ATOMS, NUCLEI, AND INTERACTIONS OF IONIZING RADIATION WITH MATTER

First Edition

By C-K Chris Wang

Georgia Institute of Technology

cognella® | ACADEMIC PUBLISHING

Bassim Hamadeh, CEO and Publisher
Kassie Graves, Director of Acquisitions
Jamie Giganti, Senior Managing Editor
Miguel Macias, Graphic Designer
Zina Craft, Senior Field Acquisitions Editor
Gem Rabanera, Project Editor
Elizabeth Rowe, Licensing Coordinator
Chelsey Schmid, Associate Editor
Brooke Knisley, Production Assistant

Cover image copyright © 2010 by iStockphoto LP / alxpin.

Printed in the United States of America

ISBN: 978-1-5165-1439-7 (pbk) / 978-1-5165-1440-3 (br)

CONTENTS

PREFACE

This book is written to serve as a textbook for an entry-level radiation physics course for students majoring in nuclear engineering, health physics, or medical physics. The purpose is to string and pack together three closely related topics (atomic and nuclear structures, radioactive decays, and interaction of ionizing radiation with matter) so that they can be taught in one semester. Such a course is meant to help students build the foundation before they take on the more specialized subjects, e.g., nuclear reactor physics, radiation transport methods, radiation dosimetry, radiation detection, and radiation shielding, …etc.

The word "radiation" here strictly refers to ionizing radiation particles, including neutrons, gamma-ray and X-ray photons, electrons, protons, and alpha particles, as well as energetic heavy ions. These particles are referred to as ionizing radiation because they are capable of breaking chemical bonds and causing ionizations in atoms and molecules (i.e., the matter) as they travel through them.

The materials included in this book are largely based on my lecture notes, which have been developed and taught over the last two decades at Georgia Tech. The book has 11 chapters. The first 10 chapters can be divided into three parts. Part I (Chapters 1–3) discusses the modern physics that is relevant to radiation interaction. Part II (Chapters 4–6) is a condensed version of nuclear physics and radioactive decay. Part III (Chapters 7–10) includes nuclear reaction kinematics and how the various types of radiation (i.e., neutron, charged particles, and gamma/X-ray photon) undergo the various types of nuclear or atomic interactions with matter. Chapter 11 uses examples to show how the various types of ionizing radiation are involved in the major applications in nuclear engineering, medical physics, and health physics.

My approach in writing this book is to treat and integrate the wide range of subjects (atomic and nuclear structure, radioactive decays, and radiation interaction with matter) with a slight flavor of quantum mechanics, just enough so that the concept of "transition probability" can be introduced to explain the probablistic nature of radioactive decays as well as the wave nature of a radiation particle undergoing interaction with a target nucleus (or atom). The materials have been taught at both undergraduate sophomore/junior and first-year graduate levels at Georgia Tech. I usually covered the same topics for both levels. The main difference between the two levels is the discussion on the involvement of angular momentum in a radioactive decay or a nuclear reaction. The discussion is qualitative for undergraduate and quantitative for graduate. It is suggested that, for an undergraduate course, one may skip the following sections without losing the continuity: 3.8–3.11, 4.6–4.10, 6.1.2–6.3, 8.3–8.6.2, and 9.2.

I am truly grateful to Professor Pedro Vaz of University of Lisbon in Portugal. As visiting professor at Georgia Tech, Dr. Vaz taught the preliminary edition of the book to the Georgia Tech undergraduate students. He and the students together helped eliminate numerous typos and errors from the preliminary edition.

C-K Chris Wang

CHAPTER 1: BASIC CONCEPTS AND DEFINITIONS

1.1 What is Ionizing Radiation?

Ionizing radiation (IR) includes neutrons, gamma-ray and X-ray photons, beta particles (or electrons), protons, and alpha particles, as well as various types of heavy ions. We call these "particles" IR because they cause atoms and molecules to ionize as they traverse through matter. The characteristics of the various types of IR and how they interact with matter form the common field of study in nuclear engineering, health physics, and medical physics. IR is generally divided into two categories: direct IR and indirect IR. Those carrying electric charge (e.g., electrons, protons, helium ions, and heavy ions) are referred to as direct IR, for they directly knock out atomic electrons via Coulomb force, and thus cause ionizations to the host atoms. Those carrying no electric charge (e.g., neutrons, gamma rays, and X rays) are referred to as indirect IR, for they must first undergo some kind of interactions with atomic electrons or nuclei to produce charged particles, which can then cause ionizations in matter via Coulomb force.

IR can be manmade or naturally existing. The manmade IR sources include nuclear reactors, particle accelerators, and the radiation-emitting radioactive sources produced by the reactors and accelerators. The energy range of concern is different for different types of IR and for different applications. Specifically, there is an energy threshold of about 10 eV for beta particles (i.e., electrons and positrons), and gamma-ray (or X-ray) photons. That is, these particles must have a minimum energy of 10 eV (corresponding roughly to the minimum ionization potential of an atom) in order to cause ionizations in matter. Neutrons, however, do not have an energy threshold because, even with no kinetic energy, they can still undergo nuclear interactions and produce energetic charged particles fully capable of causing ionizations in matter. Protons, alpha particles, and heavy ions have different energy thresholds (i.e., lower bounds) in order to be called IR. The threshold corresponds to the speed below which the ion becomes neutralized and can no longer cause ionizations in matter. Because the kinetic energy increases with the mass for an ion (when holding the speed constant), the energy threshold for an ion increases as its mass increases. For example, the approximate energy thresholds for proton and alpha particles were found to be 10 keV and 40 keV, respectively. The upper-bound energy for neutrons, alpha particles, beta particles (or electrons), and gamma rays (or X rays) for most manmade applications is around 10 MeV. Recently, however, new radiotherapy modalities (for human cancer treatment) involve the use of protons and carbon-12 (^{12}C) ions with energies up to 250 MeV and 3 GeV, respectively.

The naturally existing IR is generally divided into two groups based on their origins. The first group includes alpha and beta particles, as well as gamma photons that are emitted from the decays of naturally existing radionuclides. These nuclides include very long-lived primordial ones (e.g., potassium-40, radon-222, and radon-222) and less long-lived cosmogenic ones (e.g., tritium and carbon-14). The second group of the naturally existing IR includes neutrons, gamma photons, and muons, which arise from the instantaneous cascading/degradation processes of very high-energy cosmic rays (mainly protons) bombarding the earth's atmosphere. The naturally existing IR contributes to the overall earth background radiation, which is an important part of the study of health physics. The naturally existing IR can also cause complications in applications where the source radiation signals to be detected are weak (e.g., radiation monitoring at the US border for homeland security inspection).

A radiation particle must undergo some sort of interaction with matter, or it would be of no consequence. Because matter is made of atoms and because most IR particles (e.g. neutron, proton, electron/beta, and alpha) are the subcomponents of atoms, it is helpful to have a general idea of the dimensions and structure of matter before we discuss radiation interactions.

1.2 Dimensions, Forces of Nature, and Structure of Matter

Matter is a general term for the substance that makes up all physical objects, and it contains both mass and volume (or space). It is well known that, depending on the temperature and pressure, the same matter usually can exist in three different states (i.e., solid, liquid, and gas). Scientists in the late nineteenth century showed that the three states of the same matter are all made of the same types of fundamental units called atoms (or molecules). In early twentieth century, it was further shown that an atom (being neutral in charge) is made of interacting subatomic particles—a positively charged nucleus at the center and a cloud of negatively charged electrons orbiting the nucleus. In addition, it was shown that the mass of an atom is almost entirely possessed by the nucleus, which occupies very little volume. The diameter of an atom is in the range of 10^{-11} to 10^{-10} m, and the diameter of a nucleus is in the range of 10^{-15} to 10^{-14} m. In other words, the volume of an atom is almost entirely occupied by the cloud of electrons that carries very little mass. In 1932, an experiment conducted by James Chadwick further showed that the atomic nucleus is made of two different particles (or nucleons): the proton, which is positively charged, and the neutron, which is neutral in charge. The quantity of the electric charge of a proton is the same as that of an electron. In addition, the mass of the proton and the mass of the neutron were found to be about equal, and the diameter of each nucleon inside a nucleus is approximately 10^{-15} m. At about the same time, a fourth particle known as the neutrino ("little neutral one" in Italian) was proposed by Wolfgang Pauli, to reconcile the description of beta decay with the fundamental laws of the conservation of energy, momentum, and angular momentum. The existence of the neutrino was experimentally confirmed in the late 1950s. In other words, it seemed clear in the 1930s that electrons, protons, neutrons, and neutrinos constitute the elementary particles (or building blocks) from which all atoms and molecules are made.

In the last eighty years, with the ever more powerful particle accelerators, physicists have further shown that protons and neutrons are actually made of even smaller particles called quarks. According to the Standard Model of particle physics, there are two classes of elementary particles: the fermion, which has half-integer spin, and the boson, which has integer spin. (Povh at. al, 1995) Fermions include various types of quarks and leptons. Quarks bind together through the short-ranged strong interaction to make protons and neutrons. Leptons include electron, muon, tau, and their corresponding neutrinos. Electron, muon, and tau all carry the same negative electric charge, and they are not involved in strong reactions. Fermions (i.e., quarks and leptons) appear to be point-like particles without internal structure, and therefore, they are the ultimate building blocks of all matter. Unlike fermions, bosons are the interaction mediators. There are four fundamental interactions of matter in nature: gravitation, electromagnetic interaction, strong interaction, and weak interaction. According to the Standard Model, interactions are mediated by the exchange of bosons, including gravitons in gravitation, photons in electromagnetic interactions, gluons in strong interactions, and W^+, W^-, and Z^0 in weak interactions.

Strictly speaking, it is meaningless to talk about the size (or diameter) of a subatomic particle. In the realm of quantum mechanics, one can only discuss the likelihood of finding the particle in a certain volume in space. It is a compromise between particle and wave, the dual properties of radiation. The size of an atom (or nucleus) discussed here, therefore, corresponds to the volume within which the atom (or nucleus) can be found. It turns out that this volume is determined by the force potentials involved in the corresponding quantum system. The gravitation force in an atom is so weak it can be ignored. The electromagnetic force exerted between the nucleus and the orbiting electrons is responsible for the relatively large volume of the electron cloud, which defines the volume of the atom. While atoms are overall electrically neutral, the electromagnetic force fields at close distances between atoms do not cancel out completely. This gives rise to the attractive chemical binding force (i.e., the Van-der-Waals force) between atoms, and thus allows atoms to join together to form molecules. In other words, the fundamental interaction that gives rise to the chemical binding force is electromagnetic in nature. Quarks bind together through the short-ranged strong interaction to make nucleons (i.e., protons and neutrons). The strong interaction, as the name implies, is much stronger than the electromagnetic force, but only effective within a very short distance ($\sim 10^{-15}$ m). Similar to the electromagnetic force fields between the nearby atoms, the strong force fields between the nearby nucleons also do not cancel out completely. This gives rise to the short-ranged attractive force between nucleons, and is responsible for the tiny volume of the nucleus ($\sim 10^{-14}$ m), within which all the nucleons are clustered together. Because the electromagnetic force among atoms in a molecule is much weaker than the strong nuclear force among the nucleons in a nucleus, the binding energy of an atom in a molecule is much smaller than the binding energy of a nucleon in a nucleus. The typical binding energy of an atom in a molecule is in the order of a few eV, where 1 eV is equivalent to 1.6×10^{-19} joule. The typical binding energy of a nucleon in a nucleus, on the other hand, is in the order of a few MeV, where 1 MeV = 10^6 eV. This shows the difference in scale between nuclear energy and chemical energy.

Quarks and neutrinos can be mostly ignored in the discussion of radiation interaction. This is because quarks bind so strongly together and they do not exist individually (i.e., at least not in the energy range of IR described in Section 1.1). Neutrinos, on the other hand, are nearly massless and they hardly interact with matter. Accordingly, an atom based on the 1930s depiction should serve well for the readers of this book. The main features in such a simplified depiction of matter can be summarized as follows:

1. Atoms and molecules are the basic units of matter that makes up all physical objects.

2. Electrons, protons, and neutrons combine to form atoms, which in turn form molecules.

3. The space inside a seemingly solid object is essentially "empty," in the sense that the mass of the object is almost entirely possessed by the atomic nuclei, which occupy almost no volume.

This last feature is most important when we enter the discussion of interactions of IR with matter.

1.3 Particle–Wave Duality and the Uncertainty Principle

The nature of particle–wave duality of IR necessarily results in an important rule called the uncertainty principle, a key concept of quantum mechanics, first proposed by Werner Heisenberg in 1927. It states that the position and momentum of a particle cannot be simultaneously measured with arbitrarily high precision. There is a fundamental limit to the precision of these two measurements in that the product of their uncertainties must be greater than a certain value. Specifically, the principle is written as:

$$\Delta x \Delta p \geq \frac{\hbar}{2}, \tag{1.1}$$

where Δx and Δp are the uncertainties associated with the particle's position and momentum, respectively, and $\hbar$ is the reduced Plank constant. Equation 1.1 is not about the inaccuracy of measurement instruments, nor a reflection on the quality of experimental methods; it reveals an important fundamental property of matter: a particle cannot have a definite location and a definite momentum at the same time independently of any measurement. Even with perfect instruments and technique, the uncertainty will still be there because it is inherent in the nature of things.

The uncertainty principle is a necessary compromise between the conflicting natures of wave and particle. To illustrate this more thoroughly, let us consider a free electron traveling in the $+x$ direction. According to the formula proposed by Louis de Broglie, the electron's wave length (λ) is inversely proportional to its momentum, that is,

$$\lambda = \frac{h}{p}, \tag{1.2}$$

where p is the electron's momentum and h is the Planck constant. If one assumes that the momentum of the electron is precisely known (i.e., $\Delta p \to 0$), then equation 1.2 says that the wavelength of the electron will be constant. Such a wave form would spread probability throughout all of space, and therefore, the position of the electron becomes completely unknown (i.e., $\Delta x \to \infty$). Conversely, if one assumes that the electron's position is precisely known (i.e., $\Delta x \to 0$), then its wave form becomes a delta function, corresponding to the supposition of waves of an infinitely broad range of frequencies, meaning that its momentum is completely unknown (i.e., $\Delta p \to \infty$). The uncertainty principle described by equation 1.1 is therefore a compromise between the uncertainty of the position and that of the momentum.

1.4 Relativistic Relationships of Energy, Momentum, and Mass

In addition to the quantum effect discussed in Sections 1.2 and 1.3, the relationships of energy, momentum, and mass for IR also differ from that of classical mechanics, due to the relativistic effect. The relativistic effect becomes important when the speed of the radiation particle becomes a significant fraction of the speed of light. Let us start with the classical expression of the linear momentum ($\vec{p}$) of an object:

$$\vec{p} = m\vec{v} = m\frac{d\vec{r}}{dt}, \tag{1.3}$$

where m, $\vec{v}$, and $\vec{r}$ are the mass, velocity, and position of the object, respectively. As the speed of an object becomes a significant fraction of the speed of light, the inertia of the object increases, which, in turn, requires that equation 1.3 be modified with a correction factor γ (known as the Lorents factor):

$$\vec{p} = m\gamma\vec{v} = m\gamma\frac{d\vec{r}}{dt}, \tag{1.4}$$

where $\gamma = \dfrac{1}{\sqrt{1-\beta^2}}$, $\beta = \dfrac{v}{c}$, and c is the speed of light in vacuum. Figure 1.1 shows difference between 1.3 and 1.4, in that the relativistic effect limits the speed of an object to be less than c.

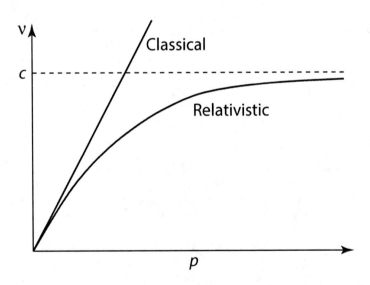

Figure 1.1. The relationship between linear momentum and speed of an object.

It should be noted that, although v of an object can never exceed c, p can keep increasing infinitely because $\gamma m \to \infty$ as $v \to c$.

Now consider an electric or magnetic force $\vec{F}$ is exerted on a charged object at position $\vec{r}$. The total work (W) being done to the object over a certain path (s) would be

$$W = \int_S \vec{F} \cdot d\vec{r} \,. \tag{1.5}$$

Since the work done on an object translates to a change in the kinetic energy of the object, if we assume that the object is initially at rest, then the final kinetic energy is equal to the total work expended on the object. In other words, equation 1.5 can be rewritten in terms of kinetic energy (K), that is,

$$K = \int_S \vec{F} \cdot d\vec{r} = \int_S \frac{d\vec{p}}{dt} \cdot d\vec{r} = \int_S \frac{d\vec{r}}{dt} \cdot d\vec{p} = \int_S \vec{v} \cdot d\vec{p} = \int_S v \, dp = m \int_0^v v \, d(\gamma v) \,.$$

Integrating by parts leads to

$$K = \gamma mc^2 - mc^2 = E - mc^2 = (\gamma - 1)mc^2 \,, \tag{1.6}$$

where $E = \gamma mc^2$, and it is referred to as the total energy of the object, including both its kinetic energy and the so-called rest energy, mc^2. Correspondingly, γm and m are referred to as the relativistic mass and rest mass. It should be noted that γ is always greater than 1 except when the object is at complete rest of which $\gamma = 1$. The relationship between E and p for relativistic object can then be derived as below:

$$E = \gamma mc^2 \implies E^2 = \gamma^2 m^2 c^4 = \frac{m^2 c^4}{1 - \beta^2} \tag{1.7}$$

$$p = \gamma m v \implies p^2 = \gamma^2 m^2 v^2 = \gamma^2 m^2 c^2 \beta^2$$

$$\implies c^2 p^2 = m^2 c^4 \gamma^2 \beta^2 = m^2 c^4 \frac{\beta^2}{1 - \beta^2} \,. \tag{1.8}$$

Equations 1.7 and 1.8 together result in

$$E^2 - c^2 p^2 = \frac{m^2 c^4}{1 - \beta^2} - m^2 c^4 \frac{\beta^2}{1 - \beta^2} = m^2 c^4 \,. \tag{1.9}$$

This well-known Pythagorean relationship is shown graphically in Figure 1.2. Equation 1.9 can be recast below to obtain the relativistic expression of p in terms of the kinetic energy K. That is,

$$c^2 p^2 = E^2 - m^2 c^4 = (E + mc^2)(E - mc^2) = (K + 2mc^2)K$$

$$\implies p = \frac{1}{c}\sqrt{(K + 2mc^2)K} \,. \tag{1.10}$$

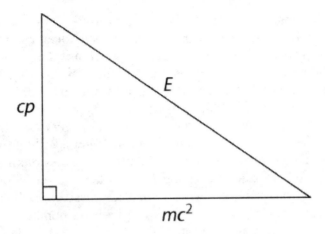

Figure 1.2. The Pythagorean relationship among E, cp, and mc^2.

It should be noted that equation 1.9 is also valid for a photon of which the rest mass is zero. In that case, it is reduced to

$$E^2 = c^2 p^2. \tag{1.11}$$

Indeed, by inserting equation 1.2 into 1.9, one obtains

$$E = cp = c\left(\frac{h}{\lambda}\right) = c\left(\frac{h}{c/v}\right) = hv, \tag{1.12}$$

where v is the frequency of the photon. This is obviously the correct formula for the photon energy first proposed by Max Planck in 1900.

1.5 Mass, Binding Energy, and Antiparticles

While in equation 1.6 we have already referred the term mc^2 as the rest energy of an object, the inventor of this famous formula himself (Albert Einstein) did not make such a claim in his early publications on mass and energy from 1905 to 1912. His early publications showed that 1.6 applies to a point-like object, and that the change of energy content of the object is proportional to the change of its mass. Indeed, if one assumes that v_1 and v_2 are respectively the initial and final speed of the object, then equation 1.6 can be re-derived as follows:

$$\Delta E = \Delta K = K_2 - K_1$$

$$= \int_s \vec{F} \cdot d\vec{r} = \int_s \frac{d\vec{p}}{dt} \cdot d\vec{r} = \int_s \frac{d\vec{r}}{dt} \cdot d\vec{p} = \int_s \vec{v} \cdot d\vec{p} = \int_s v \, dp = m \int_{v_1}^{v_2} v \, d(\gamma v)$$

$$= \gamma_2 mc^2 - \gamma_1 mc^2 = (\gamma_2 - \gamma_1)mc^2 = \Delta\gamma mc^2. \tag{1.13}$$

If one considers γm as the mass of a moving object, then equation 1.13 can be rewritten as:

$$\Delta E = \Delta mc^2. \tag{1.14}$$

Einstein's claim then was that "the mass of a body is a measure of its energy content." (Einstein, 1952). Because equation 1.13 was derived based on a charged object gaining or losing its kinetic energy in an electric or magnetic field, it can be interpreted as "the mass of an object changes proportionally with the change of the field potential." Since binding energy associated with a composite system (an atom or an atomic nucleus) is a form of potential energy, one may apply equation 1.13 to obtain the relationship between binding energy and mass difference. As mentioned in Section 1.2, the typical binding energy of an electron to an atom is in the order of a few eV, and the binding energy of a nucleon to a nucleus is in the order of several MeV. In other words, the mass of a nuclide is different from the sum of the masses of all the nucleons of which it is composed. This difference can be accounted for by the nuclear binding energy. A widely used quantity to calculate this mass difference is called "mass excess". The mass excess of a nuclide is the difference between its actual mass and its mass number in atomic units (u) , of which 1u is defined as 1/12 the mass of a carbon-12 atom (or ~931.5 MeV/c^2). To illustrate this concept more clearly, let us consider the following nuclear reaction:

$$ {}_0^1 n + {}_1^1 H \rightarrow {}_1^2 H \ . \tag{1.15} $$

According to Appendix B, the mass difference between the reactants and the product can be obtained as

$$ \Delta mc^2 = \left(m_n + m({}_1^1 H) \right) - m({}_1^2 H) = (8.071 + 7.289) - 13.136 = 2.224 \text{ MeV} \ . $$

In other words, the mass of a free neutron and the mass of a free proton together is greater than the mass of a deuteron (in which a neutron and a proton are bound together) by $\dfrac{2.224 \text{ MeV}}{c^2}$, and 2.224 MeV (which corresponds to Δmc^2) is the binding energy between the neutron and the proton. In 1912, Einstein finally made his point (not proof) that "one should view a body with inertial mass m as an energy store of magnitude mc^2 (rest-energy of the body)." (Einstein, 1952). Or more generally, one may say that mass is some form of potential.

The concept of mass and energy equivalence was most convincingly demonstrated by the observation of antiparticles. If one takes the square root of equation 1.9 for a relativistic particle, it gives

$$ E = \pm \sqrt{ \left(mc^2 \right)^2 + c^2 p^2 } \ . \tag{1.16} $$

Dirac argued in 1928 that the two signs in equation 1.16 is not a mathematical accident, and proposed that electrons can indeed have both a positive and a negative energy state. The positive-energy state corresponds to an ordinary electron carrying a negative charge, and the negative-energy state corresponds to an electron carrying a positive charge (known as the positron). The positron was experimentally discovered in 1932 by Anderson, and was recognized as the antiparticle of the electron. Today, it is relatively easy in the laboratory to observe the creation of a pair of an electron and a positron by bombarding a thin piece of high-Z material (e.g., lead or tungsten) with high-energy gamma photons. In this case, some of the energy (1.02 MeV to be exact) carried by the massless photon "disappears" to give the masses of the electron and positron. Oppositely, a positron and an electron also "annihilate" each other and during the process their masses are converted into two 511-keV gamma photons that are massless.

1.6 Cross Section and Mean Free Path

Because different forces of nature are involved for different types of IR, their interactions with matter differ drastically. For instance, a charged particle (e.g., electron, proton, or alpha particle) usually undergoes a large number of elastic and inelastic interactions (i.e., excitation and ionization events) in a very short distance (e.g., a few micrometers) in matter. This is because these interactions occur via the long-ranged Coulomb force. A neutron, on the other hand, must travel quite some distance (a few centimeters or more) before it encounters an interaction. This is because a neutron undergoes nuclear interactions via the short-ranged nuclear force. A commonly known quantity called the macroscopic cross section (denoted by Σ) has been used in radiation transport equations to calculate how radiation particles travel and interact in materials. The concept of Σ can be understood by the classical scenario of collisions between two hard spheres, as described by Figure 1.3.

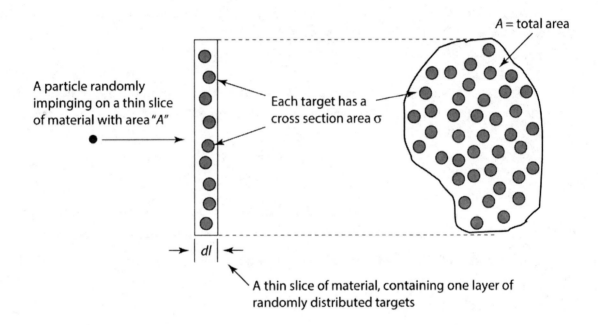

Figure 1.3. The classical scenario of collisions between two hard spheres.

As described, an incident particle randomly impinges on a thin slice of material with area "A," containing one layer of randomly distributed targets. The target may be an atom, an atomic nucleus, or an atomic electron, depending on the type of incident particle (or interaction). If we take the classical approach by assuming that both the incident particle and the target are hard spheres, that the size of the incident particle is much smaller than the size of the target, that all the targets are identical and each has a cross section area σ, and that the material contains N target spheres (electrons, atoms, or nuclei) per unit volume, then the expected probability for the incident particle to undergo a collision with a target over the thin slice of dl would be

$$P = \frac{dA}{A} = \frac{N(dV)\sigma}{A} = \frac{(NA\,dl)\,\sigma}{A} = N\sigma\,dl = \Sigma\,dl,$$

(1.17)

where dA is the total cross-section area occupied by all the targets contained in the thin slice of material; $dV = Adl$, the total volume occupied by the thin slice of material; σ is the microscopic cross section for each target; and $\Sigma = N\sigma$, the macroscopic cross section. If we take each nucleus as a target, and assign the unit of cm² nucleus⁻¹ for σ, then the unit of Σ can be obtained as follows:

$$\Sigma = N\sigma \quad \Rightarrow \quad \left(\frac{\text{nuclei}}{\text{cm}^3}\right)\left(\frac{\text{cm}^2}{\text{nucleus}}\right) = \text{cm}^{-1}.$$

(1.18)

The physical meaning of Σ is the probability of a radiation particle to undergo a collision with a nucleus per unit distance as it travels through the material.

Now, consider a beam of n particles impinging on the material; the expected number of collisions over the differential thickness of dl would be

$$dn = n\,(\Sigma\,dl).$$

(1.19)

If we further assume that a particle is removed (i.e., absorbed or scattered away by the target) from the beam after each collision, then equation 1.19 can be modified with a negative sign to represent the beam attenuation factor:

$$\frac{dn}{n} = -\Sigma\,dl.$$

(1.20)

The negative sign is needed because the change of the particle beam intensity after it passes through the differential thickness dl is negative. Now, assuming that there are n_0 particles impinging on a slab of a finite thickness l, and that n out of n_0 transmit through the slab without having an interaction, one can then calculate the transmission probability by integrating equation 1.20 over the specified thickness l:

$$\int_{n_0}^{n} \frac{dn}{n} = -\Sigma \int_0^l dl \quad \Rightarrow \quad \ln\frac{n}{n_0} = -\Sigma l \quad \Rightarrow \quad \frac{n}{n_0} = e^{-\Sigma l}.$$

(1.21)

In other words, the probability of an incident particle to undergo a collision in the thickness l is simply

$$1 - e^{-\Sigma l}.$$

(1.22)

In the case that $\Sigma l \ll 1$, equation 1.22 can be further reduced via the Taylor series expansion:

$$1 - e^{-\Sigma l} = 1 - \left(1 - \Sigma l + \frac{(\Sigma l)^2}{2!} - \frac{(\Sigma l)^3}{3!} + \dots\right) \cong \Sigma l,$$

(1.23)

which is consistent with equation 1.17 for an infinitely thin material.

It is obvious that both σ and Σ are the material properties and that they must be experimentally determined. Indeed, in the last half century many scientists all over the world have dedicated their lives to working on developing the so-called cross section data library for various types of radiation particles of a broad energy range, and for all kinds of material. The common experimental setup for measuring cross section is that of a narrow-beam geometry shown in Figure 1.4. The radiation detector measures the radiation count rates with and without the sample material in place to obtain n and n_0. One then uses equations 1.21 and 1.18 to obtain Σ and σ. That is,

$$\Sigma = -\frac{1}{l}\left(\ln\frac{n}{n_0}\right), \quad \text{and} \quad \sigma = \frac{\Sigma}{N}. \tag{1.24}$$

The σ thus obtained is denoted as σ_t, the total cross section, because, as indicated in Figure 1.4, the narrow-beam geometry ensures that as long as an interaction has taken place, a radiation particle is removed (from the incident beam) regardless of the type of interaction. In other words, the measured beam attenuation factor (n/n_0) is a result of all types of interactions, including absorption, elastic scattering, inelastic scattering, etc., of which each has its corresponding cross section (i.e., $\sigma_a, \sigma_s, \sigma_i$, etc.). Because cross section is synonymous with the probability of interaction, and because different types of interactions are independently competing with one another, the total probability should be the sum of the parts. That is

$$\sigma_t = \sigma_a + \sigma_s + \sigma_i + ... \tag{1.25}$$

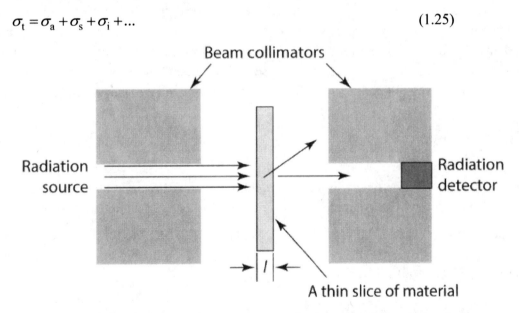

Figure 1.4. The narrow-beam geometry for cross-section measurement.

One other interesting aspect is that these measured microscopic cross sections are often significantly larger than the classical size of the target. For example, the measured cross section for a thermal neutron (with a kinetic energy of 0.025 eV) to be absorbed by a uranium-235 nucleus is about $6.8 \times 10^{-26}\,\text{m}^2$. However, the classical formula for estimating the radius of a nucleus is 7.4×10^{-15} m (from equation 4.16). This would predict a cross-section area of approximately 1.7×10^{-28} m^2, which is more than two orders of magnitude smaller than the measured one. This discrepancy has to do with the misconception of a definite size of a radiation particle and target nucleus (as alluded to in Section 1.2), and it can only be understood via quantum mechanics. This will be explored in detail in Chapters 3 and 8.

Below we show an example of how to use equation 1.18 to calculate the macroscopic cross section for 1-MeV neutron interacting with water. The data of σ_t for hydrogen and oxygen are given to be 4 barns and 3 barns, respectively, where 1 barn $= 10^{-24}$ cm^2. The number density for hydrogen and oxygen atoms in water can be calculated as

$$N_H = 2N_{H_2O} = 2\left(\frac{\rho_{H_2O}}{M_{H_2O}}\right) N_A = 2\left(\frac{1.0\,\text{g cm}^{-3}}{18\,\text{g mole}^{-1}}\right)\left(\frac{6.023 \times 10^{23}\,\text{atoms}}{\text{mole}}\right) \cong 6.7 \times 10^{22}\,\text{atoms cm}^{-3}$$

and

$$N_{Oxy} = N_{H_2O} \cong 3.35 \times 10^{22}\,\text{atoms cm}^{-3}.$$

From equation 1.18,

$$\left(\Sigma_t\right)_{H_2O} = N_H\left(\sigma_t\right)_H + N_{Oxy}\left(\sigma_t\right)_{Oxy} = \left(6.7 \times 10^{22}\,\text{atoms cm}^{-3}\right)\left(4 \times 10^{-24}\,\text{cm}^2\,\text{atom}^{-1}\right) +$$
$$\left(3.35 \times 10^{22}\,\text{atoms cm}^{-3}\right)\left(3 \times 10^{-24}\,\text{cm}^2\,\text{atom}^{-1}\right) = 0.37\,\text{cm}^{-1}.$$

The macroscopic cross section, Σ, is closely related to another important quantity called the mean free path (MFP), designated by the symbol λ, which is the average distance that a particle travels between collisions in a material. By definition, an averaged quantity of a variable, x, is obtained by weighting its value with the corresponding probability density function, $P(x)$, and then integrating over the full range of the variable. As such, λ can be obtained via

$$\lambda = \int_0^\infty xP(x)\,dx, \tag{1.26}$$

where x is the distance a particle will travel through the material without having a collision, and $P(x)dx$ is the probability that a particle will have its first collision at the interval between x and $x + dx$. Accordingly, $P(x)dx$ is the product of $e^{-\Sigma x}$ and Σdx, where the former is the probability of having no collision over the distance x, and the latter is the probability of having a collision at the interval between x and $x + dx$. That is,

$$P(x)dx = e^{-\Sigma x}\,\Sigma dx. \tag{1.27}$$

By inserting equation 1.27 into 1.26, λ can then be obtained as

$$\lambda = \int_0^\infty x\,e^{-\Sigma x}\,\Sigma\,dx = \frac{1}{\Sigma}. \tag{1.28}$$

Since Σ has the unit of μm^{-1}, mm^{-1}, cm^{-1}, and so on, λ has the unit of μm, mm, cm, and so on, which is consistent with the physical meaning of the MFP. Table 1.1 shows the estimated values of λ for various types of ionizing radiation. As shown, the values of λ for charged particles (alpha and electron) are many orders of magnitude smaller than that for neutral particles (gamma and neutron). This is consistent with the fact that charged particles constantly and directly interact with atomic electrons via the Coulomb force, and that neutral particles are neutral in charge, and thus, can travel relatively freely in media. The value of λ alone provides a rough picture on how a particle travels in a material.

Table 1.1. Estimated values of the mean free path (λ) for various types of ionizing radiation.

Radiation particle	Material	λ (cm)
5-MeV alpha	water	3.4×10^{-7}
	air	2.8×10^{-4}
	steel	8.1×10^{-8}
1-MeV electron	water	5.3×10^{-5}
	air	4.4×10^{-2}
	steel	1.3×10^{-5}
1-MeV gamma	water	$1.4 \times 10^{+1}$
	air	$1.3 \times 10^{+4}$
	steel	2.1
1-MeV neutron	water	2.7
	air	$1.1 \times 10^{+4}$
	steel	4.7

1.7 Radiation Quantities

In many applications it is of interest to calculate the reaction density (interactions cm^{-3}), R, or reaction rate density (interactions $cm^{-3} s^{-1}$), $\dot{R}$, for neutrons and gamma rays. For example, in nuclear engineering applications, the neutron-induced fission reaction rate density is proportional to the power density in a nuclear reactor. In medical and health physics applications, the gamma reaction density in tissue is proportional to the absorbed dose in the human body. A widely used quantity allowing these calculations to be carried out is called particle fluence, denoted by ϕ. For any point in a radiation field, the particle fluence is the number of particles Δn that, during some period of time, pass through an imaginary sphere of cross section ΔA centered on the point, as illustrated in Figure 1.5(a). The particle fluence is defined as

$$\phi = \lim_{\Delta A \to 0} \left[\frac{\Delta n}{\Delta A} \right]. \tag{1.29}$$

The unit of ϕ is, therefore, particles cm^{-2}. Another definition, which is found to be equivalent to equation 1.29, can be made in terms of the sum $\sum_i s_i$ of path-length segments within the sphere, as illustrated in Fig. 1.5(b). That is,

$$\phi = \lim_{\Delta V \to 0} \left[\frac{\sum_i s_i}{\Delta V} \right], \tag{1.30}$$

where ΔV is the volume of the sphere. The reader is asked to verify the equivalence of equations 1.29 and 1.30 in a homework problem at the end of this chapter.

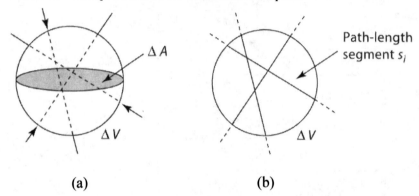

(a)   (b)

Figure 1.5. The imaginary sphere of volume ΔV and cross-sectional area ΔA used to illustrate the two definitions of particle fluence: (a) for equation 1.29, and (b) for equation 1.30. Source: Shultis and Faw (1996).

From equation 1.19, $n\,(\Sigma\,dl)$ is the number of particles that would interact in the distance dl, $\phi\Sigma\,Adl$ or $\phi\Sigma\,dV$ is then the number of interactions that would occur in the volume dV. In other words, $\Sigma\phi$ is the reaction density, or

$$R = \Sigma\phi. \tag{1.31}$$

Similarly, one defines the particle fluence rate as

$$\dot{\phi} = \frac{n}{At}, \tag{1.32}$$

where t stands for time. The reaction rate density can be obtained as

$$\dot{R} = \Sigma\dot{\phi}. \tag{1.33}$$

In medical and health physics applications, the biological effect caused by radiation is closely related to the absorbed dose (denoted by D), which is defined as energy deposited per unit mass. The SI unit of D is Gray (or Gy), and 1 Gy = 1 joule kg^{-1}.

1.8 Rutherford Scattering of Alpha Particles

The mental image of a collision between two hard spheres described in Section 1.6 is a convenient way of illustrating the concept of cross section, and it is based on the idea that the two spheres must make "contact" with each other in order to have some kind of interaction. This image works reasonably well for describing neutron interactions because the nuclear force involved in the interaction has a clearly defined range of $\sim 10^{-15}$ m. It, however, does not work for describing charged particle interactions, which are based on the long-ranged Coulomb force**Error! Bookmark not defined.**. A classical example of this is the alpha-particle scattering cross-section formula derived by Rutherford in 1911. The formula was used to explain the results of the famous gold foil experiment of H. Geiger and E. Mardsen, which resulted in the discovery of the atomic nucleus.

In the gold foil experiment, alpha particles with energy of a few MeV are brought to perpendicularly impinge on a thin gold foil. Rutherford first assumed that the mass of an atom was almost entirely possessed by the nucleus. He then assumed that both the incident alpha particle and the target gold nucleus are point-charged particles, and that the target nucleus is at rest. The geometrical relationships of the incident alpha particle with respect to the target nucleus is shown in Figure 1.6. As shown, an alpha particle travels along a straight line in the $+x$ direction towards the target nucleus, and would pass a distance b from the nucleus in the absence of the Coulomb force. The distance b is called the impact parameter. With the influence of the repulsive Coulomb force, the alpha particle will be deflected with a scattering angle θ from its initial $+x$ direction. Since no energy is converted into the internal energy of both interacting particles, the interaction is considered elastic scattering. From Figure 1.7, it is obvious that the scattering angle θ increases as the impact parameter b decreases and that $(2\pi b)db$ corresponds the differential cross section for the incident alpha particle to be scattered into a new direction between θ and $\theta + d\theta$. To obtain the relationship between θ and b, we first use the law of conservation of the linear momentum for the alpha particle before and after the scattering. That is, the direction of the alpha particle has changed (and so has its linear momentum) but its kinetic energy has remained the same (and so has the magnitude of the linear momentum) after the scattering.

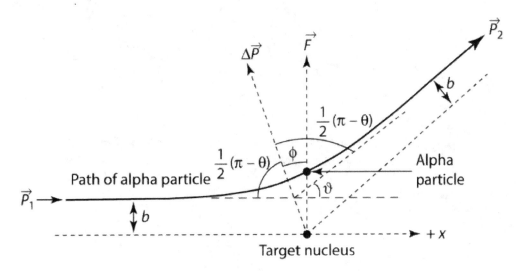

Figure 1.6. Geometrical relationships in Rutherford scattering.

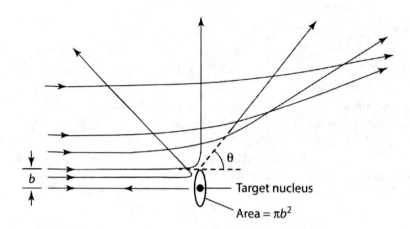

Figure 1.7. The scattering angle (θ) increases when the impact parameter (b) decreases.

Mathematically, the change of linear momentum before and after scattering can be expressed as

$$\Delta \vec{P} = \vec{P}_2 - \vec{P}_1 = \int_{\Delta t} \vec{F} \, dt, \tag{1.34}$$

where $\vec{P}_1$ and $\vec{P}_2$, respectively, represent the linear momentum of the alpha particle before and after the scattering; $\vec{F}$ is the Coulomb force involved during the scattering; and Δt is the time duration of the scattering event. Since $\left|\vec{P}_1\right| = \left|\vec{P}_2\right| = mv$, where v is the speed of the alpha particle, the magnitude of $\Delta \vec{P}$ can be obtained by using the vector diagram shown in Figure 1.8 as

$$\left|\Delta \vec{P}\right| = 2mv \sin \frac{\theta}{2}. \tag{1.35}$$

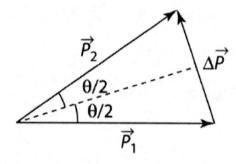

Figure 1.8. The vector diagram of the linear momentum of the alpha particle before and after scattering.

By combining equations 1.34 and 1.35, we obtain the following:

$$\left| \int_{\Delta t} \vec{F} \, dt \right| = \int_{\Delta t} F \cos \phi \, dt = 2mv \sin \frac{\theta}{2}, \tag{1.36}$$

where F is the magnitude of $\left|\vec{F}\right|$, and ϕ is the instantaneous angle between $\vec{F}$ and $\Delta\vec{P}$. To carry out the integral of equation 1.36, it is necessary to convert the variable t to ϕ so that the upper bound and lower bound of the integral are well defined. That is,

$$2mv\sin\frac{\theta}{2} = \int_{-\frac{(\pi-\theta)}{2}}^{\frac{(\pi-\theta)}{2}} F\cos\phi\left(\frac{dt}{d\phi}\right)d\phi . \qquad (1.37)$$

To obtain $\dfrac{dt}{d\phi}$, we apply the law of conservation of angular momentum during the scattering process:

$$\left|\vec{L}\right| = \left|\vec{r}\times\vec{P}\right| = mr^2\frac{d\phi}{dt} = mv\,b \quad \Rightarrow \quad \frac{d\phi}{dt} = \frac{vb}{r^2} \qquad (1.38)$$

Inserting equation 1.38 into 1.37 yields the following:

$$2mv^2 b\sin\frac{\theta}{2} = \int_{-\frac{(\pi-\theta)}{2}}^{\frac{(\pi-\theta)}{2}} Fr^2\cos\phi\,d\phi . \qquad (1.39)$$

Substituting the Coulomb force formula, $F = \dfrac{k_c e^2 zZ}{r^2}$, into equation 1.39 yields

$$\frac{2mv^2 b}{k_c e^2 zZ}\sin\frac{\theta}{2} = \int_{-\frac{(\pi-\theta)}{2}}^{\frac{(\pi-\theta)}{2}}\cos\phi\,d\phi = 2\cos\frac{\theta}{2} \quad \Rightarrow \quad b = \frac{k_c e^2 zZ}{mv^2}\cot\frac{\theta}{2}, \qquad (1.40)$$

where $k_c e^2 \cong 1.44$, MeV $\cdot$ fm , and z and Z correspond the electric charge of the alpha particle and the target nucleus, respectively.

Equation 1.40 is the algebraic expression of the relationship between b and θ shown in Figure 1.7. The differential scattering cross section for the alpha particle to be scattered into a new direction between θ and $\theta + d\theta$ can now be expressed in terms of θ:

$$d\sigma = 2\pi b\,db = \pi\,db^2 = \pi\left(\frac{k_c e^2 zZ}{mv^2}\right)^2 d\cot^2\left(\frac{\theta}{2}\right). \qquad (1.41)$$

Because the probability of the alpha particle to be scattered into a new direction between θ and $\theta + d\theta$ is proportional to the corresponding cone-shaped solid angle $d\Omega$ (see Figure 1.9), and because the scattering is azimuthally symmetric, one has

$$d\Omega = 2\pi\sin\theta\,d\theta = 4\pi\sin\frac{\theta}{2}\cos\frac{\theta}{2}\,d\theta . \qquad (1.42)$$

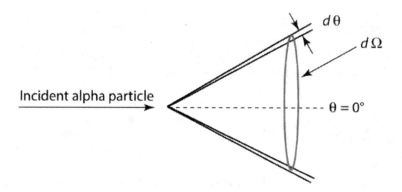

Figure 1.9. The relationship between $d\theta$ and differential solid angle $d\Omega$.

By combining equations 1.41 and 1.42, one finally obtains the famous Rutherford scattering formula:

$$\frac{d\sigma}{d\Omega} = \frac{k_c^2 e^4 z^2 Z^2}{4m^2 v^4} \left(\frac{1}{\sin^4 \dfrac{\theta}{2}} \right) = \frac{k_c^2 e^4 z^2 Z^2}{16E^2} \left(\frac{1}{\sin^4 \dfrac{\theta}{2}} \right), \tag{1.43}$$

where $E = \frac{1}{2}mv^2$, which is the classical expression of the kinetic energy of the alpha particle.

Equation 1.43 predicts that $\dfrac{d\sigma}{d\Omega} \to \infty$ when $\theta \to 0$. This is because $b \to \infty$ when $\theta \to 0$. In reality, however, θ must be greater than 0 because b must be smaller than the radius of the atom, or the charge of the target nucleus would be neutralized by the surrounding electrons of the atom. Another noteworthy aspect of equation 1.43 is that it predicts a small but finite probability for the alpha particles to be scattered with large scattering angles. If one takes 5 MeV as the kinetic energy of the incident alpha particle, and integrates equation 1.43 for θ between 90° and 180°, this gives a backscattering cross section of 1.63×10^{-27} m^2 nucleus^1. If one further assumes a thickness of 1 micrometer (or 10^{-4} cm) for the gold foil, and then applies equation 1.23, this gives a backscattering probability of 9.6×10^{-5} (see Problem 1.6). This result agrees well with that observed by Marsden and Geiger, and contributed to the monumental discovery of the atomic nucleus.

As mentioned, Rutherford's classical treatment of Coulomb scattering was published in 1911, at least one decade before the concept of quantum mechanics was solidified. Now, let us use the uncertainty principle to examine the validity of the assumptions made in the Rutherford scattering formula. According to the uncertainty principle, the position of a particle can only be known to an accuracy of approximately the de Broglie wavelength of the particle (i.e., $\Delta x \cong \lambda$). For a 5-MeV alpha particle, the uncertainty of its position can therefore be calculated as

$$\Delta x \cong \lambda = \frac{\hbar}{p} = \frac{\hbar}{\sqrt{2mE}} = \frac{\hbar c}{\sqrt{2mc^2 E}} = \frac{197.327 \text{ MeV} \cdot \text{fm}}{\sqrt{2(3728.4 \text{ MeV})(5 \text{ MeV})}} = 1.02 \text{ fm}.$$

For the Rutherford scattering formula to be valid, the distance between the two particles (i.e., r in equations 1.38 and 1.39, as well as in the Coulomb force formula) must be well defined. This means that r must be much greater than Δx. Classically, the closest distance between the two particles (r_{min}) can be obtained by setting the kinetic energy equal to the potential energy. That is,

$$5\,\text{MeV} = \frac{k_c e^2 zZ}{r_{min}} = \frac{(2)(79)(1.44)\ \text{MeV} \cdot \text{fm}}{r_{min}} \quad \Rightarrow \quad r_{min} = 45.5\ \text{fm}\ .$$

Since $r_{min} \gg \Delta x$, one concludes that the quantum uncertainty associated with the alpha particle position is negligible in the Rutherford scattering experiment. In other words, the classical approach of treating the incident alpha particle and the target nucleus as two point-charged particles is valid.

If we now take 1-MeV electron as the incident particle instead of 5-MeV alpha, the corresponding values for Δx and r_{min} become comparable to each other. In this case, one may argue that the quantum uncertainty associated with the electron position may significantly alter the Coulomb scattering formula predicted by the Rutherford's formula. Surprisingly, however, the quantum treatment of the Coulomb scattering cross section gives the same result as that of the Rutherford's formula (i.e., equation 1.43). This is because the factor r gets cancelled out in equation 1.39, and therefore does not affect the final form of equation 1.43. In other words, the successful classical treatment by Rutherford was a happy accident due to the special form of the Coulomb force, $F = k_c e^2 / r^2$, in that the quantum treatment of the Coulomb scattering cross section actually gives the same result.

1.9 Wave Behavior of Electrons

To illustrate the wave property of a particle, it has been demonstrated in the so-called double-slit experiment that a single electron passing through a wall with two opening slits can produce interference patterns, and that the interference patterns can be precisely explained by the classical wave mechanics. Since the interference pattern is most pronounced when the wavelength of the electron is comparable to the distance between the two slits, which is limited to a few hundred nanometers with today's technology, the corresponding energy of the electron in the double-slit experiment is in the range of a few hundred eV. Figure 1.10 is the schematic diagram of the electron double-slit experiment. As shown, electrons are emitted from the source one at a time. According to particle physics, each electron can only go through either slit 1 or slit 2 and will be detected at either P_1 or P_2. As such, the pattern appears on the screen predicted by particle mechanics should show two humps corresponding to P_1 and P_2. The experimental result, however, shows the interference pattern of multiple humps. This result is perfectly predicted by the wave mechanics. The interference pattern implies that each electron actually goes through both slits at the same time, and wave functions emerging from the two slits interfere with each other and thus creates the interference pattern. The interference pattern has also been shown when high energy electrons (> 100 MeV) undergo elastic scattering with an atomic nucleus (see Figure 1.11). As the wavelength of an electron becomes comparable to the size of the nucleus (Δx ~5 fm), the electron no longer sees the nucleus as a point charge. Instead, it can simultaneously interact with each proton in the nucleus, and the interference pattern is the result of the scattered wave created by all of the protons inside the nucleus.

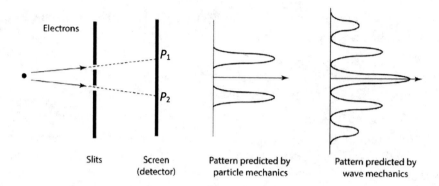

Figure 1.10. Schematic diagram of the electron double-slit interference experiment.

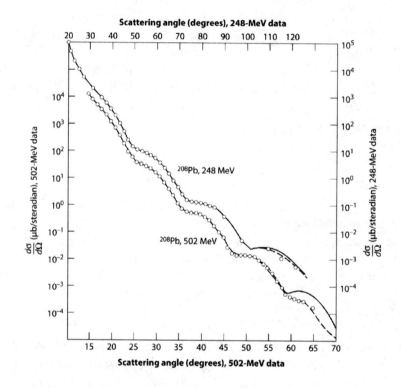

Figure 1.11. Elastic scattering of 248-MeV and 502-MeV electrons from ^{208}Pb. The diffraction pattern is clearly seen.

Source: Krane (1988).

Bibliography

Einstein, Albert *The principle of Relativity*. New York: Dover Publications, Inc., 1952.

Krane, Kenneth S. *Introductory Nuclear Physics*. New York: John Wiley & Sons, 1988.

Shultis, J. Kenneth and Faw, Richard E. *Radiation Shielding*. Upper Saddle River, NJ: Prentice-Hall, Inc., 1996.

Povh, Bogdan et al. *Particles and Nuclei: An Introduction to the Physical Concepts*. New York: Springer, 1995.

Credits

Problems

1. Consider an imaginary sphere that is passed by a uniform parallel beam of particles. Show that the particle fluence obtained from equations 1.29 and 1.30 are identical.

2. As described in the figure below, two isotropic point sources (S_1 and S_2) of radiation are located at 3 meters and 5 meters, respectively, from a point detector P.

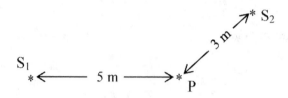

   If $S_1 = 1.0 \times 10^8$ particles sec-1 and $S_2 = 1.0 \times 10^7$ particles sec-1, and the radiation attenuation in the medium is negligible, calculate the particle fluence rate (particles cm^{-2} sec^{-1}) at P.

3. The point P is located at the origin of a spherical-surface radiation source. The diameter of the sphere is 30 cm, and the source intensity is uniform of 10^5 particles cm^{-2} sec^{-1} over the entire spherical surface. (a) Calculate the fluence rate (particles cm^{-2} sec^{-1}) at P. (b) Calculate the average fluence rate over the entire sphere. (Note: the medium is a vacuum.)

4. As shown below, a neutron beam of fluence rate 10^8 neutrons cm^{-2} sec^{-1} is perpendicularly incident on a slab of polyethylene (CH2, $\rho = 0.92$ g cm^{-3}, $\sigma_C = 1.0$ barn, $\sigma_H = 10.0$ barn, 1 barn = 10^{-24} cm^2) of thickness 1.5 cm.

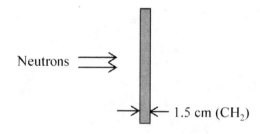

   (a) What is the macroscopic cross-section for neutrons in the material?
   (b) How manu neutrons will not interact inside the slab?
   (c) What is the mean free path of the neutrons?
   (d) Indicate which assumptions were used in the solution of (b) and (c).

5. For an electron moving with a speed of 2.9 x 10^8 m/s, determine:

   (a)   The De Broglie wavelength
   (b)   The Lorentz factor
   (c)   Its total energy

   (the mass of an electron is 9.11 x 10^{-31} kg and h= 6.62 x 10^{-34} J s)

6. Use the differential cross-section $(d\sigma/d\Omega)$ of Rutherford scattering to calculate the alpha particle microscopic scattering cross-section on a gold atoms, between $\theta = \frac{3}{4}\pi$ and $\theta = \pi$.

CHAPTER 2: STRUCTURE OF ATOMS AND CHARACTERISTIC X-RAYS

2.1 Earlier Models of an Atom

The historical account of the understanding of the internal structure of atoms began with the discovery of electrons by J. J. Thomson in 1897. Before this time, atoms were thought to be indestructible, and therefore, the fundamental building blocks of all matter. Due to the discovery of the electron, the so-called "plum pudding model" of the atom was proposed by J. J. Thomson in 1904. In this model, the atom is composed of negatively charged electrons (i.e., the plums) surrounded by a soup (i.e., the pudding) of positive charge. The positive charge is needed to balance the negative charge carried by the electrons to make the atom neutral in charge. The word "soup" implied that both the mass and the positive charge is uniformly distributed inside an atom. This model was later disproved by the famous gold foil experiment performed in 1909 by E. Rutherford's associate and student, H. Geiger and E. Marsden. In this experiment, it was found that about 1 in 8,000 α particles striking the gold foil bounced backward. Since Rutherford has already proved in 1906 that α particles were helium atoms with two positive elementary charges, he was able to show that it is impossible for α particles to bounce backward if both the mass and the positive charge were uniformly distributed inside an atom (as implied by the plum pudding model). Instead, he proposed the "nuclear model of atom" in 1911. This new model asserted that both the mass and the positive charge of an atom is held in a tiny volume, the dimension of which is 10^4 to 10^5 smaller than that of the atom. Based on this model, Rutherford derived the scattering formula for the α particles and was able to account for the backscattering probability observed by Geiger and Marsden (Section 1.8).

Historically speaking, the nuclear model of the atom proposed by Rutherford was a monumental achievement in modern physics, as it represents the discovery of the atomic nucleus. This model, however, did not receive immediate approval from his peers at the time, for one big reason: the model had great difficulty explaining how the negatively charged, point-like electrons can coexist with the positively charged, point-like nucleus to form a stable atom. It was known from classical electrodynamics that the electrons must continuously lose energy via emitting electromagnetic waves, and therefore, collapse into the nucleus. In reality, however, atoms have been found to be quite stable.

In the meantime, Niels Bohr, a young Danish physicist, applied the concept of light quanta to explain a thirty-year-old puzzle of why atoms have only spectral lines. The line spectra for various atoms had been experimentally obtained in the 1880s by J. J. Balmer and J. R. Rydberg. They came up with the following empirical formula for the spectral lines:

$$\frac{1}{\lambda} = R\left[\frac{1}{n_f^2} - \frac{1}{n_i^2} \right], \tag{2.1}$$

where λ is the wavelength of the light, n_f and n_i are integers, 1, 2, 3, 4, … and $n_f > n_i$, and R is an empirical constant called Rydberg's constant. The concept of light quantum was first proposed by M. Plank in 1900 as an attempt to explain the distribution of intensity versus wavelength in blackbody radiation. He reasoned that the exchange of electromagnetic radiation can only be in the form of quanta (i.e., $E = nh\nu$, $n = 1, 2, 3, ...$), where ν is the frequency of the quantum and is equal to c/λ, and h is called Plank's constant, which is given as 6.62618×10^{-34} J.s .

The quantum concept of electromagnetic radiation (i.e., the concept of photon) became widely accepted after Albert Einstein successfully used it to explain the photoelectric effect in 1905. Einstein determined that the energy of a photon is given by $E = h\nu$. By bringing in this new concept, Bohr put forward in 1913 his theory of the hydrogen atom. He postulated that the electron circulates the nucleus (i.e., the proton) only on certain orbits, and that each orbit corresponds to a different energy state. He further postulated that an electron would not emit electromagnetic radiation when it is rotating a stable orbit around the nucleus. Instead, a quantum of electromagnetic energy (i.e., a photon) is emitted when an electron jumps from one orbit to another. Since each orbit corresponds to a different energy state, the energy of the emitted photon is equal to the difference of the energy levels between the initial state and the final state of the transition. That is,

$$h\nu = \Delta E = E_i - E_f, \tag{2.2}$$

where E_i and E_f correspond to the energy levels of the initial state and final state, respectively. In order to satisfy the quantum emission of photons, Bohr postulated that the magnitude of the orbiting electron's angular momentum must be quantized. In classical theory, the angular momentum of an electron of mass m_e moving on a circular orbit of radius r with velocity $\vec{v}$ is

$$\vec{L} = \vec{r} \times \vec{p} = \vec{r} \times m_e \vec{v}, \tag{2.3}$$

and the magnitude of $\vec{L}$ is

$$\left| \vec{L} \right| = m_e v r, \tag{2.4}$$

where $v = \left| \vec{v} \right|$. Bohr postulated that

$$\left| \vec{L} \right| = m_e v_n r_n = n\hbar, \qquad n = 1, 2, 3, ... \tag{2.5}$$

where n denotes a specific orbit or energy state, and $\hbar = \dfrac{h}{2\pi}$. To obtain r_n and v_n, Bohr took the classical approach and assumed that the centripetal force on the orbiting electron is supplied by Coulomb force between the electron and proton, and according to classical dynamics,

$$\frac{1}{4\pi\varepsilon_0} \frac{e^2}{r_n^2} = \frac{m_e v_n^2}{r_n}. \tag{2.6}$$

By solving equations 2.5 and 2.6 simultaneously, one obtains

$$r_n = \frac{\varepsilon_0 n^2 h^2}{\pi m_e e^2} \tag{2.7}$$

and

$$v_n = \frac{e^2}{2\varepsilon_0 n h}. \tag{2.8}$$

The minimum radius of r_n is referred to as the Bohr radius, and it occurs when $n = 1$; that is,

$$r_1 = \frac{\varepsilon_0 h^2}{\pi\, m_e e^2} = \left(\frac{4\pi\varepsilon_0}{e^2}\right)\frac{(\hbar c)^2}{m_e c^2} \cong \left(\frac{1}{1.44\,\text{MeV}\cdot\text{fm}}\right)\frac{(197.329\,\text{MeV}\cdot\text{fm})^2}{0.511\,\text{MeV}}$$

$$\cong 52917\,\text{fm} \cong 0.529\,\text{Å}. \tag{2.9}$$

Bohr assumed that the total energy of the hydrogen atom is the sum of the kinetic energy (KE) and potential energy (PE) of the electron with respect to the central nucleus (i.e., the proton). Because KE and PE are classically expressed in terms of v_n and r_n, and because v_n and r_n are quantized, the total energy of the hydrogen atom is also quantized. The total energy E_n is then expressed as

$$E_n = (KE)_n + (PE)_n = \frac{1}{2}m_e v_n^2 - \frac{1}{4\pi\varepsilon_0}\frac{e^2}{r_n}. \tag{2.10}$$

Substituting r_n and v_n with equations 2.7 and 2.8 yields

$$E_n = \frac{m_e e^4}{8\varepsilon_0^2 n^2 h^2} - \frac{m_e e^4}{4\varepsilon_0^2 n^2 h^2} = -\frac{m_e e^4}{8\varepsilon_0^2 n^2 h^2}. \tag{2.11}$$

The energy of the photon emitted when a hydrogen atom undergoes a transition from an initial state i to its final state f can then be expressed as

$$\Delta E = E_i - E_f = -\frac{m_e e^4}{8\varepsilon_0^2 n_i^2 h^2} + \frac{m_e e^4}{8\varepsilon_0^2 n_f^2 h^2} = \frac{m_e e^4}{8\varepsilon_0^2 h^2}\left(\frac{1}{n_f^2} - \frac{1}{n_i^2}\right). \tag{2.12}$$

Since $\Delta E = h\nu = \dfrac{hc}{\lambda}$, a comparison of equations 2.1 and 2.12 yields

$$R = \frac{m_e e^4}{8\varepsilon_0^2 h^3 c} = \left(2\pi^2\right)\left(\frac{e^2}{4\pi\varepsilon_0}\right)^2\left(\frac{m_e c^2}{(hc)^3}\right) \cong \left(2\pi^2\right)(1.44\,\text{MeV}\cdot\text{fm})^2\left(\frac{0.511\,\text{MeV}}{(1239.853\,\text{MeV}\cdot\text{fm})^3}\right)$$

$$\cong 1.0974 \times 10^{-8}\ \text{fm}^{-1}. \tag{2.13}$$

One can also obtain the ionization energy of a ground-state hydrogen atom by replacing n_i and n_f in equation 2.12 with ∞ and 1, respectively. That is,

$$\Delta E = E_\infty - E_1 = \frac{m_e e^4}{8\varepsilon_0^2 h^2}\left(\frac{1}{1} - \frac{1}{\infty^2}\right) = \frac{m_e e^4}{8\varepsilon_0^2 h^2} = \left(2\pi^2\right)\left(\frac{e^2}{4\pi\varepsilon_0}\right)^2\left(\frac{m_e c^2}{(hc)^2}\right)$$

$$\cong \left(2\pi^2\right)\left(1.44 \text{ MeV} \cdot \text{fm}\right)^2 \left(\frac{0.511 \text{ MeV}}{\left(1239.853 \text{ MeV} \cdot \text{fm}\right)^2}\right) \cong 13.6 \text{ eV}. \qquad (2.14)$$

Both the Rydberg's constant shown in equation 2.13 and the ionization energy shown in equation 2.14 agree well with the experimentally obtained values. The Bohr's model, therefore, successfully explains the spectrum of the hydrogen atom. However, because Bohr assumed that electrons and protons are point particles and used classical mechanics to describe these particles, there were certain inherent contradictions in the model. For example, Bohr's model did not address the Rutherford's dilemma in that an atom based on a point-like electron orbiting the point-like nucleus must be unstable. Even if one assumes that each state (or orbit) is stable, how does one describe the process of quantum transition between two energy states? Does the electron simply "jump" from one orbit to another? And how does the electron decide which state it will jump to? These questions remained unanswered for almost another two decades until quantum mechanics was brought into full swing in the late 1920s.

2.2 Magnetic Moment of an Orbiting Electron

While Bohr's model was successful in matching the major atomic spectral lines, closer inspection revealed that the spectral lines contain fine structure. That is, a single line actually contains multiple closely spaced lines. This implied that there may be additional forces (other than the Coulomb force) involved in the atom. The most obvious one is that of the magnetic dipole moment produced by the electron orbital motion. According to classical electromagnetism, a circular electric current i produces a magnetic dipole moment $\vec{\mu}$ that has the same direction as its angular momentum $\vec{L}$. Let us denote the magnitudes of $\vec{L}$ and $\vec{\mu}$ by L and μ, respectively. Classical theory says that $\mu = iA$, where A is area enclosed by the circulating current. For an electron orbiting at a speed υ on a circle of radius r around the nucleus, $i = \dfrac{e\upsilon}{2\pi r}$ and $A = \pi r^2$, and therefore,

$$\mu = iA = \left(\frac{e\upsilon}{2\pi r}\right)\left(\pi r^2\right) = \frac{e\upsilon r}{2}. \qquad (2.15)$$

Because $L = m_e \upsilon r$, and because electrons are negatively charged, the relationship between $\vec{\mu}$ and $\vec{L}$ can be found as

$$\vec{\mu} = -\gamma \vec{L}, \qquad (2.16)$$

where $\gamma = \dfrac{e}{2m_e}$, and it is called gyromagnetic ratio.

In addition to the fact that the electron angular momentum in an atom is quantized, it was observed in 1921 by O. Stern and W. Gerlach that the orientation of the electron's angular momentum (or the magnetic dipole moment) in an external magnetic field is also quantized. (Yang and Hamilton, 1996) Quantization of the orientation of electron angular momentum in an external magnetic field can be expressed as

$$L_z = m_\ell \hbar, \quad m_\ell = \ell, \ell\text{-}1, \ldots, -\ell, \tag{2.17}$$

where z represents the direction of the external magnetic field. Figure 2.1 shows that both L_z and L are quantized and that

$$L = \sqrt{\ell(\ell+1)}\hbar, \quad \ell = 0, 1, 2, 3, \ldots \tag{2.18}$$

Equations 2.17 and 2.18 can be derived from quantum mechanics (Section 3.8). From equation 2.16, the magnitude of the orbital magnetic dipole moment can then be rewritten as

$$\mu_l = -\gamma L = -\sqrt{\ell(\ell+1)}\mu_B, \quad \ell = 0, 1, 2, 3, \ldots \tag{2.19}$$

where $\mu_B = \gamma \hbar = \dfrac{e\hbar}{2m_e} = 5.788 \times 10^{-5}$ eV/T (T stands for Tesla), which is called the Bohr magneton.

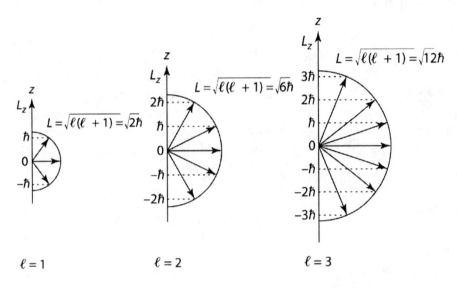

Figure 2.1. Quantization of $\vec{L}$ in the direction of the magnetic field.

According to classical theory, by applying a magnetic field $\vec{B}$ on an atom that has a magnetic moment $\vec{\mu}_\ell$, one can change the atom's energy levels by an amount of $-\vec{\mu}_\ell \cdot \vec{B}$. This means that the spectral lines of the atom will change accordingly. This effect was indeed observed by P. Zeeman in 1896. The space quantization of the magnetic moment discovered by Stern and Gerlach can now be used to explain the split of spectral lines observed by Zeeman. That is, the change of energy levels under the influence of an external magnetic field $\vec{B}$ can be calculated as

$$\Delta E = -\vec{\mu} \cdot \vec{B} = \gamma \vec{L} \cdot \vec{B} = \frac{e}{2m_e} L_z B = m_\ell \frac{e\hbar}{2m_e} B = m_\ell \mu_B B, \quad m_\ell = \ell, \ell\text{-}1, \ldots, -\ell, \tag{2.20}$$

where L_z and B are the magnitudes of $\vec{L}_z$ and $\vec{B}$, respectively.

Let us consider applying a magnetic field of 1.5 T to a helium atom. This is the typical magnetic field strength used for magnetic resonance imaging. In the case that both electrons of the helium atom are in the ground state of $\ell = 0$, the only possible value of m_ℓ is 0. Therefore, there is no shift of energy level. In the case that one electron is in the excited state $\ell = 1$, the possible values of m_ℓ are 1, 0, and -1. The energy level, therefore, is split into three equally spaced sublevels. The space between them can be calculated by equation 2.20. That is,

$$\Delta E = \mu_B B = \left(5.788 \times 10^{-5} \text{ eV T}^{-1}\right)\left(1.5\,\text{T}\right) = 8.682 \times 10^{-5} \text{ eV}.$$

The above example correctly predicts the observed spectral line splitting. In such a prediction, the number of lines would be $(2\ell+1)$, which can only be an odd number. However, it has been observed that for many atoms (especially for those with an odd atomic number) the line splitting actually shows even number of sublevels. This disagreement was later resolved by the inclusion of the electron "spin".

2.3 Hypothesis of Electron Spin

To explain the fact that atoms with an odd atomic number give rise to even numbers of sublevels in the Zeeman effect, in 1925 G. Uhlenbeck and S. Goudsmit suggested that the electron is more than just a point charge, and that it actually rotates on its own axis like a top, giving rise to a spin angular momentum $\vec{S}$, which is quantized in a similar way as that of the orbital angular momentum (equations 2.17 and 2.18), except that the quantum number is a half-integer $\frac{1}{2}$. Figure 2.2 illustrates the quantization for S and S_z. That is,

$$S_z = m_s \hbar, \quad m_s = \pm \frac{1}{2} \tag{2.21}$$

and

$$S = \sqrt{s(s+1)}\hbar, \quad s = \frac{1}{2}. \tag{2.22}$$

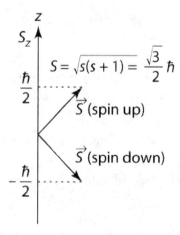

Figure 2.2. Quantization of $\vec{S}$ in the direction of the magnetic field.

As mentioned in Section 1.2, electrons belong to the elementary particle type called "fermion," which has half-integer spin. One consequence of an electron having spin is that there must be a magnetic moment accompanying the spin. Similar to equation 2.19, the magnitude of spin magnetic moment of an electron can be expressed as

$$\mu_s = -\gamma S = -\sqrt{s(s+1)}\mu_B = -\frac{\sqrt{3}}{2}\mu_B. \tag{2.23}$$

The above results, however, do not agree with the experiments. The experimental results showed that the spin gyromagnetic ratio is twice the orbital gyromagnetic ratio. Equation 2.23, therefore, must be corrected as

$$\mu_s = -\gamma S = -2\sqrt{s(s+1)}\mu_B = -\sqrt{3}\mu_B. \tag{2.24}$$

Or we may rewrite equations 2.19 and 2.23 as

$$\vec{\mu_l} = -g_l\,\gamma\,\vec{L} = -g_l\,\mu_B\,\vec{L} \tag{2.25}$$

and

$$\vec{\mu_s} = -g_s\,\gamma\,\vec{S} = -g_s\mu_B\vec{S}, \tag{2.26}$$

where g_l and g_s are 1 and 2, respectively, and they are called the Landé g-factor. The total magnetic dipole moment of an electron, therefore, can be written as

$$\vec{\mu_e} = \vec{\mu_l} + \vec{\mu_s} = -\frac{e\hbar}{2m_e}(g_l\,\vec{L} + g_s\vec{S}) = -(g_l\,\mu_B\vec{L} + g_s\mu_B\vec{S}). \tag{2.27}$$

2.4 Spin-Orbit Interaction and Energy States of a Hydrogen Atom

The introduction of electron spin necessarily changes the total angular momentum and magnetic moment, as well as the energy states of an atom. The total angular momentum and magnetic momentum of an atom can be expressed as the vector sum of the spin and orbital components. That is,

$$\vec{J} = \vec{L} + \vec{S}. \tag{2.28}$$

In 1928, P. A. Dirac included electron spin in his relativistic quantum mechanics. For an electron occupying a certain orbit with quantum number ℓ, its spin quantum number (m_s) can be either $\frac{1}{2}$ (i.e., spin up) or $-\frac{1}{2}$ (i.e., spin down). Accordingly, both J and J_z are also quantized. That is,

$$J = \sqrt{j(j+1)}\hbar, \quad j = l \pm \frac{1}{2} \tag{2.29}$$

and

$$J_z = m_j\hbar, \quad m_j = j, j-1, j-2, ..., -(j-1), -j. \tag{2.30}$$

Figure 2.3 illustrates the quantization for J and J_z for the two cases, spin-up (or parallel) and spin-down (or antiparallel). Because $j = \ell \pm \dfrac{1}{2}$ and because there are $2\ell + 1$ possible orientations for a specific ℓ, there are $2j + 1$ possible states for a specific j. By including the spin-orbit interaction, Dirac showed that the energy level of a hydrogen atom depends only on two quantum numbers n and j.

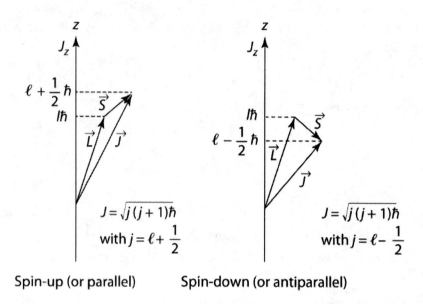

Spin-up (or parallel)   Spin-down (or antiparallel)

Figure 2.3. Quantization of $\vec{J}$ in the direction of the magnetic field.

We can now describe how the energy states of a hydrogen atom are denoted. We first introduce the spectroscopic notation of energy states according to the orbital angular momentum quantum number ℓ. The letters s, p, d, f, g, h, and i are used to represent energy states corresponding to $l = 0, 1, 2, 3, 4, 5,$ and 6, respectively.

- For $\ell = 0$, $j = \dfrac{1}{2}$. As such, there are two possible energy states ($2j + 1 = 2$), which are denoted as $s_{1/2}$.

- For $\ell = 1$, there are two possible j values: $\dfrac{3}{2}$ and $\dfrac{1}{2}$. For $j = \dfrac{3}{2}$, there are four possible energy states ($2j + 1 = 4$), which are denoted as $p_{3/2}$. For $j = \dfrac{1}{2}$, there are two possible energy states ($2j + 1 = 2$), which are denoted as $p_{1/2}$.

- For $\ell = 2$, there are two possible j values: $2 + \dfrac{1}{2} = \dfrac{5}{2}$ and $2 - \dfrac{1}{2} = \dfrac{3}{2}$. For $j = \dfrac{5}{2}$, there are six possible energy states ($2j + 1 = 6$), which are denoted as $d_{5/2}$. For $j = \dfrac{3}{2}$, there are four possible energy states ($2j + 1 = 4$), which are denoted as $d_{3/2}$.

One can follow the above procedure to obtain the number of possible energy states for each ℓ value that is greater than 2. Table 2.1 shows the quantum numbers and the notations of the various energy states for $n = 1 - 3$ according to the above procedure.

Table 2.1. The quantum numbers and the notations of the various energy states for $n = 1 - 3$.

n	ℓ	j	m_j	State notation	Number of state
1	0	$\dfrac{1}{2}$	$\pm \dfrac{1}{2}$	$1s_{1/2}$	2
2	0	$\dfrac{1}{2}$	$\pm \dfrac{1}{2}$	$2s_{1/2}$	2
	1	$\dfrac{1}{2}$	$\pm \dfrac{1}{2}$	$2p_{1/2}$	2
		$\dfrac{3}{2}$	$-\dfrac{3}{2}, -\dfrac{1}{2}, \dfrac{1}{2}, \dfrac{3}{2}$	$2p_{3/2}$	4
3	0	$\dfrac{1}{2}$	$\pm \dfrac{1}{2}$	$3s_{1/2}$	2
	1	$\dfrac{1}{2}$	$\pm \dfrac{1}{2}$	$3p_{1/2}$	2
		$\dfrac{3}{2}$	$-\dfrac{3}{2}, -\dfrac{1}{2}, \dfrac{1}{2}, \dfrac{3}{2}$	$3p_{3/2}$	4
	2	$\dfrac{3}{2}$	$-\dfrac{3}{2}, -\dfrac{1}{2}, \dfrac{1}{2}, \dfrac{3}{2}$	$3d_{3/2}$	4
		$\dfrac{5}{2}$	$-\dfrac{5}{2}, -\dfrac{3}{2}, -\dfrac{1}{2}, \dfrac{1}{2}, \dfrac{3}{2}, \dfrac{5}{2}$	$3d_{5/2}$	6

2.5 Pauli's Exclusion Principle and the Distribution of Electrons in an Atom

While the quantum numbers and available energy states discussed in Section 2.3 were for hydrogen atoms, which contain only a single electron, the principle can also be applied to allocating electrons for atoms with many electrons. The applicability has to do with the so-called Pauli's Exclusion Principle, proposed by W. Pauli in 1925. It states that no two electrons in an atom can exist in the same state. It can also be shown using quantum mechanics that, for an atom containing many electrons, the electrons tend to form pairs, of which the spin and orbital angular momenta cancel each other. Consequently, for atoms of an even atomic number, the net angular momentum (and thus the magnetic dipole moment) of the atom is zero. For atoms of odd atomic number, the net angular momentum (and thus the energy state) of the atom is determined by the unpaired valence electron. Table 2.1 shows that a state of an atomic electron can be uniquely determined by a set of quantum numbers, n, ℓ, j, and m_j. Electrons having the same principal quantum number n form a definite group, or "shell." The shells corresponding to $n = 1, 2, 3, 4, \ldots$ are named K shell, L shell, M shell, N shell, $\ldots$, respectively. Each shell may consist of many subshells, corresponding to different ℓ. The subshells corresponding to $\ell = 1, 2, 3, 4, \ldots$ are denoted by the letters s, p, d, f, $\ldots$, respectively. An interesting fact is that a subshell is filled when the sum of all the corresponding m_ℓ (or m_j) is zero. For example, for a sodium atom having eleven electrons, its energy state is designated as $1s^2 2s^2 2p^6 3s^1$, which can be abbreviated as $3s^1$, indicating that the $1s$, $2s$, and $2p$ shells are completely filled and that the energy state of the atom is determined by its valence electron occupying the $3s$ shell.

In addition to the Pauli's Exclusion Principle, for many electron atoms the order of filling the shells is determined by the minimum energy principle. According to Bohr's theory of the hydrogen atom, energy increases with increasing principle quantum number n, and therefore the electrons should be filled into the shells in the order of increasing n, beginning with $n = 1$. This, however, is not always true. Figure 2.4 shows the true order of shell filling according to the energy levels. As shown, the $3d$ level is higher than $4s$, and therefore $4s$ is first filled before $3d$. Similarly, $4d$ is higher than $5s$, and $4f$ and $5d$ are higher than $6s$, and so on. More precisely, for Z between 21 and 29, the order of filling energy levels constantly switches between $3d$ and $4s$; for Z between 39 and 47, the order of filling energy levels constantly switches between $4d$ and $5s$; for Z between 57 and 79, the order of filling energy levels constantly switches among $4f$, $5d$, and $6s$. These elements belong to the group called transition metal. Figure 2.4 also shows that many closely spaced energy levels form separate groups (or shells). The atoms with the outer shell completely filled belong to the group of inert gases, as they are extra stable chemically. Figure 2.5 shows the periodic peaks and valleys of the ionization potential for the chemical elements with Z up to 88. As shown, the peaks correspond to the inert gases (He, Ne, Ar, Kr, Xe, and Rn), which in turn correspond to the closed shells of $1s$, $2p$, $3p$, $4p$, $5p$, and $6p$, respectively. Whereas, the valleys correspond to hydrogen and the alkali metals (Li, Na, K, Rb, Cs, and Fr), which in turn correspond to the states $1s^1$, $2s^1$, $3s^1$, $4s^1$, $5s^1$, $6s^1$, and $7s^1$, respectively.

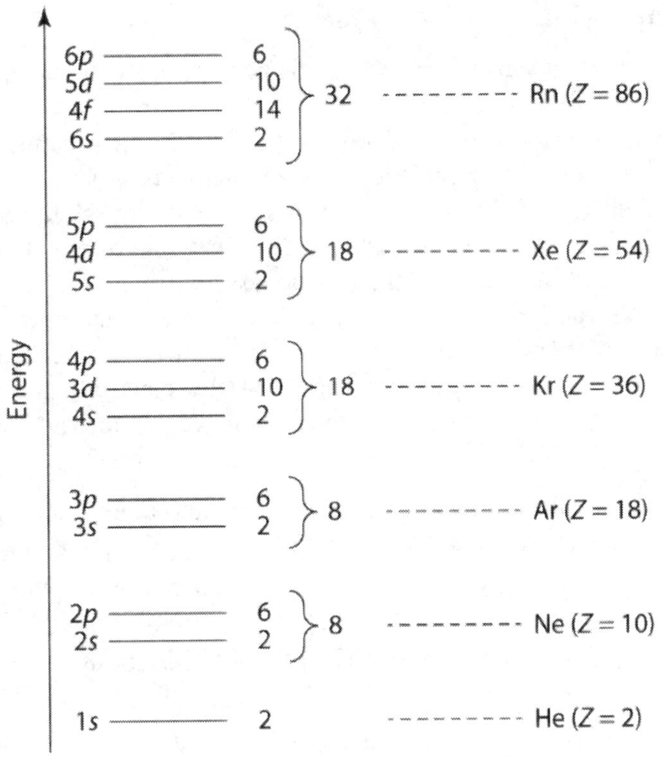

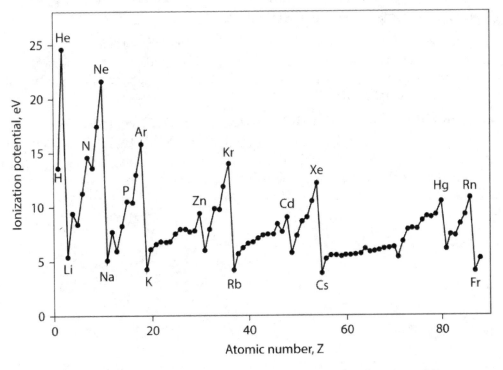

Figure 2.4. The order of shell filling according to the energy levels of the atoms.

Figure 2.5. Ionization potentials of elements as a function of Z.

2.6 Origin of Characteristic X rays

Characteristic X rays are produced when an atom is bombarded with electrons of energy greater than the binding energies of the inner-shell electrons of the atom. The term "characteristic" refers to the fact that the wavelengths of these X rays are unique to each element. The production of characteristic X rays by electron bombardment of pure elements was first observed in 1909 by C. G. Barkla and C. A. Sadler. H. G. Moseley made a systematic investigation of the characteristic X ray spectra for about forty elements (Semat, 1958). The origin of the characteristic X rays was not clear at that time. But the similarity in the uniqueness between the X ray spectral lines and the optical spectral lines for each element suggested that the two phenomena may have the same origin. Today we know that both phenomena result from an atom undergoing transition from a higher energy state to a lower energy state, and that the electromagnetic energy (a photon) emitted during the transition corresponds to the difference in energy between the two states (equation 2.12).

Conventionally, the shells corresponding to the principal quantum numbers $n = 1, 2, 3, 4, ...$ are labeled alphabetically with letters K, L, M, N, and so on. Figure 2.6 shows the so-called Moseley Plot of the K series X rays for elements of various atomic numbers versus the X ray frequency. The experimental results of Moseley were combined with Bohr's theory of the hydrogen atom and yielded the following empirical relationship for K_α X rays:

$$hv_{K_\alpha} = 13.6 \, \text{eV} \, (Z-1)^2 \left(\frac{1}{1^2} - \frac{1}{2^2} \right) = 10.2(Z-1)^2 \, \text{eV} . \tag{2.31}$$

According to the Bohr theory, the interpretation of equation 2.31 is that the K_α X ray is emitted when an electron undergoes a transition from the orbit of principal quantum number $n = 2$ (the L shell) to principal quantum number $n = 1$ (the K shell). Figure 2.7 is the energy-level diagram showing the $K_\alpha, K_\beta,$ and K_γ transitions. Since the K shell of a ground-state atom is always filled with two electrons ($1s^2$), for any of the K transitions to occur one of the two electrons in the K shell must first be removed. When a target element is bombarded with high-energy electrons, some of K-shell electrons of the target atoms are "knocked out" by the incident electrons, allowing K transitions to take place.

This explains the origin of the characteristic X rays. Equation 2.31 consists of the factor $(Z-1)$ instead of Z because there is only one electron occupying the K shell, so that the L-shell electron, which undergoes the transition, is moved in an electric field having its magnitude proportional to the positive nuclear charge (Z) plus one negative charge of the K-shell electron. According to Figure 2.7, the equivalence of equation 2.31 can be written as

$$hv_{K_\alpha} = E_L - E_K . \tag{2.32}$$

Similarly,

$$hv_{K_\beta} = E_M - E_K \tag{2.33}$$

and

$$hv_{K_\gamma} = E_N - E_K . \tag{2.34}$$

As pointed out in Section 2.1, the Bohr model was based on classical mechanics. Therefore, while it was used successfully to explain the X ray spectrum produced during atomic transitions, the Bohr model could not explain the nature of the transitions, let alone the corresponding transition probabilities. These questions will be addressed in Section 3.10 with the treatment of quantum mechanics. The quantum theory of X ray emission during an atomic transition is the same as that of γ-ray emission during a nuclear transition, in the sense that they are all caused by electromagnetic potential. The detailed treatment of γ transition probability is included in Section 6.3.

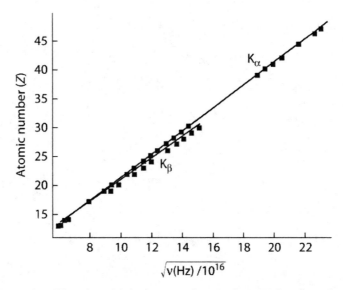

Figure 2.6. The Moseley Plot, in which the atomic number (Z) is plotted against the square root of the X ray frequency (ν) for K_α and K_β series of characteristic X rays.

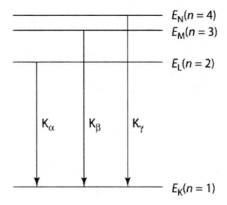

Figure 2.7. The energy-level diagram showing the K_α, K_β, and K_γ transitions.

Bibliography

Semat, Henry. *Introduction to Atomic and Nuclear Physics*, 3rd ed. New York: Rinehart & Company, Inc., 1958.

Yang, Fujia, and Joseph H. Hamilton. *Modern Atomic and Nuclear Physics*. New York: McGraw-Hill Companies, Inc., 1996.

Problems

1. Consider the Bohr model of the hydrogen atom. Calculate:
   (a) The kinetic and potential energies of an electron orbiting the hydrogen atom in the energy level corresponding to $n = 3$.
   (b) The energy released by the electron in a de-excitation process when it passes from energy level $n = 3$ to energy level $n = 2$. Explain succinctly the process of energy releasing.

2. Write the electron configurations for the following atoms: P, S, Cl, and Ar.

3. Determine the number of electrons in fully occupied $n = 4$ and $n = 5$ shells.

4. Write in a tabulated form, the quantum numbers and the notations of the various energy states for $n = 4$.

5. Moseley's experimental method was used to measure the atomic number. If the measured wavelength of a K_α X ray of an element is 0.685 Å, what is the atomic number of the element?

6. The ionization potential of an L-shell electron of a neodymium atom ($Z = 60$) is 6.5 keV. What is the ionization potential of a K-shell electron of the same atom?

CHAPTER 3: BASIC CONCEPTS OF QUANTUM MECHANICS

3.1 Wave Functions, Expectation Values, and Quantum Mechanical Operators

As hinted in Section 1.3, the quantum mechanical description of a particle involves the associated wave function $\psi(x,t)$, which is a complex function in space and time. According to the uncertainty principle, it is not possible to determine the accurate position of the particle. But it is possible to obtain the probability of finding the particle at a certain position and to specify some sort of the average position. In the one-dimensional (1-D) form, the probability of finding the particle between x and $x + dx$ is expressed by Max Born's postulation:

$$q(x,t)dx = \psi*(x,t)\psi(x,t)dx , \tag{3.1}$$

where $\psi*(x,t)$ is the conjugate of $\psi(x,t)$. The wave function must be normalized so that the probability of the particle being somewhere on the x axis is 1. That is,

$$\int_{-\infty}^{\infty} \psi*(x,t)\psi(x,t)dx = 1. \tag{3.2}$$

The average position of the particle (i.e., the expected value of x) can then be expressed as

$$\bar{x} = \int_{-\infty}^{\infty} x\, q(x,t)\, dx = \int_{-\infty}^{\infty} \psi*(x,t)\, x\, \psi(x,t)\, dx . \tag{3.3}$$

One may extend this definition of finding expected value to an arbitrary function of x. Taking momentum (p) as an example, its average value can be expressed as

$$\bar{p} = \int_{-\infty}^{\infty} \psi*(x,t)\, p\, \psi(x,t)\, dx . \tag{3.4}$$

To evaluate equation 3.4, one must express p in terms of x and t. This is not a problem in classical mechanics. But in quantum mechanics, the uncertainty principle dictates that p and x cannot be simultaneously known with complete certainty. Is there a solution for this dilemma? A clue can be found by considering the 1-D wave function traveling in the $+x$ direction:

$$\psi(x,t) = e^{i(kx-\omega t)}, \tag{3.5}$$

where $k = p/\hbar$ is the wave number, $\omega = E/\hbar$ is the wave frequency, and E is the kinetic energy of the particle. The first derivative of equation 3.5 with reference to the position variable x gives

$$\frac{\partial \psi(x,t)}{\partial x} = ike^{i(kx-\omega t)} = ik\psi(x,t) = i\frac{p}{\hbar}\psi(x,t),$$ (3.6)

which can be rewritten in the following way:

$$p[\psi(x,t)] = \frac{\hbar}{i}\frac{\partial}{\partial x}[\psi(x,t)] = -i\hbar\frac{\partial}{\partial x}[\psi(x,t)].$$ (3.7)

Equation 3.7 is the quantum mechanical operator corresponding to the classical variable of momentum. By applying equation 3.7 to 3.4, one obtains the following:

$$\bar{p} = \int_{-\infty}^{\infty} \psi^*\left(-i\hbar\frac{\partial \psi(x,t)}{\partial x}\right)dx = -i\hbar\int_{-\infty}^{\infty} \psi^*\frac{\partial \psi(x,t)}{\partial x}dx.$$ (3.8)

Similarly, the first derivative of equation 3.5 with reference to the time variable t gives

$$\frac{\partial \psi(x,t)}{\partial t} = -i\omega e^{i(kx-\omega t)} = -i\omega\psi(x,t) = -i\frac{E}{\hbar}\psi(x,t),$$ (3.9)

which can be rewritten in the following way:

$$E[\psi(x,t)] = i\hbar\frac{\partial}{\partial t}[\psi(x,t)].$$ (3.10)

The above is the quantum mechanical operator corresponding to the classical variable of energy.

3.2 The Schrödinger Equation

If one extends the variable E to include both the kinetic energy and the potential energy, then the classical nonrelativistic expression of E is simply

$$E = \frac{p^2}{2m} + V,$$ (3.11)

where m is the rest mass of the particle, and V is the potential. By applying equations 3.7 and 3.10 to 3.11, one obtains the corresponding quantum mechanical operator below:

$$i\hbar\frac{\partial}{\partial t} = \frac{\left(-i\hbar\frac{\partial}{\partial x}\right)^2}{2m} + V \quad \Rightarrow \quad -\frac{\hbar^2}{2m}\frac{\partial^2}{\partial x^2} + V(x,t) = i\hbar\frac{\partial}{\partial t}.$$ (3.12)

By applying the above operator equation on the wave function $\psi(x,t)$, one obtains the famous Schrödinger wave equation:

$$-\frac{\hbar^2}{2m}\frac{\partial^2\psi(x,t)}{\partial x^2} + V(x,t)\psi(x,t) = i\hbar\frac{\partial \psi(x,t)}{\partial t}.$$ (3.13)

The solution of the above time-dependent equation has been shown to be

$$\psi(x,t) = \varphi(x)e^{-i\omega t},$$
(3.14)

where $\varphi(x)$ is the solution of the following time-independent Schrödinger equation:

$$-\frac{\hbar^2}{2m}\frac{d^2\varphi(x)}{dx^2} + V(x)\varphi(x) = E\varphi(x).$$
(3.15)

The above equation only has solutions for certain values of E as a result of applying boundary conditions to $\varphi(x)$. These specific values E_n are known as eigenvalues, and each eigenvalue has its corresponding solution (or eigenfunction), $\varphi_n(x)$, where the subscript n corresponds to a specific state of the system. Since the time-dependent factors of ψ and $\psi*$ are $e^{-i\omega t}$ and $e^{i\omega t}$, respectively, they cancel out in 3.3 and 3.4. As such, none of the observable properties of the system depend on time.

It has been shown that any wave function (stationary or not) can be expanded in terms of the stationary-state eigenfunctions. That is,

$$\varphi(x) = \sum_n a_n\varphi_n.$$
(3.16)

In other words, for any quantum system the stationary-state eigenfunctions are a complete set for the expansion of any wave function of the system. The significance of the coefficients a_n is that $|a_n|^2$ is the probability that a measurement of the energy will result in the value E_n. To obtain a_n, one applies the orthogonality property of the stationary-state eigenfunctions; that is,

$$\int_{-\infty}^{\infty}\varphi_m(x)*\varphi_n(x)\,dx = 0 \text{ if } m \neq n$$
(3.17)

$$= 1 \text{ if } m = n$$

Multiplying both sides of equation 3.16 by $\varphi_m(x)*$ and integrating over dx, one obtains

$$\int_{-\infty}^{\infty}\varphi_m(x)*\varphi(x)\,dx = \sum_{n=0}^{\infty}a_n\int_{-\infty}^{\infty}\varphi_m(x)*\varphi_n(x)dx.$$
(3.18)

By applying the orthogonality property of equation 3.17, the right-hand side of equation 3.18 can be reduced to a_m, i.e.

$$\int_{-\infty}^{\infty}\varphi_m(x)*\varphi(x)\,dx = a_m.$$
(3.19)

The superposition principle of equation 3.16 is helpful in describing the relationship between a particle and its associated wave function. For example, the time-independent wave function of a free particle traveling in the $+x$ direction with a known momentum and energy $\left(p = k\hbar \text{ and } E = \omega\hbar\right)$ can be represented by

$$\varphi(x) = Ae^{ikx},$$

(3.20)

where A is a constant. Equation 3.2 requires that

$$\int_{-\infty}^{\infty} \varphi^*(x)\varphi(x)dx = |A|^2 \int_{-\infty}^{\infty} dx = 1,$$

(3.21)

which can only be satisfied if $|A|^2 \to 0$. This means that a free particle with a precise momentum and kinetic energy would have nowhere to be found (or can be found anywhere between $-\infty$ and $+\infty$), which is just what the uncertainty principle (equation 1.1) says. In the case that the momentum p varies over a range Δp, the coefficient A becomes a function of p. The wave function of the particle can then be expressed as

$$\varphi(x) = \int_{\Delta p} A(p)e^{ikx}dp,$$

(3.22)

where $A(p)$ to $\varphi(x)$ has the same physical meaning as that of a_n to $\varphi(x)$ of equation 3.16, in that both $A(p)$ and a_n represent the weighting factor (or relative contribution) of a specific eigenfunction to the wave function. Inserting equation 3.22 into 3.21 gives

$$\int_{-\infty}^{\infty} \varphi^*(x)\varphi(x)dx = \int_{-\infty}^{\infty} \int_{\Delta p} |A(p)|^2 dp\, dx = 1$$

(3.23)

where $|A(p)|^2 dp$ is proportional to the probability that the momentum of the particle will be found between p and $p+dp$.

3.3 Particle Current Density

For a particle traveling in a certain direction with a certain speed, the relationship between the classical quantity, "particle current density" $\vec{J}$, and the particle's wave function $\psi(x,t)$ can be established via the following conservation law of particles:

$$\frac{\partial \psi^* \psi}{\partial t} + \nabla \cdot \vec{J} = 0,$$

(3.24)

where $\psi * \psi$ represents the number of particles found in a differential volume of $dv = dxdydz$, and $\vec{J}$ is defined as the number of particles passing through an area normal to its traveling direction per unit time per unit area (i.e., particles $cm^{-2}\ sec^{-1}$). The first term of equation 3.24 can be further expanded using Schrödinger's equations as

$$\frac{\partial \psi * \psi}{\partial t} = \psi * \frac{\partial \psi}{\partial t} + \psi \frac{\partial \psi *}{\partial t} = \psi * \left[\frac{i}{\hbar} \left(\frac{\hbar^2}{2m} \nabla^2 - V \right) \right] \psi - \psi \left[\frac{i}{\hbar} \left(\frac{\hbar^2}{2m} \nabla^2 - V \right) \right] \psi *$$

$$= \frac{i\hbar}{2m} \left(\psi * \nabla^2 \psi - \psi \nabla^2 \psi * \right) = \frac{i\hbar}{2m} \left[\nabla \cdot \left(\psi * \nabla \psi - \psi \nabla \psi * \right) \right] \qquad (3.25)$$

Comparing 3.24 with 3.25, one obtains the following relationship between $\vec{J}$ and ψ :

$$\vec{J} = \frac{-i\hbar}{2m} \left(\psi * \nabla \psi - \psi \nabla \psi * \right). \qquad (3.26)$$

Since the time-dependent factors of ψ and $\psi*$ are $e^{-i\omega t}$ and $e^{i\omega t}$, they cancel each other. Equation 3.26 then becomes independent of time. That is,

$$\vec{J} = \frac{-i\hbar}{2m} \left(\varphi * \nabla \varphi - \varphi \nabla \varphi * \right). \qquad (3.27)$$

In other words, the observable properties of a system can be evaluated using the time-independent wave function $\varphi(x)$.

To verify 3.27 with a free particle traveling in the $+x$ direction, one applies equation 3.20 into 3.27, which becomes

$$\vec{J} = \frac{-i\hbar}{2m} \left(\varphi * \nabla \varphi - \varphi \nabla \varphi * \right) = \frac{-i\hbar}{2m} \left(2i\vec{k}AA* \right) = \frac{\hbar\vec{k}}{m} |A|^2. \qquad (3.28)$$

Classically, $\frac{\hbar\vec{k}}{m} = \frac{\vec{p}}{m} = \vec{v}$. Since $|A|^2$ is the probability of finding a particle in a position in space, this is the same as the number of particles existing in a position in space. Equation 3.28, therefore, is consistent with the classical definition of particle current (i.e., number of particles passing through a unit area normal to its traveling direction per unit time). (Krane, 1988)

3.4 Particle Traveling Against a Positive Potential

3.4.1 Step Potential, $E > V_0$

We now consider a 1-D problem of a particle traveling in the $+x$ direction and running into a positive step potential with height V_0; that is,

$$V(x) = 0, \text{ when } x \leq 0, \text{ region 1}$$
$$= V_0, \text{ when } x > 0, \text{ region 2.} \tag{3.29}$$

If the kinetic energy E of the particle is greater than V_0, the 1-D time-independent Schrödinger's equation takes the following form:

$$\frac{d^2\varphi(x)}{dx^2} + k^2\varphi(x) = 0. \tag{3.30}$$

The solutions for equation 3.30 for regions 1 and 2, respectively, are:

$$\varphi_1(x) = Ae^{ik_1x} + Be^{-ik_1x} \text{ and} \tag{3.31}$$

$$\varphi_2(x) = Ce^{ik_2x} + De^{-ik_2x}, \tag{3.32}$$

where $k_1 = \dfrac{\sqrt{2mE}}{\hbar}$ and $k_2 = \dfrac{\sqrt{2m(E - V_0)}}{\hbar}$.

By applying the boundary conditions of $\varphi_1(0) = \varphi_2(0)$ and $\dfrac{d\varphi_1(0)}{dx} = \dfrac{d\varphi_2(0)}{dx}$, one obtains

$$A + B = C + D \tag{3.33}$$

and

$$k_1(A - B) = k_2(C - D). \tag{3.34}$$

Since there is no reflected wave in region 2, $D = 0$. Equation 3.32 becomes

$$\varphi_2 = Ce^{ik_2x}, \tag{3.35}$$

which represents the transmitted wave. Equations 3.33 and 3.34 together give the following expressions:

$$B = A\left[\frac{1 - (k_2/k_1)}{1 + (k_2/k_1)}\right] \tag{3.36}$$

and

$$C = A\left[\frac{2}{1 + (k_2/k_1)}\right]. \tag{3.37}$$

We now rewrite equation 3.31 as $\varphi_1 = \varphi_1^+ + \varphi_1^-$, where $\varphi_1^+ = Ae^{ik_1x}$ and $\varphi_1^- = Be^{-ik_1x}$. Using equation 3.28, the incident, reflected, and transmitted particle current densities can be respectively obtained as

$$J_{incident} = -\frac{i\hbar}{2m}\left(\varphi_1^+ * \frac{d\varphi_1^+}{dx} - \varphi_1^+ \frac{d\varphi_1^+ *}{dx}\right) = -\frac{i\hbar}{2m}\left(2ik_1|A|^2\right) = \frac{\hbar k_1}{m}|A|^2, \tag{3.38}$$

$$J_{reflected} = -\frac{i\hbar}{2m}\left(\varphi_1^- * \frac{d\varphi_1^-}{dx} - \varphi_1^- \frac{d\varphi_1^- *}{dx}\right) = -\frac{i\hbar}{2m}\left(2ik_1|B|^2\right) = \frac{\hbar k_1}{m}|B|^2, \tag{3.39}$$

and

$$J_{transmitted} = -\frac{i\hbar}{2m}\left(\varphi_2 * \frac{d\varphi_2}{dx} - \varphi_2 \frac{d\varphi_2 *}{dx}\right) = -\frac{i\hbar}{2m}\left(2ik_2|C|^2\right) = \frac{\hbar k_2}{m}|C|^2 \tag{3.40}$$

The probabilities of reflection and transmission can then be obtained as

$$R = \frac{J_{reflected}}{J_{incident}} = \frac{\frac{\hbar k_1}{m}|B|^2}{\frac{\hbar k_1}{m}|A|^2} = \frac{|B|^2}{|A|^2} = \left[\frac{1-(k_2/k_1)}{1+(k_2/k_1)}\right]^2 \tag{3.41}$$

and

$$T = \frac{J_{transmitted}}{J_{incident}} = \frac{\frac{\hbar k_2}{m}|C|^2}{\frac{\hbar k_1}{m}|A|^2} = \frac{k_2|C|^2}{k_1|A|^2} = \frac{4k_2/k_1}{\left[1+(k_2/k_1)\right]^2} \tag{3.42}$$

From equations 3.41 and 3.42, it is easy to show that $R+T=1$, which is expected. It should also be noted that the de Broglie wavelength of the particle in region 2 is longer than that in region 1; that is, $(2\pi/k_2) > (2\pi/k_1)$. This is consistent with the description in classical mechanics that the incident particle loses kinetic energy as it travels against a potential barrier. Figure 3.1 shows the time-independent wave function of the particle at the interface between the two regions. In this sense, the above example is the wave-mechanics depiction of a 1-D scattering problem. The same methodology will be used again in 3-D problems in dealing with neutron and charged particle scatterings in the later chapters.

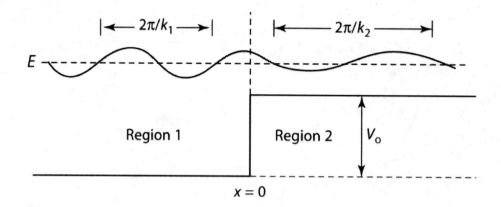

Figure 3.1. The wave function of a particle traveling against a positive-step-potential with height V_0 and $E > V_0$.

3.4.2 Step-Potential, $E < V_0$

We now consider the case when the kinetic energy E of the incident particle is less than V_0 for the same positive-step-potential problem described by equation 3.29. Because $V_0 = 0$ in region 1, the solution of $\varphi_1(x)$ remains the same as that of equation 3.31. In region 2, however, because k_2 must be a real number, the 1-D Schrödinger's equation and its general solution take slightly different forms:

$$\frac{d^2\varphi_2(x)}{dx^2} - k_2^2\varphi_2(x) = 0, \text{ where } k_2 = \frac{\sqrt{2m(V_0 - E)}}{\hbar} \tag{3.43}$$

and

$$\varphi_2(x) = Ce^{k_2 x} + De^{-k_2 x}. \tag{3.44}$$

Since $\varphi_2 \to \infty$ as $x \to \infty$, one must set $C = 0$. Equation 3.44 then becomes

$$\varphi_2(x) = De^{-k_2 x}. \tag{3.45}$$

The above result illustrates an important difference between the predictions of classical mechanics and quantum mechanics, in that the wave function is capable of penetrating into the classically forbidden region. The wave function is shown in Figure 3.2.

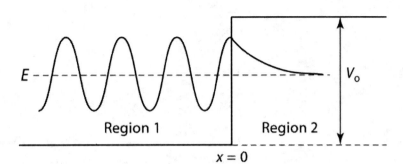

Figure 3.2. The wave function of a particle traveling against a positive-step-potential with height V_o and $E < V_o$.

3.4.3 Barrier Potential, $E > V_o$

We now consider a 1-D problem of a particle subjected to a positive barrier potential with height V_o and depth a; that is,

$$V(x) = 0, \text{ when } x < 0, \text{ region 1}$$
$$= V_o, \text{ when } 0 \le x \le a, \text{ region 2}$$
$$= 0, \text{ when } x > 0, \text{ region 3.} \tag{3.46}$$

For $E > V_o$, the 1-D Schrödinger's equation takes the same form as that of equation 3.31. The solutions for regions 1, 2, and 3, respectively, are

$$\varphi_1(x) = Ae^{ik_1 x} + Be^{-ik_1 x} \tag{3.47}$$

$$\varphi_2(x) = Ce^{ik_2 x} + De^{-ik_2 x} \tag{3.48}$$

$$\varphi_3(x) = Fe^{ik_3 x} + Ge^{-ik_3 x}, \tag{3.49}$$

where $k_1 = k_3 = \dfrac{\sqrt{2mE}}{\hbar}$ and $k_2 = \dfrac{\sqrt{2m(E - V_o)}}{\hbar}$.

By applying the boundary conditions for $x = 0$ and $x = a$, and by setting $D = G = 0$ (because there are no reflecting waves in regions 2 and 3), one may obtain the expressions of B, C, and F in terms of A, k_1, k_2, and k_3. One can then follow the same derivation of equation 3.42 to obtain the transmission probability as

$$T = \frac{|F|^2}{|A|^2} = \frac{1}{1 + \dfrac{1}{4}\dfrac{V_o^2}{E(E - V_o)}\sin^2 k_2 a}. \tag{3.50}$$

The corresponding wave function is shown in Figure 3.3.

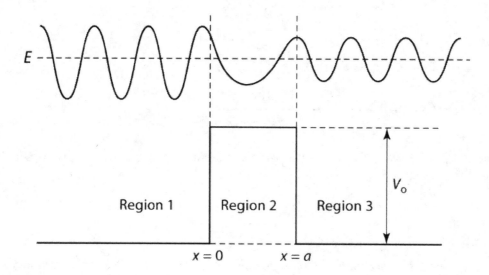

Figure 3.3. The wave function of a particle traveling against a positive-barrier-potential with height V_0 and width a, and $E > V_0$.

3.4.4 Barrier Potential, $E < V_0$

We now consider the case when $E < V_0$ for the same positive-step-potential problem described by 3.46. Because $V_0 = 0$ in regions 1 and 3, the solutions of $\varphi_1(x)$ and $\varphi_3(x)$ remain the same as in equations 3.47 and 3.49. In region 2, however, because k_2 must be a real number, the solution $\varphi_2(x)$ takes a slightly different form:

$$\varphi_2(x) = Ce^{k_2 x} + De^{-k_2 x}, \tag{3.51}$$

where $k_2 = \dfrac{\sqrt{2m(V_0 - E)}}{\hbar}$.

By applying the boundary conditions for $x = 0$ and $x = a$, and by setting $G = 0$ (because there are no reflecting waves in region 3), one may obtain the expressions of B, C, D, and F in terms of A, k_1, k_2, and k_3. One can then follow the same derivation as that of equation 3.42 to obtain the transmission probability as

$$T = \frac{|F|^2}{|A|^2} = \frac{1}{1 + \dfrac{1}{4}\dfrac{V_0^2}{E(V_0 - E)}\sinh^2 k_2 a}. \tag{3.52}$$

This non-zero barrier penetration probability is not permitted in classical mechanics for a particle having its kinetic energy less than the barrier potential (i.e., $E < V_0$). But in quantum mechanics, it is possible that the particle can tunnel through the barrier. The corresponding wave function is shown in Figure 3.4.

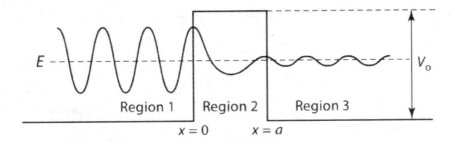

Figure 3.4. The wave function of a particle traveling against a positive-barrier-potential with height V_0 and width a, and $E < V_0$.

3.5 Infinite Square-Well Potential

Let us now consider a particle bound by an infinitely deep square well; that is,

$$V(x) = 0, \quad \text{when } 0 \le x \le a \text{ (i.e., inside the well)}$$
$$= \infty, \quad \text{when } x < 0, \text{ or } x > a \text{ (i.e., outside the well).}$$

For $0 \le x \le a$, the 1-D time-independent Schrödinger's equation takes the same form as that of Eq. 3.30:

$$\frac{d^2\varphi(x)}{dx^2} + k^2\varphi(x) = 0, \quad \text{where } k = \frac{\sqrt{2mE}}{\hbar}.$$

The general solution is

$$\varphi(x) = A\sin kx + B\cos kx . \tag{3.53}$$

Because the potential walls are infinitely high outside the well, there is no chance that the particle can be found outside the well. This sets the boundary conditions as $\varphi(0) = \varphi(a) = 0$, which in turn demands that $B = 0$. Equation 3.53 then becomes

$$\varphi(x) = A\sin kx . \tag{3.54}$$

The boundary condition $\varphi(a) = 0$ also demands that $\sin ka = 0$ for any A. This condition is satisfied if $ka = n\pi$, $n = 0, 1, 2, ...$ which gives the expression of quantized wave number:

$$k_n = \frac{n\pi}{a}, \quad n = 0, 1, 2, ... \tag{3.55}$$

and consequently the quantized momentum p_n:

$$p_n = \hbar k = \frac{n\pi\hbar}{a}, \quad n = 0, 1, 2, \ldots \tag{3.56}$$

The coefficient A in equation 3.54 can now be found by applying the normalization property that

$$\int_0^a \varphi^*(x)\varphi(x)\,dx = 1 \quad \Rightarrow \quad A^2 \int_0^a \sin^2\left(\frac{n\pi x}{a}\right)dx = 1 \quad \Rightarrow \quad A = \sqrt{\frac{2}{a}}. \tag{3.57}$$

Combining equations 3.54 and 3.55, and 3.57, one obtains the final solution of the wave function for the particle inside the well (i.e., $0 \le x \le a$) as

$$\varphi_n(x) = \sqrt{\frac{2}{a}}\sin\left(\frac{n\pi x}{a}\right). \tag{3.58}$$

One can also obtain the total energy (or kinetic energy in this case) of the particle as

$$E_n = \frac{p_n^2}{2m} = \frac{n^2\pi^2\hbar^2}{2ma^2}, \quad n = 1, 2, \ldots \tag{3.59}$$

The case of $n = 0$ is removed because it corresponds to the trivial solution of $\varphi(x) = 0$ inside the well. Equation 3.59 shows that E_n increases as n increases and decreases as a increases. If we now extend the problem from 1-D to 3-D, the solutions become

$$\varphi(x, y, z) = X(x)Y(y)Z(z), \tag{3.60}$$

where

$$X(x) = A\sin k_x x, \quad k_x = \frac{n_x \pi}{a},$$

$$Y(y) = B\sin k_y y, \quad k_y = \frac{n_y \pi}{a},$$

$$Z(z) = C\sin k_z z, \quad k_z = \frac{n_z \pi}{a},$$

And $p_x = \hbar k_x$, $p_y = \hbar k_y$, $p_z = \hbar k_z$. $\tag{3.61}$

Because p_x, p_y, and p_z are the magnitude of momentum vectors $\vec{p}_x$, $\vec{p}_y$, and $\vec{p}_z$, and because $\vec{p} = \vec{p}_x + \vec{p}_y + \vec{p}_z$, the magnitude of $\vec{p}$ can be found as

$$p_n = \sqrt{p_x^2 + p_y^2 + p_z^2} = \sqrt{\frac{\pi^2\hbar^2}{a^2}\left(n_x^2 + n_y^2 + n_z^2\right)}, \tag{3.62}$$

where $n^2 = n_x^2 + n_y^2 + n_z^2$, and $n_1 = 1, 2, 3, \ldots$ with $i = x$, y, or z

Accordingly, some states will exhibit degeneracy in energy in the sense that each state has the same n but a different set of (n_x, n_y, n_z). Figure 3.5 shows the energy levels and degeneracies for the three lowest energy levels.

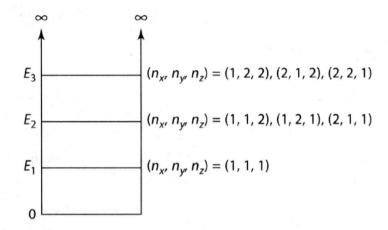

Figure 3.5. The energy levels and degeneracies for the three lowest energy levels.

The above 3-D particle-in-the-box example can serve as a crude model for a nucleus. For example, if one replaces a with the diameter of a nucleus, then equation 3.59 becomes

$$E_n = \frac{n^2 \pi^2 (\hbar c)^2}{2mc^2 (2r)^2},$$
(3.63)

where m is the mass of a nucleon and r is the radius of the nucleus. Now let us take an average nucleus with $r \cong 6$ fm, $mc^2 \cong 939$ MeV, and $\hbar c = 197.329$ MeV·fm. Equation 3.63 becomes

$$E_n = \frac{n^2 \pi^2 (197.329 \text{ MeV} \cdot \text{fm})^2}{2(939 \text{ MeV})(12 \text{ fm})^2} \cong 1.42 \, n^2 \text{ MeV}.$$
(3.64)

For the lowest energy state, $(n_x, n_y, n_z) = (1, 1, 1)$, $n^2 = 3 \Rightarrow E_1 \cong (3)(1.42) = 4.26$ MeV.

For the next energy state, $(n_x, n_y, n_z) = (2, 1, 1), (1, 2, 1),$ or $(1, 1, 2)$, $n^2 = 6$,

$$\Rightarrow E_2 \cong (6)(1.42) = 8.52 \text{ MeV}.$$

Thus, $\Delta E = E_2 - E_1 = 8.52 - 4.26 = 4.26$ MeV.

This result is consistent with the observed binding energies of a nucleon in a nucleus. If one replaces m and a in equation 3.58 with the electron rest mass and the diameter of an atom, respectively, then ΔE would be in the order of a few eV, which is consistent with the binding energies of an electron in an atom. The above results can also be obtained from the uncertainty principle. That is,

$$\Delta E = \frac{(\Delta p)^2}{2m} \cong \frac{\left(\frac{\hbar}{2\Delta x}\right)^2}{2m} = \frac{(\hbar c)^2}{8mc^2(\Delta x)^2}. \tag{3.65}$$

By inserting $\Delta x \cong 1\,\text{fm}$, $mc^2 \cong 939\,\text{MeV}$, and $\hbar c = 197.329\,\text{MeV} \cdot \text{fm}$, one obtains

$$\Delta E = \frac{(197.329\,\text{MeV} \cdot \text{fm})^2}{8(939)(1\,\text{fm})^2} = 5.18\,\text{MeV}.$$

3.6 Finite Square-Well Potential, $E < V_o$

We now consider a particle bound by a square well potential of a finite depth V_o; that is,

$$V(x) = V_o, \text{ when } x < 0, \text{ region I}$$
$$= 0, \text{ when } 0 \le x \le a, \text{ region II}$$
$$= V_o, \text{ when } x > a, \text{ region III}.$$

For region II, the general solution of the wave function has the same forms as that shown in equation 3.53:

$$\varphi_2(x) = A\sin k_2 x + B\cos k_2 x, \tag{3.66}$$

where $k_2 = \dfrac{p}{\hbar} = \dfrac{\sqrt{2mE}}{\hbar}$.

For regions I and III, the general solution has the same forms as that of equations 3.47 and 3.49:

$$\varphi_1(x) = Ce^{ik_1 x} + De^{-ik_1 x} \text{ and}$$

$$\varphi_3(x) = Fe^{ik_3 x} + Ge^{-ik_3 x}, \tag{3.67}$$

where $k_1 = k_3 = \dfrac{p}{\hbar} = \dfrac{\sqrt{2m(E - V_o)}}{\hbar}$. If we redefine $k_1 = k_3 = \dfrac{p}{\hbar} = \dfrac{\sqrt{2m(V_o - E)}}{\hbar}$, then 3.67 can be reduced to the following:

$$\varphi_1(x) = Ce^{k_1 x} + De^{-k_1 x}$$

$$\varphi_3(x) = Fe^{k_3 x} + Ge^{-k_3 x}. \tag{3.68}$$

For a particle in region I, $x \to -\infty$ leads to $e^{-k_1 x} \to \infty$ and $\varphi_1 \to \infty$. Since this cannot be true, that means $D = 0$. With the same argument, one finds that $F = 0$ for particles in region III. Equation 3.68 therefore becomes

$$\varphi_1(x) = Ce^{k_1 x}$$

$$\varphi_3(x) = Ge^{-k_3 x}. \tag{3.69}$$

There now exist five knowns in the three wave functions: A, B, C, G, and E. The unknowns can be obtained by using the four boundary conditions, $\varphi_1(0) = \varphi_2(0)$, $\varphi_1'(0) = \varphi_2'(0)$, $\varphi_2(a) = \varphi_3(a)$, $\varphi_2'(a) = \varphi_3'(a)$, and the normalization of the wave function. The boundary conditions $\varphi_1(0) = \varphi_2(0)$ and $\varphi_1'(0) = \varphi_2'(0)$ lead to

$$A\sin(0) + B\cos(0) = C \quad \Rightarrow \quad B = C \tag{3.70}$$

and

$$k_2 A\cos(0) - k_2 B\sin(0) = k_1 C \quad \Rightarrow \quad A = \left(\frac{k_1}{k_2}\right)C. \tag{3.71}$$

The boundary conditions $\varphi_2(a) = \varphi_3(a)$ and $\varphi_2'(a) = \varphi_3'(a)$ lead to:

$$A\sin k_2 a + B\cos k_2 a = Ge^{-k_3 a} \quad \Rightarrow \quad G = e^{k_3 a}\left[\left(\frac{k_1}{k_2}\right)\sin k_2 a + \cos k_2 a\right]C \tag{3.72}$$

and

$$k_2 A\cos k_2 a - k_2 B\sin k_2 a = -k_3 Ge^{-k_3 a} \quad \Rightarrow \quad G = e^{k_3 a}\left[-\left(\frac{k_1}{k_3}\right)\cos k_2 a + \left(\frac{k_2}{k_3}\right)\sin k_2 a\right]C. \tag{3.73}$$

Dividing equation 3.72 by 3.73 yields

$$\left(\frac{k_1}{k_2}\right)\sin k_2 a + \cos k_2 a = -\left(\frac{k_1}{k_3}\right)\cos k_2 a + \left(\frac{k_2}{k_3}\right)\sin k_2 a = -\cos k_2 a + \left(\frac{k_2}{k_1}\right)\sin k_2 a$$

$$\Rightarrow \quad \left(\frac{k_1}{k_2}\right)\tan k_2 a + 2 = \left(\frac{k_2}{k_1}\right)\tan k_2 a$$

$$\Rightarrow \quad \tan k_2 a = \frac{2k_1 k_2}{k_2^2 - k_1^2}. \tag{3.74}$$

Substituting $k_1 = \dfrac{\sqrt{2m(V_0 - E)}}{\hbar}$ and $k_2 = \dfrac{\sqrt{2mE}}{\hbar}$ into equation 3.74 yields

$$2\sqrt{(V_0 - E)E} = (2E - V_0)\tan\left(\frac{a}{\hbar}\sqrt{2mE}\right). \tag{3.75}$$

One may then obtain E by solving equation 3.75 numerically. We will leave this as an exercise for the readers. We will simply make two notable remarks below:

1. The non-zero wave functions of φ_1 and φ_3 in region I and III indicate that there is a non-zero probability of finding the particle in these regions that is classically forbidden.

2. Equation 3.75 leads to a finite number of allowed energy levels. In fact, there is a possibility that no energy level is allowed if a potential well is too narrow or too shallow. This is different from that of the infinite square-well case (Section 3.5), where the number of allowed energy levels is infinite.

3.7 Infinite Spherical Well

Let us now consider a particle bound by a spherically symmetric potential, $V(r)$. The 3-D time-independent Schrödinger's equation expressed in the spherical coordinates can be found as

$$-\frac{\hbar^2}{2m}\nabla^2\varphi + [E - V(r)]\varphi = 0, \tag{3.76}$$

where, $\nabla^2 = \frac{1}{r^2}\frac{\partial}{\partial r}\left(r^2\frac{\partial}{\partial r}\right) + \frac{1}{r^2}\left[\frac{1}{\sin\theta}\frac{\partial}{\partial\theta}\left(\sin\theta\frac{\partial}{\partial\theta}\right) + \frac{1}{\sin^2\theta}\frac{\partial^2}{\partial\phi^2}\right].$ \hfill (3.77)

By using the separation-of-variable method, and assuming that $\varphi = \varphi(r, \theta, \phi) = R(r)\Theta(\theta)\Phi(\phi)$, one can recast equation 3.76 into the following three separate ordinary differential equations:

$$\frac{d^2\Phi}{d\phi^2} + m_\ell^2\Phi = 0 \tag{3.78}$$

$$\frac{1}{\sin\theta}\frac{\partial}{\partial\theta}\left(\sin\theta\frac{d\Theta}{d\theta}\right) + \left[\ell(\ell+1) - \frac{m_\ell^2}{\sin^2\theta}\right]\Theta = 0 \tag{3.79}$$

$$-\frac{\hbar^2}{2m}\left(\frac{d^2R}{dr^2} + \frac{2}{r}\frac{dR}{dr}\right) + \left[V(r) + \frac{\ell(\ell+1)\hbar^2}{2mr^2}\right]R = ER. \tag{3.80}$$

The solutions for equations 3.78 and 3.79, respectively, are as follows:

$$\Phi(\phi) = \frac{1}{\sqrt{2\pi}}e^{im_\ell\phi} \tag{3.81}$$

$$\Theta(\theta) = \left[\left(\frac{2\ell+1}{2}\right)\frac{(\ell-m_l)!}{(\ell+m_l)!}\right]^{1/2} p_\ell^{m_\ell}(\theta), \tag{3.82}$$

where $p_\ell^{m_\ell}(\theta)$ is the associated Legendre polynomials given in Table 3.1.

Table 3.1. The associated Legendre polynomials for some low ℓ values.

ℓ	m_ℓ	$p_\ell^{m_\ell}$
0	0	1
1	0	$\cos\theta$
	± 1	$\sin\theta$
2	0	$(3\cos^2\theta - 1)/2$
	± 1	$3\sin\theta\cos\theta$
	± 2	$\sin^2\theta$

To solve *R(r)* for equation 3.80, let us consider the following infinite potential well:

$$V(r) = 0, \ r < a$$
$$= \infty, \ r \geq a. \tag{3.83}$$

Equation 3.83 requires that $R(r) = 0$ for $r \geq a$. Because $V(r) = 0$ for $r < a$, equation 3.80 is reduced to

$$-\frac{\hbar^2}{2m}\left(\frac{d^2R}{dr^2} + \frac{2}{r}\frac{dR}{dr}\right) + \frac{\ell(\ell+1)\hbar^2}{2mr^2}R = ER. \tag{3.84}$$

The solution of 3.84 can be found as

$$R_\ell(r) = j_\ell(kr), \tag{3.85}$$

where $k = \dfrac{\sqrt{2mE}}{\hbar}$, $l = 0, 1, 2, ...$ and $j_\ell(kr)$ is the Spherical Bessel Functions given in Table 3.2.

Table 3.2. The Spherical Bessel Functions.

ℓ	$j_\ell(kr)$
0	$\dfrac{\sin kr}{kr}$
1	$\dfrac{\sin kr}{(kr)^2} - \dfrac{\cos kr}{kr}$
2	$\dfrac{3\sin kr}{(kr)^3} - \dfrac{3\cos kr}{(kr)^2} - \dfrac{\sin kr}{kr}$
ℓ	$\cong \dfrac{(kr)^\ell}{1\cdot 3\cdot 5\cdots(2\ell+1)}$ when $kr \to 0$ $\cong \dfrac{\sin\left(kr - \dfrac{\ell\pi}{2}\right)}{kr}$ when $kr \to \infty$

To find the energy eigenvalues, we apply the boundary conditions for $r = a$. That is,

$$R_\ell(a) = j_\ell(ka) = 0. \tag{3.86}$$

Equation 3.86 is a transcendental equation, and the values of k can be obtained by finding the zeros of $j_\ell(ka)$. For example, for $\ell = 0$, $j_0(ka) = 0$ occurs at $ka = 3.14, 6.28, 9.42, 12.37, \dots$.

for $n = 1, 2, 3, 4, \dots$ and so on. For $n = 1$, $ka = 3.14 \Rightarrow k_1 = \dfrac{3.14}{a}$, which in turn gives

$$E_{n,l} = E_{1,0} = \frac{p^2}{2m} = \frac{k_1^2 \hbar^2}{2m} = \frac{(3.14)^2 \hbar^2}{2ma^2}. \tag{3.87}$$

For $n = 2$, $ka = 6.28 \Rightarrow k_2 = \dfrac{6.28}{a}$, which in turn gives

$$E_{n,l} = E_{2,0} = \frac{p^2}{2m} = \frac{k_2^2 \hbar^2}{2m} = \frac{(6.26)^2 \hbar^2}{2ma^2}. \tag{3.88}$$

From equations 3.87 and 3.88, one obtains

$$\frac{E_{2,0}}{E_{1,0}} = \frac{(6.28)^2}{(3.14)^2} = 4.0 \, .$$

Similarly, for $l = 1$, $j_1(ka) = 0$ occurs at $ka = 4.49, 7.73, 10.90, 14.07, \ldots$ for $n = 1, 2, 3, 4, \ldots$

For $n = 1$, $ka = 4.49 \Rightarrow k_1 = \frac{4.49}{a}$, which in turn gives

$$E_{n,l} = E_{1,1} = \frac{p^2}{2m} = \frac{k_1^2 \hbar^2}{2m} = \frac{(4.49)^2 \hbar^2}{2ma^2} \, . \tag{3.89}$$

For $n = 2$, $ka = 7.73 \Rightarrow k_2 = \frac{7.73}{a}$, which in turn gives

$$E_{n,l} = E_{2,1} = \frac{p^2}{2m} = \frac{k_2^2 \hbar^2}{2m} = \frac{(7.73)^2 \hbar^2}{2ma^2} \, . \tag{3.90}$$

From equations 3.87 to 3.90, one obtains

$$\frac{E_{1,1}}{E_{1,0}} = \frac{(4.49)^2}{(3.14)^2} = 2.05$$

and

$$\frac{E_{2,1}}{E_{1,0}} = \frac{(7.73)^2}{(3.14)^2} = 6.06 \, .$$

By repeating the above process for $\ell = 2, 3, \ldots$ we would be able to construct the entire spectrum of energy states of the system. Similar to that of the 3-D Cartesian well, the states are degenerate. That is, for each ℓ there are $2\ell + 1$ different wave functions (each with different m_l values; i.e., $0, \pm 1, \pm 2, \ldots, \pm \ell$) that all have the same energy. The different wave functions are represented by the so-called spherical harmonics, defined by

$$Y_{\ell,m_\ell}(\phi, \theta) = \Phi_{m_\ell}(\phi) \Theta_{\ell,m_\ell}(\theta) = \left[\left(\frac{2\ell+1}{4\pi} \right) \frac{(\ell - m_\ell)!}{(\ell + m_\ell)!} \right]^{1/2} p_\ell^{m_\ell}(\theta) e^{im_\ell \phi} \, . \tag{3.91}$$

For example, for $\ell = 2$, $m_\ell = 0, \pm 1, \pm 2$. The five wave functions $Y_{2,0}, Y_{2,1}, Y_{2,-1}, Y_{2,2}$, and $Y_{2,-2}$ all have the same energy (i.e., five-fold degeneracy).

The probability of locating the particle in a differential volume $d\tau$ is given by $|\varphi|^2 d\tau$. Therefore, by replacing $d\tau$ with $r^2 \sin\theta \, dr \, d\theta \, d\phi$ (or $r^2 dr \, d\Omega$), the probability of locating the particle between r and $r+dr$ can be obtained as

$$P(r)dr = \int |\varphi|^2 d\tau = r^2 |R(r)|^2 dr \int_{4\pi} |Y_{l,m_l}|^2 d\Omega = r^2 |R(r)|^2 dr. \tag{3.92}$$

3.8 Quantum Theory of Angular Momentum

In Section 3.7, the solutions of the 3-D spherical symmetric potential, ℓ, is referred to as the angular momentum quantum number. Because the classical expression of angular momentum is $\vec{L} = \vec{r} \times \vec{p}$, and because the momentum operator in quantum mechanics is $(\vec{p})_{op} = -i\hbar \vec{\nabla}$, we can obtain the angular momentum operator as $(\vec{L})_{op} = \frac{\hbar}{i}(\vec{r} \times \vec{\nabla})$, where $\vec{\nabla} = \frac{\partial}{\partial x}\vec{i} + \frac{\partial}{\partial y}\vec{j} + \frac{\partial}{\partial z}\vec{k}$. In Cartesian coordinates, the corresponding angular momentum on each axis therefore is

$$\left(\vec{L}_x\right)_{op} = \frac{\hbar}{i}\left(y\frac{\partial}{\partial z} - z\frac{\partial}{\partial y}\right)$$

$$\left(\vec{L}_y\right)_{op} = \frac{\hbar}{i}\left(z\frac{\partial}{\partial x} - x\frac{\partial}{\partial z}\right)$$

$$\left(\vec{L}_z\right)_{op} = \frac{\hbar}{i}\left(x\frac{\partial}{\partial y} - y\frac{\partial}{\partial x}\right), \tag{3.93}$$

where $\vec{L} = \vec{L}_x + \vec{L}_y + \vec{L}_z$. The corresponding equations in the spherical coordinates are

$$\left(\vec{L}_x\right)_{op} = i\hbar\left(\sin\phi\frac{\partial}{\partial\theta} + \cot\theta\cos\phi\frac{\partial}{\partial\phi}\right)$$

$$\left(\vec{L}_y\right)_{op} = -i\hbar\left(\cos\phi\frac{\partial}{\partial\theta} - \cot\theta\sin\phi\frac{\partial}{\partial\phi}\right) \left(\vec{L}_y\right)_{op} = -i\hbar\left(\cos\phi\frac{\partial}{\partial\theta} - \cot\theta\sin\phi\frac{\partial}{\partial\phi}\right)$$

$$\left(\vec{L}_z\right)_{op} = -i\hbar\frac{\partial}{\partial\phi}, \tag{3.94}$$

and

$$\left(L^2\right)_{op} = \left(L_x^2\right)_{op} + \left(L_y^2\right)_{op} + \left(L_z^2\right)_{op} = -\hbar^2\left[\frac{1}{\sin\theta}\frac{\partial}{\partial\theta}\left(\sin\theta\frac{\partial}{\partial\theta}\right) + \frac{1}{\sin^2\theta}\frac{\partial^2}{\partial\phi^2}\right]. \tag{3.95}$$

We now define the commutator of two operators, A_{op} and B_{op}, as:

$$[A_{op}, B_{op}] = A_{op}B_{op} - B_{op}A_{op}. \tag{3.96}$$

If $[A_{op}, B_{op}]\varphi = 0$, then the operators A_{op} and B_{op} are said to be "commute." From equations 3.93 and 3.96, it can be shown that

$$\left[\left(\vec{L}_x\right)_{op}, \left(\vec{L}_y\right)_{op}\right] = -\hbar^2\left(y\frac{\partial}{\partial z} - z\frac{\partial}{\partial y}\right)\left(z\frac{\partial}{\partial x} - x\frac{\partial}{\partial z}\right) + \hbar^2\left(z\frac{\partial}{\partial x} - x\frac{\partial}{\partial z}\right)\left(y\frac{\partial}{\partial z} - z\frac{\partial}{\partial y}\right)$$

$$= -\hbar^2\left(y\frac{\partial}{\partial x} - x\frac{\partial}{\partial y}\right) = i\hbar\left[\frac{\hbar}{i}\left(x\frac{\partial}{\partial y} - y\frac{\partial}{\partial x}\right)\right] = i\hbar\left(\vec{L}_z\right)_{op}.$$

$$(3.97)$$

Similarly, one can show that

$$\left[\left(\vec{L}_y\right)_{op}, \left(\vec{L}_z\right)_{op}\right] = i\hbar\left(\vec{L}_x\right)$$

and

$$.\left[\left(\vec{L}_z\right)_{op}, \left(\vec{L}_x\right)_{op}\right] = i\hbar\left(\vec{L}_y\right)$$

From the above, one concludes that none of the operators $\left(\vec{L}_x\right)_{op}, \left(\vec{L}_y\right)_{op}$, and $\left(\vec{L}_z\right)_{op}$ commute with one another. In other words, if one finds an eigenfunction of one of the components, that component will be determined precisely for a state, but the other two components will not be precisely defined. However, from equation 3.96 it can be shown that

$$\left[\left(L^2\right)_{op}, \left(\vec{L}_x\right)_{op}\right] = \left[\left(L^2\right)_{op}, \left(\vec{L}_x\right)_{op}\right] = \left[\left(L^2\right)_{op}, \left(\vec{L}_x\right)_{op}\right] = 0, \qquad (3.98)$$

which means that $\left(L^2\right)_{op}$ commutes with each of the components $\left(\vec{L}_x\right)_{op}, \left(\vec{L}_y\right)_{op}$, and $\left(\vec{L}_z\right)_{op}$. The relationship between $\vec{L}$ and any of the Cartesian components can be further illustrated in Figure 3.6; that is, if one keeps L and L_z constant, then $\vec{L}$ corresponds to a vector in precession about the z axis. As such, L_x and L_y are totally undetermined.

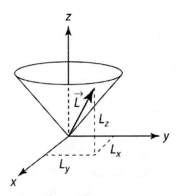

Figure 3.6. The relationship between $\vec{L}$ and any of the Cartesian components.

One can, therefore, summarize an important finding in quantum mechanics: because the total angular momentum is conserved for an isolated system, the square of the total angular momentum (which measures its magnitude) and one of the Cartesian components can have the same eigenfunction. In other words, each state of the system will be characterized by discrete values of both L and one of the Cartesian components, L_x, L_y, or L_z. Conventionally, one uses L_z. The values of L_z can be calculated from equations 3.81 and 3.94:

$$\left(\bar{L}_z\right)_{op}\Phi = -i\hbar\frac{\partial\Phi}{\partial\phi} = -i\hbar\frac{\partial}{\partial\phi}\left(\frac{1}{\sqrt{2\pi}}e^{im_\ell\phi}\right) = \frac{m_\ell\hbar}{\sqrt{2\pi}}e^{im_\ell\phi} = m_\ell\hbar\Phi, \tag{3.99}$$

which means L_z has values of $m_\ell\hbar$, where $m_\ell = 0,\pm 1,\pm 2,...,\pm\ell$. Similarly, the values of L can be calculated from equations 3.91 and 3.95:

$$\left(L^2\right)_{op}Y_{\ell,m_\ell}(\phi,\theta) = -\hbar^2\left[\frac{1}{\sin\theta}\frac{\partial}{\partial\theta}\left(\sin\theta\frac{\partial}{\partial\theta}\right) + \frac{1}{\sin^2\theta}\frac{\partial^2}{\partial\phi^2}\right]Y_{\ell,m_\ell}(\phi,\theta)$$

$$= \ell(\ell+1)Y_{\ell,m_\ell}(\phi,\theta), \tag{3.100}$$

which means L has the values of $\sqrt{\ell(\ell+1)}\hbar$, where $\ell = 0,1,2,...$

3.9 Spin and Parity

3.9.1 Spin

As mentioned in Section 2.3, the complete description of an electronic state in an atom requires the inclusion of the intrinsic spin of the electron. The intrinsic spin can be treated as an inherent angular momentum associated with the particle. The electron spin has a spin quantum number $s = \frac{1}{2}$. This same property is also possessed by protons and neutrons. As mentioned in Section 1.2, electrons, protons, and neutrons are fermions, which have a half-integer spin quantum number. The magnitudes S and S_z can be expressed in a similar way as that of the orbital angular momentum L. That is,

$$S = \sqrt{s(s+1)}\hbar, \text{ where } s = \frac{1}{2} \tag{3.101}$$

and

$$S_z = m_s\hbar, \text{ where } m_s = \pm\frac{1}{2}. \tag{3.102}$$

3.9.2 Parity

Parity is a property associated with symmetry of the wave function. The parity operation causes a spatial reflection through the origin (i.e., $\vec{r} \rightarrow -\vec{r}$). In Cartesian coordinates, this means $x \rightarrow -x, y \rightarrow -y, z \rightarrow -z$. In spherical coordinates, this means $r \rightarrow r, \theta \rightarrow \pi - \theta, \phi \rightarrow \phi + \pi$. A wave function is said to possess even parity if $\psi(\vec{r}) = \psi(-\vec{r})$, and it is said to possess odd parity if $\psi(\vec{r}) = -\psi(-\vec{r})$. In Schrödinger's equation, where the potential is an even function, there always exist both an odd and an even solution. The parity of the wave function is found to be conserved by both the electromagnetic and strong interactions, but not conserved for the weak interaction. Parity conservation has important implications with respect to nuclear structure and transitions between nuclear states. For example, certain α and γ decays are forbidden solely because the parity is not conserved (see Chapter 6).

3.10 Transitions Between States

As shown in Sections 3.4 to 3.7, the energy levels we obtain by solving the time-independent Schrödinger's equation for a bound particle are stationary states. The orthogonal property of the eigenfunctions (equation 3.17) does not allow a quantum system to undergo transition between two different stationary states. That is, a system that originally exists in a particular state will always remain in that state. In reality, however, the uncertainty principle says that the energy level of a system is never perfectly defined. As such, there is a chance for a quantum system to undergo transition from one state to another. The source of uncertainty of the energy level can either be internal (e.g., a radioactive nuclide) or external (e.g., a neutron-induced nuclear reaction). The transition probability between two states can be obtained by solving the time-dependent Schrödinger's equation that contains an additional small perturbation potential.

We begin by defining H_0, the time-independent Hamilton operator, as

$$H_0 = -\frac{\hbar^2}{2m}\frac{\partial^2}{\partial x^2} + V(x).$$

(3.103)

The time-independent Schrödinger's equation can therefore be written as

$$H_0 \varphi(x) = E\varphi(x).$$

(3.104)

It has been shown in equations 3.14 to 3.16 that $\varphi(x) = \sum_n a_n \varphi_n$, where φ_n is an eigenfunction corresponding to a specific state of the system, and that $\psi(x,t) = \varphi(x)e^{-i\omega t}$. Now at $t = 0$, one introduces a perturbation term H' into the system (i.e., $H = H_0 + H'$); then $\psi(x,\Delta t)$ can be approximated by

$$\psi(x,\Delta t) \cong \psi(x,0) + \frac{\Delta t}{i\hbar}H\psi(x,0) = \varphi_n(x) + \frac{\Delta t}{i\hbar}(H_0 + H')\varphi_n(x)$$

$$= (1 - i\omega_n \Delta t)\varphi_n(x) - \frac{i\Delta t}{\hbar}H'\varphi_n(x),$$

(3.105)

where $\omega_n = E_n/\hbar$. The first term on the right-hand side of equation 3.105 is the same as the first-order approximation of the Taylor series expansion of $\psi(x,t) = \varphi_n(x)e^{-i\omega_n t}$, which does not allow transition of state to take place. The second term of equation 3.105, however, represents a small component of a different stationary state, φ_m. That is, the effect of switching on a perturbation potential H' is to add to an initial eigenfunction φ_n the extra term of equation 3.105 proportional to $H'\varphi_n$, which contains small components of several different eigenfunctions φ_m. For each $m \neq n$, there is therefore a definite probability $P(n \to m)$ that a system that started out in the state φ_n will be found in state φ_m. This probability can be evaluated by setting $\varphi(x) = \varphi_n$ and then expanding the extra term of equation 3.105 as follows:

$$-\frac{i\Delta t}{\hbar} H' \varphi_n = \sum_m a_m \varphi_m \,, \tag{3.106}$$

where a_m can be obtained by applying the orthogonal property of φ_n as

$$a_m = -\frac{i\Delta t}{\hbar} \int_{-\infty}^{\infty} \varphi_m^* H' \varphi_n dx \quad. \tag{3.107}$$

The transition probability can then be found as

$$P(n \rightarrow m) = |a_m|^2 = \left(\frac{i\Delta t}{\hbar}\right)^2 \left(\int_{-\infty}^{\infty} \varphi_m^* H' \varphi_n dx\right)^2 = \left(\frac{\Delta t}{\hbar}\right)^2 |H'_{mn}|^2 \,, \tag{3.108}$$

where $H'_{mn} = \int_{-\infty}^{\infty} \varphi_m^* H' \varphi_n dx$, and is referred to as the matrix element. The total probability for an initial state n to undergo transition is then the integral of equation 3.108 with reference to all the available final state m. That is,

$$P(n) = \int P(n \rightarrow m) \rho_m \, dE_m \,, \tag{3.109}$$

where ρ_m is the state density. It can be shown (without proof here) that $P(n) \cong \frac{2\pi}{\hbar} |H'_{mn}|^2 \rho_m t$.

As such, the transition probability per unit time for the initial state n can be expressed as

$$\lambda_n = \frac{P(n)}{t} = \frac{2\pi}{\hbar} |H'_{mn}|^2 \rho_m \,. \tag{3.110}$$

The above formula is referred to as Fermi's Golden Rule, which will be used to explain radioactive decay rate as well as nuclear reaction rate in future chapters.

3.11 Wave-Mechanical Description of Scattering

In this section, we will use wave mechanics to describe scattering as opposed to the classical description, such as the Rutherford scattering discussed in Section 1.8. As shown in equation 3.5, an incident free particle traveling in the +x direction can be represented by a plane wave:

$$\varphi_{in} = e^{ikx} \,, \tag{3.111}$$

where $k = \dfrac{1}{\lambdabar} = \dfrac{p}{\hbar} \cong \dfrac{mv}{\hbar}$. As shown in Figure 3.7, we consider a central spherical potential (presented by a nucleus or an atom) being placed in front of the traveling particle wave. The force nature of the potential can be either strong force or Coulomb force. The infinite transverse dimension of a plane wave is justified because the incident wave is effectively relative to the dimension of the nuclear potential, which is typically in the order of 10^{-8} to 10^{-12} cm.

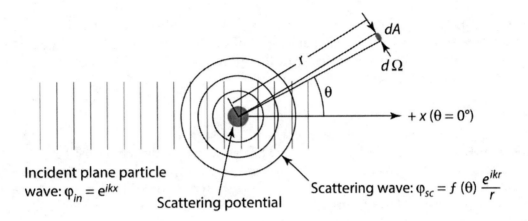

Figure 3.7. The quantum-mechanical picture of a free particle traveling in the $+x$ direction and scattered by a spherical nuclear potential.

The incident particle current density can be expressed via equation 3.28 as

$$J_{in} = \frac{\hbar}{2mi}\left(\varphi_{in}^{*} \frac{d\varphi_{in}}{dx} - \varphi_{in} \frac{d\varphi_{in}^{*}}{dx} \right) = \frac{\hbar}{2mi}(ik + ik) = \frac{\hbar k}{m} \cong v. \tag{3.112}$$

For an elastic scattering interaction, the magnitude of the scattered wave must be inversely proportional to r, because the scattered particle current density must be proportional to $1/r^2$, where r is the distance from the center of the scattering potential. As such, the scattered wave must have the following form:

$$\varphi_{sc} = f(\theta) \frac{e^{ikr}}{r}, \tag{3.113}$$

where $f(\theta)$ is the amplitude of the scattered wave, and it implies that the scattering is only dependent on the polar angle θ and not on the azimuthal angle ϕ. The scattered particle current density, which is directed radially outward, is therefore given by

$$J_{sc} = \frac{\hbar}{2mi}\left(\varphi_{sc}^{*} \frac{d\varphi_{sc}}{dr} - \varphi_{sc} \frac{d\varphi_{sc}^{*}}{dr} \right) = \frac{\hbar k}{m} \frac{|f(\theta)|^2}{r^2} \cong v \frac{|f(\theta)|^2}{r^2}. \tag{3.114}$$

The differential scattering cross section at angle θ can then be obtained as

$$d\sigma_s(\theta) = \frac{J_{sc}dA}{J_{in}} = \frac{J_{sc}\,r^2 d\Omega}{J_{in}} = |f(\theta)|^2 d\Omega,$$

or

$$\frac{d\sigma_s(\theta)}{d\Omega} = |f(\theta)|^2 = f(\theta)^* f(\theta), \qquad (3.115)$$

which shows that the problem of finding the differential scattering cross section is now reduced to the problem of determining the amplitude, $f(\theta)$, of the scattered wave. We will discuss below two widely used methods for obtaining $f(\theta)$: the Born Approximation method and the partial-wave analysis method. (Anderson, 1971)

3.11.1 Born Approximation

In this method, we consider the force potential (presented by the target nucleus or atom) described in Figure 3.7, so weak that it can be treated as a perturbation to the incident particle. That is, the potential is turned on when the incident particle comes into the scattering zone, and turned off when the scattered particle goes out of the scattering zone. Then, according to Fermi's Golden Rule (equation 3.110), the transition rate for the particle to go from its initial state i to its final state f under the influence of the perturbation potential $v(\vec{r})$ is given by

$$R = \frac{2\pi}{\hbar} \left[\int_\tau \varphi_f^* \, v(\vec{r}) \, \varphi_i \, d\tau \right]^2 \rho_f, \qquad (3.116)$$

where ρ_f is the final state density of the particle, and it is known to be

$$\rho_f = \frac{mL^3 k_f}{2\pi^2\hbar^2}, \qquad (3.117)$$

where L is the length of the side of a cubic encompassing the scattering zone.

The transition rate of the particle from the initial state, $\vec{k}_i$, to its final state, $\vec{k}_f$, lies in a small solid angle ($d\Omega$) centered around $\vec{k}_f$:

$$\frac{R}{4\pi} = J_{in} \frac{d\sigma(\theta)}{d\Omega}. \qquad (3.118)$$

By setting $J_{in} = \dfrac{\hbar k_i}{m}$ and substituting equations 3.116 and 3.117 into 3.118, the angular-dependent differential cross section then becomes

$$\frac{d\sigma(\theta)}{d\Omega} = \frac{R}{4\pi J_{in}} = \left(\frac{m^2 L^3}{4\pi^2\hbar^4} \right)\left(\frac{k_f}{k_i} \right)\left[\int_\tau \varphi_f^* \, v(\vec{r}) \, \varphi_i \, d\tau \right]^2, \qquad (3.119)$$

where φ_i and φ_f^* can be found as

$$\varphi_i = L^{-3/2} \, e^{i\vec{k}_i \cdot \vec{r}} \tag{3.120}$$

and

$$\varphi_f^* = L^{-3/2} \, e^{-i\vec{k}_f \cdot \vec{r}} \, . \tag{3.121}$$

Equations 3.120 and 3.121 are obtained by the normalization principle that

$$\int_{L^3} \varphi^* \varphi \, d\tau = 1 \, . \tag{3.122}$$

For elastic scattering, $k_f = k_i$. Equation 3.119 is then reduced to

$$\frac{d\sigma(\theta)}{d\Omega} = \frac{R}{4\pi I} = \left(\frac{m^2 L^3}{4\pi^2 \hbar^4} \right) \left[\int_\tau L^{-3} e^{-i\vec{k}_f \cdot \vec{r}} \, v(\vec{r}) \, e^{i\vec{k}_i \cdot \vec{r}} \, d\tau \right]^2$$

$$= \left[\frac{m}{2\pi\hbar^2} \int_\tau v(\vec{r}) \, e^{i(\vec{k}_i - \vec{k}_f) \cdot \vec{r}} \, d\tau \right]^2 \, . \tag{3.123}$$

By comparing equation 3.123 with 3.115, one obtains

$$|f(\theta)| = \frac{m}{2\pi\hbar^2} \int_\tau v(\vec{r}) \, e^{i(\vec{k}_i - \vec{k}_f) \cdot \vec{r}} \, d\tau \, . \tag{3.124}$$

The above approach is referred to as the Born Approximation method. For elastic scattering, $\vec{k}_i$ and $\vec{k}_f$ have the same length. If we define $\vec{K} = \vec{k}_i - \vec{k}_f$, then from Figure 3.8 one obtains

$$K = 2k_i \sin\frac{\theta}{2} \, . \tag{3.125}$$

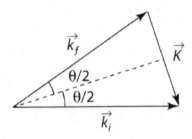

Figure 3.8. The geometric relationship of $\vec{k}_i$ and $\vec{k}_f$ and $\vec{K}$.

By defining an auxiliary set of polar coordinates with the polar axis directed along $\vec{K}$, one has

$$\int_\tau v(\vec{r}) \, e^{i\vec{K} \cdot \vec{r}} \, d\tau = \int_0^\infty \int_0^\pi v(r) \, e^{iKr\cos\theta} (2\pi r^2 \sin\theta \, dr \, d\theta)$$

$$= 2\pi \int_0^\infty \mathrm{v}(r)\, r^2\, dr \int_0^\pi e^{iKr\cos\theta} \sin\theta\, d\theta$$

$$= \frac{4\pi}{K} \int_0^\infty \mathrm{v}(r)\cdot \sin Kr \cdot r\, dr \,. \tag{3.126}$$

Thus, from equations 3.123 and 3.126, one obtains the differential cross section as

$$\frac{d\sigma}{d\Omega} = \left[\frac{2m}{\hbar^2 K} \int_\tau \mathrm{v}(r)\cdot \sin Kr \cdot r\, dr \right]^2 . \tag{3.127}$$

To re-derive the Rutherford scattering formula, we let v(r) be the Coulomb potential. That is,

$$\mathrm{v}(r) = \frac{a}{r}, \tag{3.128}$$

where $a = k_c e^2 zZ$. Equation 3.127 then becomes

$$\frac{d\sigma}{d\Omega} = \left[\frac{2ma}{\hbar^2 K} \int_0^\infty \sin Kr\, dr \right]^2 = \left[\frac{a}{E(2\sin\theta/2)^2} \right]^2$$

$$= \frac{k_c^2 z^2 Z^2 e^4}{16 E^2 \sin^4(\theta/2)}, \tag{3.129}$$

where $E = \dfrac{k^2 \hbar^2}{2m}$, which is the classical expression of the kinetic energy of the incident particle.

We therefore have used the quantum-mechanical approach and derived the same formula obtained from the classical particle-mechanics approach as that shown in equation 1.24. This is not surprising, because Rutherford scattering is extremely forwardly directed; that is, $\dfrac{d\sigma}{d\Omega} \propto \sin^{-4}(\theta/2)$, hence the change of the wave function of the particle during the scattering is so little so that the perturbation theory (i.e., Fermi's Golden Rule) is valid. While equation 3.129 is for elastic scattering, the Born Approximation is also valid for inelastic scattering of charged particles with atoms. As such, equation 3.123 will be used in Section 9.2 in charged-particle interactions with atoms.

3.11.2 Partial-Wave Analysis Method

In this method, we consider that the force potential (presented by the target nucleus or atom) described in Figure 3.7 is strong enough that the Born Approximation is not valid. In this case, to find $f(\theta)$ and thus $d\sigma_s/d\Omega$, one needs to first obtain the total wave function as a function of r and θ. According to the superposition principle of quantum mechanics, the total wave function of a particle can be expressed as the sum of the incident wave function and scattered wave function. From equations 3.111 and 3.113, the total wave function is therefore

$$\varphi_t = \varphi_{in} + \varphi_{sc} = e^{ikx} + f(\theta)\frac{e^{ikr}}{r} \,. \tag{3.130}$$

Mathematically, it has been shown that the incident plane wave can be expressed as a supposition of spherical waves:

$$\varphi_{in} = e^{ikx} = e^{ikr\cos\theta} = \sum_{\ell=0}^{\infty}(2\ell+1)i^{\ell}j_{\ell}(kr)p_{\ell}(\cos\theta), \qquad (3.131)$$

where $j_{\ell}(kr)$ are the Spherical Bessel Functions given in Table 3.2, and $p_{\ell}(\cos\theta)$ are the Legendre polynomials given in Table 3.1 for $m_l=0$. Each term in equation 3.131 is called a partial wave of the total incident wave. As a convention, the partial waves corresponding to $\ell = 0,1,2,3,...$ are called the s-wave, p-wave, d-wave, f-wave, ... respectively. The expression of equation 3.112 is significant in that, from a quantum-mechanical viewpoint of collision, the incident particle can be broken into many partial particles, of which each carries a different angular momentum ($\ell\hbar$) and interacts separately with the force potential, be it a nucleus or an atom, during collision. The end result of the collision can be obtained by the superposition of all the partial waves.

As $r\to\infty$, $j_{\ell}(kr)$ can be further expressed as

$$j_{\ell}(kr)\xrightarrow{r\to\infty}\frac{1}{kr}\sin(kr-\frac{\ell\pi}{2})=\frac{1}{kr}\left(\frac{e^{i(kr-\frac{\ell\pi}{2})}-e^{-i(kr-\frac{\ell\pi}{2})}}{2i}\right). \qquad (3.132)$$

Since $i^{\ell}=e^{i(\frac{\ell\pi}{2})}$, one may then replace equation 3.131 with

$$\varphi_{in} = e^{ikx} = \sum_{\ell=0}^{\infty}\frac{(2\ell+1)}{2ikr}\left[e^{ikr}-(-1)^{\ell}e^{-ikr}\right]p_{\ell}(\cos\theta), \qquad (3.133)$$

where the first term in the bracket represents the outgoing waves and the second term represents the incoming waves. We now assume that the total wave function can also be expressed as a sum of incoming and outgoing spherical waves asymptotically for large r:

$$\varphi_t = \sum_{\ell=0}^{\infty}\frac{\alpha_{\ell}(2\ell+1)}{2ikr}\left[e^{i(kr+\delta_{\ell})}-(-1)^{\ell}e^{-i(kr+\delta_{\ell})}\right]p_{\ell}(\cos\theta), \qquad (3.134)$$

where α_{ℓ} and δ_{ℓ} are the coefficients allowing the amplitude and the phase of the total wave to be different from that of the incident wave. Since φ_t can also be expressed by substituting equation 3.133 into 3.130 as

$$\varphi_t = \varphi_{in}+\varphi_{sc} = e^{ikx}+f(\theta)\frac{e^{ikr}}{r}$$

$$= \sum_{\ell=0}^{\infty} \frac{(2\ell+1)}{2ikr} \left[e^{ikr} - (-1)^{\ell} e^{-ikr} \right] p_{\ell}(\cos\theta) + f(\theta) \frac{e^{ikr}}{r}, \tag{3.135}$$

a comparison between equations 3.134 and 3.135 yields

$$\varphi_{sc} = f(\theta) \frac{e^{ikr}}{r} = \sum_{\ell=0}^{\infty} \frac{(2\ell+1)}{2ikr} p_{\ell}(\cos\theta) \left[\alpha_{\ell} \left(e^{i(kr+\delta_{\ell})} - (-1)^{\ell} e^{-i(kr+\delta_{\ell})} \right) - \left(e^{ikr} - (-1)^{\ell} e^{-ikr} \right) \right]. \tag{3.136}$$

Since the left-hand side of equation 3.136 is a pure outgoing wave, the right-hand side must not contain waves directed toward the scattering center. This requires that

$$\alpha_{\ell} e^{-i(kr+\delta_{\ell})} = e^{-ikr} \quad \Rightarrow \quad \alpha_{\ell} = e^{i\delta_{\ell}}. \tag{3.137}$$

Equations 3.135 and 3.136 are then reduced to

$$\varphi_{t} = \sum_{\ell=0}^{\infty} \frac{(2\ell+1)}{2ikr} p_{\ell}(\cos\theta) \left[e^{i(kr+2\delta_{\ell})} - (-1)^{\ell} e^{-ikr} \right] \tag{3.138}$$

and

$$\varphi_{sc} = f(\theta) \frac{e^{ikr}}{r} = \sum_{\ell=0}^{\infty} \frac{(2\ell+1)}{2ikr} p_{\ell}(\cos\theta)(e^{2i\delta_{\ell}} - 1) e^{ikr}. \tag{3.139}$$

Equation 3.139 leads to

$$f(\theta) = \sum_{\ell=0}^{\infty} \frac{(2\ell+1)}{2ik} (e^{2i\delta_{\ell}} - 1) p_{\ell}(\cos\theta)$$

$$= \sum_{\ell=0}^{\infty} \frac{(2\ell+1)}{k} e^{i\delta_{\ell}} \sin\delta_{\ell} p_{\ell}(\cos\theta), \tag{3.140}$$

where δ_{ℓ} is the phase shift of the ℓth partial wave. From equations 3.115 and 3.140, the differential scattering cross section can finally be expressed as

$$\frac{d\sigma_{s}(\theta)}{d\Omega} = |f(\theta)|^{2} = f(\theta)^{*} f(\theta) = \frac{1}{k^{2}} \left| \sum_{\ell=0}^{\infty} (2\ell+1) e^{i\delta_{\ell}} \sin\delta_{\ell} p_{\ell}(\cos\theta) \right|^{2}. \tag{3.141}$$

The terms with different ℓ in equation 3.141 interfere with one another, and they explain the observed interference pattern of Figure 1.10. In other words, the oscillatory pattern of $d\sigma_{s}/d\Omega$ is caused by the partial waves interfering with one another.

The total scattering cross section can be obtained by integrating equation 3.141 over the entire solid angle; that is,

$$\sigma_s = \int_{4\pi} \frac{d\sigma_s(\theta)}{d\Omega} d\Omega = \int_0^\pi \frac{d\sigma_s(\theta)}{d\Omega} 2\pi \sin\theta \, d\theta$$

$$= \frac{2\pi}{k^2} \sum_{\ell=0}^{\infty} \int_{-1}^{1} (2\ell+1)(2\ell'+1) e^{i(\delta_\ell - \delta_{\ell'})} \sin\delta_\ell \sin\delta_{\ell'} \, p_\ell(\cos\theta) p_{\ell'}(\cos\theta) \, d\cos\theta .$$

$$(3.142)$$

By using the orthogonality property

$$\int_{-1}^{1} p_\ell(\cos\theta) p_{\ell'}(\cos\theta) \, d\cos\theta = \frac{2}{2\ell+1} \quad \text{for } \ell = \ell'$$

$$= 0 \quad \text{for } \ell \neq \ell', \quad (3.143)$$

equation 3.142 then becomes

$$\sigma_s = \frac{4\pi}{k^2} \sum_{\ell=0}^{\infty} (2\ell+1)\sin^2\delta_\ell = 4\pi\lambda^2 \sum_{\ell=0}^{\infty} (2\ell+1)\sin^2\delta_\ell = \sum_{\ell=0}^{\infty} \sigma_{s,\ell} , \quad (3.144)$$

where $\sigma_{s,\ell} = 4\pi\lambda^2(2\ell+1)\sin^2\delta_\ell$, and it represents the scattering cross section for each partial wave ℓ. Equation 3.144 shows that the scattering cross section in general has little to do with the "size" of the target (a nucleus or an atom). It corresponds more to the wavelength of the incident particle. Or oppositely, the wavelength λ in a sense defines the size of the incident particle. Equation 3.144 can also be interpreted quantum-mechanically as the total scattering cross section being a sum of parts, each of which corresponds to an angular momentum quantum number ℓ. Since $\sin^2\delta_\ell$ varies between 0 and 1 as δ_ℓ varies, the contribution of each partial-wave scattering to the total scattering varies accordingly. That phase shifts δ_ℓ can be obtained by solving Schrödinger's equation with the known $V(r)$. In the simplest case, where the total scattering is dominated by the s-wave ($\ell = 0$), equation 3.141 gives

$$\frac{d\sigma_s(\theta)}{d\Omega} = \frac{1}{k^2} \left[e^{-i\delta_0} \sin\delta_0 \, p_0(\cos\theta) \right]\left[e^{i\delta_0} \sin\delta_0 \, p_0(\cos\theta) \right] = \lambda^2 \sin^2\delta_0 . \quad (3.145)$$

Since δ_0 is a constant, equation 3.145 shows that an s-wave–dominated scattering is isotropic. Similarly, equation 3.144 gives

$$\sigma_s = 4\pi\lambda^2 \sin^2\delta_0 . \quad (3.146)$$

The above results will be further discussed in Chapter 8, on neutron interactions.

Bibliography

Anderson, Elmer E. *Modern Physics and Quantum Mechanics*. Philadelphia: W. B. Saunders Company, 1971.

Krane, Kenneth S. *Introductory Nuclear Physics*. New York: John Wiley & Sons, 1988.

Problems

1. Derive equation 3.52 and plot the transmission coefficient as a function of E.

2. Write the 3-D time-independent Schröedinger equation in spherical coordinates, for a Coulomb-like potencial V(r).

3. In the 1-D problem shown below, a 5-MeV alpha particle is approaching a square potential barrier.

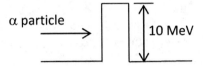

Calculate the transmission probability for the barrier widths of 1 fm and 5 fm, respectively.

4. (a) Find the wave functions and energy levels for a particle confined to a 2-D rectangular box, with

$$V(x,y) = 0 \quad -a \leq x \leq +a, -b \leq y \leq +b$$
$$= \infty \quad |x| > a, |y| > b$$

   (b) Make a diagram similar to Figure 3.5, showing the levels and degeneracies for $b = a$ and for $b = 2a$.

5. Calculate a three-dimensional infinite square well potential of dimensions a,b and c in the x,y and z dimensions, respectively.

   (a) Write time-independent 3D Schröedinger equation in Cartesian coordinates and the corresponding general solution.

   (b) How many and which are the quantum numbers (n_x, n_y, n_z) degenerate states will exist for the fourth energy state (E_4)?

6. Consider a particle bound by an infinite spherically symmetric well potential V(r). Write the wavefunctions of the system for $\ell = 2$.

7. Derive the expression for the Quantum Mechanics angular momentum operator in cartesian coordinates.

8. Find the solutions to the 1-D infinite square well when the potential extends from $-a/2$ to $+a/2$ instead of from 0 to $+a$. Is the potential invariant with respect to parity? How about the wave functions? Discuss the assignment of odd and even parity to the solutions.

9. Assume that eight fermions of the same type are confined to a 1-D infinite potential well. If the dimension of the well is 5 fm and the mass of the particle is 940 MeV c^{-2}, calculate the kinetic energies of these particles.

10. Find the angle between the angular momentum vector $\vec{L}$ and the z axis for all possible orientations when $\ell = 3$.

11. (a) What are the possible values of j for f states?

   (b) What are the corresponding m_j?

   (c) How many total m_j states are there?

   (d) How many states would there be if we used the labels m_ℓ and m_s?

12. Assume a fermion is initially at the ground state of a 1-D infinite square well and is exposed to a constant force field $\mathcal{E}$ for a short time Δt. Use equations 3.58 and 3.108 to obtain the transition probability $P(1 \rightarrow m)$ for $m = 2, 3$, and 4, respectively.

13. Use the Born Approximation to:

   (a) calculate $d\sigma / d\Omega$ for a shallow $(V_o << E)$ spherical square-well potential:
   $$V(r) = -V_o \qquad (r < R),$$
   $$V(r) = 0 \quad (r > R),$$

   (b) sketch $d\sigma / d\Omega$ versus θ for various values of kR, and compare this differential cross section with the one obtained classically for the same potential.

CHAPTER 4: PROPERTIES AND STRUCTURE OF ATOMIC NUCLEI

4.1 Size and Components of Atomic Nuclei

As briefly discussed in Section 1.2, the space occupied by matter (atoms and molecules) is essentially empty, in the sense that the mass of matter is almost entirely possessed by the atomic nuclei, which occupy almost no volume. On the other hand, the atomic electrons occupy almost all of the space but possess very little mass in comparison with the atomic nuclei. Section 2.1 then described the first model of the atom containing a point-like nucleus, proposed by E. Rutherford in 1911. In this model, Rutherford asserted that both the mass and the positive charge of an atom are held in a tiny volume (the nucleus), the dimension of which is 10^4 to 10^5 smaller than that of the atom. The diameter of an atom was known to be in the range of a few Å (or 10^{-10} m). Therefore, the diameter of the nucleus should be in the range of 10^{-15} to 10^{-14} m.

Yet in 1919, when Rutherford discovered the proton, a positively charged particle inside the nucleus, it was immediately recognized that the strong repulsive Coulomb force exerted among the positively charged protons would push them apart, unless there is an even stronger attractive force involved in holding them together. Since Rutherford also observed in a number of different atoms that the atomic mass (average mass of the atom) is often twice the atomic number (number of protons in the nucleus), he put out the idea that there could be a new particle with mass similar to that of the proton, but with no charge. He called it a neutron, and imagined it as a paired proton and electron. Rutherford's idea about the existence of neutrons was experimentally confirmed in 1932 by J. Chadwick, who estimated that the neutron's mass was about 0.1 percent more than the proton's mass. Soon after Chadwick's discovery of neutrons, W. Heisenberg showed that the neutron could not be a paired proton and electron, and that it had to hold its own identity as a new particle. Heisenberg's argument was based on the uncertainty principle, which shows that if an electron is trapped inside a nucleus with a dimension of a few fm, then the energy of the electron would be greater than 100 MeV. But there was no experimental evidence that an electron inside a nucleus can have such a high energy.

4.2 The Strong Nuclear Force

In 1935, E. Wigner suggested that there is a new kind of force that is short-ranged and acts between protons and protons, protons and neutrons, and neutrons and neutrons. This force is stronger than the repulsive force acting between the protons, and therefore is the reason why the nucleus can be held together. Wigner's idea is consistent with the liquid drop model of atomic nuclei proposed by G. Gamow a few years earlier. In this model, G. Gamow made an analogy between an atomic nucleus and a drop of incompressible liquid, in that the strong nuclear force acting between the neighboring nucleons (i.e., protons and neutrons) is similar to the van der Waals force acting between the neighboring molecules in a drop of liquid. The difference, however, is that in a nucleus there is also the repulsive Coulomb forces exerted among protons. The strong nuclear force acting between nucleons is now understood as the residual strong force or the nuclear force. As briefly mentioned in Section 1.2, quarks are bound together by the strong interaction to form proton and neutron. Unlike the gravitational and electromagnetic forces, the strong nuclear force does not diminish in strength with increasing distance. According to the

Standard Model of particle physics, the strong nuclear force that acts between quarks is mostly neutralized because nearly all of it goes toward binding the quarks together. As a result, the force is confined mostly within the nucleon. However, there is a tiny fraction of the force that does act outside of the proton or neutron. This fraction of the force is the residual strong force or the nuclear force. The strength of the nuclear force does diminish rapidly with distance, and it is what holds atomic nuclei together in spite of the repulsive Coulomb force between the positively charged protons. The strength of the nuclear force is about a hundred times greater than the Coulomb force inside the nucleus.

Besides its strength and short range, there are three other properties of the nuclear force. First, the nuclear force is independent of charge. That is, the force between two protons is the same as that between two neutrons, and that between one proton and one neutron. Second, while the nuclear force is attractive between two nucleons, the two nucleons do not get infinitely close to each other. At even closer distances (<0.8 fm), the force becomes highly repulsive. This indicates that the nucleon has a repulsive core, which gives the size of the nucleon. Figure 4.1a shows the potential between two protons (V_{pp}) as a function of distance between them. Figure 4.1b shows the potential between one proton and one neutron (V_{pn}). These results were derived from the p-p and p-n scattering experiments. (Yang and Hamilton, 1996) It is not possible to carry out the n-n scattering experiment because there are no solid neutron targets available, but many indirect experiments indicate that the behavior of V_{nn} should be the same as that of V_{pn}.

Last, the nuclear force between two nucleons depends on their relative spin directions. This can be illustrated by analyzing the ground state deuteron, $^{2}_{1}H$, of which the orbital angular momentum $L = 0$ and the nuclear spin can be either 1 (when the spins of proton and neutron are parallel) or 0 (when the spins of proton and neutron are antiparallel). If the nuclear force between the neutron and proton is independent of their spin directions, then the spin states 1 and 0 should be at the same energy. In reality, however, only the spin state 1 was found to be stable, indicating that the nuclear force is stronger when the proton and neutron spins are parallel.

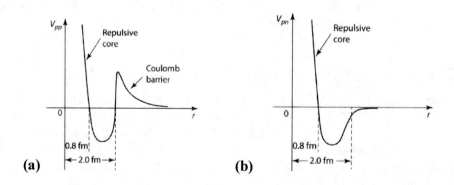

Figure 4.1. (a) The potential between two protons. **(b)** The potential between a proton and a neutron. In both cases, the sharp rise of the potential at smaller r (~0.8 fm) is the effect of the very strong repulsive core, which gives the size of the nucleon.

4.3 The Chart of Nuclides

Figure 4.2 is the chart of nuclides. It includes more than two thousand nuclides, of which 263 are stable and the rest are unstable. More than half of the stable nuclides contain an even number of protons and an even number of neutrons; they are referred to as even-even nuclides. There are only four stable nuclides that happen to be odd-odd nuclides. As shown, the stable nuclides tend to follow a relatively smooth Z-versus-N curve with the N/Z ratio slowly increasing from 1.0 for light nuclides to about 1.6 for heavy nuclides. The increase of the N/Z value can be understood as follows. As the number of protons of a nucleus increases, the nucleus becomes less and less stable due to the increased repulsive Coulomb force. Adding more neutrons to a nucleus brings in the attractive nuclear force without increasing the repulsive Coulomb force, and therefore, makes the nucleus more stable. The repulsive Coulomb force, however, diminishes more slowly, so it acts across the entire nucleus. Therefore, in heavy nuclei, particularly those with atomic numbers greater than 82 (lead), while the short-ranged nuclear force acting on nucleons remains nearly constant, the total Coulomb force acting on the nucleus increases with atomic number to the point that it eventually pushes the nucleus apart. This is indicated by the fact the heaviest stable nuclide found in nature is $^{209}_{83}\text{Bi}$.

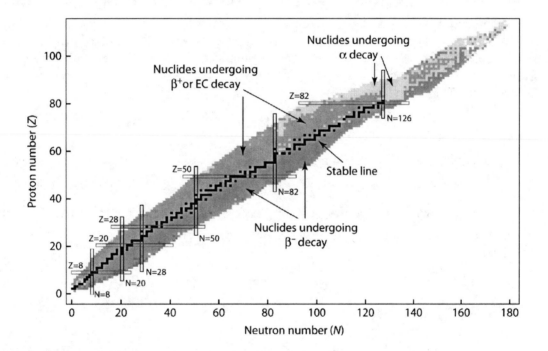

Figure 4.2. The chart of nuclides, showing the distribution of more than two thousand nuclides in terms of their neutron number (N) and proton number (Z).
Notes: β^+ = positron; EC = electron capture.

In general, the nuclides located above the stable line are deficient in neutrons and tend to undergo positron (β^+) or electron capture (EC) decay to migrate towards the stable line. This is because β^+ or EC decay converts a proton into a neutron in a nucleus (Section 6.3). Similarly, the nuclides located below the stable line are rich in neutrons and tend to undergo negatron (β^-) decay to migrate towards the stable line. This is because β^- decay converts a neutron into a proton in a nucleus (Section 6.3). For heavy nuclides with $A > 209$ (tip of stable line), there are too many nucleons in the nucleus to be stable. They mostly undergo α decay to migrate towards the stable line. This is because α decay reduces two protons and two neutrons at one time. For even heavier unstable nuclides with $A > 230$, they occasionally undergo spontaneous fission (SF), during which the nucleus is split into two fragments (Section 5.3.4). In a sense, SF can be thought of as a tug of war between the attractive nuclear force and the repulsive Coulomb force. In fission reactions, Coulomb repulsion wins.

Figure 4.2 also indicated the so-called magic numbers: 8, 20, 28, 50, 82, and 126. The nuclides containing a magic number of either protons or neutrons are extra stable, and their ground-state nuclei tend to have the shape of a sphere. The existence of the magic numbers among atomic nuclei indicates that some kind of "shell structure" of nucleons exists inside a nucleus, and that the nuclei with magic numbers containing nucleons of closed shells (similar to the noble gas atoms containing electrons of closed shells), therefore, are extra stable. The shell model of the nucleus will be discussed in Section 4.8.

4.4 Nuclear Binding Energy and the Semi-Empirical Mass Formula

Based on the liquid drop model, von Weizsäcker developed a semi-empirical mass formula, which can be used to approximate the mass, binding energy, and various other properties of an atomic nucleus from its proton number and neutron number. Weizsäcker included three types of energy in the nuclear binding energy formula: the volume energy, the surface energy, and the Coulomb energy. That is,

$$B = B_v + B_s + B_c, \tag{4.1}$$

where B_v, B_s, and B_c are the three binding energy terms associated with volume, surface, and Coulomb. B_v refers to when many nucleons are packed together into the smallest volume, such that each interior nucleon is in contact with (or glued to) certain other nucleons. As such, B_v is proportional to the number of nucleons which, in turn, is proportional to the volume of the nucleus. That is,

$$B_v = a_v A, \tag{4.2}$$

where A is the mass number, and a_v is a constant.

The surface term, B_s, is actually a correction term to B_v because not all nucleons are interior nucleons. Compared to the interior nucleons, the nucleons on the nucleus surface are in contact with fewer numbers of neighboring nucleons. So, the binding energy of the surface nucleons must be smaller than those in the interior. In other words, B_s should have a negative sign with respect to B_v and it should be proportional to the number of surface nucleons. If one assumes that the shape of a nucleus is a perfect sphere of radius R and that the nucleon density is constant over the entire nucleus, then $A \propto R^3$ or $R \propto A^{1/3}$. Since $B_s \propto R^2$, this leads to

$$B_s = -a_s A^{2/3}, \tag{4.3}$$

where a_s is a constant. The Coulomb term, B_c, should also have a negative sign with respect to B_v because the Coulomb forces exerted among protons are repulsive. Because there are a total of $\frac{Z(Z-1)}{2}$ pairs of protons, because the Coulomb potential is inversely proportional to the mean distance between two protons, and because this mean distance is proportional to R (more accurately, it is $\frac{6R}{5}$), B_c can be expressed as

$$B_c = -a_c Z(Z-1)A^{-1/3},$$

(4.4)

where a_c is a constant. Substituting equations 4.2, 4.3, and 4.4 into 4.1 yields

$$B = a_v A - a_s A^{2/3} - a_c Z(Z-1)A^{-1/3}.$$

(4.5)

Dividing equation 4.5 by A, one obtains the binding-energy-per-nucleon formula:

$$\frac{B}{A} = a_v - a_s A^{-1/3} - a_c Z(Z-1)A^{-4/3}.$$

(4.6)

Figure 4.3 is the plot of average binding energy per nucleon (B/A) versus the mass number A, based on the experimental data. Figure 4.4 shows the three major contributors, namely the volume, surface, and Coulomb, to the total binding energy per nucleon (B/A) versus the mass number A, based on equation 4.6. As shown, the overall shape of the B/A-versus-A curve based on this equation agrees reasonably well with that of the experimentally measured data. To fit the experimental data more closely, over the years more terms have been added to equation 4.6. The widely used mass-binding energy formula today is shown below:

$$\frac{B}{A} = a_v - a_s A^{-1/3} - a_c Z(Z-1)A^{-4/3} - a_{sym}\frac{(A-2Z)^2}{A^2} + a_p A^{-3/2}.$$

(4.7)

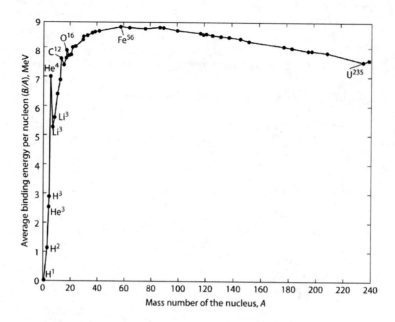

Figure 4.3. The average binding energy per nucleon (B/A) versus the mass number (A), based on the experimental data.
Source: Krane (1988).

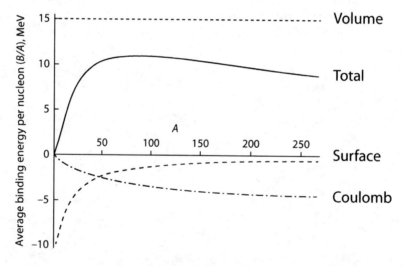

Figure 4.4. The curve of average binding energy per nucleon (B/A) versus the mass number (A), including the three major contributors: volume, surface, and Coulomb.

Meanwhile, an instrument called a mass spectrograph had been developed, allowing the rest masses of many atoms and nuclei to be measured to precisions of order 10^{-6}. The masses of the neutron and proton were measured to be $m_n = 1.008665$ u and $m_p = 1.007277$ u, respectively. It was soon recognized that the mass of a nucleus is smaller than the sum of the masses of its components (neutrons and protons) and that the difference is the binding energy divided by c^2. That is,

$$m(Z,A) = Zm_p + Nm_n - \frac{B}{c^2}, \qquad (4.8)$$

where $m(Z,A)$ is the mass of the nucleus, having atomic number Z and mass number A; m_p and m_n, respectively, are the rest mass of proton and neutron; N is the number of neutrons in the nucleus; and B is the binding energy of the nucleus. The term B/c^2 converts energy unit into mass unit based on Einstein's famous law of $E = mc^2$. Because measured mass values are usually made for atoms instead of for atomic nuclei, and because $N = A - Z$, equation 4.8 can be rewritten as

$$M(Z,A) = Zm_p + (A-Z)m_n + Zm_e - \frac{B}{c^2} = ZM(^1H) + (A-Z)m_n - \frac{B}{c^2}, \quad (4.9)$$

where m_e is the mass of the electron, $M(Z,A)$ is the mass of the atom having atomic number Z and mass number A, and $M(^1H)$ is the mass of ^1H atom. Equation 4.9 can be further reduced to

$$B = \left[ZM(^1H) + (A-Z)m_n - M(Z,A)\right]c^2. \qquad (4.10)$$

By applying the empirical binding energy formula of equation 4.7 into 4.9, one obtains the so-called semi-empirical mass formula (SEMF).

The fourth term in equation 4.7 is the adjustment for the symmetry between the neutron number and the proton number of the nucleus. This term is negligible for light nuclides because $N = (A - Z) \cong Z$, which makes this term zero. This term obviously becomes significant for heavy nuclides when N is much larger than Z. According to the Pauli exclusion principle, when the number of one kind of nucleon is greater than the number of the other kind in a nucleus, the excess nucleon (mostly neutron for heavy nuclides) must be in higher energy states. As such, there must be less binding energy associated with the nucleus. The fifth term in equation 4.10 is referred to as the pairing term, which is the adjustment for whether the neutron number and proton number are even or odd. As mentioned in Section 4.3, nature is in favor of even-even nuclides (i.e., those with even N and Z). Out of the total 263 stable nuclides, 148 are even-even nuclides and only five are odd-odd nuclides, namely ^2_1H, ^6_3Li, $^{10}_5B$, $^{14}_7N$, and $^{180}_{73}Ta$. This implies that pairing neutrons or protons tends to make the nucleus more stable; that is, increasing the binding energy or reducing the mass. Figure 4.5 shows the masses as a function of Z of nuclei with $A=76$, including two curves for even-even and odd-odd nuclei, respectively. The effect of the pairing term is clearly shown. The constants for the five terms of equation 4.7 were calculated by fitting it to the experimentally measured data (Figure 4.3). Values can vary depending on the fitting method. One set of often quoted values is $a_v = 15.74$ MeV, $a_s = 17.62$ MeV, $a_c = 0.715$ MeV, $a_{sym} = 23.4$ MeV, and

$$
\begin{aligned}
a_p = \;& 12.6 \text{ MeV} && \text{for even} - \text{even nucleus} \\
& 0 \text{ MeV} && \text{for odd-}A \text{ nucleus} \\
& -12.6 \text{ MeV} && \text{for odd-odd nucleus.}
\end{aligned}
$$

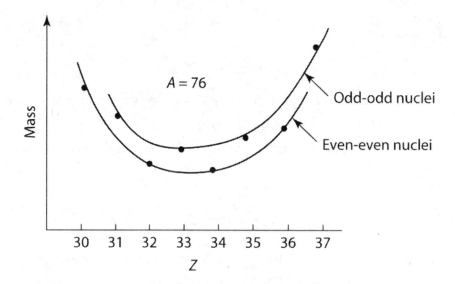

Figure 4.5. The masses as a function of Z of nuclei with $A = 76$, including the two curves for even-even and odd-odd nuclei, respectively.

As shown in Figure 4.5, equation 4.9 represents a parabola of mass versus Z for an isobar (A=constant). The minimum mass makes the nuclide most stable, and it occurs when

$$\frac{\partial M(Z,A)}{\partial Z} = 0 . \tag{4.11}$$

By substituting equation 4.9 (after combining with 4.7) into 4.11, one obtains

$$M(^1H) - m_n + \frac{1}{c^2}\left[a_c \frac{(2Z-1)}{A^{1/3}} - 4a_{sym}\frac{(A-2Z)}{A} \right] = 0 . \tag{4.12}$$

Solving for Z yields

$$Z_{min} \cong \frac{A}{2}\left[\frac{4a_{sym} + \dfrac{a_c}{A^{1/3}} - \left(m_n - M(^1H)\right)c^2}{4a_{sym} + a_c A^{2/3}} \right]. \tag{4.13}$$

By plugging in the values of m_n, $m(^1H)$, a_c, and a_{sym}, one obtains $Z_{min} \cong \frac{A}{2}$ for small A, and $Z_{min} \cong 0.4A$ for large A. These results are consistent with the observed results of the stable nuclides shown in Figure 4.2.

To illustrate the relationship between nuclear binding energy and mass, we use the following example of a nuclear reaction:

$$^2_1H + ^3_1H \rightarrow ^4_2He + ^1_0n . \tag{4.14}$$

The energy released from a nuclear reaction is referred to as the Q-value, which is the same as the difference in binding energy between the reactants and the products, and therefore, can be calculated from equation 4.9 in terms of the difference in mass between the reactants and the products. That is,

$$Q = -\Delta B = B_{\text{Products}} - B_{\text{Reactants}} = \Delta M c^2 = \left(M_{\text{Reactants}} - M_{\text{Products}} \right) c^2 , \tag{4.15}$$

where $M_{\text{Reactants}}$ and M_{Products} are the atomic masses of the reactants and products, respectively. According to Appendix B, the Q-value for the reaction shown by equation 4.14 can be calculated as

$$Q = 13.136 + 14.95 - 2.425 - 8.071 \cong 17.59 \text{ MeV}.$$

In other words, the original form of this energy (the nuclear binding energy) is hidden in $_{1}^{2}\text{H}$ and $_{1}^{3}\text{H}$. The reaction converts this hidden energy into the form of kinetic energy carried by $_{2}^{4}\text{He}$ and $_{0}^{1}\text{n}$. The above example is the well-known deuterium-tritium (or D-T) nuclear fusion reaction, which is responsible for the huge amount of energy released by hydrogen bombs. The reaction has also been selected to power controlled fusion reactors in the future. More detailed discussion on nuclear fusion reactions is included in Section 7.5.

4.5 Nucleon Distribution in Atomic Nuclei

Experimental information about nucleon distributions in nuclei are derived mainly from particle scattering experiments. The particles used include alpha, proton, electron, and neutron. Alpha particles and protons both can be used to give a rough estimation of the size of a nucleus, in that they exert both Coulomb and nuclear forces on a target nucleus. The size of a nucleus should be defined by the range of the nuclear force. Taking alpha particles as the example, the classical approach shows that the closest distance (r_{min}) between a 5-MeV alpha particle and a gold nucleus is 45.5 fm (Section 1.8), which corresponds to the distance where the kinetic energy of the alpha particle (E_{α}) equals to the Coulomb potential. The fact that the classically derived Rutherford scattering formula agreed well with the experimental results indicated that the range of the nuclear force is smaller than 45.5 fm. Since r_{min} decreases as the alpha particle energy increases, one should expect a threshold value of E_{α} where r_{min} becomes small enough and the nuclear force starts to become effective. Figure 4.6 shows the results of just such an experiment, with lead as the target material. It shows that the intensity of the scattered alpha particles departs from the Rutherford scattering formula at E_{α} of about 27 MeV. Using the classical approach, r_{min} can be estimated as

$$r_{\text{min}} \cong \frac{1}{4\pi\varepsilon_0} \frac{zZe^2}{E_{\alpha}} = (1.44 \text{ MeV fm}) \frac{(2)(82)}{27 \text{ MeV}} = 8.74 \text{ fm}.$$

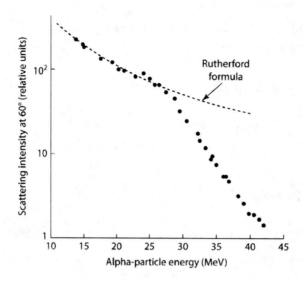

Figure 4.6. The intensity of alpha particles scattered by lead at 60 ° as a function of the alpha-particle energy.
Source: Krane (1988).

According to Heisenberg's uncertainty principle, to probe the details of the nucleon distribution in a nucleus one needs to use particles with the de Broglie wavelength smaller than the size of the nucleus. Because electrons are electrically charged and because they do not feel the strong nuclear force, beams of electrons with energies from 100 MeV to 1 GeV (with the wavelength between 1 and 10 fm) have been used to study the charged distributions in nuclei. Figure 4.7 shows the radial charge distribution of several nuclei determined from electron scattering experiments. Two unique features are: 1) the charge densities are reasonably constant at the center of the nucleus for all nuclei, and 2) the boundary region (the so-called "skin thickness," defined as the distance in which the charge density falls from 90% of its central value to 10%) of the nuclei for various nuclei is roughly constant at 2.3 fm. If one assumes that neutrons are uniformly mixed with protons in a nucleus, then the nucleon density distribution would be similar to that of the charge distribution shown in Figure 4.7. While in theory one can use neutron beams to determine the neutron density distribution in a nucleus, in reality, it is quite difficult to come up with monoenergetic neutron beams with the proper wavelength for such an experiment. As such, the neutron density is still an open question. In fact, recent studies on very neutron-rich nuclei indicated that some valence neutrons may form halos (or neutron clouds) outside the dense core of the nucleus.

If one assumes that the nucleon density is constant, independent of the mass number A, and that the shape of the nucleus is a perfect sphere with radius R, it then follows that $A \propto \dfrac{4}{3}\pi R^3$, or

$R \propto A^{1/3}$. This leads to the empirical formula of nuclear radius:

$$R = R_0 A^{1/3},$$ (4.16)

where $R_0 \cong 1.2$ fm, which is determined from the experimental results shown in Figure 4.7. Equation 4.16 is a widely used formula for quick estimation of the size of a nucleus.

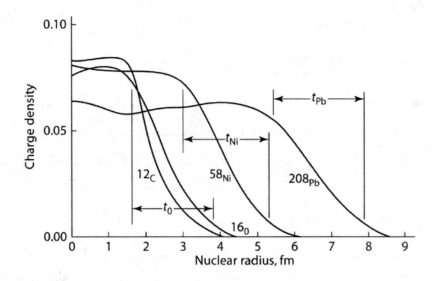

Figure 4.7. The radial charge distribution for several nuclei determined from electron scattering experiments. The skin thickness t is shown for O, Ni, and Pb; its value is roughly constant at 2.3 fm.
Source: Krane (1988).

4.6 Nuclear Spin, Magnetic Moment, and Parity

From experiments, it was found that each nucleus also has a unique angular momentum similar to that of an atom. Similar to an atomic electron that possesses its own orbital angular momentum $\vec{L}$ and spin $\vec{S}$ (Sections 2.2 and 2.3), so does a nucleon in a nucleus. The nuclear angular momentum is usually called the nuclear spin, which is represented by the symbol I. It is the total angular momentum of the nucleus, which is the vector sum of the $\vec{L}$ and $\vec{S}$ of all nucleons in the nucleus. It was found from the experiments that the neutron and proton are fermions that have intrinsic spin like the electron ($\frac{1}{2}\hbar$). The experimental data also show the following three rules for the ground-state nuclei: 1) all even-even nuclei have spin zero, 2) all odd-A nuclei have half integer spin ($\frac{1}{2}, \frac{3}{2}, \frac{5}{2}, \ldots$), and 3) all odd-odd nuclei have integer spin of 1 or 2. The above rules give a strong indication that neutrons and protons in a nucleus form pairs just like the electrons in atoms, in that the angular momenta of the paired nucleons are completely canceled out, and that the nuclear spin is solely determined by the valence unpaired nucleon(s). The nuclear spins for excited nuclei do not follow the above rule, and will be discussed in Section 4.9.

The experimental data showed that protons and neutrons also have magnetic dipole moments. Similar to the electron magnetic dipole moment in an atom (Section 2.2), the magnetic dipole moment for proton, $\vec{\mu}_p$, should also be separately contributed from $\vec{L}$ and $\vec{S}$, except that the proton carries a positive electric charge. The expression of $\vec{\mu}_p$ can then be written as

$$\vec{\mu}_p = \vec{\mu}_l + \vec{\mu}_s = \frac{e\hbar}{2m_p}(g_{p,l}\vec{L} + g_{p,s}\vec{S}) = \mu_N(g_{p,l}\vec{L} + g_{p,s}\vec{S}), \qquad (4.17)$$

where $\left|\vec{L}\right|^2 = l(l+1)\hbar$ and $\left|\vec{S}\right|^2 = s(s+1)\hbar$, and $\mu_N = \frac{e\hbar}{2m_p} = 3.152\times10^{-8}$ eV/T, which is called

the nuclear Bohr magneton. Dirac's theory initially predicted that $g_{p,l}$ and $g_{p,s}$ should be the same as $g_{e,l}$ and $g_{e,s}$ (i.e., 1 and 2, respectively). The experimental data later showed that the value of $g_{p,l}$ was indeed 1, but the correct value of $g_{p,s}$ was actually 5.58, which is quite different from the theoretical prediction. It should be noted that, while the formula of $\vec{\mu}_p$ (equation 4.17) and the formula of $\vec{\mu}_e$ (equation 2.27) resemble each other, the magnitude of $\vec{\mu}_p$ is much smaller than that of $\vec{\mu}_e$. This is because m_p is a factor of 1836 times that of m_e. Without the orbital contribution, the magnitude of the proton magnetic dipole moment can be obtained from equation 4.17 as

$$\mu_p = \mu_N(g_{p,s}S_z) = \mu_N(5.58)(1/2) = 2.79\mu_N, \qquad (4.18)$$

where S_z is the projection of $\vec{S}$ on the z axis, which is 1/2.

The experimental data showed that neutrons also have a non-zero magnetic dipole moment, $\vec{\mu}_n$. Since the neutron carries no electric charge, its magnetic moment must be from its intrinsic spin, $\vec{S}$. The expression of $\vec{\mu}_n$, therefore, can be written as

$$\vec{\mu}_n = \vec{\mu}_l + \vec{\mu}_s = \frac{e\hbar}{2m_n}g_{n,s}\vec{S}, \qquad (4.19)$$

where the value of $g_{n,s}$ was found to be -3.82, indicating that the sign of neutron magnetic moment is the same as that of the electron, and opposite to that of the proton. While neutron as a particle by itself does not carry electric charge, its non-zero magnetic moment indicates that there is some charge distribution inside the neutron. From equation 4.19, the magnitude of the neutron magnetic dipole moment can be obtained as

$$\mu_n = \mu_N(g_{n,s}S_z) = -\mu_N(3.82)(1/2) = -1.91\mu_N. \qquad (4.20)$$

Similar to the electrons in an atom, the nucleons in a nucleus tend to form pairs, of which the angular momenta and spins of the two nucleons in each pair cancel each other out. As such, the paired nucleons in a nucleus do not contribute to the total nuclear spin. In other words, the total nuclear spin is solely determined by one or few unpaired valence nucleons. This is evidenced by the fact that one rarely finds a nucleus having a magnetic dipole moment larger than $6\mu_N$. Table 4.1 shows some experimental values of nuclear magnetic dipole moments for a few nuclei. All values refer to the nuclear ground states.

In addition to the nuclear spin, the state of a nucleus also includes the parity. As discussed in Section 3.9, parity can be either + (even parity) or − (odd parity). In theory, the nuclear parity can be determined by multiplying together the parities of each of the A nucleons (i.e., $\pi = \pi_1\pi_2..\pi_A$). In reality, however, the parities for the nucleons (i.e., $\pi_1, \pi_2, ..., \pi_A$) are not known because we do not know the wave functions of all the nucleons. As such, the nuclear parity is usually regarded as a property of the whole nucleus, and it can be directly measured with a variety of experimental techniques. The spin and parity associated with a nuclear state are usually expressed together by the symbol I^π. For example, I^π for the ground-state nuclei ^{1}H, ^{2}H, ^{4}He, and ^{7}Li can be found from Appendix B to be $\frac{1}{2}^+$, 1^+, 0^+, and $\frac{3}{2}^-$, respectively.

Table 4.1. Some experimental values of nuclear magnetic dipole moments for a few nuclei.

Nuclide	Magnetic dipole moment (μ_N)
n	-1.9131
p	2.7928
$^2_1$H	0.8574
$^4_2$He	0
$^7_3$Li	3.2563
$^{57}_{27}$Co	4.733
$^{93}_{41}$Nb	6.1705
$^{235}_{92}$U	-0.35
$^{238}_{92}$U	0

4.7 Nuclear Electric Quadrupole Moment

Experimentally it was found that many ground-state nuclei do not have the shape of a sphere. Instead, they have the shape of either a prolate spheroid (football-like) or an oblate spheroid (pumpkin-like). The non-spherical shapes of the nuclei greatly influence the spins and parities of the ground state, as well as the low-level density of the excited states of these nuclei. The electric quadrupole moment (Q) is a quantity that can be used to determine whether a nucleus is a sphere, a prolate spheroid, or an oblate spheroid. $Q = 0$ indicates that the charge distribution of the nucleus is spherical; $Q > 0$ indicates that the charge distribution of the nucleus is in the shape of a prolate spheroid; and $Q < 0$ indicates that the charge distribution of the nucleus is in the shape of a oblate spheroid. One must not confuse the electric quadrupole moment with the Q-value of a nuclear reaction defined by equation 4.15. The electric quadrupole moment of a classical point charge e has the form $e(3z^2 - r^2)$, where $r^2 = x^2 + y^2 + z^2$. In quantum mechanics, one evaluates the expectation value of the quantity via its corresponding operator. Let us consider a nucleus with a single proton, each with a wave function ψ_i. The expectation value of Q can be expressed as

$$e\langle Q \rangle = e \int_{Nucleus} \psi_i^* (3z^2 - r^2)\psi \, dv. \qquad (4.21)$$

$\langle Q \rangle = 0$ if $|\psi|^2$ is spherically symmetric as $\langle z^2 \rangle = \langle x^2 \rangle = \langle y^2 \rangle = \dfrac{\langle r^2 \rangle}{3}$. If $|\psi|^2$ is concentrated along the z axis ($x = y = 0$, and an extreme case of the prolate spheroid), then $\langle Q \rangle = 2\langle r^2 \rangle$. While if $|\psi|^2$ is concentrated in the xy plane ($z = 0$, and an extreme case of the oblate spheroid), then $\langle Q \rangle = -\langle r^2 \rangle$. Since most nucleons form pairs and the paired nucleons tend to move in spherically symmetric orbits, they do not contribute to $\langle Q \rangle$. As such, the value of $\langle Q \rangle$ for a many-nucleon nucleus is mainly contributed from the valence nucleon, which is located near the surface with $r \cong R_0 A^{1/3}$. The magnitude of $e\langle Q \rangle$ is, therefore, estimated to be in the order of $R_0^2 A^{2/3}$, which is expressed in the unit of barn (1 barn = 10^{-24} cm^2). Table 4.2 shows some experimental values of nuclear electric quadrupole moments for a few nuclei. All values refer to the nuclear ground states.

Table 4.2. Some experimental values of nuclear electric quadrupole moments for a few nuclei.

Nuclide	$e\langle Q \rangle$ (barn)
n	0
p	0
^2_1H	0.00282
^4_2He	0
^7_3Li	-0.045
$^{59}_{27}\text{Co}$	0.40
$^{176}_{71}\text{Lu}$	8.0
$^{209}_{83}\text{Bi}$	-0.37

4.8 Shell Model of the Nucleus

While the liquid drop model of the nucleus was successful in predicting the average binding energy per nucleon for most nuclei (Section 4.4), it fell short especially for the magic nuclei. A magic nuclide contains one of the following numbers of either protons or neutrons: 2, 8, 20, 28, 50, 82, and 126 (Section 4.3). These nuclides are extra stable and their ground-state nuclei tend to have the shape of a sphere. The existence of the magic nuclides indicates that some kind of shell structure of nucleons exists inside a nucleus, similar to that of an atom. The magic nuclides are similar to the noble gas atoms in that they both contain closed shells. Figure 4.8 provides clear evidence of the existence of the magic nuclides. As shown, the difference between measured two-neutron separation energy and that predicted by the SEMF is most pronounced for the magic nuclides. This is similar to Figure 2.5, where the peak values of the ionization potential occur for the noble gas atoms. The plot uses two-neutron separation energy instead of one-neutron so that the nucleon pairing energy is excluded from the effect. Since the magic numbers also apply to protons, one may find a plot similar to Figure 4.8 for two-proton separation energy versus proton number. A similar effect supporting the nuclear shell structure is that a large binding energy is released in a nuclear reaction when the addition of one nucleon yields one of the magic numbers, and that there is only a small energy release when a nucleon is added to a magic nuclide.

The development of shell model for the nucleus was less straightforward than that for the atom. It is easier to imagine that in an atom all the electrons independently move around and are bound by the Coulomb force supplied by the nucleus. With the known formula of Coulomb potential, one can solve the Schrödinger equation, add the Pauli exclusion principle, and thus obtain the shell structure for an atom. In a nucleus, however, the force potential is not known in the closed form. To solve the Schrödinger equation for nucleus, an earlier approach was to assume a mean potential of the following form:

$$V(r) = \frac{-V_0}{1 + \exp\left[(r\text{-}R)/a\right]}, \tag{4.22}$$

which is known as the Woods-Saxon potential. The parameter V_0 is a constant representing the full depth of the potential, r is the distance to the center of the nucleus, $R = R_0 A^{1/3}$ is the nuclear radius (equation 4.16), and a is a parameter adjusting the skin thickness of the potential. Typical values of V_0 and a are 50 MeV and 0.5 fm, respectively. Figure 4.9 shows such a nuclear potential.

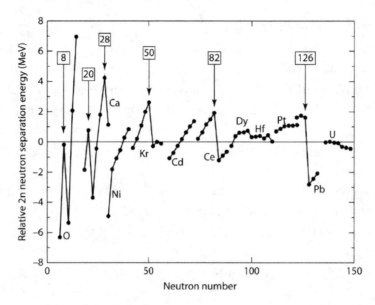

Figure 4.8. The difference between measured two-neutron separation energies and those predicted by the SEMF, plotted against neutron number.

Note: SEMF = semi-empirical mass formula.

Source: Lilley (2001).

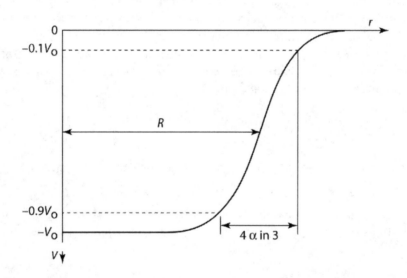

Figure 4.9. The Wood-Saxon form of a realistic nuclear potential used for the shell model. The "skin thickness" $4a \ln 3$ is the distance over which the potential changes from $0.1V_0$ to $0.9V_0$.

Source: Krane (1988).

Figure 4.10a shows the allowed energy states obtained from solving the Schrödinger equation with the use of the Woods-Saxon potential. Similar to that of the atomic spectroscopic notation (Table 2.1), the nuclear energy states are also labelled in terms of s, p, d, f, g, and so on, according to the orbital angular momentum quantum number $\ell = 0, 1, 2, 3, 4, ...$ One exception here is that the index number is not the principal quantum number, but simply represents the energy level for the particular ℓ value. As such, 1p and 1d denote the first (lowest) p state and d state, respectively, and 2p and 2d denote the second p state and d state, respectively, and so on. In atomic spectroscopic notation, however, the first (lowest) p state and d state are labelled as 2p and 3d, respectively. The energy-level gaps that appear in Figure 4.10a do match the experimentally observed magic numbers of 2, 8, and 20. But the gaps for the higher nucleon numbers (occurring at 40, 58, 92, and 112) do not match the experimentally observed magic numbers. Many attempts were made in the 1940s using a variety of different potential wells, but without success. Triumph was finally achieved in 1949 by Mayer, Haxel, Suess, and Jensen, who showed that the inclusion of the spin-orbit coupling would change the energy levels that match the rest of the experimentally observed magic numbers: 28, 50, 82, and 126 (Figure 4.10b). The spin-orbit coupling in atoms involves the electromagnetic force, and its effect on the energy levels of an atom is insignificant. The spin-orbit coupling in nuclei involves the strong nuclear force, and therefore, it has a huge effect on the energy levels of a nucleus.

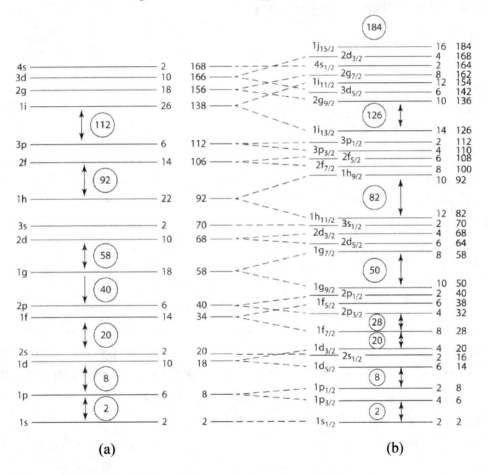

(a)   (b)

Figure 4.10. The energy states predicted by the shell model using **(a)** the Wood-Saxon well, and **(b)** the Wood-Saxon well with spin-orbit coupling.
Source: Krane (1988).

The spin-orbit interaction is typically written in the form $-V_{so}(r)(\vec{L} \cdot \vec{S})$, where $\vec{L}$ and $\vec{S}$ are respectively the orbital and spin angular momenta of a nucleon moving in the nuclear potential well and $V_{so}(r)$ is related to the nuclear force potential at distance r from the center of the nucleus. To show how spin-orbit interaction affects the energy levels, one first applies the law of cosines to equation 2.28 and obtains

$$J^2 = L^2 + S^2 + 2\vec{L} \cdot \vec{S}. \tag{4.23}$$

Substituting $J^2 = j(j+1)\hbar^2$, $L^2 = \ell(\ell+1)\hbar^2$, and $S^2 = s(s+1)\hbar^2$ into equation 4.23 yields

$$\left|\vec{L} \cdot \vec{S}\right| = \frac{1}{2}\left[j(j+1) - \ell(\ell+1) - s(s+1)\right]\hbar^2. \tag{4.24}$$

Since $s = \dfrac{1}{2}$, its follows that

- for the parallel case where $j = \ell + \dfrac{1}{2}$,

$$\left|\vec{L} \cdot \vec{S}\right| = \frac{1}{2}\left[j(j+1) - \ell(\ell+1) - s(s+1)\right]\hbar^2 = \frac{\ell\hbar^2}{2} \text{ ; and} \tag{4.25}$$

- for the antiparallel case where $j = \ell - \dfrac{1}{2}$,

$$\left|\vec{L} \cdot \vec{S}\right| = \frac{1}{2}\left[j(j+1) - \ell(\ell+1) - s(s+1)\right]\hbar^2 = -\frac{(\ell+1)\hbar^2}{2}. \tag{4.26}$$

The difference (or split) between the parallel and the antiparallel energy states can then be obtained from equations 4.25 and 4.26 as

$$\Delta\left|\vec{L} \cdot \vec{S}\right| = \frac{\ell\hbar^2}{2} + \frac{(\ell+1)\hbar^2}{2} = \frac{(2\ell+1)\hbar^2}{2}, \tag{4.27}$$

which shows that effect of spin-orbit coupling on the parallel and antiparallel energy states is proportional to $(2\ell+1)$. Because $V_{so}(r)$ is related to the strong nuclear force, it can have a rather large value for large values of ℓ. Consequently, the split of the parallel and antiparallel energy states can be in the several-MeV range. Good examples for the split of energy states are that of 1f ($\ell = 3$), 1g ($\ell = 4$), 1h ($\ell = 5$), and 1i ($\ell = 6$) shown in Figure 4.10b. As shown, the wide gap between parallel state ($1f_{7/2}$) and antiparallel state ($1f_{5/2}$) help create the magic number 28. The splits of energy states are even wider for 1g, 1h, and 1i, and help create the magic numbers 50, 82, and 126.

4.9 Spin and Parity of Spherical Nuclei

In addition to its ability to correctly produce the magic numbers, the shell model was also successful in predicting the nuclear spin and parity (I^π) for spherical nuclei when it was combined with the premise that in a nucleus all nucleons but one are paired, and that the nuclear spin and parity are solely determined by the spin and parity of the single unpaired nucleon. The second premise is the same as saying that the angular momenta of all paired nucleons cancel out completely and do not contribute to the nuclear spin. This premise is supported by the observed fact that all stable even-even nuclei have I^π of 0^+ regardless of whether they are spherical. This particular application of the shell model is known as the independent particle shell model (IPSM). We now compare the I^π predicted by the IPSM with that obtained by the experiment for the following ground-state stable, odd-A nuclides, ^7_3Li, $^{39}_{19}\text{K}$, $^{91}_{40}\text{Zr}$, $^{143}_{60}\text{Nd}$, and $^{209}_{83}\text{Bi}$.

- For ^7_3Li, the unpaired nucleon is the 3rd proton, which, according to Figure 4.10b, occupies the $1p_{3/2}$ state. Since p corresponds to $\ell=1$, $\pi=(-1)^\ell=-$, the I^π for ^7_3Li, therefore, should be $\frac{3}{2}^-$.

- For $^{39}_{19}\text{K}$, the unpaired nucleon is the 19th proton, which, according to Figure 4.10b, occupies the $1d_{3/2}$ state. Since d corresponds to $\ell=2$, $\pi=(-1)^\ell=+$, the I^π for $^{39}_{19}\text{K}$, therefore, should be $\frac{3}{2}^+$.

- For $^{91}_{40}\text{Zr}$, the unpaired nucleon is the 51st neutron, which, according to Figure 4.10b, occupies the $1g_{7/2}$ state. Since g corresponds to $\ell=4$, $\pi=(-1)^\ell=+$, the I^π for $^{91}_{40}\text{Zr}$, therefore, should be $\frac{7}{2}^+$.

- For $^{143}_{60}\text{Nd}$, the unpaired nucleon is the 83rd neutron, which, according to Figure 4.10b, occupies the $1h_{9/2}$ state. Since h corresponds to $\ell=5$, $\pi=(-1)^\ell=-$, the I^π for $^{143}_{60}\text{Nd}$, therefore, should be $\frac{9}{2}^-$.

- For $^{209}_{83}\text{Bi}$, the unpaired nucleon is the 83rd proton, which, according to Figure 4.10b, occupies the $1h_{9/2}$ state. Since h corresponds to $\ell=5$, $\pi=(-1)^\ell=-$, the I^π for $^{209}_{83}\text{Bi}$, therefore, should be $\frac{9}{2}^-$.

Comparison of the above results with the experimental data (Appendix B) shows that Figure 4.10b correctly predicted the I^π for all the nuclides except for $^{91}_{40}\text{Zr}$ and $^{143}_{60}\text{Nd}$. The experimentally measured I^π for $^{91}_{40}\text{Zr}$ and $^{143}_{60}\text{Nd}$ are $\frac{5}{2}^+$ and $\frac{7}{2}^-$, respectively. Closer examination of Figure 4.10b shows that the orbital energy states near the magic numbers 50 and 82 are closely spaced, so that the unpaired nucleon may occupy any one of the these orbitals as its ground state. In the case of $^{91}_{40}\text{Zr}$, Figure 4.10b shows that the unpaired 51st neutron may occupy $2d_{5/2}$ instead of $1g_{7/2}$. As such, it would have correctly predicted the I^π of $\frac{5}{2}^+$ for $^{91}_{40}\text{Zr}$. Similarly in the case of

$^{143}_{60}$Nd, Figure 4.10b shows that the unpaired 83rd neutron may occupy $2f_{7/2}$ instead of $1h_{9/2}$, as its ground state. As such, the $2f_{7/2}$ orbital would correctly predict the I^π of $\frac{7}{2}^-$ for $^{143}_{60}$Nd. All the nuclei we have discussed so far are either of low-Z or have Z or N next to magic numbers, which makes their nuclear potentials near spherical. Since the IPSM was based on the assumption that the nuclear potential is spherical, it is no surprise that Figure 4.10b gives good predictions of ground-state I^π for these nuclei. For high-Z nuclei with both Z and N away from magic numbers of which the nuclear potentials are non-spherical, a modified shell model called "the Nilsson Model" had been developed to more correctly predict the ground state I^π. (Prussin, 2007)

Now, what about the odd-odd nuclei? Let's use the example of $^{10}_{5}$B, where there are two unpaired nucleons (a proton and a neutron) both occupying $1p_{3/2}$. In this case, the nuclear spin I cannot be uniquely determined, but it must lie in the range:

$$\left| \vec{j}_n - \vec{j}_p \right| \le I \le \left| \vec{j}_n + \vec{j}_p \right|, \tag{4.28}$$

where $\vec{j}_n$ and $\vec{j}_p$ are the angular momentum quantum numbers associated with the unpaired neutron and proton, respectively. Since both of the unpaired nucleons occupy $1p_{3/2}$, $j_n = j_p = \frac{3}{2}$. From equation 4.28, the nuclear spin I can be $0, 1, 2,$ or 3. The corresponding parity is given by the product of the parities of the two unpaired nucleons. Since the parity for $1p_{3/2}$ is $-$, the parity for the ground state $^{10}_{5}$B should be $+$. As such, the I^π for the ground state $^{10}_{5}$B can be $0^+, 1^+, 2^+,$ or 3^+. It turns out that nature is overwhelmingly in favor of 3^+.

While the above examples only include ground state nuclei, the IPSM also works well for predicting the I^π for the excited states of spherical nuclei. Let us use $^{17}_{8}$O as an example. Figure 4.11 shows the energy levels of $^{17}_{8}$O, with the lowest as the ground state. If one assumes that the I^π of the excited states are solely determined by the unpaired nucleon and that all the paired nucleons are unbreakable, then according to Figure 4.10b, the available states for the 9th unpaired proton of $^{17}_{8}$O should be sequentially $1d_{5/2}$, $2s_{1/2}$, $1d_{3/2}$, $1f_{7/2}$, and so on. The first two orbitals are consistent with the measured ground state and first excited states of $\frac{5}{2}^+$ (0 MeV) and $\frac{1}{2}^+$ (0.87 MeV). But the next two orbitals, $1d_{3/2}$ and $1f_{7/2}$, are inconsistent with the next two excited states, $\frac{1}{2}^-$ (3.06 MeV) and $\frac{5}{2}^-$ (3.84 MeV), shown in Figure 4.11. This inconsistency can be explained by the erroneous assumption that all the paired nucleons are unbreakable. In fact, this is a good example to show that the nucleon pairing energy is on the order of 2-3 MeV. That is, if the excitation energy is more than 2-3 MeV, then it is possible to break a paired nucleon from a lower level. In this case, the lower level is $1p_{1/2}$. In other words, one of the two paired protons in $1p_{1/2}$ is promoted to form a pair with the initially unpaired proton in $1d_{5/2}$, rendering the unpaired proton to be in $1p_{1/2}$, which is consistent with the measured second excited state. Similarly, as the excitation energy increases, one of the two paired protons in $1p_{3/2}$ is promoted to form a pair with the initially unpaired proton in $1d_{5/2}$, rendering the unpaired proton to be in $1p_{3/2}$, which is consistent with the measured fourth excited state $\frac{3}{2}^-$ (4.55 MeV). As the excitation energy is even higher, the favor of state transition switches back to promoting the initially unpaired proton from $1d_{5/2}$ to $1d_{3/2}$, which is consistent with the measured fifth excited state $\frac{3}{2}^+$ (5.08 MeV). The third excited state, $\frac{5}{2}^-$ (3.84 MeV), however, is still left unexplained. One possibility is that a pair of neutrons in $1p_{1/2}$ is promoted to $2s_{1/2}$, rendering three unpaired neutrons in $1p_{1/2}$, $1d_{5/2}$, and $2s_{1/2}$. In this case, the angular momenta for $1p_{1/2}$ and $2s_{1/2}$ may be antiparallel and cancel each other out, which leaves $\frac{5}{2}$ as the nuclear spin. The parity can be calculated as $\pi = \pi(1p_{1/2})\pi(1d_{5/2})\pi(2s_{1/2}) = (-)(+)(+) = -$. The I^π of this state is, therefore, $\frac{5}{2}^-$, which is consistent with that of the measured third excited state.

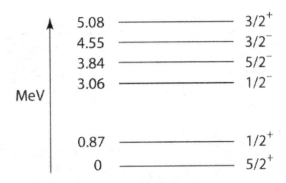

Figure 4.11. The energy levels of $^{17}_{8}O$.

Another interesting example is at the other end of the nuclide chart, $^{209}_{83}Bi$. Figure 4.12 shows the energy levels for $^{208}_{82}Pb$ and $^{209}_{83}Bi$, with the lowest as the ground state. $^{209}_{83}Bi$ is to $^{208}_{82}Pb$ just like $^{17}_{8}O$ is to $^{16}_{8}O$, in that $^{209}_{83}Bi$ and $^{17}_{8}O$ both have one unpaired nucleon outside their respective double-magic cores. According to Figure 4.10b, the available energy states for the 83rd unpaired proton should be, sequentially, $1h_{9/2}, 2f_{7/2}, 2f_{5/2}, 3p_{3/2}, 3p_{1/2},$ and $1i_{13/2}$. The first two orbitals are consistent with Figure 4.12 in that the I^π of the ground state and first excited states are $\frac{9}{2}^-$ (0

MeV) and $\frac{7}{2}^{-}$ (0.90 MeV). The second excited state of $\frac{13}{2}^{+}$ (1.61 MeV), however, does not match the next orbital of the sequence, $2f_{5/2}$, but it does match $1i_{13/2}$. This can be explained by the significantly reduced Coulomb energy for a proton in the $1i_{13/2}$ orbital ($\ell = 6$), because the average proton position is close to the edge of the nucleus. In fact, for a sphere of radius R containing a uniformly distributed charge of Q, one can easily show that the Coulomb energy $V_c(r)$ inside the sphere obeys the following formula:

$$V_c(r) = \frac{Q}{2R}\left(3 - \frac{r^2}{R^2}\right), \quad r \leq R. \tag{4.29}$$

In other words, unlike what is shown in Figure 4.10b, the energy for a proton in the $1i_{13/2}$ orbital is actually lower than that in the $2f_{5/2}, 3p_{3/2},$ and $3p_{1/2}$ orbitals. The $2f_{5/2}$ and $3p_{3/2}$ orbitals seem to match the top two excited states, $\frac{5}{2}^{-}$ (2.83 MeV) and $\frac{3}{2}^{-}$ (3.12 MeV). But how do we explain the seven closely spaced excited states in between? These states are not predicted by the IPSM, and they are the result of the coupling of the spin of the 83rd proton ($\frac{9}{2}^{-}$) with the spin of the excited core (3^-) of $^{208}_{82}$Pb. The excited state of $^{208}_{82}$Pb of 3^- (2.61 MeV) is a collective state, which will be discussed in Section 4.10.

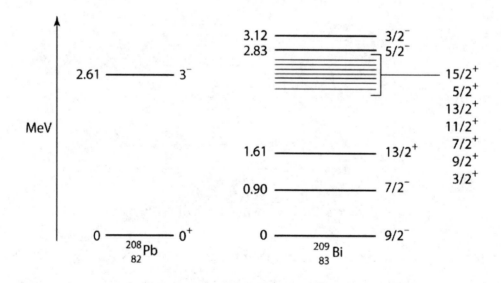

Figure 4.12 The energy levels for $^{208}_{82}$Pb and $^{209}_{83}$Bi.

All the nuclei we discussed so far are more or less spherical, and the IPSM has been shown to be successful in predicting the I^{π} for both the ground and the various excited states. For non-spherical nuclei, specifically those with mass regions 150<A<190 and A>230, the IPSM no longer works. This is because for non-spherical potential the angular momentum quantum number ℓ cannot be used to uniquely identify a specific orbital (s, p, d, f, et cetera). For example, Appendix B shows that the I^{π} are, respectively, $\frac{7}{2}^{+}, \frac{1}{2}^{+}, \frac{1}{2}^{-}$, and $\frac{7}{2}^{-}$ for the ground states $^{167}_{68}$Er, $^{169}_{69}$Tm, $^{171}_{70}$Yb, and $^{235}_{92}$U . But none of these states could be deciphered from the orbitals shown in Figure 4.10b.

4.10 Collective States of the Nucleus

As the name suggested and as shown in Section 4.9, the success of IPSM in predicting the I^{π} of a nuclear state is limited to when there is only one single unpaired nucleon. The IPSM becomes less and less useful as the number of unpaired nucleons increases. For these nuclei, many of the excited states can be understood as the "collective states," which means they are created by the collective behavior of the nucleons in the nucleus. The best example of a collective state is the lowest excited state of $I^{\pi} = 2^{+}$, which exists for almost all even-even nuclei. As shown in Figure 4.13, $E(2^{+})$ slowly decreases as A increases, except for the nuclei with Z or N near the magic numbers. This behavior can be explained via two different collective behaviors of the nuclei: the vibrational mode and the rotational mode. For nuclei with Z or N near the magic numbers, they have a spherical shape and the collective states are mainly due to the various vibrational modes. In addition, these collective states are generally at relatively high levels (> 1 MeV). For nuclei with Z or N away from the magic numbers, they have an ellipsoid shape and the collective states are mainly due to the various rotational modes. In addition, these collective states are generally at relatively low levels. Figure 4.13 shows that for nuclei with 150<A<190 and A>230, the $E(2^{+})$ lies only a few tens of keV above their ground states. The details of the various vibrational states and rotational states are discussed below.

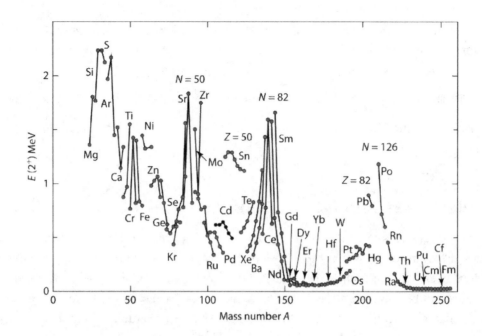

Figure 4.13. Energy levels of the lowest excited state of $I^{\pi} = 2^{+}$ of even-even nuclei plotted as a function of mass number.
Source: Lilley (2001).

4.10.1   Vibrational States

Because the nucleus is literally incompressible, for a spherical nucleus to change energy via a collective motion the nucleus must change its shape. The lowest energy corresponds to when it is a sphere. To show the various vibrational quanta, the coordinates of an arbitrary point on the surface of a deformed shape can be written in the form of a multipole expansion:

$$R(t) = R_{\text{av}} + \sum_{\lambda=1}^{\infty} \sum_{\mu=-\lambda}^{\lambda} \alpha_{\lambda,\mu}(t) Y_{\lambda,\mu}(\theta,\phi), \tag{4.30}$$

where each pole is represented by a spherical harmonic $Y_{\lambda,\mu}(\theta,\phi)$ (equation 3.91). The subscripts λ and μ are used to represent the collective motion, to distinguish from ℓ and m, used to represent a single particle. The $\lambda = 0$ term (i.e., the monopole) has been incorporated into the average radius R_{av}, which can be estimated with $R_{\text{o}}A^{1/3}$ (equation 4.16). Figure 4.14 shows 2-D depictions for $\lambda = 0, 1, 2,$ and 3. The $\alpha_{\lambda,\mu}(t)$ describes the time-varying behavior of a vibration mode. Each mode has its unique vibrational frequency, ω_{λ}, which corresponds to a quantized energy of $\hbar\omega_{\lambda}$. A quantum of vibrational energy is called a phonon. The spin and parity of a phonon are given by λ and $(-1)^{\lambda}$, respectively. The monopole vibration is nearly impossible because it is an expansion and contraction of the nucleus, and because nucleus is essentially incompressible. The dipole vibration is also not observable, because it represents a shift of the center of mass that can only occur with the action of an external force. So the observable collective states are mainly due to quadrupole and octupole vibrations. For the quadrupole vibration, $\lambda = 2$ and $(-1)^\lambda = +$, and therefore $I^\pi = 2^+$. This is responsible for the $E(2^+)$ states of the spherical nuclei having Z or N near the magic numbers, and their energy levels are relatively high (>1 MeV), as shown in Figure 4.13. For the octupole vibration, $\lambda = 3$ and $(-1)^\lambda = -$, and therefore $I^\pi = 3^-$. The first excited state of $^{208}_{82}\text{Pb}$ at 3^- (2.61 MeV) shown in Figure 4.12 is a good example of the octupole vibration.

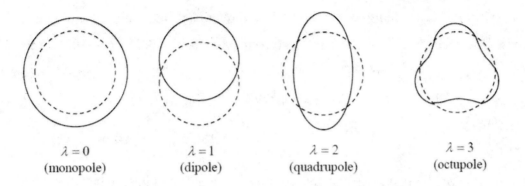

$$\lambda = 0 \qquad \lambda = 1 \qquad \lambda = 2 \qquad \lambda = 3$$
(monopole)   (dipole)   (quadrupole)   (octupole)

Figure 4.14. The 2-D depictions of the lowest four vibrational modes of a nucleus.

4.10.2   Rotational States

In quantum mechanics, a wave function representing a spherically symmetrical system has no direction preference, and a rotation of such a system leads to no observable change of the system. As such, collective rotational states are only observed in non-spherical nuclei, which are mostly found in the mass regions $150<A<190$ and $A>230$. These nuclei are non-spherical because their shells are about half-filled. Their shapes are mostly prolate or oblate. In classical mechanics, the kinetic energy of a rigid rotating object is known to be $\frac{1}{2}\mathcal{I}\omega^2$, where $\mathcal{I}$ is the moment of inertia of the object and ω the angular velocity of the rotation. For a nucleus of arbitrary shape, $\mathcal{I}$ can be calculated by

$$\mathcal{I} = \int_{\substack{\text{Nuclear} \\ \text{volume}}} \rho\, r^2 d\mathrm{v}\,, \qquad (4.31)$$

where ρ is the mass density within the nucleus, and r is the vertical distance between an arbitrary point in the nucleus and the rotating axis. Since the angular momentum can be expressed as $L = \mathcal{I}\omega$, the kinetic energy associated with the rotation can then be expressed as

$$E = \frac{1}{2}\mathcal{I}\omega^2 = \frac{1}{2}\mathcal{I}\left(\frac{L}{\mathcal{I}}\right)^2 = \frac{1}{2}\frac{L^2}{\mathcal{I}}\,. \qquad (4.32)$$

Substituting L^2 with $\hbar^2\lambda(\lambda+1)$ yields

$$E = \frac{\hbar^2}{2\mathcal{I}}\lambda(\lambda+1), \tag{4.33}$$

where λ is the angular momentum quantum number. Increasing λ corresponds to adding rotational energy to the nucleus.

For even-even nuclei with zero spin as their ground state, the rotational angular momentum is the same as the total nuclear angular momentum. Since the angular part of the wave function is a spherical harmonic, $Y_{\lambda,\mu}(\theta,\phi)$, the parity of this function is $(-1)^{\lambda}$. It can also be shown that, due to the symmetry of an ellipsoid, the only allowed rotational states are those of which λ is even. These states are $0^+, 2^+, 4^+, 6^+, 8^+, 10^+,...$ corresponding to $\lambda = 0, 2, 4, 6, 8, 10, ...$ According to equation 4.33, the energy levels of these states are $E(0^+)=0$, $E(2^+)=3\hbar^2/\mathcal{I}$, $E(4^+)=10\hbar^2/\mathcal{I}$, $E(6^+)=21\hbar^2/\mathcal{I}$, $E(8^+)=36\hbar^2/\mathcal{I}$, $E(10^+)=55\hbar^2/\mathcal{I}$, ... These formulae lead to the following ratios: $\frac{E(4^+)}{E(2^+)}=3.33$, $\frac{E(6^+)}{E(2^+)}=7$, $\frac{E(8^+)}{E(2^+)}=12$, $\frac{E(10^+)}{E(2^+)}=18.33$, ... We now arbitrarily pick a nucleus with $150<A<190$ (e.g., $^{170}_{70}$Yb), and examine if the above ratios predicted by the theory agree with the experimental data. According to the energy levels shown in Figure 4.15,
$$\frac{E(4^+)}{E(2^+)}=\frac{277.4}{84.3}=3.29 \quad, \quad \frac{E(6^+)}{E(2^+)}=\frac{573.3}{84.3}=6.8 \quad, \quad \frac{E(8^+)}{E(2^+)}=\frac{963.3}{84.3}=11.43 \quad, \quad \text{and}$$

$\frac{E(10^+)}{E(2^+)}=\frac{1437.5}{84.3}=17.05$. These values agree reasonably well with the theory. But the theory always over predicts the ratios, and the over prediction seems to increase as λ increases. This discrepancy can be explained by the fact that a nucleus, in reality, is more like a liquid drop than a rigid body, and that as the rotation speed (or angular momentum) increases, the nuclear body is stretched away from the rotational axis. This effect of centrifugal stretching necessarily increases the moment of inertia as it increases the effective value of r in equation 4.31. The increased moment of inertia, therefore, makes the experimentally obtained ratios of $E(\lambda^+)/E(2^+)$ smaller than that predicted by the theory.

For odd-A nuclei with non-zero spin as their ground state, the description of low-level excited states is significantly more complicated, because it involves the various couplings of the angular momentum of the single unpaired nucleon to the rotational angular momentum of the nucleus. Interested readers are referred to the more in-depth textbooks in nuclear physics. (Yang and Hamilton, 1996, and Prussin, 2007)

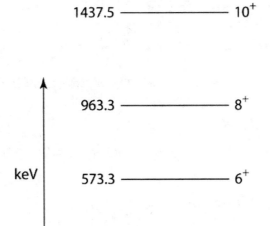

Figure 4.15. The experimentally measured low-level excited states of $^{170}_{70}$Yb.

Bibliography

Krane, Kenneth S. *Introductory Nuclear Physics*. New York: John Wiley & Sons, New York, 1988.

Lilley, John S. *Nuclear Physics: Principles and Applications*. Chichester, UK: John Wiley & Sons, Ltd., 2001.

Prussin, Stanley G. *Nuclear Physics for Applications: A Model Approach*. Weinheim, Germany: Wiley-VCH Verlag GmbH & Co. KGaA, 2007.

Yang, Fujia, and Joseph H. Hamilton. *Modern Atomic and Nuclear Physics*. New York: McGraw-Hill Companies, Inc., 1996.

Credits

Problems

1. (a) From the known masses of ^{15}O and ^{15}N, calculate the difference in binding energy. (b) Assuming this difference arises from the difference in Coulomb energy, calculate the nuclear radius of ^{15}O and ^{15}N.

2. From the difference in mass of a hydrogen atom to the mass of a proton and an electron, estimate the binding energy of the electron in the hydrogen atom. Compare this to the ionization energy of the ground state electron as calculated by the Bohr model. What fraction of the total mass is lost as the electron bonds to the proton?

3. From each of the following nuclei, use the semi-empirical mass formula to compute the total binding energy and the Coulomb energy: (a) ^{21}Ne, (b) ^{57}Fe, (c) ^{209}Bi, (d) ^{256}Fm.

4. Evaluate (a) the neutron separation energies of ^{7}Li, ^{91}Zr, and ^{236}U; (b) the proton separation energies of ^{20}Ne, ^{55}Mn, and ^{197}Au.

5. The spin-parity of ^{9}Be and ^{9}B are both $\frac{3}{2}^{-}$. Assuming in both cases that the spin and parity are characteristic only of the odd nucleon, show how it is possible to obtain the observed spin-parity of ^{10}B(3^{+}). What other spin-parity combinations could also appear? (These are observed as excited states of ^{10}B.)

6. Let's suppose we can form ^{3}He or ^{3}H by adding a proton or a neutron to ^{2}H, which has spin equal to 1 and even parity. Let ℓ be the orbital angular momentum of the added nucleon relative to the ^{2}H center of mass. What are the possible values of the total angular momentum of ^{3}H or ^{3}He? Given that the ground-state parity of ^{3}H and ^{3}He is even, which of these can be eliminated? What is the most likely value of the ground-state angular momentum of ^{3}H or ^{3}He? Can you make a similar argument based on removing a proton or a neutron from ^{4}He? (What is the ground-state spin-parity of ^{4}He?) How would you account for the spin-parity of ^{5}Li and ^{5}He ($\frac{3}{2}^{-}$)?

7. Assuming that the spin-orbit potential is given by $V_{sl} = -\frac{a^{2}}{R\hbar^{2}}\frac{\partial V}{\partial r}\Big|_{r=R} < \vec{\ell}\cdot\vec{s} >$, where $V(r) = \frac{-V_{0}}{1 + e^{(r-R)/a}}$, use $V_{0} = 50$ MeV, $R = 1.2 \times A^{1/3}$ fm and $a = 0.8$ fm to calculate the spin-orbit splitting of the shell-model states 1p, 1d, and 1f, for a nucleus with $A = 100$.

8. Use the IPSM with Figure 4.10b of the textbook to obtain the I^{π} for the ground states of (a) ^{7}Li, (b) ^{15}C, (c) ^{31}P, and (d) ^{141}Pr.

9. The low-lying levels of ^{13}C are ground state $\frac{1}{2}^{-}$; 3.09 MeV, $\frac{1}{2}^{+}$; 3.68 MeV, $\frac{3}{2}^{-}$; and 3.85 MeV, $\frac{5}{2}^{+}$. The next states are about 7 MeV and above. Use the IPSM with Figure 4.10b to decipher these four states.

10. ^{34}Cl has a ground state with a half-life of 1.526 s and spin and parity of 0^{+}, and an isomeric first excited state with a half-life of 32.0 min and spin and parity of 3^{+}. Use the IPSM with Figure 4.10b to demonstrate that the I^{π} of these two states are consistent with the

assumption that they arise from the same nucleon configuration with different angular momentum couplings.

11. Use the IPSM with Figure 4.10b to predict the I^π of the ground state and first excited state of ^{99}Mo.

12. Go to the website http://www.nndc.bnl.gov/nudat2/ and view the level diagram for ^{148}Sm. For the first six levels assigned to the ground-state rotational band, compare the experimental energies with those obtained from the simple rigid rotor model using the experimental energy difference between 0^+ and 2^+ levels to determine the magnitude of $\hbar^2/2\mathcal{I}$.

13. The excitation energies of the first 2^+ levels in ^{154}Gd and ^{238}U are 123.07 keV and 44.92 keV, respectively. Compare the ratio of level energies to the ratio estimated from a comparison of the moments of inertia estimated classically. Note: To simplify the calculation for the moments of inertia, you may assume the nuclei are constant density spheres.

14. Use Appendix B to calculate the Q-value for the following nuclear reaction. Note: n_{th} is a thermal neutron whose kinetic energy is negligible.

$$^6_3\text{Li} + {}^1n_{th} \rightarrow {}^3_1\text{H} + {}^4_2\text{He}$$

15. Use Appendix B to calculate the Q-value for the following reaction. What will be the energies of ^2H and γ, respectively?

$$^1\text{H} + {}^1n_{th} \rightarrow {}^2\text{H} + \gamma$$

16. Use Figure 4.3 to estimate the energy released as a result of a spontaneous fission reaction of a ^{252}Cf nuclide, if the reaction follows the following formula:

$$^{252}\text{Cf} \rightarrow {}^{150}\text{X} + {}^{100}\text{Y} + 2{}^1n$$

CHAPTER 5: UNSTABLE NUCLEI, RADIOACTIVITY, RADIOACTIVE DECAY MODES AND SCHEMES, AND RADIOACTIVE DECAY AND BUILDUP

5.1 Origins of Unstable Nuclei

Unstable atomic nuclei (or radionuclides) can be found in nature. They can also be produced at manmade facilities. Naturally occurring radionuclides are divided into two categories according to their origin: the primordial and the cosmogenic. Primordial radionuclides are those that have existed since the earth was first formed. Some of these radionuclides (e.g., ^{238}U), have half-lives comparable to the age of the earth (~5 billion years), and therefore, have not completely decayed away. Others (e.g., ^{222}Rn), have much shorter half-lives (~4 days). They can still be found naturally because they are the products associated with the decay chain of the three long-lived primordial radionuclides, ^{238}U, ^{235}U, and ^{232}Th. Figures 5.1 and 5.2 show the decay chains of these three radionuclides. Other long-lived primordial radionuclides are singly occurring. The well-known ones include ^{40}K, ^{50}V, ^{87}Rb, ^{115}In, ^{123}Te , ^{138}La , ^{142}Ce , ^{144}Nd , ^{147}Sm, ^{152}Gd, ^{174}Hf , ^{176}Lu , ^{187}Re, and ^{190}Pt . The cosmogenic radionuclides have half-lives significantly shorter than the age of the earth, and they are constantly being produced via the interactions of high-energy cosmic rays (mainly protons and ^{4}He nuclei) and their derivatives (neutrons, mesons, pions, kaons, muons, and gamma rays) with the earth's environment. A well-known cosmogenic radionuclide is ^{14}C ($T_{1/2} = 5700$ years), which is produced via the nuclear reaction ^{14}N(n,p)^{14}C (Section 6.1) in the earth's atmosphere. Some other cosmogenic radionuclides include ^{3}H , ^{7}Be, ^{10}Be, ^{22}Na, ^{26}Al, ^{32}P, ^{35}S , ^{36}Cl, ^{41}Ar, ^{41}Ca , and ^{53}Mn .

Radionuclides can also be artificially produced via nuclear weapons testing, in nuclear reactors, and at particle accelerators. The largest quantities of artificially produced radionuclides have been produced and released into the atmosphere via nuclear weapons testing during the period from 1945 to 1970 or so. These fallout radionuclides include several hundred different species, of which most are referred to as fission products, because they are produced via nuclear fission reactions (Sections 6.4 and 7.4). Most of the fission products have half-lives shorter than a few years (e.g., ^{131}I with $T_{1/2} = 8$ days), and therefore, have decayed away. There are a few longer-lived ones, most notably ^{90}Sr ($T_{1/2} = 28.9$ years) and ^{137}Cs ($T_{1/2} = 30.2$ years) , which can still be found in the soil today. Large quantities of fission products have also been released into the atmosphere due to commercial nuclear power accidents, such as Chernobyl in 1986 and Fukushima in 2011. The huge quantity of radionuclides produced by the commercial power reactors are considered radioactive waste. They currently remain in the spent fuel assemblies and are stored either in water pools or in dry storage casks. A small number of reactor-produced radionuclides, however, are purposely made for research or medical and industrial applications. The notable ones include ^{60}Co, ^{90}Sr , ^{90}Y , ^{99}Mo, ^{99m}Tc , ^{123}I , ^{125}I , ^{131}I , ^{137}Cs , ^{153}Sm,

^{186}Re, ^{188}Re, ^{225}Ac, ^{238}Pu, ^{241}Am, and ^{252}Cf. Relative to nuclear power reactors, the amount of radionuclides produced at particle accelerators is much smaller. Most of these nuclides are purposely made for use in medical diagnostic imaging or the treatment of cancer. A well-known accelerator-produced radionuclide is ^{18}F. It has a short half-life of 110 minutes, and is widely used with a diagnostic imaging modality called position emission tomography. The main method of production is via the nuclear reaction ^{18}O(p, n)^{18}F, by bombarding the naturally existing ^{18}O atoms in the form of ^{18}O-enriched liquid water with 18-MeV protons. Other notable accelerator-produced radionuclides include ^{11}C, ^{13}N, ^{15}O, ^{32}P, ^{64}Cu, ^{75}Se, ^{99}Mo/^{99m}Tc, ^{103}Pd, ^{169}Yb, and ^{192}Ir.

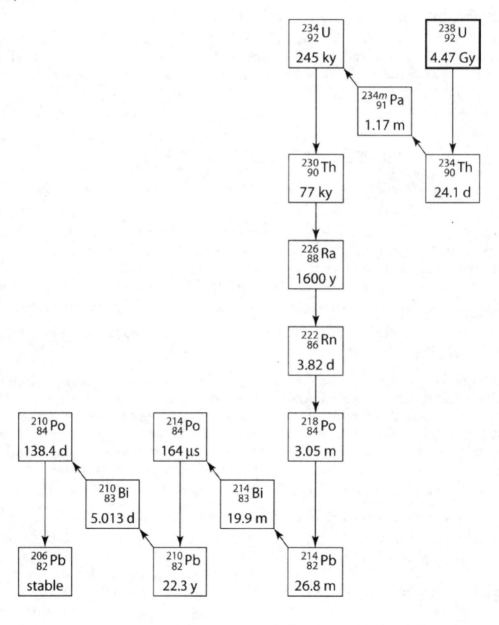

Figure 5.1. The decay chain of ^{238}U.
Source: Shultis and Faw (2008).

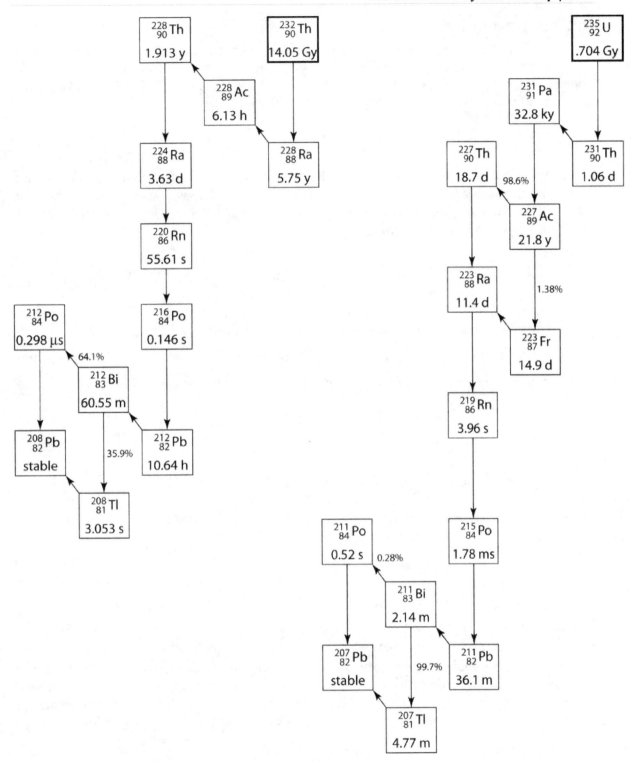

Figure 5.2. The decay chains of ^{235}U and ^{232}Th.
Source: Shultis and Faw (2008).

5.2 Radioactivity

An unstable atomic nucleus is called a radionuclide. It has been found that the probability of per unit time that a radionuclide will decay is a constant. This so-called decay constant can be understood via the transition probability (Section 3.10 and equations 3.108–3.110). The decay rate (decay per unit time) of a radionuclide can then be expressed as:

$$\frac{dN}{dt} = -\lambda N , \qquad (5.1)$$

where N is the number of atoms and λ the decay constant. The negative sign on the right-hand side of equation 5.1 indicates that the radionuclide population decreases with respect to time. The term λN is defined as the radioactivity (or activity) of the radionuclide and is denoted by A. Equation 5.1 can be solved as follows:

$$\frac{dN}{N} = -\lambda\, dt \;\Rightarrow\; \int_{N_0}^{N} \frac{dN}{N} = -\lambda \int_{0}^{t} dt \;\Rightarrow\; \ln\!\left(\frac{N}{N_0}\right) = -\lambda t \;\Rightarrow\; N = N_0 e^{-\lambda t}, \quad (5.2)$$

where N_0 is the initial number of atoms (i.e., at $t = 0$). Equation 5.2 shows that the decay rate of a radionuclide follows a simple exponential function, $e^{-\lambda t}$. By applying 5.2 and by setting $N = \dfrac{N_0}{2}$, one can obtain the expression of the half-life ($T_{1/2}$) in terms of λ. That is,

$$N = N_0 e^{-\lambda T_{1/2}} = \frac{N_0}{2} \quad\Rightarrow\quad e^{-\lambda T_{1/2}} = \frac{1}{2}$$

$$\Rightarrow\; -\lambda T_{1/2} = \ln\!\left(\frac{1}{2}\right) \quad\Rightarrow\quad T_{1/2} = \frac{\ln 2}{\lambda} \cong \frac{0.693}{\lambda}. \qquad (5.3)$$

The standard unit of radioactivity is Becquerel (or Bq), which is defined as

$$1\,\text{Bq} = 1 \ \text{disintegration sec}^{-1}. \qquad (5.4)$$

5.3 Radioactive Decay Modes

The common types of radioactive decay (or transformation) include alpha (α), negative beta (β^-), positive beta (β^+), electron capture (EC), gamma (γ), and internal conversion (IC). Some less common types include spontaneous fission (SF), proton (p), and neutron (n). In all nuclear interactions (including radioactive decay), the law of conservation applies to several quantities, including electric charge, number of nucleons, energy, linear momentum, and angular momentum. The phenomenology of these decay modes is described individually below.

5.3.1 Alpha Decay

Alpha decay typically occurs in the heavy nuclides with $A > 170$, and it is the predominate decay mode for transuranic radionuclides. When a radionuclide $_Z^A X$ undergoes α decay, it emits an α particle (i.e., a $_2^4 He$ nucleus). Since the numbers of neutrons and protons are conserved in α decay, the residual nucleus Y, therefore, has a proton number of Z-2 and a mass number of A-4. The generic representation of α decay is expressed as

$$_Z^A X \rightarrow {_{Z-2}^{A-4}} Y + \alpha .\tag{5.5}$$

For example, uranium-238 undergoing α decay is written as

$$_{92}^{238} U \rightarrow {_{90}^{234}} Th + \alpha .$$

Alpha decay is the most common form of cluster decay, where the parent atom ejects a defined daughter collection of nucleons, leaving another defined product behind. It is the most common form because of the combined extremely high binding energy and relatively small mass of the α particle. Alpha decay is fundamentally a quantum tunneling process (Section 3.4), and it is governed by the interplay between the nuclear force and the electromagnetic force. The kinetic energy of an α particle typically is in the range of 4-8 MeV. The half-life of an α decay in general is inversely proportional to the kinetic energy of the α particle (or the Q-value). The relationship between the half-life (or decay constant) and the kinetic energy of the α particle (or the Q-value) can be explained by the semi-classical theory of α decay, which is described in Section 6.1.

As defined by equation 4.15, the Q-value of a nuclear reaction is the difference in mass before and after the reaction. That is,

$$Q/c^2 = \Delta m = m\left(_Z^A X\right) - \left[m\left(_{Z-2}^{A-4} Y\right) + m\left(_2^4 He\right)\right]$$
$$\cong \Delta M = M\left(_Z^A X\right) - \left[M\left(_{Z-2}^{A-4} Y\right) + M\left(_2^4 He\right)\right]\tag{5.6}$$

where m and M represent the mass of the nucleus and the atom, respectively. The $\cong$ sign indicates that there is a slight difference between Δm and ΔM due to the difference in electron binding energies between the initial nuclide and the decay products. If one ignores this difference, then the Q-value for any α decay can be obtained by using the atomic mass values available from Appendix B.

In a typical α decay, where the radionuclide is originally at rest, both the kinetic energy and the linear momentum are zero. The laws of conservation for energy and linear momentum can respectively be expressed below:

$$Q = \Delta M c^2 = E_\alpha + E_Y = \frac{1}{2} M_\alpha v_\alpha^2 + \frac{1}{2} M_Y v_Y^2\tag{5.7}$$

and

$$M_\alpha v_\alpha = M_Y v_Y ,\tag{5.8}$$

where v_α and v_Y are the speed for the α particle and the residual nucleus, respectively, $M_\alpha = M\left(^4_2\text{He}\right)$, and $M_Y = M\left(^{A-4}_{Z-2}Y\right)$. The kinetic energies E_α and E_Y can be obtained by solving the two unknowns v_α and v_Y with equations 5.7 and 5.8. That is, by substituting v_Y with $\dfrac{M_\alpha}{M_Y} v_\alpha$ (from 5.8), 5.7 becomes

$$Q = \frac{1}{2}\frac{M_\alpha^2}{M_Y}v_\alpha^2 + \frac{1}{2}M_\alpha v_\alpha^2 = \frac{1}{2}M_\alpha v_\alpha^2\left(\frac{M_\alpha}{M_Y}+1\right) = E_\alpha\left(\frac{M_\alpha + M_Y}{M_Y}\right). \qquad (5.9)$$

That is,

$$E_\alpha = Q\left(\frac{M_Y}{M_\alpha + M_Y}\right) \cong Q\left(\frac{M_Y}{M_X}\right) \cong Q\left(\frac{A-4}{A}\right) \qquad (5.10)$$

and

$$E_Y = Q - E_\alpha \cong Q - Q\left(\frac{M_Y}{M_X}\right) = Q\left(1 - \frac{M_Y}{M_X}\right) = Q\left(\frac{M_X - M_Y}{M_X}\right) \cong Q\left(\frac{4}{A}\right) \quad (5.11)$$

We now take the α decay of uranium-238 as an example. From equation 5.6, the Q-value can be obtained as

$$Q \cong \Delta M c^2 = \left[M(^{238}_{92}\text{U}) - M\left(^4_2\text{He}\right) - M\left(^{234}_{90}\text{Th}\right)\right]c^2$$
$$= [47.310 - 2.425 - 40.615]\,\text{MeV} = 4.27\ \text{MeV}.$$

From equations 5.10 and 5.11, one has

$$E_\alpha \cong Q\left(\frac{A-4}{A}\right) = 4.27\left(\frac{238-4}{238}\right) \cong 4.198\ \text{MeV}$$

and

$$E_Y = Q - E_\alpha = 4.27 - 4.198 = 0.072\ \text{MeV, or } 72\ \text{keV}.$$

5.3.2 Beta Decays and Electron Capture

When an unstable nucleus has too many neutrons or too many protons, it can undergo β decays or electron capture (EC). There are two types of β decay: negative beta decay (β^-) and positive beta decay (β^+). When a radionuclide $^A_Z X$ undergoes β^- decay, it throws out an electron and an antineutrino, and at the same time, a neutron is switched into a proton inside the nucleus. The residual nucleus Y, therefore, has an increased proton number of $Z+1$ and its mass number stays the same. The generic form is written as

$$^A_Z X \rightarrow\, ^A_{Z+1}Y + e^- + \bar{v}, \qquad (5.12)$$

where $\bar{v}$ is the symbol for antineutrino. Historically, antineutrino was a "ghost particle," proposed by Wolfgang Pauli in 1930 as a desperate rescue of the conservation laws of energy, linear momentum, and angular momentum. Without it, none of the conservation laws will hold for β decay. The experimental confirmation of the existence of the antineutrino had to wait until a quarter of a century later.

Similar to β^- decay, when a radionuclide $^A_Z X$ undergoes β^+ decay, it throws out a positively charged electron (e^+ or positron) and a neutrino. The positron is the antiparticle of the electron. In this case, a proton is switched into a neutron inside the nucleus. As such, the residual nucleus Y has a decreased proton number of $Z-1$ and its mass number stays the same. The generic form is written as

$$^A_Z X \rightarrow\, ^A_{Z-1}Y + e^+ + \nu, \tag{5.13}$$

where ν is the symbol for neutrino. The antineutrino is the antiparticle of the neutrino.

EC is an alternative (or competing) decay mode to β^+ decay. The EC transition occurs when the radionuclide $^A_Z X$ absorbs an atomic electron (most likely from the closest K-shell) and undergoes the transition to become $^A_{Z-1}Y$, same as that in β^+ decay. The generic form of an EC is written as:

$$^A_Z X + e^- \rightarrow\, ^A_{Z-1}Y + \nu. \tag{5.14}$$

One may experimentally distinguish EC events from β^+ events via observing the characteristic X rays following the EC events. The characteristic X rays are emitted following EC events as a result of the missing K-shell electrons (Section 2.6).

From conservation of energy, the Q-values for β^- and β^+ decay can be written, respectively, as

$$Q/c^2 = \Delta m = m\left(^A_Z X\right) - \left[m\left(^A_{Z+1}Y\right) + m_e + m_{\bar\nu}\right] \cong \Delta M = M\left(^A_Z X\right) - \left[M\left(^A_{Z+1}Y\right) + m_{\bar\nu}\right] \tag{5.15}$$

and

$$Q/c^2 = \Delta m = m\left(^A_Z X\right) - \left[m\left(^A_{Z-1}Y\right) + m_e + m_\nu\right]$$
$$\cong \Delta M = M\left(^A_Z X\right) - \left[M\left(^A_{Z-1}Y\right) + 2m_e + m_\nu\right] \tag{5.16}$$

where m_e, $m_{\bar\nu}$, and m_ν are the masses of the electron, antineutrino, and neutrino, respectively. Since $m_{\bar\nu}$ and m_ν are negligible for all practical matters, 5.15 and 5.16 are reduced to

$$Q = \left[M\left(^A_Z X\right) - M\left(^A_{Z+1}Y\right)\right]c^2 \tag{5.17}$$

and

$$Q = \left[M\left(^A_Z X\right) - M\left(^A_{Z-1}Y\right) - 2m_e\right]c^2. \tag{5.18}$$

Similarly, the Q-values for EC can be written as

$$Q = \left[M\left(_Z^A X\right) - M\left(_{Z-1}^A Y\right) \right] c^2 - B, \tag{5.19}$$

where B is the binding energy of the electron. Because $B \ll 2m_e c^2$, nuclei that can undergo β^+ decay can always also undergo EC, but the reverse is not true.

We now take the β^- decay of phosphorus-32 as an example: $^{32}P \rightarrow {}^{32}S + e^- + \bar{\nu}$. From equation 5.17, the Q-value can be obtained as

$$Q \cong \Delta M c^2 = \left[M(^{32}P) - M(^{32}S) \right] c^2 = \left[-24.304 + 26.015 \right] \text{MeV} = 1.711 \, \text{MeV}.$$

Another example is that of a free neutron, which spontaneously undergoes β^- decay to become a proton. The half-life of a free neutron is approximately 10.2 minutes. From equation 5.17, the Q-value can be obtained as

$$Q \cong \Delta M c^2 = \left[M(n) - M(^1H) \right] c^2 = \left[8.071 - 7.289 \right] \text{MeV} = 0.782 \, \text{MeV}.$$

A free proton, however, cannot spontaneously undergo β^+ decay to become a neutron. This is because the Q-value for such a decay is negative.

One major difference between β decay and other decay modes is that the particle emitted (i.e., e^- or e^+) is not monoenergetic. This is because a β decay involves three bodies: the e^- or e^+, the antineutrino or neutrino, and the residual nucleus; the Q-value must be shared by the three bodies. From the conservation laws of energy and linear momentum, and because the mass of the residual nucleus is so much greater that of the e^- (or e^+) and the antineutrino (or neutrino), almost all the Q-value goes to the kinetic energies of the e^- (or e^+) and the antineutrino (or neutrino). As discussed in Section 6.2, there is an infinite number of ways that the Q-value can be distributed between the e^- and the antineutrino (or between the e^+ and the neutrino); the kinetic energy of the e^- (or e^+) follows a continuous energy spectrum spanning from 0 to $\sim Q$. In the case of ^{32}P, the electron emitted from the decay can have energy as high as 1.71 MeV (see Figure 5.3). But the average energy of the electrons is only about one-third, which is approximately 0.7 MeV. The other two-thirds of the Q-value go to the antineutrino.

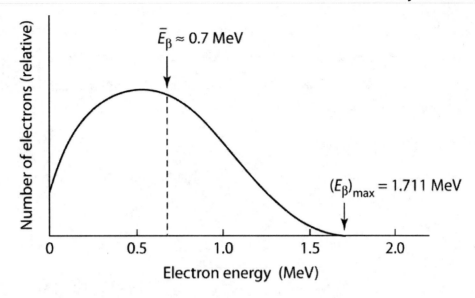

Figure 5.3. The energy spectrum of the electrons emitted from β decays of ^{32}P.

Unlike that for α decay, for β decay there is no simple relationship between the half-life (or decay constant) and the Q-value. For example, $T_{1/2} \cong 12.4$ years for ^{3}H undergoing β^{-} decay where $Q = 18$ keV. Whereas for ^{14}C undergoing β^{-} decay where $Q = 156$ keV (being much greater), the half-life is actually much longer, ~ 5700 years. The transition probability of β decay can be understood via Fermi's Golden Rule (equation 3.110) and is further discussed in Section 6.2.

5.3.3 Gamma Decay and Internal Conversion

When an excited nucleus undergoes γ decay, it throws out a gamma photon and then goes down to a lower energy state. The representation of γ decay can be expressed as

$$_{Z}^{A}X^{i} \rightarrow {}_{Z}^{A}X^{i-1} + \gamma,\tag{5.20}$$

where $_{Z}^{A}X^{i}$ and $_{Z}^{A}X^{i-1}$, respectively, represent the excited states i and $i-1$ of the nucleus $_{Z}^{A}X$. From conservation of energy, the Q-value of the above γ decay can be obtained as

$$Q = \Delta mc^{2} = \left[m\left(_{Z}^{A}X^{i}\right) - m\left(_{Z}^{A}X^{i-1}\right)\right]c^{2} = E_{i} - E_{i-1},\tag{5.21}$$

where E_{i} and E_{i-1} are respectively the energies of $_{Z}^{A}X^{i}$ and $_{Z}^{A}X^{i-1}$, relative to their ground state. The data of E_{i} and E_{i-1} for the various nuclides are available from the NuDat 2 database at the National Nuclear Data Center (http://www.nndc.bnl.gov/nudat2/). From conservation of linear momentum, one has

$$P_{\gamma} = P_{X} \quad \Rightarrow \quad \frac{E_{\gamma}}{c} = \sqrt{2m_{X}E_{X}} \quad \Rightarrow \quad E_{\gamma} = c\sqrt{2m_{X}E_{X}} \quad \Rightarrow \quad E_{\gamma}^{2} = 2m_{X}c^{2}E_{X},\tag{5.22}$$

where P_γ and E_γ, respectively, are the linear momentum and energy of the gamma photon, and P_X, m_X, and E_X, respectively, are the linear momentum, mass, and kinetic energy of the residual nucleus ${}^A_Z X^{i-1}$. Because $2m_X c^2 >> E_X$, equation 5.22 requires that $E_\gamma >> E_X$. The energy conservation then leads to

$$Q = E_\gamma + E_X \approx E_\gamma. \tag{5.23}$$

In other words, almost the entire Q-value goes to E_γ. The tiny amount that goes to E_X can be estimated via equations 5.22 and 5.23 as

$$E_X = \frac{E_\gamma^2}{2m_X c^2} \approx \frac{Q^2}{2m_X c^2}. \tag{5.24}$$

Because E_γ for most γ decays is less than 5 MeV, and because $2m_X c^2 \geq 3751$ MeV (two times the mass of the deuteron), E_X is smaller than Q by more than three orders of magnitude.

Unlike α decay and β decay, most γ decays occur instantly ($<10^{-9}$ s). They are typically the result of nuclear reactions or of α or β decays, of which the residual nuclei are left in excited states. However, there are a few excited nuclei that have much greater lifetimes—up to minutes or hours. These long-lived γ-emitting nuclides are called *metastable nuclei* or *isomers*. The generic symbol of an isomer is represented as ${}^{Am}X$, where the additional m after A represents "metastable." For example, ${}^{99m}Tc$ represents an isomer of ${}^{99}Tc$. The transition probability of γ decays is further discussed in Section 6.3.

Internal conversion (IC) is an alternative (or competing) decay mode to γ decay. IC occurs when the excited radionuclide ${}^A_Z X^i$ directly transfers its energy to an atomic electron (most likely in the closest K-shell), and then undergoes the transition to become ${}^A_Z X^{i-1}$, same as that in γ decay. The generic form of an IC is written as:

$$\tag{5.25} {}^A_Z X^i \rightarrow {}^A_Z X^{i-1} + e^-.$$

One may experimentally distinguish IC events from γ events via observing the characteristic X rays following the IC events. The characteristic X rays are emitted following IC events as a result of the missing K-shell electrons (Section 2.6). One may also experimentally distinguish IC events from β^- events by the electron spectrum (i.e., the electrons emitted from IC events are monoenergetic, whereas the electrons emitted from β^- events follow a continuous spectrum).

5.3.4 Spontaneous Fission

Spontaneous fission (SF) is only observed in heavy nuclides with $A > 230$. It is an alternative (or competing) mode to α decay. The most notable radionuclide that undergoes SF is ${}^{252}Cf$. When a radionuclide ${}^A_Z X$ undergoes SF, it is typically split into two fragments, C and D, which are mostly unequal in mass. The generic representation of SF is expressed as:

$$\tag{5.26} {}^A_Z X \rightarrow {}^{A_C}_{Z_C} C + {}^{A_D}_{Z_D} D,$$

where $A_C + A_D = A$ and $Z_C + Z_D = Z$. Because nuclides C and D are both highly excited and neutron-rich, they immediately throw out a few neutrons and gamma rays. The remaining fission fragments are less excited, but still neutron-rich; they would continue to undergo several β^- decays.

Like α decay, SF is a form of cluster decay, but the probability is usually much smaller than that of α decay (see Section 6.4). According to Figure 4.3, one expects a large amount of energy (a large positive Q-value) to be released in a fission reaction when a nuclide of A > 150 is split into two fragments of equal mass. For example, the binding energy per nucleon for $A = 100$ and 200 are approximately 8.6 MeV and 7.9 MeV, respectively. As such, when a nuclide of $A = 200$ is split into two equal-mass fragments of $A = 100$, the expected total amount of energy released can be estimated as

$$\left(8.6 \frac{\text{MeV}}{\text{nucleon}} - 7.9 \frac{\text{MeV}}{\text{nucleon}}\right)(200 \text{ nucleons}) = 140 \text{ MeV} .$$

Surprisingly, when a nuclear fission reaction occurs it does not split into two equal-mass fragments, even though an equal-mass split would give the largest Q-value. In the case of ^{252}Cf, the masses of two fission fragments tend to be around 143 and 109. Because the binding energy per nucleon for A = 109, 143, and 252 are approximately 8.5 MeV, 8.3 MeV, and 7.4 MeV, respectively, the Q-value can be estimated as

$$(8.5 \text{ MeV})(109) + (8.3 \text{ MeV})(143) - (7.4 \text{ MeV})(252) = 248.6 \text{ MeV} .$$

According to energy and momentum conservation, this energy is unequally shared by the two fission fragments, according to their masses. The lighter fragment (with $A = 109$) will have a kinetic energy of 248.6 MeV $\left(\frac{143}{252}\right) \cong 141.1 \text{ MeV}$, and the heavy one (with $A = 143$) will have a kinetic energy of 248.6 MeV $\left(\frac{109}{252}\right) = 107.5 \text{ MeV}$. A more detailed theory on SF is provided in Section 6.4.

5.3.5 Decay via Neutron Emission

As mentioned in Section 5.3.3, many residual nuclei following a β decay are left in an excited state and would undergo instant decay by emitting a gamma photon. Rarely, however, a nucleus may be left at an excited state that decays by emitting a neutron. One example is that of ^{87}Br, which undergoes a β decay to an excited state of ^{87}Kr, which in turn decays via emitting a neutron to the ground state of ^{86}Kr. Another example is that of ^{137}I, which undergoes a β decay to an excited state of ^{137}Xe, which in turn decays via emitting a neutron to the ground state of ^{136}Xe. The fact that two excited nuclei (^{87}Kr and ^{137}Xe) opt to undergo neutron emission, instead of the common gamma emission, has to do with the fact that the two corresponding residual nuclei (^{86}Kr and ^{136}Xe) are both magic nuclei. The neutrons emitted from these decays are referred to as "delayed neutrons," because they are the decay products of ^{87}Kr and ^{137}Xe, which have half-lives of 54.5 s and 24.4 s, respectively. In other words, the emission of neutrons is delayed according to the half-lives of their precursors, ^{87}Kr and ^{137}Xe. The delayed neutrons play a critical role in safe control of a nuclear reactor. More discussion on this topic is included in Section 7.4.3.

5.4 Radioactive Decay Schemes

In addition to the various decay processes, each decay process can also have many pathways. The complex decay pathways for each nuclide are commonly described by the decay scheme shown in Figure 5.4. (Shultis and Faw, 2008) In this diagram, the x-axis represents the proton number and the y-axis represents the energy of the state. Each state of a nuclide is shown by a horizontal line with the thick one representing the ground state. Because a nuclide loses energy in each decay pathway, the various decay modes and pathways are shown by descending arrows. The daughter nuclide is shifted to the left or right from the parent nuclide depending on if the decay results in a decrease or increase in proton number. For example, the daughter nuclide is shifted to the left by two units for an α decay and by one unit for β^+ decay and EC. The decay scheme also includes the probability (or yield) for each pathway. For example, Figure 5.4 shows that there are two β^- decay pathways, $\beta_1^-(f_1)$ and $\beta_2^-(f_2)$, where f_1 and f_2 are the probabilities for β_1^- and β_2^-, respectively. The sum of the fractions of all pathways should add up to 100%.

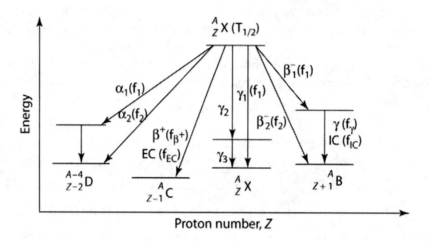

Figure 5.4. A hypothetical decay scheme showing the various decay modes and pathways.

Figure 5.5 shows a partial decay scheme of ^{99}Mo/^{99}Tc. As shown, ^{99}Mo first undergoes β^- decay via four different pathways. Each pathway leads to a different excited state of ^{99}Tc. Each excited state of ^{99}Tc then undergoes γ decay via multiple pathways. The probability (or yield) associated with each decay pathway is dictated by the quantum-mechanical principle of transitions between the initial state and the corresponding final state of each pathway (Section 3.8). The decay rate of a radionuclide is characterized by the decay constant, λ, which is defined as the probability of disintegration per unit time (Section 5.2). Since there can be many decay pathways where each has its own decay constant, λ is therefore the sum of the decay constants for all pathways. That is, $\lambda = \sum_i \lambda_i$, where λ_i is the decay constant for a specific pathway i.

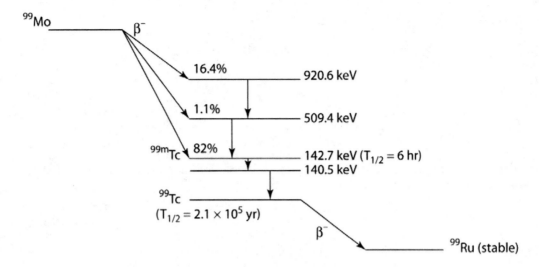

Figure 5.5. A partial decay scheme of ^{99}Mo/^{99}Tc.

5.5 Radioactive Decay Chains

Let's now consider a serial decay chain that involves three nuclide species — 1, 2, and 3 shown below:

That is, the first two are radioactive and the third one is stable. If we let N_1 and N_2 be the number of atoms for nuclides 1 and 2, respectively, then the rate of change equations and their solutions can then be written as:

$$\frac{dN_1}{dt} = -\lambda_1 N_1 \qquad\qquad (5.27)$$

and

$$\frac{dN_2}{dt} = \lambda_1 N_1 - \lambda_2 N_2 . \qquad\qquad (5.28)$$

According to equation 5.2, the solution for 5.27 is simply $N_1 = N_1(0)e^{-\lambda_1 t}$. As such, 5.28 becomes

$$\frac{dN_2}{dt} = \lambda_1 N_1(0)e^{-\lambda_1 t} - \lambda_2 N_2 . \qquad\qquad (5.29)$$

Multiplying by the integrating factor $e^{\lambda_2 t}$, 5.29 then follows that:

$$e^{\lambda_2 t} dN_2 = \lambda_1 N_1(0)e^{(\lambda_2 - \lambda_1)t} dt - \lambda_2 N_2 e^{\lambda_2 t} dt$$

$$\Rightarrow \quad e^{\lambda_2 t} dN_2 + \lambda_2 N_2 e^{\lambda_2 t} dt = \lambda_1 N_1(0)e^{(\lambda_2 - \lambda_1)t} dt$$

$$\Rightarrow \quad d\left(N_2 e^{\lambda_2 t}\right) = \lambda_1 N_1(0)e^{(\lambda_2 - \lambda_1)t} dt$$

$$\Rightarrow \quad N_2 e^{\lambda_2 t} = \frac{\lambda_1}{\lambda_2 - \lambda_1} N_1(0)e^{(\lambda_2 - \lambda_1)t} + C, \qquad (5.30)$$

where C is a constant that can be obtained by applying the initial condition of $N_2 = 0$ to 5.30, as

$$C = -\left(\frac{\lambda_1 N_1(0)}{\lambda_2 - \lambda_1}\right). \qquad (5.31)$$

Substituting 5.31 into 5.30, the final solution of N_2 can be found as

$$N_2 = \frac{\lambda_1 N_1(0)}{\lambda_2 - \lambda_1}\left(e^{-\lambda_1 t} - e^{-\lambda_2 t}\right). \qquad (5.32)$$

Figure 5.6 shows a typical decay and buildup curve of the activities A_1 and A_2 as function of time, where $A_1 = \lambda_1 N_1$ and $A_2 = \lambda_2 N_2$. According to equation 5.28, the two curves A_1 and A_2 intersect each other when $\lambda_1 N_1 = \lambda_2 N_2$, or $\dfrac{dN_2}{dt} = 0$, which also corresponds to when A_2 reaches its maximum value. From equation 5.20, it follows that

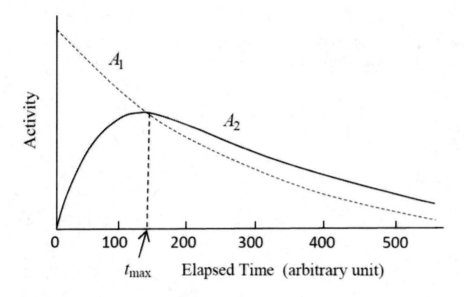

Figure 5.6. The decay and buildup of the activities A_1 and A_2 as function of time.

$$\frac{dN_2}{dt} = \frac{\lambda_1 N_1(0)}{\lambda_2 - \lambda_1}\left(\lambda_2 e^{-\lambda_2 t} - \lambda_1 e^{-\lambda_1 t}\right). \qquad (5.33)$$

By setting the right-hand side of 5.33 to zero and solving for t, one obtains t_{max} as

$$t_{max} = \frac{\ln(\lambda_2 / \lambda_1)}{\lambda_2 - \lambda_1}. \tag{5.34}$$

There are two scenarios under which simple relationships between A_1 and A_2 can be found. The first one is called secular equilibrium, which occurs for $\lambda_2 \gg \lambda_1$ and when $\lambda_2 t \gg 1$. (Turner, 2007) Under such a condition, A_2 can be derived and simplified from 5.32 as:

$$A_2 = \lambda_2 N_2 = \frac{\lambda_1 \lambda_2 N_1(0)}{\lambda_2 - \lambda_1}\left(e^{-\lambda_1 t} - e^{-\lambda_2 t}\right) \cong \lambda_1 N_1(0)\left(e^{-\lambda_1 t}\right) \cong \lambda_1 N_1 = A_1. \tag{5.35}$$

That is, when a decay chain is under secular equilibrium, the parent activity A_1 and the daughter activity A_2 are equal to each other. Figure 5.7 shows how A_2 approaches A_1 under the secular equilibrium condition.

Two good examples of secular equilibrium decay chains are

$^{90}\text{Sr}\xrightarrow{T_{1/2}=288\,\text{yr}}{}^{90}\text{Y}\xrightarrow{T_{1/2}=2.7\text{d}}{}^{90}\text{Zr}$ and $^{226}\text{Ra}\xrightarrow{T_{1/2}=1600\,\text{yr}}{}^{222}\text{Rn}\xrightarrow{T_{1/2}=3.8\text{d}}{}^{218}\text{Po}$.

A simple rule of thumb for satisfying the condition of $\lambda_2 t \gg 1$ is when t is greater than five times the half-life of nuclide 2. For an isolated ^{90}Sr source, it approaches secular equilibrium when $t > 5(2.7\,\text{d}) = 13.5\,\text{days}$. For an isolated ^{226}Ra source, it approaches secular equilibrium when $t > 5(3.8\,\text{d}) = 19\,\text{days}$.

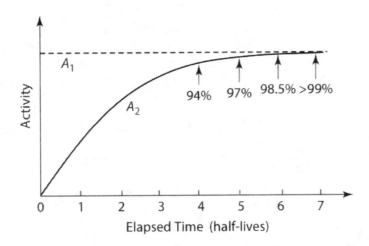

Figure 5.7. The secular equilibrium condition between the parent activity A_1 and the daughter activity A_2.

The second scenario is called the transient equilibrium, which occurs for $\lambda_1 < \lambda_2$ and when t is rather large, so that $e^{-(\lambda_2 - \lambda_1)t} \to 0$. Under such a condition, A_2 can be derived and simplified from equation 5.35 as:

$$A_2 = \lambda_2 N_2 = \frac{\lambda_1 \lambda_2 N_1(0)}{\lambda_2 - \lambda_1}\left(e^{-\lambda_1 t} - e^{-\lambda_2 t}\right) \cong \left(\frac{\lambda_2}{\lambda_2 - \lambda_1}\right)\lambda_1 N_1(0) e^{-\lambda_1 t}\left[1 - e^{-(\lambda_2 - \lambda_1)t}\right]$$

$$\cong \left(\frac{\lambda_2}{\lambda_2 - \lambda_1}\right)\lambda_1 N_1 = \left(\frac{\lambda_2}{\lambda_2 - \lambda_1}\right)A_1. \tag{5.36}$$

That is, when a decay chain is under transient equilibrium, the daughter activity A_2 is proportional to the parent activity A_1 with a simple ratio $(\lambda_2 / \lambda_2 - \lambda_1)$. Figure 5.8 shows how A_1 and A_2 approach the transient equilibrium.

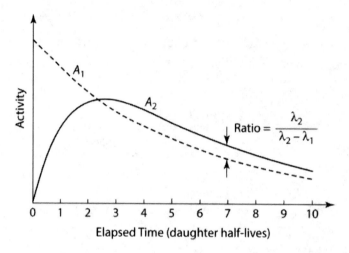

Figure 5.8 The relationship between A_1 and A_2 under transient equilibrium.

A good example of transient equilibrium decay chain is:

$$^{99}\text{Mo} \xrightarrow{\;T_{1/2}=66\text{ hr}\;} {}^{99m}\text{Tc} \xrightarrow{\;T_{1/2}=6\text{ hr}\;} {}^{99}\text{Tc} .$$

To satisfy the condition of $e^{-(\lambda_2 - \lambda_1)t} \rightarrow 0$ to within 3%, $(\lambda_2 - \lambda_1)t$ must be greater than 5; that is, $t > \dfrac{5}{\lambda_2 - \lambda_1}$. Since $\lambda_1 = \dfrac{0.693}{66\text{ hr}} = 0.0105$ hr^{-1} and $\lambda_2 = \dfrac{0.693}{6\text{ hr}} = 0.1155$ hr^{-1} , the transient equilibrium occurs after $\dfrac{5}{(0.1155 - 0.0105)\text{ hr}^{-1}}$, which is approximately 47.6 hours.

Bibliography

Shultis, J. Kenneth, and Faw, Richard E.. *Fundamentals of Nuclear Science and Engineering*, 2nd ed. Boca Raton, FL: CRC Press, Taylor & Francis Group, 2008.

Turner, James E. *Atoms, Radiation, and Radiation Protection*, 3rd ed. Weinheim, Germany: Wiley-VCH Verlag GmbH & Co. KGa, 2007.

Credits

Fig. 5.1: J. Kenneth Shultis and Richard E. Faw, from *Fundamentals of Nuclear Science and Engineering*, 2nd ed., p. 117. Copyright © 2008 by CRC Press.

Fig. 5.2: J. Kenneth Shultis and Richard E. Faw, from *Fundamentals of Nuclear Science and Engineering*, 2nd ed., p. 118. Copyright © 2008 by CRC Press.

Problems

1. Three radioactive sources each have activities of 1.0×10^5 Bqs at $t = 0$. Their half-lives are, respectively, 1.0 min, 1.0 hr, and 1.0 d. (a) How many radioactive nuclei are present at $t = 0$? (b) How many nuclei of each source decay between $t = 0$ and $t = 1$ min? (c) How many nuclei decay of each source decay between $t = 0$ and $t = 1$ hr?

2. Naturally occurring potassium includes 0.01% of the radioisotope ^{40}K. Given that the half-life of ^{40}K is 1.25×10^9 years, what is the activity of 1 gram of natural potassium?

3. The naturally occurring carbon contains 1 part per trillion of ^{14}C, which has a half-life of 5730 years. The human body contains on the average about 18% carbon and 0.2% potassium by weight. Compute the intrinsic radioactivity of the average person (70 kg) from ^{14}C and ^{40}K.

4. There are two decay modes of ^{252}Cf: spontaneous fission (3.1%) and alpha decay (96.9%). Given that the half-life of ^{252}Cf is 2.6 years and that each spontaneous fission releases 3.7 neutrons, how many neutrons are emitted in 1 mg of ^{252}Cf per second?

5. A 1.0 mg sample of ^{90}Sr ($T_{1/2} = 29.1$ yr) is in secular equilibrium with its daughter ^{90}Y ($T_{1/2} = 64$ hr). (a) How many Bq of ^{90}Sr are present? (b) How many Bq of ^{90}Y are present? (c) What will be the activity of ^{90}Y be after 100 years?

6. A 10-mg sample of pure ^{226}Ra is encapsulated. (a) How long will it take for the activity of ^{222}Rn to build up to 1 mCi? (b) What will be the maximum activity of ^{222}Rn? (c) What will be the activity of ^{222}Rn after 1000 years?

7. Charcoal found in a deep layer of sediment in a cave is found to have an atomic ^{14}C/^{12}C ratio of only 30% that of a charcoal sample from a higher level with a known age of 3000 yr. What is the age of the deeper layer?

8. The $^{226}_{88}$Ra nucleus emits a 4.78 MeV alpha particle when it decays to $^{222}_{86}$Rn.

   (a) Use Appendix B to calculate the Q-value for this decay.
   (b) What is the recoil energy of the $^{222}_{86}$Rn atom?

9. In the following beta decay, use the atomic-mass table to calculate the energy released in this decay: $^{32}_{15}P \rightarrow ^{32}_{16}S + \beta^- + \bar{\nu}$. If a beta particle has 650 keV, how much energy does the antineutrino have?

CHAPTER 6: THEORIES OF THE VARIOUS RADIOACTIVE DECAY MODES

6.1 Theory of α Decay

In general, the half-life of an α decay is strongly dependent on the α particle energy in that the higher the α particle energy is, the shorter the half-life becomes. Table 6.1 shows the values of α particle energies versus half-lives for six α decays associated with the uranium-238 decay series. Figure 6.1 shows the inverse relationship between the α decay half-life and the Q-value of the decay.

Table 6.1. Half-lives and α particle energies of six well-known α decays.

α decays	$T_{1/2}$	E_{α} (MeV)
$^{238}_{92}U \rightarrow {}^{234}_{90}Th + \alpha$	4.47×10^{9} years	4.198
$^{234}_{92}U \rightarrow {}^{230}_{90}Th + \alpha$	2.45×10^{5} years	4.775
$^{226}_{88}Ra \rightarrow {}^{222}_{86}Rn + \alpha$	1.60×10^{3} years	4.784
$^{210}_{84}Po \rightarrow {}^{206}_{82}Pb + \alpha$	1.38×10^{2} days	5.304
$^{222}_{86}Rn \rightarrow {}^{218}_{84}Po + \alpha$	3.82 days	5.489
$^{214}_{84}Po \rightarrow {}^{210}_{82}Pb + \alpha$	1.64×10^{-4} seconds	7.687

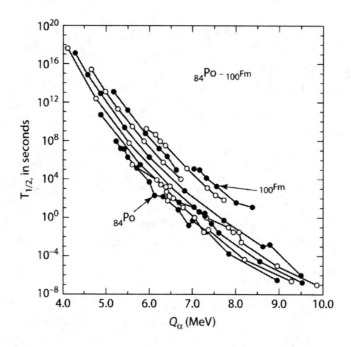

Figure 6.1. The inverse relationship between the α decay half-life and the *Q*-value of the decay. (Souce: Prussin, 2007)

6.1.1 Semi-Classical Theory of Alpha Decay

The inverse relationship between the α decay half-life and α particle energy (shown in Table 6.1 and Figure 6.1) was noticed soon after Rutherford's discovery of the nucleus in 1909. But it wasn't until 1928 that Gamow and Gurney came up with the theory explaining this relationship. In this theory, the α particle is assumed to be trapped inside the negative nuclear potential. Figure 6.2 shows the relative potential between an α particle and the residual nucleus. While the typical kinetic energy of an α particle of a few MeV is significantly smaller than the barrier height of the Coulomb potential (~25-30 MeV for A > 200), there is a small but fixed probability that the α particle may penetrate the barrier.

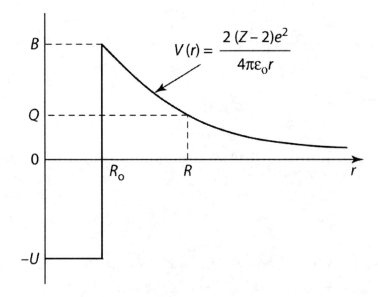

Figure 6.2. The relative potential between an α particle and the residual nucleus.

According to equation 3.52, the probability for an α particle with kinetic energy E_α to penetrate a positive step potential barrier of height V_0 (where $V_0 > E_\alpha$) and width a can be expressed as

$$P = \frac{1}{1 + \dfrac{1}{4}\dfrac{V_0^2}{E_\alpha(V_0 - E_\alpha)}\sinh^2 k_2 a} = \left[1 + \frac{V_0^2 \sinh^2 k_2 a}{4E_\alpha(V_0 - E_\alpha)}\right]^{-1}, \qquad (6.1)$$

where $k_2 = \dfrac{\sqrt{2m_\alpha(V_0 - E_\alpha)}}{\hbar}$. In the case when $k_2 a \gg 1$ (which is the case for α decay), equation 6.1 can be approximated as

$$P \cong \left[1 + \frac{V_0^2 e^{2k_2 a}}{E_\alpha(V_0 - E_\alpha)}\right]^{-1} \cong \left[1 + e^{2k_2 a}\right]^{-1} \cong e^{-2k_2 a}. \qquad (6.2)$$

Since the Coulomb barrier height is a function of r (instead of a constant V_0) and $E_\alpha \approx Q$, equation 6.2 should be further modified as

$$P \cong \exp\left(-2\int_{R_0}^{R} \sqrt{(2m_\alpha/\hbar^2)[V(r) - Q]}\,dr\right) = e^{-2G}, \qquad (6.3)$$

where $V(r) = \dfrac{2(Z-2)e^2}{4\pi\varepsilon_0 r}$, R corresponds to the value of r where $V(r) = Q$, and G is known as the Gamow factor. It can be evaluated as

$$G = \sqrt{\left(\frac{2m_\alpha}{\hbar^2 Q}\right)} \frac{2(Z-2)e^2}{4\pi\varepsilon_0} \left[\cos^{-1}\sqrt{x} - \sqrt{x(1-x)}\right],$$ (6.4)

where $x = R_0/R = Q/B$, and $B = \dfrac{2(Z-2)e^2}{4\pi\varepsilon_0 R_0}$.

Assuming that the α particle exists and is trapped inside the nuclear potential well, one may then imagine it bouncing back and forth with a frequency:

$$f \approx \frac{v_\alpha}{2R_0},$$ (6.5)

where v_α is the speed of the α particle. Since each back-and-forth bounce is an α particle's attempt to escape the nucleus, the α decay constant can be estimated as

$$\lambda = fP \approx \frac{v_\alpha}{2R_0}e^{-2G}.$$ (6.6)

The above theory of α decay is referred to as semi-classical because a full-blown quantum-mechanical theory would need to calculate the transition probability from the initial state of the nucleus, $^A_Z X$, to the final state including the residual nucleus, $^{A-4}_{Z-2}Y$, and the α particle. According to equation 3.110, this calculation is too complex to implement, as it would require the knowledge of the wave functions of all the three particles, $^A_Z X$, $^{A-4}_{Z-2}Y$, and α.

We now use the semi-classical theory described above to calculate the α decay constant for a typical α-decaying nuclide. Let's assume the values of A, Z, and Q to be 230, 90, and 5 MeV, respectively. R_0 is then estimated to be $\approx 1.2\left[(230)^{1/3} + (4)^{1/3}\right]$ fm, or 9.3 fm. Let's further assume that the depth of the nuclear potential well, U, due to the stong force, is 100 MeV. The speed of the α particle inside the well is then estimated to be

$$v_\alpha \approx \sqrt{\frac{2(Q+U)}{m_\alpha}} = c\sqrt{\frac{2(Q+U)}{m_\alpha c^2}} \approx \left(3\times10^8\ \frac{m}{s}\right)\sqrt{\frac{2(5+100)\ \text{MeV}}{3726\ \text{MeV}}} \approx 7.1\times10^7\ \frac{m}{s}.$$

The parameters f, B, and x can calculated, respectively, as

$$f \approx \frac{v_\alpha}{2R_0} = \frac{7.1\times10^7\ \text{m/s}}{2(9.3\times10^{-15}\ \text{m})} \approx 3.83\times10^{21}\ \text{s}^{-1},$$

$$B = \frac{2(Z-2)e^2}{4\pi\varepsilon_0 R_0} = \frac{2(90-2)(1.44\ \text{MeV}\cdot\text{fm})}{9.3\ \text{fm}} \approx 27.3\ \text{MeV},$$

and

$$x = \frac{Q}{B} \approx \frac{5\ \text{MeV}}{27.3\ \text{MeV}} \approx 0.183 .$$

According to equation 6.4, one can then calculate the Gamow factor as

$$G = \frac{1}{\hbar c} \sqrt{\left(\frac{2m_\alpha c^2}{Q}\right)} \frac{2(Z-2)e^2}{4\pi\varepsilon_0} \left[\cos^{-1}\sqrt{x} - \sqrt{x(1-x)}\right]$$

$$= \frac{1}{197.3\,\text{MeV}\cdot\text{fm}} \sqrt{\frac{2(3726\,\text{MeV})}{5\,\text{MeV}}} [2(90-2)(1.44\,\text{MeV}\cdot\text{fm})]\left[\cos^{-1}\sqrt{0.183} - \sqrt{0.183(1-0.183)}\right]$$

$$\cong 36.8.$$

Finally, from equation 6.6 the decay constant can be obtained as

$$\lambda = fP \approx \frac{v_\alpha}{2R_o}e^{-2G} = \left(3.82\times10^{21}\,\text{s}^{-1}\right)e^{-2(36.8)} \cong 4.15\times10^{-11}\,\text{s}^{-1},$$

which gives a half-life of

$$T_{1/2} = \frac{0.693}{4.15\times10^{-11}\,\text{s}^{-1}} \cong 1.67\times10^{10}\,\text{s} = 530\,\text{years}.$$

This half-life is in the right order of magnitude when compared with that of the isotopes shown in Table 6.1, specifically, of ^{226}Ra, which has similar values of A and Q. The readers can take it as a homework problem by going through the above exercise for Q-values of 4 MeV, 5 MeV, 6 MeV, 7 MeV, and 8 MeV, and obtain the corresponding values of f, x, G, λ, and $T_{1/2}$. The results are shown in Table 6.2. As shown, a relatively small change of the Q-value from 4 to 5 MeV results in a $T_{1/2}$ change by 7-8 orders of magnitude. This change rate reduces to 3-4 orders of magnitude for Q-value changing from 7 to 8 MeV. These estimated change rates of $T_{1/2}$ agree very well with the measured results shown in Figure 6.1, indicating the validity of the semi-classical theory of α decay. Table 6.2 also shows that the parameter, x, is proportional to the Q-value and that the G factor is inversely proportional to the Q-value. Physically, G is proportional to the width of the Coulomb barrier. In other words, as Q-value increases, the barrier width proportionally decreases. Because the barrier penetration probability of the α particle increases exponentially as the barrier width decreases, this results in a dramatic decrease in $T_{1/2}$.

Table 6.2. The corresponding values of f, x, G, λ, $T_{1/2}$ for the Q-value range of 4-8 MeV.

Q (MeV)	f (s^{-1})	x	G	λ (s^{-1})	$T_{1/2}$
4 MeV	3.81×10^{21}	0.147	45.7	7.71×10^{-19}	2.85×10^{10} years
5 MeV	3.83×10^{21}	0.183	36.8	4.15×10^{-11}	5.3×10^2 years
6 MeV	3.85×10^{21}	0.212	30.3	1.87×10^{-5}	10.3 hours
7 MeV	3.87×10^{21}	0.256	25.3	0.408	1.7 seconds
8 MeV	3.88×10^{21}	0.293	21.3	1.22×10^3	5.67×10^{-4} seconds

6.1.2 Angular Momentum and Parity in α Decay

It is known that the angular momentum and the parity are both conserved during an α decay. The equation of conservation of angular momentum can be expressed as

$$\vec{I}_X = \vec{I}_Y + \vec{I}_\alpha + \vec{L}_\alpha, \tag{6.7}$$

where $\vec{I}_X$ is the spin of the parent nucleus $^A X$, $\vec{I}_Y$ is the spin of the residual nucleus $^{A-4} Y$, $\vec{I}_\alpha$ is the spin of the α particle, and $\vec{L}_\alpha$ is the orbital angular momentum of the α particle. Since $\vec{I}_\alpha = 0$ for the ground-state α particle, equation 6.7 is reduced to

$$\vec{I}_X = \vec{I}_Y + \vec{L}_\alpha. \tag{6.8}$$

Because the angular momentum can take any allowed values projection on a space-fixed z-axis, the allowed values of the orbital angular momentum quantum number (ℓ_α) of the α particle are given by

$$|I_X - I_Y| \le \ell_\alpha \le |I_X + I_Y|, \tag{6.9}$$

where I_X and I_Y are the quantum numbers of $\vec{I}_X$ and $\vec{I}_Y$, respectively. The α particle wave function is then represented by a spherical harmonics, Y_{ℓ,m_ℓ}, where $\ell = \ell_\alpha$. Thus, the parity change associated with α decay is determined by $(-1)^{\ell_\alpha}$. Since parity is conserved for α decay, the parities of the parent and daughter nuclei should be the same if ℓ_α is even and they should be switched if ℓ_α is odd.

The exercise for determining ℓ_α is quite simple for the even-to-even α decays. We will use the α decay of ^{238}U as an example. As shown in Figure 6.3, when ^{238}U undergoes α decay there are three possible states for the residual nucleus ^{234}Th. The I^π of the three states are, respectively, $0^+, 2^+$, and 4^+. According to equation 6.9, for the transition to the ground state, 0^+, it follows that $|0-0| \le \ell_\alpha \le |0+0|$, or $\ell_\alpha = 0$. For the transition to the first excited state, 2^+, it follows that $|0-2| \le \ell_\alpha \le |0+2|$, or $\ell_\alpha = 2$. Similarly, one finds that $\ell_\alpha = 4$ for the transition to the second excited state, 4^+. The above exercise is so simple because the I^π of the initial state is 0^+ and because there is no change of parity between the parent nucleus and the residual nucleus.

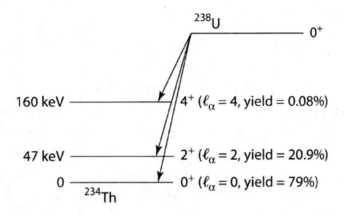

Figure 6.3. A partial decay scheme of the three ^{238}U α-decay transitions.

The exercise for determining ℓ_α is a bit more complex for the odd-to-odd α decays. We will use the α decay of ^{239}Pu as an example. As shown in Figure 6.4, when ^{239}Pu undergoes α decay there are three possible states for the residual nucleus ^{235}U. According to equation 5.35, the transition to the ground state follows that $\left|\frac{1}{2} - \frac{7}{2}\right| \le \ell_\alpha \le \left|\frac{1}{2} + \frac{7}{2}\right|$, or $3 \le \ell_\alpha \le 4$. This means ℓ_α can be either 3 or 4. However, because there is a change of parity, ℓ_α must be an odd number. We therefore determine that $\ell_\alpha = 3$ for this transition. Similarly, one can determine that $\ell_\alpha = 2$ for the other two transitions.

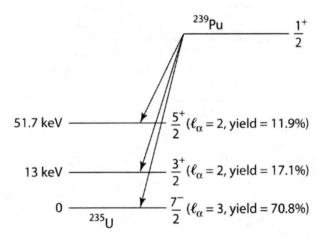

Figure 6.4. A partial decay scheme to illustrate how ℓ_α is associated with each of the three ^{239}Pu α-decay transitions.

6.1.3 Effect of Angular Momentum on α Decay Constant

According to equation 3.80, the orbital angular momentum contributes an additional term, $\ell(\ell+1)\hbar^2/2mr^2$, to the potential. This term is often referred to as the "centrifugal potential."

Since it adds to the Coulomb barrier, it should reduce the α particle's penetration probability and thus the decay constant. By letting $V(r) = \dfrac{2(Z-2)e^2}{4\pi\varepsilon_0 r} + \dfrac{\ell_\alpha(\ell_\alpha+1)\hbar^2}{2\mu r^2}$, where μ is the reduced mass of the α particle, and numerically carrying out equation 6.4, one obtains the corresponding values of G for the various values of ℓ_α. By taking $f = 3.83\times10^{21}\,\text{s}^{-1}$ (the same value used in the previous example) and using equation 6.6, one then obtains the corresponding decay constants shown in Table 6.3. As indicated, the decay constant is reduced by approximately one order of magnitude as ℓ_α increases from 0 to 5. Let's now return to Figures 6.3 and 6.4, and examine the yields that appear in the parentheses. These are the relative decay yields associated with the corresponding transitions, and they should add up to 1.0. As shown, the relative decay yields are smaller for transitions to higher-level excited states. The smaller yields are mainly caused by the smaller Q-values of the transitions. However, as just discussed, the value of ℓ_α also plays a minor role in that a high value of ℓ_α further reduces the yield.

Table 6.3. The effect of orbital angular momentum on the α decay constant.

ℓ	G	$\lambda\ (\text{s}^{-1})^{*}$
0	36.8	4.15×10^{-11}
1	36.88	3.53×10^{-11}
2	37.05	2.51×10^{-11}
3	37.29	1.55×10^{-11}
4	37.62	8.14×10^{-12}
5	38.04	3.49×10^{-12}

* The values of λ are calculated based on $f = 3.83\times10^{21}\,\text{s}^{-1}$.

6.1.4 Alpha Decay of Odd-A Nuclides

The simple, semi-classical theory of α decay described in this chapter works well for most α decays, especially for the even-A transitions. But it often fails badly for the odd-A transitions. An example of the failure can be illustrated by the ^{241}Am decay scheme shown in Figure 6.5. Instead of having the largest yield for the transitions to the ground state, the largest yield actually goes to the second excited state of ^{237}Np. This is generally explained by how the α particle is formed within the nucleus. In an odd-A nucleus, the valence nucleon usually does not participate in forming the α particle because it will need a lot of energy to break a pair of nucleons of the lower energy states. Instead, the α particle is likely formed from a pair of neutrons and a pair of protons occupying the levels just below that of the valence nucleon. This renders the valence nucleon able to stay in the original orbital of the parent nucleus, causing the daughter nucleus to be at an excited state. This explanation is consistent with equation 3.110, in that the overlap between the initial and final nuclear states gives a large value of the matrix element, H'_{mn}, which in turn, gives a high transition probability.

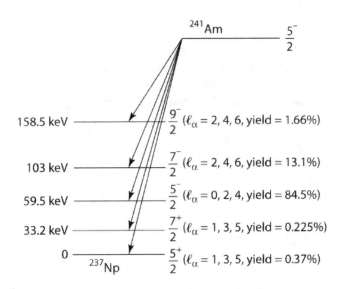

Figure 6.5. A partial decay scheme of the various ^{241}Am α-decay transitions.

6.2 Theory of β Decay and Electron Capture

As mentioned in Section 5.3.2, there is no simple relationship between the half-life and the Q-value for β decays. In 1934, Fermi published a successful theory of β decay based on Pauli's neutrino hypothesis. He proposed that the neutron and the proton can be viewed as two different states of the nucleon. The conversion of a neutron into a proton corresponds to a transition from one quantum state to another in which the electron and the neutrino are created and emitted. This is analogous to the creation and emission of a photon when an atom undergoes a transition between two different energy states. By assuming the decay-causing interaction is a weak perturbation, the decay constant can be obtained from Fermi's Golden Rule (equation 3.110):

$$\lambda = \frac{2\pi}{\hbar}|H_\beta|^2 \rho(E_f),\tag{6.10}$$

where $H_\beta = \int \psi_f^* H \psi_i \, d\tau$, of which H represents the small perturbative "weak interaction" that stimulates the β decay, $d\tau$ is the volume element of the nucleus, and ψ_i and ψ_f are the wave functions of the initial state and final state, respectively. Because the final state include two new particles, an electron and a neutrino, ψ_f^* should be expressed as $\psi_f^* = \psi_{fN}^* \psi_e^* \psi_\nu^*$, where ψ_e, ψ_ν, and ψ_{fN} are, respectively, the wave functions of the electron, the neutrino, and the daughter nucleus. The factor $\rho(E_f)$ is the density of the final states, and it can be written as dN/dE_f, where N is the number of energy states.

6.2.1 Energy Spectrum of β Particles

The shape of the β energy spectrum is determined by the density of the final state. To obtain the final state density, one needs to find the number of states available to the electron and neutrino. For a particle trapped inside a 3-D cubical box of infinite potential at the boundaries, equations 3.59 and 3.62 show that the energy and momentum of the particle are quantized and can be expressed as

$$E_n = \frac{p_n^2}{2m} = \frac{n^2 \pi^2 \hbar^2}{2mL^2} \tag{6.11}$$

and

$$p_n = \sqrt{p_x^2 + p_y^2 + p_z^2} = \sqrt{\frac{\pi^2 \hbar^2}{L^2}\left(n_x^2 + n_y^2 + n_z^2\right)}, \tag{6.12}$$

where L is the length of the cubical box, $n^2 = n_x^2 + n_y^2 + n_z^2$, and $n_i = 1,2,3,...$ with $i = x$, y, or z. Each set of integers of n_x, n_y, and n_z corresponds to an available state for the particle. The state density of the particle can be estimated using the coordinate system shown in Figure 6.6.

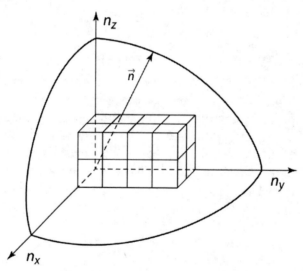

Figure 6.6. Diagram showing the possible energy states of the particle. Each set of integers of n_x, n_y, and n_z is a possible energy state. (Source: Enge, 1966)

Since $n = \frac{p_n L}{\pi \hbar}$, if one replaces the notation of p_n with p, the number of states with momenta lower than p would be

$$N = \frac{1}{8}\left(\frac{4}{3}\pi n^3\right) = \frac{1}{8}\left[\frac{4}{3}\pi\left(\frac{pL}{\pi\hbar}\right)^3\right] = \frac{Vp^3}{6\pi^2\hbar^3},$$ (6.13)

where $V = L^3$, which is the volume of the box. The number of states in the momentum interval dp between p and $p + dp$ is then obtained by taking the differentiation of equation 6.13:

$$dN = \frac{Vp^2 dp}{2\pi^2\hbar^3}.$$ (6.14)

Equation 6.14 holds for both the electron and the neutrino. Therefore, the total number of states for the electron that is emitted with momentum between p_e and $p_e + dp_e$ and the neutrino emitted with momentum between p_ν and $p_\nu + dp_\nu$ would be

$$dN_{total} = dN_e\, dN_\nu = \left(\frac{V}{2\pi^2\hbar^3}\right)^2 p_e^2\, p_\nu^2\, dp_e\, dp_\nu.$$ (6.15)

If one assumes the mass of the neutrino is negligibly small, so that p_ν can be approximated by E_ν/c, then from energy conservation one obtains:

$$Q = E_e + E_\nu = E_e + p_\nu c$$

or (6.16)

$$p_\nu = \frac{Q - E_e}{c},$$

where E_e and E_ν are the energies of the electron and neutrino, respectively. For a fixed value of E_e, the differentiation of equation 6.16 yields

$$dp_\nu = \frac{dQ}{c}.$$ (6.17)

By substituting equations 6.16 and 6.17 into 6.15, one obtains the energy state density available to the emitted electron:

$$\frac{dN_{total}}{dE_e} = \rho(E_e) = \left(\frac{V}{2\pi^2\hbar^3}\right)^2 \frac{1}{c^3}(Q - E_e)^2 p_e^2\, dp_e.$$ (6.18)

Equation 6.18 predicts a symmetric distribution as a function of p_e. The experimentally determined electron and positron spectra, however, were shifted to the left and right, respectively (Figure 6.7). This spectrum-shifting effect is attributed to influence of the nuclear Coulomb field on the emitted electrons or positrons. The correction factor for the spectrum is called the Fermi function, $F(Z, E_e)$, where Z is the atomic number of the daughter nucleus. Figure 6.8 shows the log-log plot of $F(Z,E_e)$ versus E_e. By incorporating the Fermi function into equation 6.18 and substituting it into 6.10, one obtains the differential decay constant as a function of p_e:

$$d\lambda(p_e) = C\left|H_\beta\right|^2 F(Z,E_e)(Q-E_e)^2 p_e^2\, dp_e, \qquad (6.19)$$

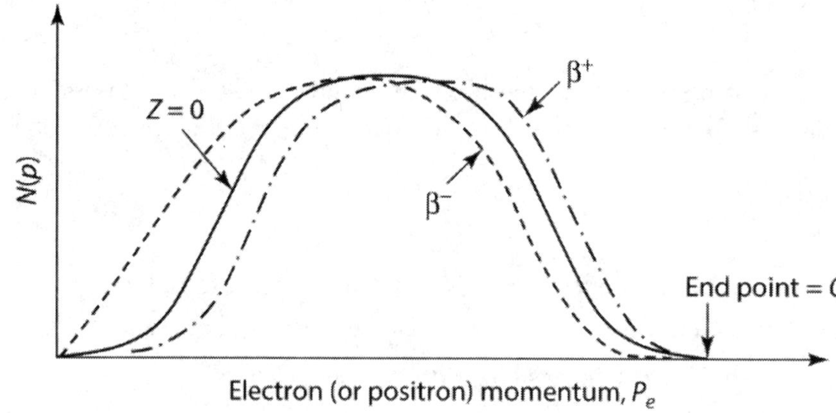

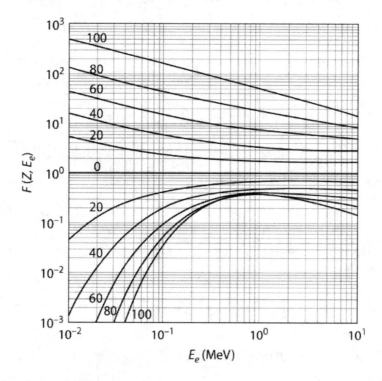

Figure 6.7. The influence of the nuclear Coulomb field on the momentum distribution of electrons (and positrons emitted from β decays).

Figure 6.8. The log-log plot of $F(Z,E_e)$ versus E_e. The curves with $F(Z,E_e)>1$ are for β^+ decay and the curves with $F(Z,E_e)<1$ are for β^- decay. The number indicated on each curve corresponds to the atomic number of the daughter nucleus. (Source: Prussin, 2007)

where C is a constant that is proportional to the strength of the weak interaction, and $\left|H_\beta\right|^2$ is the nuclear matrix element, representing the overlap between the initial and final nuclear states. The strength of the nucleon-nucleon weak interaction has been estimated to be five orders smaller than the strong interaction, or two orders of magnitude smaller than the electromagnetic interaction inside a nucleus.

To further examine $\left|H_\beta\right|^2$, we first express ψ_e and ψ_ν in the normalized free-particle form:

$$\psi_e(\vec{r}) = \frac{1}{\sqrt{V}} e^{i\vec{k}_e \cdot \vec{r}}$$

$$\psi_\nu(\vec{r}) = \frac{1}{\sqrt{V}} e^{i\vec{k}_\nu \cdot \vec{r}}, \tag{6.20}$$

where V is the volume of the nucleus. For a typical Q-value of 1 MeV, being equally shared by the electron and the neutrino, $k_e r \cong k_\nu r \ll 1$. The exponential terms in equation 6.20 can, therefore, be approximated by unity. That is,

$$e^{i\vec{k}_e \cdot \vec{r}} = 1 + \vec{k}_e \cdot \vec{r} + \ldots \cong 1$$

$$e^{i\vec{k}_\nu \cdot \vec{r}} = 1 + \vec{k}_\nu \cdot \vec{r} + \ldots \cong 1. \tag{6.21}$$

This approximation is known as the allowed approximation. By using the property that H is independent of the momentum of the electron, and taking the allowed approximation of the wave function of the electron (or neutrino), one may obtain the decay constant by integrating equation 6.19:

$$\lambda = C\left|H_\beta\right|^2 \int F(Z, E_e)(Q - E_e)^2 p_e^2 \, dp_e = C\left|H_\beta\right|^2 f(Z, Q), \tag{6.22}$$

where $f(Z, Q)$ is called the Fermi integral. Figure 6.9 shows the Fermi integral plotted against the end-point kinetic energy of the electron (or positron) $\left(E_e\right)_{max}$.

Equation 6.22 shows that λ is proportional to the product of the nuclear matrix element and the Fermi integral. Since $f(Z, Q)$ can be accurately evaluated for any transition, equation 6.22 is conveniently rewritten as

$$fT_{1/2} \propto \frac{1}{\left|H_\beta\right|^2}, \tag{6.23}$$

where $fT_{1/2}$ is called the comparative half-life (where $T_{1/2}$ is in seconds), or the "ft value," which can be readily measured by experiments. The ft value, therefore, is a measure of $\left|H_\beta\right|^2$.

The values fall into groups that can be correlated with the spin and parity change in the β decay. This correlation helps us understand why certain β transitions are more likely to take place than others, even though their Q-values may be similar.

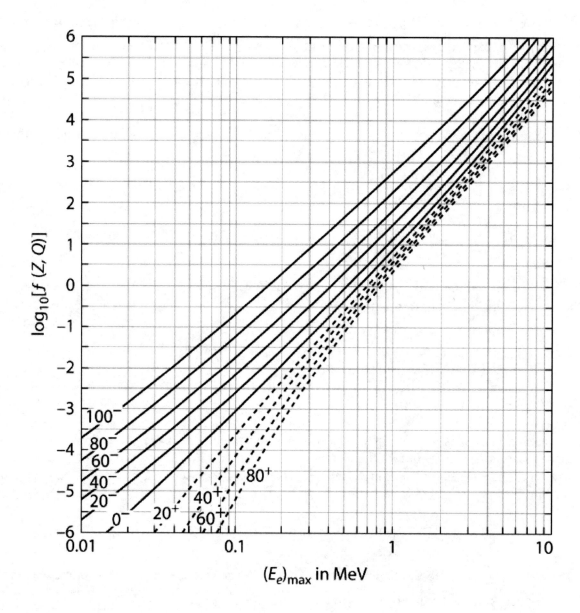

Figure 6.9. The Fermi integral versus the end-point kinetic energy of the electron (or positron) $\left(E_e\right)_{max}$. (Source: Prussin, 2007)

6.2.2 Allowed Transitions and Forbidden Transitions

In quantum mechanics, a transition is referred to as "allowed" if the value of the matrix element is large. Oppositely, it is referred to as "forbidden" if the value of the matrix element is small. Unfortunately, there is no easy way to carry out the calculation of the nuclear matrix element ($\left|H_\beta\right|^2$) for β decay. A practical way to tell whether the transition is allowed or forbidden is based on the spin and parity change of the transition. From conservation of angular momentum,

$$\vec{I}_i = \vec{I}_f + \vec{L} + \vec{s}_e + \vec{s}_v, \qquad (6.24)$$

where $\vec{I}_i$ and $\vec{I}_f$ are the spins of the parent and daughter nucleus, respectively, $\vec{s}_e$ and $\vec{s}_v$ are the spins of the electron and neutrino, respectively, and $\vec{L}$ is the orbital angular momentum carried away by the two leptons. Equation 3.131 shows that the planar wave functions of the electron and neutrino can be specifically expressed in terms of the spherical Bessel functions, as well as the Legendre polynomials:

$$e^{i\vec{k}\cdot\vec{r}} = e^{ikr\cos\theta} = \sum_{\ell=0}^{\infty} (2\ell+1)i^\ell j_\ell(kr) p_\ell(\cos\theta), \qquad (6.25)$$

where each term of ℓ is referred to as a partial wave, with $\ell = 0, 1, 2, 3, \ldots$ corresponding to the s-wave, p-wave, d-wave, f-wave, $\ldots$, respectively. The allowed approximation of equation 6.21 is also called the allowed transition. It is called "allowed" because it correlates well with the β decays having high transition probabilities (or small ft values). The allowed transitions must correspond to the s-wave transition ($\ell = 0$) because $e^{i\vec{k}\cdot\vec{r}}$ is independent of ℓ. In this case, equation 6.24 becomes

$$\vec{I}_i = \vec{I}_f + \vec{s}_e + \vec{s}_v. \qquad (6.26)$$

Since both leptons have quantum spin $\frac{1}{2}$, the two spins together give a total spin of $s = 1$ (if two spins are parallel) or 0 (if two spins are antiparallel). The $s = 0$ case is called the Fermi type (F) transition, and the $s = 1$ case is called the Gamow-Teller type (G-T) transition. For an allowed F transition ($s = 0$ and $\ell = 0$), there can be no change in the nuclear spin; that is, $\Delta I = \left|I_i - I_f\right| = 0$, where I_i and I_f are the quantum numbers of $\vec{I}_i$ and $\vec{I}_f$, respectively. For an allowed G-T transition ($s = 1$ and $\ell = 0$), the two leptons carry a total angular momentum of 1 unit. This may occur if $\Delta I = (0)$ or 1 where the parenthese excludes a $0 \to 0$ transition.

The transitions corresponding to $\ell > 0$ are called forbidden transitions, with $\ell = 1, 2, 3, \ldots$ corresponding to the first forbidden, second forbidden, third forbidden, $\ldots$, respectively. They are called "forbidden" because the transition probability decreases drastically as ℓ increases. Because $\ell \neq 0$, the selection rules for the forbidden transitions are more complex than for the allowed transitions. In the case of F-type first forbidden transition ($s = 0$ and $\ell = 1$), it can occur only if $\Delta I = (0)$ or 1. In the case of G-T type first forbidden transition ($s = 1$ and $\ell = 1$), it can occur only if $\Delta I = 0, 1,$ or 2. The classifications of various β-decay transitions in regard to ℓ, ΔI, $\Delta \pi$, and Log_{10} ft are shown in Table 6.4. As shown, the rule for $\Delta \pi$ for β decay follows the simple formula $\Delta\pi = (-1)^{\ell}$, the same as that of α decay. As a general rule, the decay constant for a beta transition is significantly affected by the orbital angular momentum (ℓ) involved in the transition. As ℓ increases, the decay constant decreases drastically. This effect is more pronounced than in the alpha decay (see Section 6.1.3).

Table 6.4. Classifications of various β-decay transitions. The parentheses of (I) exclude the transition of $I_i = I_f = I$.

Transition type	ℓ	$\Delta\pi$	ΔI		$\text{Log}_{10} ft$
			Fermi	Gamow-Teller	
Allowed	0	No	0	(0), 1	3-7
First forbidden	1	Yes	(0), 1	0, 1, 2	5-9
Second forbidden	2	No	(1), 2	2, 3	10-13
Third forbidden	3	Yes	(2), 3	3, 4	15-18
Fourth forbidden	4	No	(3), 4	4, 5	~21

We now examine a well-known beta decay: $^3\text{H} \rightarrow {}^3\text{He} + e^- + \bar{\nu}$. Since I^{π} is identical for the initial and final states ($\frac{1}{2}^+$ for both ^3H and ^3He), $\Delta I = 0$ and $\Delta\pi = \text{No}$. As such, according to Table 6.4, this decay belongs to the Fermi type with $\ell = 0$. For the ^3H case, $Q = 18.6\,\text{keV}$. From Figure 6.9, the corresponding value of $\log_{10}[f(Z,Q)]$ is shown to be $\sim 5 \times 10^{-6}$. The $\text{T}_{1/2}$ for ^3H is 12.3 years, or 3.88×10^8 seconds. The value of $\log_{10} f\text{T}_{1/2}$ can, therefore, be obtained as

$$\log_{10} f\text{T}_{1/2} = \log_{10} f + \log_{10} \text{T}_{1/2} = \log_{10}(5 \times 10^{-6}) + \log_{10}(3.88 \times 10^8) \cong 3.3.$$

Let us now examine another well-known β decay: $^{90}\text{Sr} \rightarrow {}^{90}\text{Y} + e^+ + \bar{\nu}$, where $I^{\pi} = 0^+$ and 2^- for ^{90}Sr and ^{90}Y, respectively. In this case, $\Delta I = 2$ and $\Delta\pi = \text{Yes}$. According to Table 6.4, this decay can be either the 1st forbidden G-T type or the 3rd forbidden F type. The $(E_e)_{max}$ for this decay is found to be 546 keV. From Figure 6.9, the corresponding value of $\log_{10}[f(Z,Q)]$ is shown to be ~0.45. The $\text{T}_{1/2}$ for ^{90}Sr is 28.9 years, or 9.114×10^8 seconds. The value of $\log_{10} f\text{T}_{1/2}$ can, therefore, be obtained as

$$\log_{10} f\text{T}_{1/2} = \log_{10} f + \log_{10} \text{T}_{1/2} \cong 0.45 + \log_{10}(9.114 \times 10^8) = 9.41.$$

The above two examples show that the decay constant of a beta decay is a function of both the Q-value and the value of $|H_{\beta}|^2$. That is, the ^{90}Sr decay has a higher Q-value than that of the ^3H decay. But the ^{90}Sr decay also has a smaller $|H_{\beta}|^2$ value than that of the ^3H decay. Since the effect of $\left|H_\beta\right|^2$ outweighs the effect of the Q-value, the decay constant of ^{90}Sr ends up to be smaller than that of ^{3}H .

6.2.3 The Fermi-Kurie Plot

As an attempt to experimentally validate the Fermi theory of β decay, the measured electron spectrum is divided by $F(Z, E_e)p_e^2$, and the square root of the result is then plotted as a function of E_e. According to equation 6.19, the graph for an allowed transition should be a straight line intersecting the x-axis at $E_e = Q$. Figure 6.10 shows the Fermi-Kurie plot of the allowed transition ^{32}P $\rightarrow$ ^{32}S $+ e^- + \bar{\nu}$, of which the straight line and the extrapolated end point at $E_e = Q$ strongly agree with the Fermi theory. The Fermi-Kurie plot is often used as a way to obtain the end-point energy of the electron (or positron), instead of using the direct graph of $N(E_e)$-versus-E_e. This is because the number of events becomes fewer and fewer as E_e approaches Q, so one has no clear way to identify the end-point energy.

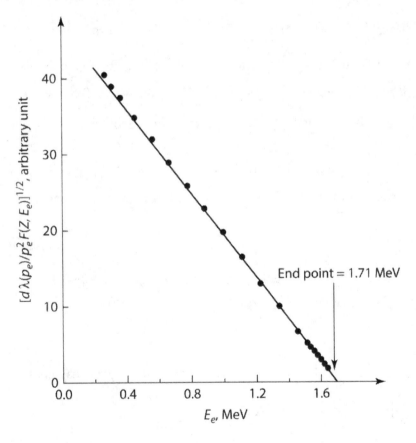

Figure 6.10. The Fermi-Kurie plot of ^{32}P $\rightarrow$ ^{32}S $+ e^- + \bar{\nu}$.

6.2.4 Theory of Electron Capture

The electron capture (EC) transition is a competing (or alternative) decay mode to the β^+ decay. The theory of EC transition is the same as that of β^+ decay except that the electron exists before the transition takes place. The electron is mostly from one of the two shells (K or L) near the nucleus, so that there is a significant overlap of the wave functions between the electrons and the protons in the nucleus. Because the Q-value essentially all goes to the neutrino, the decay constant can be written as

$$\lambda_{EC} = \frac{2\pi}{\hbar}\left|H_{EC}\right|^2 \frac{dN}{dE_\nu},\tag{6.27}$$

where $\left|H_{EC}\right|^2$ is the matrix element representing the overlap between the initial and final nuclear states of the EC. Since both EC and β^+ decay are based on the nuclear weak interaction, the perturbative potential involved in EC should have the same form as that in β^+ decay. However, because the wave functions of the matrix element for EC are different from that for β decay, the magnitude of $\left|H_{EC}\right|^2$ should be different from $\left|H_{\beta^+}\right|^2$. That is, $H_{EC} = \int \psi_f^* H \psi_i \, d\tau$, of which H is the same as that for β^+ decay, $d\tau$ is the volume element that includes the nucleus and the atom, $\psi_i = \psi_p \psi_e$, where ψ_p and ψ_e are respectively the wave functions of the proton and electron of the initial state, and $\psi_f = \psi_n \psi_\nu$, where ψ_n and ψ_ν are, respectively, the wave functions of the neutron and neutrino of the final state. One may further express the electron wave function ψ_e in terms of its shells K, L, M, … (i.e., $\psi_e = \psi_{e,K} \psi_{e,L} \psi_{e,M},\cdots$). From equation 6.14, the number of states available for a neutrino with momentum between p_ν and $p_\nu + dp_\nu$ is

$$dN_\nu = \frac{V p_\nu^2 dp_\nu}{2\pi^2 \hbar^3}.\tag{6.28}$$

By applying $E_\nu = p_\nu c = (Q - B_i)$, where B_i is the binding energy of the electron of the corresponding shell i, equation 6.28 can be rewritten as

$$\frac{dN_\nu}{dE} = \frac{V(Q - B_i)^2}{2\pi^2 \hbar^3 c^3}.\tag{6.29}$$

Substituting equation 6.29 into 6.27 and using 6.22, one obtains the decay constant for EC as

$$\lambda_{EC} = \frac{2\pi}{\hbar}\left|H_{EC}\right|^2 \frac{V(Q - B_i)^2}{2\pi^2 \hbar^3 c^3} = \frac{2\pi}{\hbar} C\left|H_{\beta^+}\right|^2 \left|\psi_e(0)\right|^2 \frac{(Q - B_i)^2}{2\pi^2 \hbar^3 c^3}$$

$$= C\left|H_{\beta^+}\right|^2 \left|\psi_e(0)\right|^2 \frac{(Q - B_i)^2}{\pi \hbar^4 c^3},\tag{6.30}$$

where C is the same constant indicated in equation 6.22, and $\psi_e(0)$ is the electron wave function at the origin. The wave function of the K-shell electron at the origin has been shown to be:

$$\psi_{e,K}(0) \cong \pi^{-1/2}\left(\frac{Z m_e e^2}{4\pi\varepsilon_o \hbar^2}\right)^{3/2}. \tag{6.31}$$

Substituting $\psi_e(0)$ in equation 6.30 with $\psi_{e,K}(0)$ in 6.31, one obtains the decay constant for EC associated with the K-shell electron:

$$(\lambda_{EC})_K = C|H_{\beta^+}|^2 \frac{Z^3 m_e^3 e^6 (Q - B_K)^2}{64\pi^5 \varepsilon_o^3 \hbar^{10} c^3}. \tag{6.32}$$

Similarly, one may obtain the formulas for $(\lambda_{EC})_L$, $(\lambda_{EC})_M$, ... if the algebraic expressions of $\psi_{e,L}(0)$ and $\psi_{e,M}(0)$ are available. Since $\psi_e = \psi_{e,K}\psi_{e,L}\psi_{e,M},\cdots$ it can be shown that

$$\lambda_{EC} = (\lambda_{EC})_K + (\lambda_{EC})_L + (\lambda_{EC})_M + ... \tag{6.33}$$

Because the overlap of the electron wave functions with the nucleus decreases drastically for L shell and M shell, in general it follows that $(\lambda_{EC})_K \gg (\lambda_{EC})_L \gg (\lambda_{EC})_M$. But when $Q < B_K$, K-capture cannot take place. In such cases, the L-capture will be the dominant one if $Q > B_L$. An example of such a case is ^{205}Po decay. It is also important note that $(\lambda_{EC})_K \propto Z^3$, which means EC events are much more commonly observed in high-Z nuclei than in low-Z nuclei. It should also be noted that, because $2m_e c^2 \gg B_K$ (equations 5.18 and 5.19), a nucleus that can undergo β^+ decay always has EC as a competing mode. An example of this is ^{22}Na, which undergoes either EC or β^+ decay to an excited state of ^{22}Ne with relative yields 10.2% and 89.8%, respectively. However, if $B_K < M\binom{A}{Z}X) - M\binom{A}{Z+1}Y) < 2m_e c^2$, then only EC can take place. An example is ^{55}F, of which the atomic mass is only 0.231 MeV greater than ^{55}Mn, so only EC can occur.

6.3 Theory of Gamma Decay and Internal Conversion

6.3.1 Theory of Gamma Decay

Gamma radiation is a form of electromagnetic radiation of very high frequencies. It is generated in the nucleus by either an oscillating electric charge or a varying electric current or magnetic moment. In Section 4.7 we described electric distribution of a nucleus in terms of quadrupole moment. In classical electrostatics, the electric potential outside the volume of an arbitrary charge distribution $\rho(r')$ can be written as a multipole expansion in spherical harmonics (Jackson, 1975):

$$V(r) = \int_\tau \frac{\rho(r')}{|r - r'|} d\tau = \sum_{\ell=0}^{\infty} \sum_{m=-\ell}^{\ell} \frac{4\pi}{2\ell+1} q_{\ell m} \frac{Y_{\ell m}(\theta,\phi)}{r^{\ell+1}}, \tag{6.34}$$

where τ represents the volume of an arbitrary charge distribution, and r and r' are, respectively, the position inside and outside volume τ. One defines the multipole order by 2^ℓ; that is, the term corresponding to $\ell = 0$ is the monopole, $\ell = 1$ the dipole, and $\ell = 2$ the quadrupole, and so on. The corresponding coefficients $q_{\ell m}$ are called the multipole moments and can be obtained from

$$q_{\ell m} = \int_\tau Y_{\ell m}^*(\theta',\phi')\, r^\ell \rho(r')\, d\tau. \tag{6.35}$$

The magnetic fields arise from electric current. Expansion similar to equation 6.34 can be made for the magnetic field outside the volume of an arbitrary current distribution, except that there is no magnetic monopole.

Classically, radiation is produced when a charge or current distribution (or magnetic moment) varies with time. Radiation produced from the former mechanism is called the called electric (E) radiation and the latter is referred to as the magnetic (M) radiation. For example, as shown in Figure 6.11, the electric dipole moment (p) formed by two point charges ($+q$ and $-q$) separated by a distance z is qz. Similarly, the magnetic dipole moment (μ) formed by an electric current i moving around a circular loop of area A is iA. Electric dipole ($E1$) radiation is produced when the electric dipole moment qz oscillates in time (e.g., $p(t) = qz \cos \omega t$, where ω is the angular frequency of the oscillation). Similarly, magnetic dipole ($M1$) radiation is produced when the magnetic dipole moment oscillates in time (e.g., $\mu(t) = iA \cos \omega t$). An electric or magnetic dipole does not radiate energy along its axis. Quadrupole radiation (i.e., $E2$ and $M2$) and higher multipoles will have different angular distributions. The total radiated power for an $E1$ radiation is given as

$$W(E1) = \frac{1}{12\pi\varepsilon_0}\frac{\omega^4}{c^3}p^2, \tag{6.36}$$

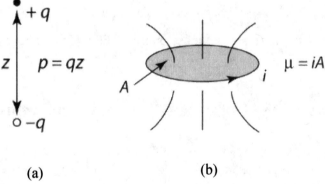

(a)   (b)

Figure 6.11. (a) An electric dipole moment formed by positive charge ($+q$) and negative charge ($-q$) separated by a distance z. (b) A magnetic dipole moment formed by an electric current i moving around a circular loop of area A.

where p is the amplitude of the time-varying electric dipole moment, and c is the speed of light in a vacuum. The total radiated power for a $M1$ radiation is given as

$$W(M1) = \frac{1}{12\pi\varepsilon_0}\frac{\omega^4}{c^5}\mu^2, \tag{6.37}$$

where μ is the amplitude of the time-varying magnetic dipole moment.

The general expression of the radiated power of a specific type of radiation ($\sigma\ell$, where $\sigma = E$ or M and $\ell = 1, 2, 3, ...$) is given as

$$W(\sigma\ell) = \frac{2(\ell+1)c}{\varepsilon_0 \ell[(2\ell+1)!!]^2}\left(\frac{\omega}{c}\right)^{2\ell+2}[m(\sigma\ell)]^2, \tag{6.38}$$

where $(2\ell+1)!! = (2\ell+1)\times(2\ell-1).......3\times1$, and $m(\sigma\ell)$ is the corresponding multipole moment of the radiation.

To carry the classical theory into quantum mechanics, one replaces multipole moments with multiple operators. The transition probability is then determined by the square of the matrix element M_{fi}, where

$$M_{fi}(\sigma\ell) = \int \psi_f^* \mathfrak{m}(\sigma\ell)\psi_i d\tau, \tag{6.39}$$

where ψ_i and ψ_f are, respectively, the wave functions of the initial state and final state of the nucleus, and $\mathfrak{m}(\sigma\ell)$ is the corresponding multipole operator that converts the nucleus from the initial state to the final state. Since equation 6.39 gives the energy emitted per unit time, one may obtain the γ decay constant by simply dividing it with the energy of the γ photon, $\hbar\omega$, as below:

$$\lambda(\sigma\ell) = \frac{W(\sigma\ell)}{\hbar\omega} = \frac{2(\ell+1)}{\varepsilon_0 \ell[(2\ell+1)!!]^2}\left(\frac{\omega}{c}\right)^{2\ell+1}|M_{fi}(\sigma\ell)|^2. \tag{6.40}$$

Equation 6.40 is the probability per unit time for the corresponding γ photon ($\sigma\ell$) to be emitted when a nucleus undergoes transition between two states, and from conservation of energy, $\hbar\omega$ must equal the difference between the energies of the two states.

To quantitatively obtain the value of $\lambda(\sigma\ell)$, one needs to know the wave functions ψ_i and ψ_f of the transition. While the exact wave functions are too complex to calculate, it is possible to find the approximated ones by assuming that the transition is due to a single proton changing from one shell-model state to another. In the case of electric transition, the multipole operator includes a term $er^\ell Y_{\ell m}(\theta,\phi)$, which reduces to ez for $\ell = 1$, and to $e(3z^2 - r^2)$ for $\ell = 2$ (see equation 4.21). If one takes the radial parts of the wave functions to be constant up to the nucleus R and zero for $r > R$, where $R = 1.2A^{1/3}$ fm, this approximation method (by Blatt and Weisskopf) eventually leads to the following empirical formulas of $\lambda(\sigma\ell)$:

$$\lambda(E1) \cong 1.0\times10^{14}\, A^{2/3}E_\gamma^3 \qquad\qquad \lambda(M1) \cong 3.1\times10^{13}\, E_\gamma^3$$

$$\lambda(E2) \cong 7.3\times10^7\, A^{4/3}E_\gamma^5 \qquad\qquad \lambda(M2) \cong 2.2\times10^7\, A^{2/3}E_\gamma^5$$

$$\lambda(E3) \cong 3.4\times10^1\, A^2 E_\gamma^7 \qquad\qquad \lambda(M3) \cong 1.0\times10^1\, A^{4/3}E_\gamma^7$$

$$\lambda(E4) \cong 1.1\times10^{-5}\, A^{8/3}E_\gamma^9 \qquad\qquad \lambda(M4) \cong 3.3\times10^{-6}\, A^2 E_\gamma^9, \tag{6.41}$$

where E_γ is the γ photon energy in MeV and $\lambda(\sigma\ell)$ is in s^{-1}. The results of equation 6.41 are plotted in Figure 6.12. In general, λ is large for small ℓ. For the same ℓ, $\lambda(E\ell)$ is greater than $\lambda(M\ell)$ by ~100.

While the γ photon itself does not carry spin (because it is a boson), it does carry away an orbital angular momentum, and ℓ is the quantum number of the angular momentum carried away by the γ photon. Since the angular momentum is conserved during a γ decay, it follows that

$$\vec{I}_i = \vec{I}_f + \vec{L}_\gamma, \tag{6.42}$$

where $\vec{I}_i$ and $\vec{I}_f$ are the spins of the initial state and final state of the nucleus, respectively, and $\vec{L}_\gamma$ is the orbital angular momentum carried away by the gamma photon. Equation 6.42 leads to the following selection rule:

$$\left|I_i - I_f\right| \leq \ell \leq \left|I_i + I_f\right|, \tag{6.43}$$

where I_i and I_f are the quantum numbers of $\vec{I}_i$ and $\vec{I}_f$, respectively, and ℓ is the quantum number of $\vec{L}_\gamma$.

The parity of a nucleus may or may not change during a γ transition, and it obeys the following rule according to the type of transition:

$$\pi(E\ell) = (-1)^\ell \quad \text{and} \quad \pi(M\ell) = (-1)^{\ell+1}. \tag{6.44}$$

In other words, electric and magnetic fields of the same multipole have opposite parities. For example, there is a parity change for $E1$ transition because $\pi = (-1)^1 = -$, and there is no parity change for $M1$ transition because $\pi = (-1)^2 = +$.

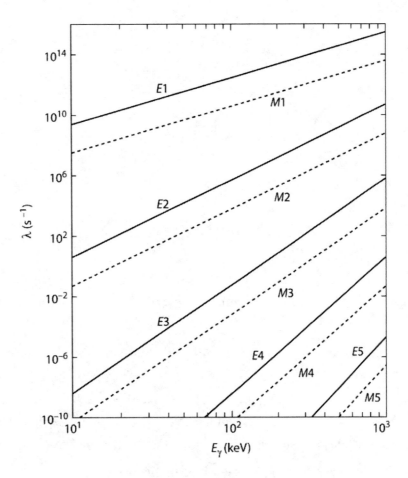

Figure 6.12. Estimated decay constants for the various types of γ transitions according to equation 6.41 for A=125. (Source: Lilley, 2001)

We now take the decay schemes of ^{60}Co and ^{137}Cs (Figure 6.13) to illustrate how I^{π} can be used to decide the type of γ transition between two nuclear states. For the ^{60}Co scheme, Figure 6.13 (a) shows that there are two excited states of ^{60}Ni : 4^+ (2.506 MeV) and 2^+ (1.333 MeV). According to the selection rules (equations 6.43 and 6.44), the decay from 4^+ to 2^+ has five allowed transitions: $E2$, $M3$, $E4$, $M5$, and $E6$. However, because $\lambda(E2) \gg \lambda(M3) \gg \lambda(E4) \gg \lambda(M5) \gg \lambda(E6)$, the transition is dominated by $E2$. For the decay from 2^+ to the ground (0^+), on the other hand, $E2$ is the only allowed transition. Equation 6.41 shows that $\lambda(E2)$ for both decays are of the order of 10^{10} s^{-1}, which translates to half-lives of 10^{-10} s. The transition directly from 4^+ to 0^+ in theory is also allowed. But the corresponding decay constant of $\lambda(E4)$ is much smaller than $\lambda(E2)$, making it negligible. We therefore conclude that the two γ photons, γ_1 and γ_2 shown in Figure 6.13 (a), are emitted immediately after the β^- decay occurs, and that the emission of γ_3 is negligible. Lastly, from energy conservation, the energy of the γ photon is simply the difference in energy between the two states of the transition (i.e., $E_{\gamma_1} = 2.506 - 1.333 = 1.173$ MeV and $E_{\gamma_2} = 1.333 - 0 = 1.333$ MeV). The above conclusions fully agree with the measured results.

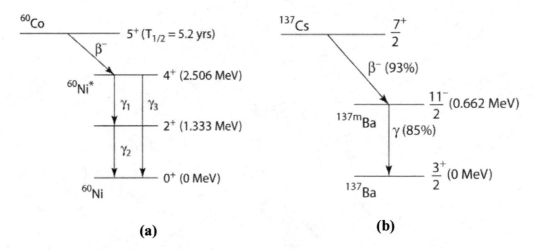

Figure 6.13. Partial decay schemes of ^{60}Co **(a)** and ^{137}Cs **(b)**. They are used to illustrate how I^π can be used to determine the type of γ transition between two nuclear states.

As for the decay scheme of ^{137}Cs, Figure 6.13 (b) shows that there is only one excited state of ^{137}Ba, $\frac{11}{2}^-$ (0.662 MeV). The decay of ^{137}Ba from $\frac{11}{2}^-$ to the ground $\frac{3}{2}^+$ has four allowed transitions: M4, E5, M6, and E7, among which M4 dominates. The small value of $\lambda(M4)$ translates to a half-life of ~2.5 minutes, which is long enough to be called the "isomeric" transition. Accordingly, the $\frac{11}{2}^-$ state is referred to as the "metastable" state, denoted by ^{137m}Ba. Isomeric transitions are rare among γ decays. They are mainly the result of the big difference in nuclear spins of the two states (i.e., $|I_i - I_f|$). Another well-known isomeric transition is that of ^{99m}Tc, which has a half-life of ~ 6 hours (see Problem 6.6).

6.3.2 Theory of Internal Conversion

The internal conversion (IC) transition is a competing (or alternative) decay mode to the γ decay. The IC occurs when the excited radionuclide $^A_Z X^i$ directly transfers its energy to a bound atomic electron and then undergoes the transition to become $^A_Z X^{i-1}$, same as that in γ decay (Section 5.3.3). One requirement for IC transition to occur, of course, is that the transition energy (ΔE) between the two nuclear states must be greater than the binding energy of the electron. The emitted electron is monoenergetic, and its kinetic energy can be obtained as

$$E_e = \Delta E - B, \tag{6.45}$$

where B is the binding energy of the electron. Because the IC process is electromagnetic in nature, the calculation of the transition probability is similar to that of equation 6.40 γ decay, except that (1) the wave function of the initial state includes a bound atomic electron (i.e., $\psi_i = \psi_{i,N} \psi_{i,e}$), where N stands for the nuclear wave function and e stands for the bound electron wave function; and (2) the wave function of the final state includes a free electron wave function (i.e., $\psi_f = \psi_{f,N} \psi_{f,e}$), where $\psi_{f,e}$ is the free electron wave function, which can be expressed as

$e^{-i\vec{k}\cdot\vec{r}_e}$. Without going through all the derivation, we simply argue that because both γ decay and IC are based on the same electromagnetic multipole operator $\mathfrak{m}(\sigma\ell)$, it can be shown that

$$\lambda_\gamma(\sigma\ell) \propto \left| M_{\mathrm{fi}}(\sigma\ell) \right|^2$$

$$\lambda_{\mathrm{IC}}(\sigma\ell) \propto \left| M_{\mathrm{fi}}(\sigma\ell) \right|^2. \tag{6.46}$$

Because $\psi_{\mathrm{i,N}}$ and $\psi_{\mathrm{f,N}}$ are the same for both γ decay and IC, the ratio of $\lambda_{\mathrm{IC}}(\sigma\ell)$ to $\lambda_\gamma(\sigma\ell)$ is independent of the initial and final states of the nucleus. This ratio is called the internal conversion coefficient α, which depends on the atomic number of the atom. The high-Z atoms tend to have higher α values because there is more overlap of the bound electron wave function with the nucleus. In addition, because the bound electron in each shell has its own wave function, there is a corresponding decay constant of IC for each shell. That is, $\lambda_{\mathrm{IC}} = \lambda_{\mathrm{IC,K}} + \lambda_{\mathrm{IC,L}} + \lambda_{\mathrm{IC,M}} + \dots$ or

$$\alpha = \frac{\lambda_{\mathrm{IC}}}{\lambda_\gamma} = \frac{\lambda_{\mathrm{IC,K}} + \lambda_{\mathrm{IC,L}} + \lambda_{\mathrm{IC,M}} + \dots}{\lambda_\gamma} = \alpha_{\mathrm{K}} + \alpha_{\mathrm{L}} + \alpha_{\mathrm{M}} + \dots \tag{6.47}$$

More detailed quantum mechanics treatment of the electron wave functions shows the following features of the IC coefficients: 1) they increase rapidly with increasing Z, 2) they decrease rapidly with increasing transition energy, 3) they increase rapidly as the multipole order increases, and 4) they decrease rapidly for higher atomic shells (i.e., M, N, ...). The above features are illustrated in Figure 6.14 for $Z = 60$.

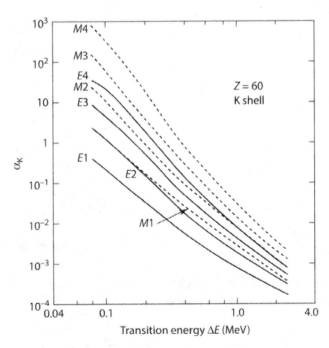

Figure 6.14. The K-electron internal conversion coefficient α_{K} for various multipole transitions for $Z = 60$. (Source: Lilley, 2001)

6.4 Theory of Spontaneous Fission

Nuclear fission reaction is one of the most remarkable discoveries of the twentieth century. It is the basis of commercial nuclear power reactors as well as nuclear fission bombs. As such, it is of most interest to nuclear engineers as well as to those working in safeguarding special nuclear materials for national security reasons. There are two major types of nuclear fission: spontaneous fission (SF) and neutron-induced fission. While the physics is the same for both types, the current section focuses only on SF. The discussion of neutron-induced fission is delayed to Section 7.4 as part of nuclear interactions.

According to Figure 4.3, one expects a large amount of energy (>100 MeV) to be released in a fission reaction when a large nuclide with $A > 150$ is split into two smaller nuclides (Section 5.3.4). In reality, however, one rarely observes SF of nuclides with $A < 240$. The small yield of SF decay can be explained by the potential energy-versus-distance curve shown in Figure 6.15. (Foderaro, 1971) This curve is analogous to that of alpha decay (Figure 6.2) in that there is a potential barrier preventing the nucleus from "fissioning."

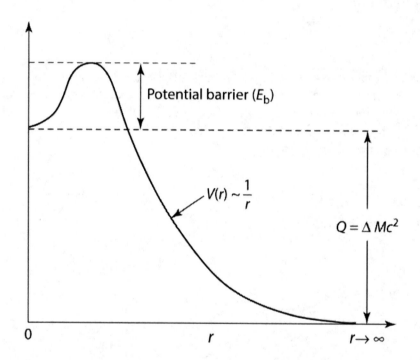

Figure 6.15. The potential energy versus distance between two fission fragments.

The maximum height of the barrier corresponds to the Coulomb potential of the two fission fragments at their closest possible distance from each other. This distance can be approximately estimated by $R_1 + R_2$, where $R_1 \approx 1.2 A_1^{1/3}$ fm and $R_2 \approx 1.2 A_2^{1/3}$ fm, respectively. The maximum height of the potential barrier can then be estimated as

$$V_{max} \cong \frac{Z_1 Z_2 k_c}{R_1 + R_2} = \frac{Z_1 Z_2 (1.44 \text{ MeV} \cdot \text{fm})}{1.2(A_1^{1/3} + A_2^{1/3}) \text{ fm}} \cong \frac{Z_1 Z_2}{A_1^{1/3} + A_2^{1/3}} \text{ MeV}. \qquad (6.48)$$

If one assumes that $A_1 = A_2 = A/2$, and $Z_1 = Z_2 = Z/2$, equation 6.48 is then reduced to

$$V_{max} \cong 0.16 Z^2 / A^{1/3} \text{ MeV.} \tag{6.49}$$

For ^{238}U, equation 6.49 gives $V_{max} \cong 218$ MeV. Since the average Q-value for ^{238}U is estimated to be about 212 MeV, the potential barrier height (E_b) is therefore about 6 MeV. This barrier quickly increases as the mass number decreases. For example, $E_b \approx 20$ MeV for ^{208}Pb. The following empirical formula has been derived for the barrier energy:

$$E_b = \frac{19.0 - 0.36 Z^2}{A + \delta} \text{ MeV,} \tag{6.50}$$

where δ is a parameter that is equal to zero for even-even, 0.7 for odd-odd, and 0.4 for even-odd and odd-even nuclei. Since the barrier penetration probability quickly diminishes as E_b increases, one rarely observes SF for nuclides with $A < 240$. The probability of SF for ^{238}U is estimated to be 5×10^{-7} per alpha decay (see Appendix B). This probability is significantly smaller for ^{235}U, ^{239}Pu, and ^{233}U. Spontaneous fission only becomes noticeable for $A > 250$. For example, californium-252 (^{252}Cf) has a half-life of 2.64 years, and it undergoes alpha decay with 96.9% chance and spontaneous fission with 3.1% chance. It is the most widely available spontaneous fission neutron source, emitting approximately 2.31×10^6 fission neutrons per microgram. The more widely known fission reactions occur when a thermal neutron is absorbed into a nucleus, such as ^{235}U, ^{239}Pu, or ^{233}U. These reactions are referred to as "neutron-induced fissions" and will be discussed separately in Section 7.4.

Surprisingly, when a nuclear fission reaction occurs it does not split into two equal-mass fragments, even though an equal-mass split would give the largest Q-value. Instead, it follows a "double-hump" probability distribution. Figure 6.16 shows such a distribution (i.e., fission yield) for ^{252}Cf. As shown, the two fragments immediately coming out of the SF tend to have masses around 110 and 142, instead of two equal pieces of 126. This uneven split can be explained by a combination of the liquid-drop model and the shell model. Based on the liquid-drop model, as the excited nucleus rapidly oscillates back and forth, its lobes tend to maintain core configurations corresponding to the magic numbers of 50 and 82 of protons and neutrons. As shown in Figure 6.17, the two most likely combinations of the core configurations are $Z = 50, N = 82$, which constitutes the heavy lobe, and $Z = 48, N = 50$, which constitutes the light lobe. The remaining 22 neutrons (the neck) are then equally shared by the two cores, resulting in mass numbers of 143 and 109 for the two fragments. Because the newly split fragments are at highly excited states, and because they also have too many neutrons, they promptly emit several neutrons and gamma rays (the so-called prompt neutrons and gamma rays), typically within 10^{-14} seconds. The cooled-down fragments are still neutron-rich and will then undergo a series of beta decays. Among the prompt energy release (in $< 10^{-14}$ sec), approximately 80% goes to the kinetic energy of the two fragments. The rest of it goes to the kinetic energy of the neutrons and gamma rays. More detailed discussion on the energy distribution among various components involved in a fission reaction will be covered in Section 7.4 in neutron-induced fission.

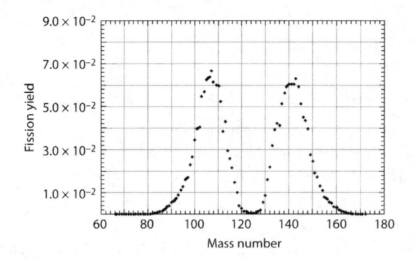

Figure 6.16. Mass distribution of the fission products for ^{252}Cf.

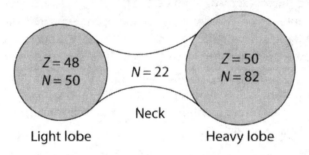

Figure 6.17. The ^{252}Cf nucleus shortly before fission.

Bibliography

Foderaro, Anthony *The Elements of Neutron Interaction Theory*. Cambridge, MA: MIT Press, 1971.

Prussin, Stanley G. *Nuclear Physics for Applications: A Model Approach*. Weinheim, Germany: Wiley-VCH Verlag GmbH & Co. KGa, 2007.

Enge, Harald A. *Introduction to Nuclear Physics*. Reading, Massachusetts: Addison-Wesley Pub. Co., 1966.

Lilley, John S. *Nuclear Physics: Principles and Applications*. Chichester, UK: John Wiley & Sons, Ltd., 2001

Jackson, John D. *Classical Electrodynamics*, 2nd edition, New York: John Wiley & Sons, Inc., 1975.

Credits

Problems

1. The following Figure depicts, in a semi-quantitative manner, the relative potential between an alpha particle and the residual nucleus, in alpha decay of ^{226}Ra. Assume U=100 MeV.

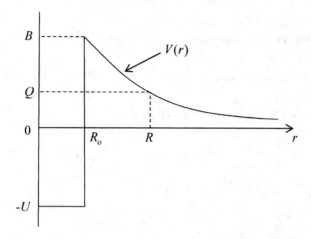

(a) Characterize $V(r)$.

(b) Assuming that the Q-value of the reaction is 4.8 MeV, compute the probability that the beta will penetrate the potential barrier.

(c) Estimate the half-life ($T_{1/2}$) of ^{226}Ra.

2. The alpha decay of ^{244}Cm populates a 0^+ excited state in ^{240}Pu at 0.861 MeV, with an intensity of 1.6×10^{-4} %, while the 0^+ ground state is populated with an intensity of 76.7 %. Estimate the ratio between these decay intensities from the theory of alpha decay and compare with the experimental values.

3. In the following two β-decay schemes, calculate the ft values, respectively, and then use Table 6.4 to determine the type of β-decay transition (e.g., allowed, first forbidden, et cetera).

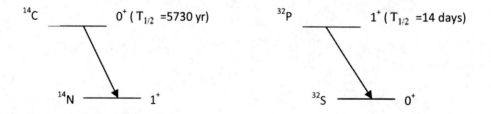

4. For the following γ transitions, give all permitted multipoles and indicate which multipole might be the most intense in the emitted radiation: (a) $\frac{9^-}{2} \rightarrow \frac{7^+}{2}$, (b) $1^- \rightarrow 2^+$, and (c) $3^+ \rightarrow 3^+$.

5. A nucleus has the following sequence of states beginning with the ground state: $\frac{3^+}{2}$, $\frac{5^+}{2}$, $\frac{7^+}{2}$, $\frac{1^-}{2}$, and $\frac{3^-}{2}$. Draw a decay scheme showing the various γ transitions that are likely to be emitted and indicate their multipole assignments (e.g., E1, M2, et cetera).

6. Refer to the following decay scheme for ^{99}Mo/^{99m}Tc. (a) Apply the beta decay theory and use the tables/figures from the text/notes to determine the beta decay mode (i.e., allowed, first forbidden, second forbidden, et cetera) and estimate the half-life for ^{99}Mo. (b) Apply the gamma decay theory and use the figures/formula from the text to determine the gamma decay mode (i.e., E1, M1, E2, M2, et cetera) and estimate the half-life of ^{99m}Tc.

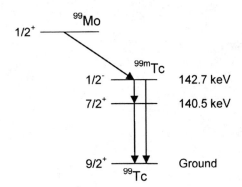

7. In a spontaneous fission of $^{238}_{92}$U, assuming that the two most likely combinations of the core configurations are $Z = 50, N = 82$ and $Z = 42, N = 50$, and that the remaining neutrons are equally shared by the two cores, (a) what are the masses of the two fission fragments? (b) Use Figure 4.3 and the results of (a) to estimate the Q-value of this SF reaction.

CHAPTER 7: NUCLEAR REACTIONS AND KINEMATICS

When an energetic particle comes into the vicinity of a stable target nucleus, many types of nuclear reactions may take place. Similar to decay pathways in a radioactive decay process, the probability associated with each nuclear reaction pathway is dictated by the quantum-mechanical principle of transitions between the initial state and the final state of each pathway (see Section 3.8). As indicated in Section 1.7, the interaction probability for an incident particle to interact with the target material per unit distance is given by the macroscopic cross section $\Sigma = N\sigma$, where N is the atomic number density with the unit of atoms cm^3, and σ is the microscopic cross section with the unit of cm^2 $atom^{-1}$ of the target material. In the classical sense, σ can be thought of as the size of the target area per target nucleus. As described in Figure 1.4 and equation 1.24, σ can be experimentally obtained by bombarding a thin target with a narrow beam of the incident particles. Since there can be many reaction pathways where each has its own cross section, σ_i, the total cross section σ is therefore the sum of the cross sections of all pathways. That is,

$$\sigma = \sum_i \sigma_i .$$

(7.1)

7.1 Types of Nuclear Reactions

The generic representation of a typical nuclear reaction is expressed as

$$a + X \rightarrow b + Y ,$$

(7.2)

where a, X, b, and Y, respectively, represent the incoming particle (or projectile), the target nucleus, the outgoing particle, and the residual nucleus. In elastic scattering and inelastic scattering, the incoming and outgoing particles are the same. They can be expressed as

$$a + X \rightarrow a + X \quad \text{(elastic)}$$

(7.3)

$$a + X \rightarrow a + X^* \quad \text{(inelastic)},$$

(7.4)

where X^* is an excited state of X. Obviously, the kinetic energy is conserved in an elastic scattering event and its corresponding Q-value is zero. On the other hand, the kinetic energy is not conserved in an inelastic scattering event and the corresponding Q-value is negative, the value of which equals the amount of kinetic energy lost by the incoming particle a. An alternative representation for equation 7.2 is $X(a,b)Y$, or simply (a,b). Some nuclear reaction examples that can be represented by equation 7.2 are provided in Table 7.1.

Table 7.1. A list of nuclear reaction examples that can be represented by $X(a,b)Y$.

Reaction	Q-Value (MeV)
$^3_1H(^2_1d, {}^1_0n)^4_2He$	17.59
$^3_2He(^1_0n, {}^1_1p)^3_1H$	0.764
$^7_3Li(^1_1p, {}^1_0n)^7_4Be$	−1.644
$^9_4Be(^2_1d, {}^1_0n)^{10}_5B$	4.36
$^9_4Be(^4_2\alpha, {}^1_0n)^{12}_6C$	5.7
$^{10}_5B(^1_0n, {}^4_2He)^7_4Li$	2.79

There are other types of nuclear reactions that result in more than one outgoing particle and cannot be represented by equation 7.2. These reactions are abbreviated as (*a*, reaction type). For example, a neutron-induced fission reaction is abbreviated as (n, fission), a proton-induced spallation reaction is abbreviated as (p, spallation), a neutron absorption reaction producing three neutrons is abbreviated as (n, 3n), and so on.

Most nuclear reactions can be classified into two categories: direct reactions and compound-nucleus reactions. This classification is based on the mechanistic model and time duration of the reaction process. A direct reaction refers to a one-step process in that the core of the target nucleus is not involved in the process and that the process takes less than 10^{-22} seconds. A compound-nucleus reaction refers to a two-step process in that the projectile and the target nucleus momentarily merge together and form an excited compound nucleus, which then decays by emitting one or more secondary particles. The process of a compound-nucleus reaction takes between 10^{-18} to 10^{-14} seconds. As it will be discussed below, both elastic and inelastic scattering may take place as either a direct reaction or a compound-nucleus reaction. More details of the different types of reactions are discussed below.

7.1.1 Direct Reactions

Potential scattering

Potential scattering reaction is a type of elastic scattering of which the projectile and the target nucleus first come close to each other and then scatter away from each other. The kinetic energy is conserved before and after the event (i.e., the kinetic energy of the reactants is the same as the kinetic energy of the products). The potential scattering is also called shape elastic scattering because it is simply the result of the force field existing between the projectile and the target nucleus. It is specifically named to differentiate itself from the elastic compound-nucleus reaction (see Section 7.1.2). The Rutherford scattering discussed in Section 1.8 is an example of a potential scattering with the Coulomb force. Elastic scatterings also occur between a neutron and a nucleus via the short-ranged strong nuclear force.

Direct inelastic scattering

Direct inelastic scattering occurs when an incoming particle knocks the target nucleus into an excited state and emerges with a reduced energy. As such, the kinetic energy is not conserved in this process. Similar to that in potential scattering, the force involved in direct inelastic scattering can also be either Coulomb or strong nuclear force in nature. It is specifically named to differentiate itself from the inelastic compound-nucleus reaction (see 7.1.2).

Pickup reactions

A pickup reaction occurs when the projectile passes through the periphery of the nucleus and picks up one nucleon from the nucleus. One example is $^{16}_{8}O(^{2}_{1}d,^{3}_{1}H)^{15}_{8}O$, in which the projectile $^{2}_{1}d$ picks up a neutron from $^{16}_{8}O$ and becomes $^{3}_{1}H$.

Stripping reactions

A stripping reaction is the opposite of the pickup reaction in that the projectile loses one nucleon to the nucleus. One example is $^{16}_{8}O(^{2}_{1}d,^{1}_{1}p)^{17}_{8}O$, in which the projectile $^{2}_{1}d$ loses a neutron to $^{16}_{8}O$ and becomes $^{1}_{1}p$.

7.1.2 Compound-Nucleus Reactions

As mentioned, a compound-nucleus reaction is a two-step process in that the projectile and the target nucleus momentarily merge together and form an excited compound nucleus, which rattles for a short period time and then decays by emitting one or more secondary particles. Since it is a two-step process, equation 7.2 is modified as

$$a + X \rightarrow C^{*} \rightarrow b + Y, \qquad (7.5)$$

where C^{*} stands for the excited compound nucleus.

It should be noted that there can be many different incoming channels to form C^{*} and there can also be many exiting channels for C^{*} to decay through. In addition, the final state may consist of more than one outgoing particle. Figure 7.1 is a better presentation of a compound-nucleus reaction than equation 7.5.

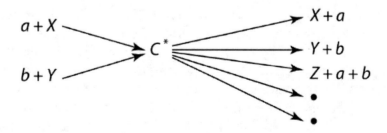

Figure 7.1. A multichannel representation of a compound-nucleus reaction.

As indicated earlier, both elastic scattering and inelastic scattering may occur as a compound-nucleus reaction, because it is possible that they follow a two-step process. That is, the incoming particle is first absorbed into the target nucleus to form an excited compound nucleus, which rattles a bit and then decays by emitting a particle that is of the same type as the incoming one. They will be called compound elastic scattering and compound inelastic scattering, to distinguish from "potential scattering" and "direct inelastic scattering".

Another important feature of a compound-nucleus reaction is that the relative probability of a specific exiting channel for C^* is independent of the incoming channel. This is because the model assumes that C^*, once formed, immediately loses its memory of which incoming channel it came from. As a result, the direction of all outgoing particles is expected to be random, and the angular distribution is therefore isotropic in the center-of-mass (COM) frame. The relative probability associated with each decay channel is specified by its corresponding decay constant λ_i. As discussed in Section 5.4, any excited nucleus decays with a specific decay constant λ, and $\lambda = \sum_{i=1}^{n} \lambda_i$, where n is the total number of decay channels. Because the compound-nucleus reaction is considered as two independent steps, the first being the formation of the compound nucleus and the second its decay at a later time, the cross section for a reaction $X(a,b)Y$ that takes place via this mechanism can be expressed as the product of the cross section for the incoming channel ($\sigma_{a+X \to C^*}$) and the relative probability for the specific exiting channel $C^* \to b + Y$. That is,

$$\sigma_{a,b} = \sigma_{a+X \to C^*} \cdot \frac{\lambda_b}{\lambda}. \tag{7.6}$$

7.2 Conservation Laws of Nuclear Reactions

The conservation laws that apply to nuclear reactions include: 1) conservation of total energy and linear momentum, 2) conservation of proton and neutron number, 3) conservation of angular momentum, and 4) conservation of parity. (Krane, 1988)

7.3 Kinematics of Nuclear Reactions

Kinematics of a nuclear reaction concerns the motion (i.e., speed and direction) of the outgoing particles of the reaction. As will be shown below, the motion of the outgoing particles of a nuclear reaction is determined by: 1) the masses of all the particles involved, 2) the kinetic energy of the incident particle, and 3) the Q-value of the reaction. The governing equations are the conservations of energy and linear momentum. While the conservation equations can be worked out in the laboratory (LAB) frame, algebraically it is much simpler to work them on the COM frame. As shown in Figure 7.2, the COM of the two-particle system of a nuclear reaction can be defined by the position vector $\vec{\rho}$ as

$$\vec{\rho} = \frac{m\vec{r_l} + M\vec{R_l}}{m+M}, \tag{7.7}$$

where m and M are the masses of the projectile and the target nucleus, respectively, and $\vec{r}_l$, $\vec{R}_l$ are the position vectors in the LAB frame for the projectile and the target nucleus, respectively. As shown in Figure 7.2, the position vectors in the COM frame for the projectile a and the target nucleus X can be respectively expressed as

$$\vec{r}_c = \vec{r}_l - \vec{\rho}$$
$$\vec{R}_c = \vec{R}_l - \vec{\rho}.$$

(7.8)

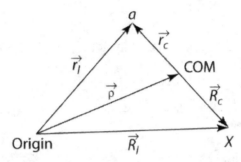

Figure 7.2. The relationship between the position vectors in the COM and that in the LAB frame.
Source: Lamarsh (1966)
Notes: COM = center of mass; LAB = laboratory.

Taking the first derivatives with reference to time for all the quantities in equation 7.8, one obtains the corresponding velocity vectors as

$$\vec{v}_c = \vec{v}_l - \vec{v}_0$$
$$\vec{V}_c = \vec{V}_l - \vec{v}_0,$$

(7.9)

where $\vec{v}_0$ is the velocity vector of the COM with reference to the LAB frame,

$\vec{v}_l$ is the velocity vector of the projectile a in the LAB frame,

$\vec{v}_c$ is the velocity vector of the projectile a in the COM frame,

$\vec{V}_l$ is the velocity vector of the target nucleus X in the LAB frame, and

$\vec{V}_c$ is the velocity vector of the target nucleus X in the COM frame.

In addition, taking the first derivative of equation 7.7 with reference to time gives

$$\frac{d\vec{\rho}}{dt} = \vec{v}_0 = \frac{m\vec{v}_l + M\vec{V}_l}{m + M}.$$

(7.10)

If one assumes that $|\vec{V}_l| = 0$ (i.e., the target nucleus is at rest), then equation 7.10 becomes

$$\vec{v}_o = \frac{m\vec{v}_l}{m+M}.$$

(7.11)

Substituting equation 7.11 into 7.9 gives

$$\vec{v}_c = \vec{v}_l - \frac{m\vec{v}_l}{m+M} = \frac{M\vec{v}_l}{m+M}$$

(7.12)

and

$$\vec{V}_c = \vec{V}_l - \vec{v}_o = -\vec{v}_o = -\frac{m\vec{v}_l}{m+M}.$$

(7.13)

The total linear momentum of the two-particle system in the COM frame can then be expressed as

$$\vec{P}_c = m\vec{v}_c + M\vec{V}_c = \frac{mM\vec{v}_l}{m+M} + M\left(-\frac{m\vec{v}_l}{m+M}\right) = 0.$$

(7.14)

Yes, the total linear momentum of the system is zero in the COM frame! In other words, the linear momenta of the two particles with reference to the COM have the same magnitude but in opposite directions (see Figure 7.2), and therefore, they cancel each other out exactly. As shown below, the null linear momentum in the COM frame makes the kinematics of nuclear reactions much simpler.

Because the kinetic energy of an incoming particle is usually given in the LAB frame, we need to convert it to the COM frame. Again, if we assume the target nucleus is at rest in the LAB frame, then the initial total kinetic energy of the system in the LAB frame is just that of the incoming particle; that is,

$$E_l = \frac{1}{2}mv_l^2.$$

(7.15)

The initial total kinetic energy of the system in the COM frame, however, contains two terms, one for the projectile and the other for the target. This is because both particles have non-zero velocities in the COM frame. That is,

$$E_c = \frac{1}{2}mv_c^2 + \frac{1}{2}MV_c^2.$$

(7.16)

From equations 7.12 and 7.13, 7.16 can be expressed as

$$E_c = \frac{1}{2}m\left(\frac{M}{m+M}\right)^2 v_l^2 + \frac{1}{2}M\left(\frac{m}{m+M}\right)^2 v_l^2 = \frac{1}{2}\frac{\left(mM^2 + m^2M\right)}{\left(m+M\right)^2}v_l^2$$

$$= \frac{1}{2}\left(\frac{mM}{m+M}\right)v_l^2 = \frac{1}{2}\mu v_l^2,$$

(7.17)

where $\mu = \dfrac{mM}{m+M}$, and is referred to as the "reduced mass" because it is always smaller than

m. Equations 7.15 and 7.17 then give the simple relationship between E_c and E_l below:

$$E_c = \frac{M}{m+M} E_l . \tag{7.18}$$

This is the total kinetic energy of the system in the COM frame before the reaction. Because a nuclear reaction often involves a non-zero Q-value, the total kinetic energy of the system in the COM frame after the reaction becomes

$$E_c' = E_c + Q . \tag{7.19}$$

This amount of energy will be shared by all of the reaction products, which can be more than two. But for the simplicity of derivation, we assume that there are only two reaction products—the outgoing particle b and the residual nucleus Y. The kinematics of such a reaction are illustrated in Figures 7.3a and 7.3b for LAB and COM, respectively, in terms of the velocity vectors of the projectile and the reaction products.

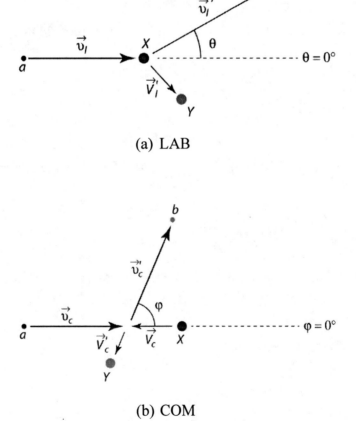

(a) LAB

(b) COM

Figure 7.3. The kinematics of a two-particle reaction system for the LAB and COM frames.

Since the total available energy in the COM is to be shared by the two reactant products b and Y, equation 7.19 can be written in terms of the kinetic energies of b and Y. That is,

$$E_c' = E_c + Q = \frac{1}{2}m'v_c'^2 + \frac{1}{2}M'V_c'^2, \tag{7.20}$$

where m' and M' are, respectively, the masses of b and Y, and v_c' V_c' are, respectively, the speed of b and Y in the COM frame. Since the total linear momentum of the system is zero in the COM, the linear momentum of the two reaction products must have the same magnitude but in opposite directions. That is,

$$m'v_c' = M'V_c' \quad \Rightarrow \quad V_c' = \frac{m'}{M'}v_c'. \tag{7.21}$$

Substituting equation 7.21 into 7.20 and using 7.17, one has

$$E_c' = \frac{1}{2}m'v_c'^2 + \frac{1}{2}M'\left(\frac{m'}{M'}\right)^2 v_c'^2 = \frac{1}{2}m'\left(1 + \frac{m'}{M'}\right)v_c'^2 = E_c + Q = \frac{1}{2}\mu v_I^2 + Q. \tag{7.22}$$

The portion that goes to the kinetic energy of the outgoing particle in COM is then

$$\frac{\frac{1}{2}m'v_c'^2}{\frac{1}{2}m'\left(1 + \frac{m'}{M'}\right)v_c'^2} = \frac{1}{1 + \frac{m'}{M'}} = \frac{M'}{m' + M'}. \tag{7.23}$$

In other words, the kinetic energy of the outgoing particle in COM is related to E_c' as

$$\frac{1}{2}m'v_c'^2 = \left(\frac{M'}{m' + M'}\right)E_c'. \tag{7.24}$$

From energy conservation, the kinetic energy of the residual nucleus in COM gets the rest of E_c'. That is,

$$\frac{1}{2}M'V_c'^2 = \left(\frac{m'}{m' + M'}\right)E_c'. \tag{7.25}$$

From equation 7.24, v_c' can then be solved as

$$v_c' = \sqrt{\frac{2M'E_c'}{m'\left(m' + M'\right)}}. \tag{7.26}$$

From equation 7.21, V_c' can be obtained as:

$$V_c' = \frac{m'}{M'} v_c' = \frac{m'}{M'} \sqrt{\frac{2M'E_c'}{m'(m'+M')}}.$$ (7.27)

To convert v_c' and V_c' back to the LAB frame, we need to use the relationships of the velocity vectors; that is,

$$\vec{v}_l' = \vec{v}_0 + \vec{v}_c'$$
$$\vec{V}_l' = \vec{v}_0 + \vec{V}_c'.$$ (7.28)

These relationships are better presented graphically. Figure 7.4 shows the relationships of the velocity vectors, $\vec{v}_0, \vec{v}_c'$, and $\vec{v}_l'$.

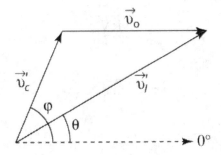

Figure 7.4. The relationships of the velocity vectors, $\vec{v}_0, \vec{v}_c'$, and $\vec{v}_l'$.

From Figure 7.4, one has

$$v_l' \sin\theta = v_c' \sin\varphi$$
$$v_l' \cos\theta = v_0 + v_c' \cos\varphi.$$ (7.29)

It follows that

$$\tan\theta = \frac{v_c' \sin\varphi}{v_0 + v_c' \cos\varphi} \quad \text{or} \quad \theta = \tan^{-1}\left(\frac{v_c' \sin\varphi}{v_0 + v_c' \cos\varphi}\right).$$ (7.30)

Equation 7.30 allows the direction angle in the COM frame to be converted to the LAB frame. It can be seen from Figure 7.4 that v_l' has its maximum value when $\varphi = 0°$, and it has its minimum value when $\varphi = 180°$. When $\varphi = 0°$, $v_l' = (v_l')_{max} = v_c' + v_0$, which also corresponds the maximum kinetic energy for the outgoing particle b. When $\varphi = 180°$, $v_l' = (v_l')_{min} = v_c' - v_0$, which also corresponds the minimum kinetic energy for the outgoing particle b. As such, the kinetic energy of the outgoing particle depends on the angle φ and it varies between $\frac{1}{2}m'\left(v'_c + v_o\right)^2$ and $\frac{1}{2}m'\left(v'_c - v_o\right)^2$.

Example 7.3.1 ($Q > 0$)

A 1-MeV deuteron beam impinges on a tritium target to produce neutrons via the $^3H(d,n)^4He$ reaction. Assuming that the direction of outgoing neutrons is isotropic in the COM frame, find: (a) the maximum and minimum energies of the emerging neutrons, and (b) the percentage of neutrons emitted in the forward direction (i.e., for $\theta < 90°$).

Solution

(a) From Appendix B, $Q = \Delta mc^2 = 14.95 + 13.136 - 8.071 - 2.425 = 17.59$ MeV.

$$E_I = 1 \text{ MeV} = \frac{1}{2}m_d v_d^2 \quad \Rightarrow \quad v_d = \sqrt{\frac{2 \text{ MeV}}{m_d}}$$

$$E_c = \left(\frac{m_t}{m_d + m_t}\right)E_I \cong \left(\frac{A_t}{A_d + A_t}\right)E_I = \left(\frac{3}{5}\right)(1 \text{ MeV}) = 0.6 \text{ MeV}$$

From equation 7.11, $v_o = \left(\frac{m_d}{m_d + m_t}\right)v_d \cong \left(\frac{2}{5}\right)\sqrt{\frac{2 \text{ MeV}}{m_d}}$.

$$E'_c = E_c + Q = 0.6 \text{ MeV} + 17.59 \text{ MeV} = 18.19 \text{ MeV}$$

From equation 7.26, one finds

$$v'_c = \sqrt{\frac{2m_{He}E'_c}{m_n\left(m_n + m_{He}\right)}} \cong \sqrt{\frac{2}{m_n}\left(\frac{4}{1+4}\right)(18.19 \text{ MeV})} = \sqrt{\frac{29.12 \text{ MeV}}{m_n}}.$$

As indicated earlier, the maximum energy of emerging neutrons corresponds to those emitted in the most forward direction (i.e., $\theta = 0°$), at which

$$v'_I = v'_c + v_o = \sqrt{\frac{29.12 \text{ MeV}}{m_n}} + \left(\frac{2}{5}\right)\sqrt{\frac{2 \text{ MeV}}{m_d}} \cong \sqrt{\frac{29.12 \text{ MeV}}{m_n}} + \left(\frac{2}{5}\right)\sqrt{\frac{1 \text{ MeV}}{m_n}}.$$

It then follows that

$$\left(\frac{1}{2}m_n v_l'^2\right)_{max} = \frac{1}{2}m_n\left(\sqrt{\frac{29.12\ \text{MeV}}{m_n}} + \left(\frac{2}{5}\right)\sqrt{\frac{1\ \text{MeV}}{m_n}}\right)^2$$

$$= \frac{1}{2}m_n\left(\frac{29.12\ \text{MeV}}{m_n} + \frac{0.16\ \text{MeV}}{m_n} + \frac{2\sqrt{(29.12)(0.16)}\ \text{MeV}}{m_n}\right)$$

$$= \frac{1}{2}(33.6\ \text{MeV}) = 16.8\ \text{MeV}.$$

Similarly, the minimum energy of emerging neutrons corresponds to those emitted in the most backward direction (i.e., $\theta = 180°$), at which

$$v_l' = v_c' - v_o = \sqrt{\frac{29.12\ \text{MeV}}{m_n}} - \left(\frac{2}{5}\right)\sqrt{\frac{2\ \text{MeV}}{m_d}} \cong \sqrt{\frac{29.12\ \text{MeV}}{m_n}} - \left(\frac{2}{5}\right)\sqrt{\frac{1\ \text{MeV}}{m_n}}.$$

It then follows that

$$\left(\frac{1}{2}m_n v_l'^2\right)_{min} = \frac{1}{2}m_n\left(\sqrt{\frac{29.12\ \text{MeV}}{m_n}} - \left(\frac{2}{5}\right)\sqrt{\frac{1\ \text{MeV}}{m_n}}\right)^2$$

$$= \frac{1}{2}\left(29.12\ \text{MeV} + 0.16\ \text{MeV} - 2\sqrt{(29.12)(0.16)}\ \text{MeV}\right)$$

$$= \frac{1}{2}(24.96\ \text{MeV}) = 12.48\ \text{MeV}.$$

(b) The angular distribution of neutrons is isotropic in the COM frame. To figure out the percentage of the neutrons emitted in the forward direction in the LAB frame, one needs to find the angle φ in the COM frame that corresponds to θ of 90° in the LAB frame. According to equation 7.29, for $\theta = 90°$,

$$-v_c'\cos\varphi = v_o \quad \Rightarrow \quad \cos\varphi = -\frac{v_o}{v_c'} = -\frac{\sqrt{0.16}}{\sqrt{29.12}} = -0.074625 \quad \Rightarrow \quad \varphi \cong 94.25°.$$

Since $\dfrac{d\sigma(\varphi)}{d\Omega} = \text{constant (i.e., isotropic)}$, % of neutrons emitted in the forward direction can be calculated as

$$\% = \frac{\displaystyle\int_{0°}^{94.25°}\frac{d\sigma(\varphi)}{d\Omega}d\Omega}{\displaystyle\int_{0°}^{180°}\frac{d\sigma(\varphi)}{d\Omega}d\Omega} = \frac{\displaystyle\int_{0°}^{94.25°}2\pi\sin\varphi\,d\varphi}{\displaystyle\int_{0°}^{180°}2\pi\sin\varphi\,d\varphi} = \frac{1}{2}\int_{0°}^{94.25°}\sin\varphi\,d\varphi = 0.537,\ \text{or}\ 53.7\%.$$

Example 7.3.2 ($Q < 0$)

Consider the reaction $^7\text{Li} + p \rightarrow {}^7\text{Be} + n$. (a) Calculate the threshold energy (E_{th}) for the incident proton for this reaction to occur. (b) For a proton of $E_{th} + 0.01$ MeV, calculate the maximum angle with respect to the incident beam direction at which neutrons will be observed. (c) Calculate the energies of the emitted neutrons at $0°$ and the maximum angle found in part (b).

Solution

(a) From Appendix B, $Q = \Delta mc^2 = 14.907 + 7.289 - 8.071 - 15.768 = -1.643$ MeV. Since $Q < 0$, the reaction is endothermic and there should be a corresponding threshold energy for the incident proton. Since a proton is positively charged, one also needs to consider the Coulomb barrier. The Coulomb barrier for this reaction can be estimated as

$$\frac{Z_1 Z_2 (1.44 \text{ MeV} \cdot \text{fm})}{1.2(A_1^{1/3} + A_2^{1/3}) \text{ fm}} = \frac{(1)(3)(1.44 \text{ MeV} \cdot \text{fm})}{1.2(1 + 7^{1/3}) \text{fm}} = 1.235 \text{ MeV},$$

which is smaller than $-Q$. As such, E_{th} corresponds to Q converted to the LAB frame; that is,

$$E_{th} = \left(\frac{m_p + m_{\text{Li}}}{m_{\text{Li}}}\right)(-Q) \cong \left(\frac{8}{7}\right)(1.643 \text{ MeV}) = 1.8777 \text{ MeV}.$$

(b) The maximum angle occurs when $\frac{d\theta}{d\varphi} = 0$. From equation 7.30, it follows that

$$\frac{d\theta}{d\varphi} = \frac{d\left[\tan^{-1}\left(\frac{v_c' \sin\varphi}{v_0 + v_c' \cos\varphi}\right)\right]}{d\varphi} = \left[1 + \left(\frac{v_c' \sin\varphi}{v_0 + v_c' \cos\varphi}\right)^2\right]^{-1} \frac{d\left(\frac{v_c' \sin\varphi}{v_0 + v_c' \cos\varphi}\right)}{d\varphi} = 0$$

$$\Rightarrow \frac{d\left(\frac{v_c' \sin\varphi}{v_0 + v_c' \cos\varphi}\right)}{d\varphi} = \left[v_0 + v_c' \cos\varphi\right]^{-1} \frac{d v_c' \sin\varphi}{d\varphi} + v_c' \sin\varphi \frac{d\left[v_0 + v_c' \cos\varphi\right]^{-1}}{d\varphi} = 0$$

$$\Rightarrow \frac{v_c' \cos\varphi}{v_0 + v_c' \cos\varphi} + \frac{\left(v_c' \sin\varphi\right)^2}{\left(v_0 + v_c' \cos\varphi\right)^2} = \frac{v_0 v_c' \cos\varphi + v_c'^2}{\left(v_0 + v_c' \cos\varphi\right)^2} = 0 \Rightarrow v_0 v_c' \cos\varphi + v_c'^2 = 0$$

$$\Rightarrow v_0 \cos\varphi + v_c' = 0 \Rightarrow \cos\varphi = -\frac{v_c'}{v_0}. \tag{7.31}$$

$$E_l = E_{th} + 0.01 \text{ MeV} = 1.8777 + 0.01 = 1.8877 \text{ MeV} = \frac{1}{2}m_p v_p^2 \implies v_p = \sqrt{\frac{3.7754 \text{ MeV}}{m_p}}$$

$$E_c = \left(\frac{m_{Li}}{m_p + m_{Li}}\right)E_l \cong \left(\frac{7}{8}\right)(1.8877 \text{ MeV}) = 1.6517 \text{ MeV}$$

From equation 7.11, $v_o = \left(\dfrac{m_p}{m_p + m_{Li}}\right)v_p \cong \left(\dfrac{1}{8}\right)\sqrt{\dfrac{3.7754 \text{ MeV}}{m_p}} = \sqrt{\dfrac{0.05899 \text{ MeV}}{m_p}}$.

$$E_c' = E_c + Q = 1.6517 \text{ MeV} - 1.643 \text{ MeV} = 0.0087 \text{ MeV}$$

From equation 7.26, one finds

$$v_c' = \sqrt{\frac{2 m_{Be} E_c'}{m_n(m_n + m_{Be})}} \cong \sqrt{\frac{2}{m_n}\left(\frac{7}{8}\right)(0.0087 \text{ MeV})} = \sqrt{\frac{0.015225 \text{ MeV}}{m_n}} .$$

Equation 7.31 then becomes

$$\cos\varphi = -\frac{v_c'}{v_o} = -\frac{\sqrt{0.015225 \text{ MeV}}}{\sqrt{0.05899 \text{ MeV}}} = -0.50803 \implies (\varphi)_{max} \cong 120.5° .$$

Finally,

$$\theta_{max} = \tan^{-1}\left(\frac{v_c' \sin\varphi}{v_o + v_c' \cos\varphi}\right) = \tan^{-1}\left(\frac{\sqrt{0.015225 \text{ MeV}} \sin(120.5°)}{\sqrt{0.05899 \text{ MeV}} + \sqrt{0.015225 \text{ MeV}} \cos(120.5°)}\right)$$

$$= \tan^{-1}(0.5896) \cong 30.5° .$$

It should be noted that φ_{max} and θ_{max} exist only if $v_c' < v_o$. Should $v_c' > v_o$, equation 7.31 would predict $|\cos\varphi| > 1$, which is impossible.

(c) Since $v_c' < v_o$, there are two different energies of neutrons for $\theta = 0°$. The higher energy corresponds to those emitted in the forward direction in the COM frame ($\varphi = 0°$), at which

$$v_l' = v_c' + v_o = \sqrt{\frac{0.015225 \text{ MeV}}{m_n}} + \sqrt{\frac{0.05899 \text{ MeV}}{m_p}} \cong \sqrt{\frac{0.015225 \text{ MeV}}{m_n}} + \sqrt{\frac{0.05899 \text{ MeV}}{m_n}} .$$

It then follows that

$$\left(\frac{1}{2}m_n v_l'^2\right)_{max} = \frac{1}{2}m_n\left(\sqrt{\frac{0.015225 \text{ MeV}}{m_n}} + \sqrt{\frac{0.05899 \text{ MeV}}{m_n}}\right)^2$$

$$= \frac{1}{2}\left(0.015225 \text{ MeV} + 0.05899 \text{ MeV} + 2\sqrt{(0.015225)(0.05899)} \text{ MeV}\right)$$

$$= 0.0671 \text{ MeV}.$$

Similarly, the lower energy corresponds to the neutrons emitted in the backward direction in the COM frame ($\varphi = 180°$), at which

$$v_l' = v_c' - v_o = \sqrt{\frac{0.015225 \text{ MeV}}{m_n}} - \sqrt{\frac{0.05899 \text{ MeV}}{m_n}}.$$

It then follows that

$$\left(\frac{1}{2}m_n v_l'^2\right)_{min} = \frac{1}{2}m_n\left(\sqrt{\frac{0.015225 \text{ MeV}}{m_n}} - \sqrt{\frac{0.05899 \text{ MeV}}{m_n}}\right)^2$$

$$= \frac{1}{2}\left(0.015225 \text{ MeV} + 0.05899 \text{ MeV} - 2\sqrt{(0.015225)(0.05899)} \text{ MeV}\right)$$

$$= 0.00714 \text{ MeV}.$$

For $\theta_{max} = 30.5°$ (i.e. $\varphi_{max} = 120.5°$), v_l' can be obtained using the simple trigonometry shown below

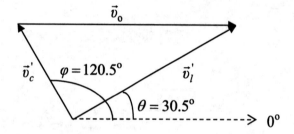

That is, $v_l' = v_o \cos 30.5° = \sqrt{\frac{0.05899 \text{ MeV}}{m_p}}(0.861629)$. The outgoing neutron energy can therefore be obtained as

$$\frac{1}{2}m_n v_l'^2 = \frac{1}{2}m_n\left(\frac{0.05899 \text{ MeV}}{m_p}\right)(0.861629)^2 \cong 0.0219 \text{ MeV}$$

Example 3 ($Q = 0$)

A 1-MeV neutron undergoes elastic scattering with a hydrogen nucleus. Given that the scattering is isotropic in the COM frame, show that the scattered neutron must be forwardly directed in the LAB frame.

Solution

Elastic scattering by definition means $Q = 0$. To show that the scattered neutron must be forwardly directed in the LAB frame is the same as to show that $v_c' \leq v_0$. As such, we again need to calculate v_0 and v_c'.

$$E_l = 1 \text{ MeV} = \frac{1}{2}m_n v_n^2 \Rightarrow v_n = \sqrt{\frac{2 \text{ MeV}}{m_n}}$$

From equation 7.11, $v_0 = \left(\frac{m_n}{m_n + m_H}\right)v_n \cong \left(\frac{1}{2}\right)\sqrt{\frac{2 \text{ MeV}}{m_n}} = \sqrt{\frac{0.5 \text{ MeV}}{m_n}}$.

$$E_c = \left(\frac{m_H}{m_n + m_H}\right)E_l \cong \left(\frac{1}{2}\right)(1 \text{ MeV}) = 0.5 \text{ MeV}$$

Because $Q = 0$, $E_c' = E_c = 0.5 \text{ MeV}$.

From equation 7.26, one finds

$$v_c' = \sqrt{\frac{2m_H E_c'}{m_n(m_n + m_H)}} \cong \sqrt{\frac{2}{m_n}\left(\frac{1}{1+1}\right)(0.5 \text{ MeV})} = \sqrt{\frac{0.5 \text{ MeV}}{m_n}}.$$

The above shows that $v_c' = v_0$, and therefore, the scattered neutron must be forwardly directed in the LAB frame.

7.4 Neutron-Induced Fission Reactions

7.4.1 Theory

As discussed in Section 6.4, spontaneous fissions hardly occur for nuclides with $A < 240$. This is because there is a Coulomb barrier (E_b) of approximately 6 MeV (see Figure 6.15). However, it is well known that some heavy nuclides can undergo fissions upon absorbing a thermal neutron. Because a thermal neutron has a negligible amount of kinetic energy (~0.025 eV), this means there is no neutron energy threshold for these neutron-induced fission reactions. These nuclides are capable of sustaining a nuclear fission chain reaction, and are called fissile material. Commonly known fissile material includes ^{233}U, ^{235}U, and ^{239}Pu, among which only ^{235}U exists in nature. As such, ^{235}U also serve as the major fuel in the commercial nuclear power reactors.

Fissile material is a subset of fissionable material, which also includes nuclides (e.g., ^{238}U) that can undergo fission upon absorbing a neutron with a relatively low energy threshold (E_t). Neutron-induced fissions can easily occur in the fissionable nuclides, mainly because the binding energy resulting from the absorption of a neutron is enough to overcome the Coulomb barrier (E_b). In fact, fissions may occur via the tunneling effect even when the neutron binding energy is less than E_b. As shown in Figure 7.5, the activation energy (E_a) for fissions to occur is estimated to be about 0.9 MeV less than E_b. At this energy, fissions occur in less than 10^{-14} s, which corresponds to the half-life of the excited compound nuclei that would undergo $E1$ or $M1$ gamma transitions otherwise.

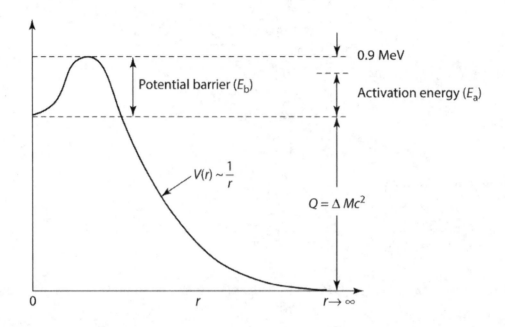

Figure 7.5. The potential energy versus distance between two fission fragments.

The binding energy resulting from the absorption of a neutron is the same as the neutron separation energy (S_n) of the compound nucleus. Table 7.2 shows the characteristic data for the commonly known fissionable nuclides. The values of E_a are taken to be 0.9 MeV less than E_b estimated with equation 6.50. As shown, the top three nuclides are fissile nuclides, as they have negative values of $E_a - S_n$, indicating that the binding energy brought in by the incident neutron is more than enough to overcome the activation energy for fission to take place. As such, there is no energy threshold for the incident neutron for the fissile nuclides. The rest of the nuclides in Table 7.2 all have positive values of $E_a - S_n$, indicating that the binding energy brought in by the incident neutron is not enough to overcome the activation energy for fission to take place. As such, there is a corresponding energy threshold for the incident neutron for these nuclides. Because $E_a - S_n$ represents the minimum energy required for the fission reaction to occur, the experimentally observed values of E_t is often slightly greater than the values of $E_a - S_n$.

Table 7.2. The characteristic data for the commonly known fissionable nuclides.
Source: Foderaro (1971)

Nuclide	E_a (MeV)	S_n (MeV)	$E_a - S_n$ (MeV)	E_t (MeV)
^{233}U	5.1	6.8	-1.7	0
^{235}U	5.2	6.5	-1.3	0
^{239}Pu	4.8	6.4	-1.6	0
^{232}Th	6.0	4.9	1.1	1.6
^{234}U	5.5	5.2	0.3	0.3
^{236}U	5.6	5.3	0.3	0.8
^{238}U	5.7	4.8	0.9	0.9
^{237}Np	5.7	5.5	0.2	0.35

7.4.2 Energy Release in Nuclear Fissions

The energy release in nuclear fission can be obtained from the mass and energy balance equation. If one considers a neutron-induced binary fission where a neutron with kinetic energy E_n is absorbed by a fissionable nuclide with mass $M(Z,A)$, then the mass and energy balance equation gives

$$E_n + m_n + M(Z,A) = T_L(Z_L,A_L) + M^*(Z_L,A_L) + T_H(Z_H,A_H) + M^*(Z_H,A_H), \tag{7.32}$$

where T_L and T_H are the kinetic energies of the light and heavy fragments, respectively, and $M^*(Z_L,A_L)$ $M^*(Z_H,A_H)$ are their corresponding masses immediately after scission. The * notation indicates that the fission fragments are in the excited states.

The total energy release, E_r, in binary fission is defined as the ground-state mass of the compound nucleus undergoing fission minus the ground-state masses of the two fission fragments. That is,

$$E_r = M(Z,A+1) - M(Z_L,A_L) - M(Z_H,A_H), \tag{7.33}$$

where $M(Z,A+1)$ is the mass of the compound nucleus, and it can be obtained as

$$m_n + M(Z,A) = M(Z,A+1) + B_n, \tag{7.34}$$

where B_n is the neutron binding energy, which can be obtained from the Q-value for neutron capture. By inserting equation 7.34 into 7.32, one obtains

$$E_n + B_n + M(Z,A+1) = T_L(Z_L,A_L) + M^*(Z_L,A_L) + T_H(Z_H,A_H) + M^*(Z_H,A_H)$$

$$= T_L(Z_L,A_L) + M(Z_L,A_L) + T_H(Z_H,A_H) + M(Z_H,A_H)$$

$$+ E^*(Z_L,A_L) + E^*(Z_H,A_H), \tag{7.35}$$

where $E^* = M^* - M$. It represents the excitation energy of the nuclide and will be dissipated by the emission of prompt neutrons and gamma rays. Inserting 7.33 into 7.35 yields

$$E_r = T_L(Z_L, A_L) + T_H(Z_H, A_H) + E^*(Z_L, A_L) + E^*(Z_H, A_H) - (E_n + B_n).$$
(7.36)

Since the fission fragments consist of a large number of possible nuclide species, energy terms in the above equation must be replaced by their average values as determined by weighting, with the corresponding fission fragment yielding Y_f. That is,

$$\langle E_r \rangle = \langle T_f^{tot} \rangle + \langle E_{tot}^* \rangle - (E_n + B_n),$$
(7.37)

with

$$\langle T_f^{tot} \rangle = \frac{\sum Y_f [T_L(Z_L, A_L) + T_H(Z_H, A_H)]}{\sum Y_f}$$
(7.38)

$$\langle E_{tot}^* \rangle = \frac{\sum Y_f [E^*(Z_L, A_L) + E^*(Z_H, A_H)]}{\sum Y_f}.$$
(7.39)

It should be noted that the term $(E_n + B_n)$ that appears in equation 7.36 and 7.37 should be replaced with 0 for spontaneous fission and E_γ for photofission.

To be more specific about the prompt energy release in a fission process, one must consider the detailed time evolution of the process. Figure 7.6 is a schematic diagram of neutron-induced binary fission. As shown at the bottom of this figure, the fission process is divided into four stages: The first stage is compound nucleus formation, which takes no time. The second stage is the scission and Coulomb acceleration of the fission fragments, which takes approximately 10^{-20} s. The third stage is the prompt emission of neutrons and gamma-rays, which takes less than 10^{-7} s. The prompt energy release of the fission is the amount that is released by the end of stage 3 (i.e., $<10^{-7}$ s), indicated by the dotted line. The experimental data of $\langle T_f^{tot} \rangle$ as a function of E_n for the $n + {}^{235}U$ system is shown in Figure 7.7. The value of $\langle E_{tot}^* \rangle$ can be approximated by the sum of the average total kinetic energy of prompt neutrons $\langle E_{pn}^{tot} \rangle$ and the average total energy of prompt gamma rays $\langle E_{p\gamma}^{tot} \rangle$. The experimental data of $\langle E_{pn}^{tot} \rangle$ and $\langle E_{p\gamma}^{tot} \rangle$ are provided in Figures 7.8 and 7.9, respectively.

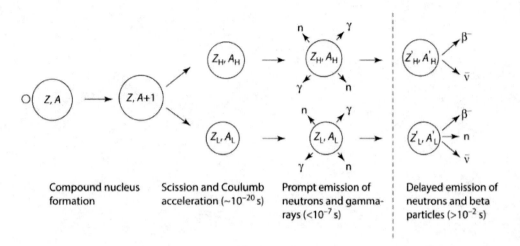

Figure 7.6. A schematic diagram describing the multiple stages of a neutron-induced binary fission of target nucleus (Z, A).
Source: Madland(2006).

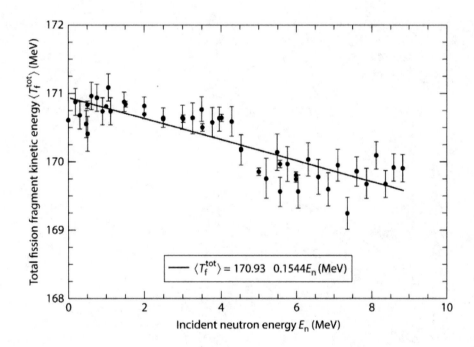

Figure 7.7. The experimental data of the average total fission-fragment kinetic energy (pre-prompt neutron emission) as a function of incident neutron energy E_n for the $n+^{235}U$ system.
Source: Madland (2006).

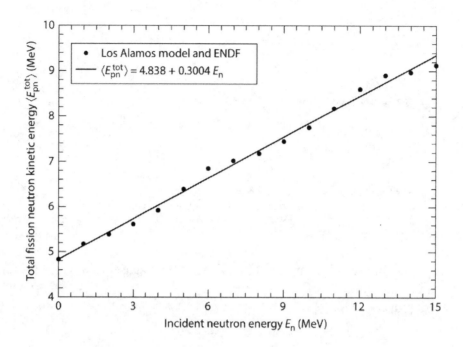

Figure 7.8. The average total prompt fission neutron kinetic energy $\left\langle E_{pn}^{tot} \right\rangle$ as a function of incident neutron energy E_n for the $n+^{235}U$ system.
Source: Madland (2006).

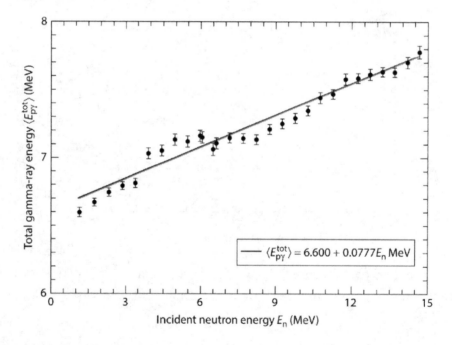

Figure 7.9 The experimental data of total prompt fission gamma-ray energy $\left\langle E_{p\gamma}^{tot} \right\rangle$ as a function of incident neutron energy E_n for the $n+^{235}U$ system.
Source: Madland (2006).

For a $n+{}^{235}U$ fission where the incident neutron is a thermal neutron ($E_n \cong 0.025\,eV$), Figures 7.7 to 7.9 show that the total prompt energy release is about 182.5 MeV, of which the fission fragments carry 171 MeV, the neutrons carry 5 MeV, and the gamma rays carry 6.5 MeV. As shown in Figure 7.6, the two fission fragments $\left(Z'_H, A'_H\right)$ and $\left(Z'_L, A'_L\right)$ will continue to undergo a series of beta decays for some time. This is because they are far too neutron-rich (Section 6.4). In fact, these "fission products," produced in commercial nuclear reactors (which are mainly based on the $n+{}^{235}U$ system), represent the lion's share among all manmade radioactivities. These fission products are currently contained in the used nuclear fuel. A typical nuclear power plant in a year generates twenty metric tons of used fuel.

7.4.3 Prompt and Delayed Neutrons

The neutrons emitted in a fission reaction are essential to the development of nuclear power. These neutrons make it possible to build and operate self-sustaining chain reaction systems. It turns out that not all neutrons are promptly emitted at the moment of fission. As mentioned in Section 5.3.5, there exist several indirect fission products (e.g., ${}^{87}Kr$ and ${}^{137}Xe$) that happen to be neutron emitters. Since these nuclides are the products of beta decays from the direct fission fragments, ${}^{87}Br$ and ${}^{137}I$, having half-lives of 54.5 s and 24.4 s, respectively, the corresponding average delays of neutrons emitted from ${}^{87}Kr$ and ${}^{137}Xe$ are 78.6 s and 35.2 s after the initial fission takes place. These delayed neutrons are of great importance to the safe operation of a nuclear power reactor. In a typical commercial nuclear reactor, approximately 99.3% are prompt neutrons directly emitted from fission reactions and 0.7% are the delayed neutrons emitted from fission products such as ${}^{87}Kr$ and ${}^{137}Xe$. Because the neutron lifetime in a reactor is so short ($\sim 10^{-4}$ s), without the delayed neutrons it would be impossible to safely control the neutron population (and thus the power level) of a nuclear reactor.

The average number of prompt fission neutrons emitted per fission as a function of incident neutron energy E_n for the three types of fission, $n+{}^{235}U$, $n+{}^{238}U$, and $n+{}^{239}Pu$, are provided in Figure 7.10. In the case that the incident neutron is a thermal neutron, Figure 10 shows that the average number of prompt fissions is approximately 2.4 for $n+{}^{235}U$ and $n+{}^{238}U$, and 2.85 for $n+{}^{239}Pu$. Since Figure 7.8 shows that the total kinetic energy carried by prompt neutrons per fission of $n+{}^{235}U$ is approximately 5 MeV, the average energy of a prompt neutron for $n+{}^{235}U$ would be about 2.1 MeV (i.e., 5 MeV/2.4).

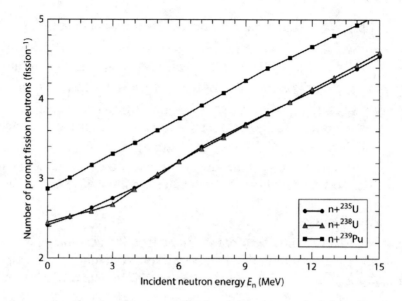

Figure 7.10. The average number of prompt fission neutrons as a function of incident neutron energy E_n for three systems: n+^{235}U, n+^{238}U, and n+^{239}Pu.
Source: Madland (2006).

The full prompt fission neutron spectra for various types of fission have been carefully evaluated both experimentally and computationally over the last many years. Figure 7.11 shows the neutron spectra for the various thermal and fast neutron-induced nuclides, as well for the spontaneous fission nuclide ^{252}Cf. As shown, the neutron energies of the spectra extend up to between 15 to 20 MeV. All spectra have a maximum at about 0.7 MeV and then smoothly drop off by many orders of magnitude as energy increases. These spectra all look alike and can be described by a simple formula called Watt distribution:

$$\chi(E) = ae^{-E/b} \sinh \sqrt{cE}, \tag{7.40}$$

where the coefficients a, b, and c are constants, and their values are different for the various types of fission shown in Table 7.3.

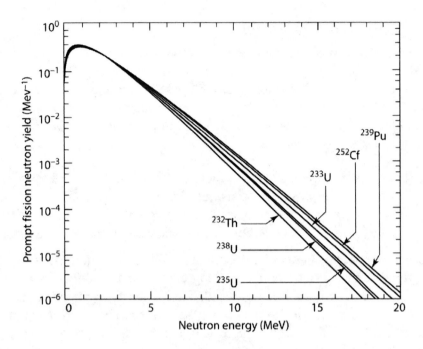

Figure 7.11. Energy distribution of the prompt fission neutrons produced by the neutron-induced fissions of ^{232}Th, ^{233}U, ^{235}U, ^{238}U, and ^{239}Pu. The results for ^{252}Cf are for spontaneous fission.
Source: Shultis and Faw (1996).

Table 7.3. The values of a, b, and c of the Watt distribution (equation 7.40) for the various types of fission.

Nuclide	Type of fission	a	b	c
^{233}U	Thermal	0.6077	1.1080	1.2608
^{235}U	Thermal	0.5535	1.0347	1.6214
^{239}Pu	Thermal	0.5710	1.1593	1.2292
^{232}Th	Fast (2 MeV)	0.5601	0.9711	1.8262
^{238}U	Fast (2 MeV)	0.5759	1.0269	1.5776
^{252}Cf	Spontaneous	0.6400	1.1750	1.0401

The delayed neutron energy spectra for the various neutron-emitting fission products (e.g., ^{87}Kr and ^{137}Xe) have also been evaluated both experimentally and computationally. These spectra are softer than the prompt neutron spectra. The mean energies typically vary between 250 keV and 560 keV.

7.5 Nuclear Fusion Reactions

As an opposite to nuclear fission, Figure 4.3 also shows that a large amount of energy (a large positive Q-value) can be released in a nuclear fusion reaction when two nuclei of A < 20 are fused into one bigger nucleus. Considering two ^{10}B nuclei forming a ^{20}Ne nucleus, the Q-value is about 30 MeV, or 1.5 MeV per nucleon. For this reaction to take place, however, the kinetic energy of each ^{10}B nucleus must be greater than the Coulomb barrier, which can be estimated as $\frac{Z_1 Z_2 (1.44\,\text{MeV·fm})}{1.2(A_1^{1/3}+A_2^{1/3})\,\text{fm}} = 6.963\,\text{MeV}$. This type of fusion reaction can be easily demonstrated in the laboratory using particle accelerators. A nuclear fusion device based on an accelerator, however, produces too little power to be useful, because a typical ion accelerator produces beams in the nanoampere to microampere range. Even if all of the ions undergo fusion reactions with the target nuclei, it would produce no more than a few watts of power.

An alternate approach is to heat up the atoms, making them into the form of plasma, and then to try to trap the plasma in a container long enough that enough fusion reactions occur and a useful amount of power can be produced. This process is called thermonuclear fusion, because the thermal energy is used to overcome the Coulomb barrier for fusion to take place. The temperature needed for the two ^{10}B nuclei to overcome the Coulomb barrier of 6.684 MeV can be calculated by setting the mean kinetic energy of a ^{10}B nucleus equal to one half of the barrier height. That is, $\frac{3}{2}kT = \frac{6.684\,\text{MeV}}{2} = 3.342\,\text{MeV}$. Since $kT \approx 0.025\,\text{eV}$ at room temperature, 3.342 MeV of kinetic energy would require a temperature about $3 \times 10^{10}\,°\text{K}$, which is not practically achievable. As such, for several decades research has been focused on plasma made of low-Z nuclides (e.g., ^{1}H, ^{2}H, ^{3}H, ^{4}He), in which the Coulomb barriers are much lower and the required plasma temperatures are achievable. The major reactions include

$$^{1}\text{H}+^{1}\text{H}\rightarrow ^{2}\text{H}+e^{+}+\nu \quad (Q=1.44\,\text{MeV}) \tag{7.41}$$

$$^{1}\text{H}+^{2}\text{H}\rightarrow ^{3}\text{He}+\gamma \quad (Q=5.49\,\text{MeV}) \tag{7.42}$$

$$^{2}\text{H}+^{2}\text{H}\rightarrow ^{3}\text{He}+n \quad (Q=3.27\,\text{MeV}) \tag{7.43}$$

$$^{2}\text{H}+^{2}\text{H}\rightarrow ^{3}\text{H}+p \quad (Q=4.03\,\text{MeV}) \tag{7.44}$$

$$^{2}\text{H}+^{3}\text{H}\rightarrow ^{4}\text{He}+n \quad (Q=17.6\,\text{MeV}) \tag{7.45}$$

$$^{2}\text{H}+^{3}\text{He}\rightarrow ^{4}\text{He}+^{1}H \quad (Q=18.3\,\text{MeV}). \tag{7.46}$$

Equation 7.41 is the first step in a series of fusion processes occurring in the sun. This reaction involves a weak interaction process (converting a proton into a neutron), and therefore has too small a cross section to be considered in a thermonuclear fusion device. Equation 7.42 is not very useful either, because it also has a small cross section. In addition, the Q-value mainly goes to the gamma ray, whose energy is difficult to convert into a usable form. Equations 7.43 to 7.45 are the reactions being widely considered for a thermonuclear fusion device. Equations 7.43 and 7.44 are called deuterium-deuterium (or D-D) reactions. Equation 7.45 is called deuterium-tritium (or D-T) reaction.

Bibliography

Foderaro, Anthony *The Elements of Neutron Interaction Theory*. Cambridge, MA: MIT Press, Cambridge, 1971.

Krane, Kenneth S. *Introductory Nuclear Pfhysics*. New York: John Wiley & Sons, 1988.

Lamarsh, John R. *Introduction to Nuclear Reactor Theory*. Reading, MA: Addison-Wesley Publishing Company, Inc., 1966.

Madland, David G. "Total Prompt Release in the Neutron-Induced Fission of ^{235}U, ^{238}U, and ^{239}Pu." *Nuclear Physics A* 772(2006): 112–37.

Shultis, J. Kenneth, and Faw. Richard E. *Radiation Shielding*. Upper Saddle River, NJ: Prentice-Hall, 1996.

Credits

Problems

1. A portable neutron source is made of a mixture of ^{241}Am and Be (100% ^{9}Be). Neutrons are produced via the (α, n) reactions on Be. Assuming that the maximum α particle energy is 5.5445 MeV, calculate the maximum energy of the emitted neutrons.

2. It is desired to study the first excited state of ^{16}O, which is at energy of 6.049 MeV. (a) Using the (α, n) reaction on a target of ^{13}C, what is the minimum alpha particle energy needed to populate the excited state? (b) In what direction will the resulting neutrons travel? (c) If it is desired to detect neutrons at 90° to the incident beam, what is the minimum alpha particle energy that can result in the excited state being populated?

3. (a) In Coulomb scattering of 7.5-MeV protons by a target of ^{7}Li, what is the energy of the elastically scattered protons at 90°? (b) What is the energy of the inelastically scattered protons at 90° when the ^{7}Li is left in its first excited state (0.477 MeV)?

4. For the reaction $^2\mathrm{H} + {}^2\mathrm{H} \rightarrow {}^3\mathrm{He} + \mathrm{n}$, plot the energy of the outgoing neutron as a function of angle for ^{2}H incident on ^{2}H at rest. Use incident energies of 0.0, 2.5, and 5.0 MeV.

5. A 3-MeV deuteron beam impinges on a tritium target to produce neutrons via the $^3\mathrm{H}(d,n)^4\mathrm{He}$ reaction. Assuming that the direction of outgoing neutrons is isotropic in the COM frame, determine: (a) the Q-value of this reaction, (b) the COM velocity, (c) the total kinetic energy of the system in the COM frame, (d) the velocity and kinetic energy of the final state particles in both the LAB and COM frames, and (2) the maximum and minimum energies of the emerging neutrons.

6. In the reaction $^7\mathrm{Li} + \mathrm{p} \rightarrow {}^4\mathrm{He} + {}^4\mathrm{He}$ (18.6-MeV protons incident on a lithium target), the differential cross section (in the COM frame) reaches a maximum of about 1.67 barns/steradian at a COM angle of 75°. (a) Sketch the reaction kinematics in the LAB system, labeling all momenta, directions, and energies. (b) Assuming a target thickness of 1.0 mg cm^{-2} and a proton beam current of 1.0 μA spread over an area of 1 cm^2, find the number of α particles per second in the above geometry that would strike a detector of area 0.5 cm^2 located 12.0 cm from the target.

7. In a Coulomb excitation experiment, α particles are inelastically scattered from ^{160}Dy nuclei. (a) If the incident α particle energy is 5.6 MeV, what is the energy of the elastically scattered α particles observed at $\theta = 150°$? (b) States in ^{160}Dy are known at 2^+ (0.087 MeV), 4^+ (0.284 MeV), and 2^+ (0.966 MeV). Considering only the E2 excitation mode, find the energies of the inelastically scattered α particles observed at 150°.

CHAPTER 8: INTERACTIONS OF NEUTRONS WITH MATTER

8.1 Various Types of Neutron Interactions

Since a neutron is a nucleon and is neutral in charge, it mainly interacts with a nucleus via the strong nuclear force. There are many types of neutron interactions; for example, elastic scattering, inelastic scattering, (n, γ), (n, p), (n, α), (n, 2n), (n, fission), and so on. As such, the total neutron cross section for a nucleus can be written as:

$$\sigma_t = \sigma_s + \sigma_i + \sigma_\gamma + \sigma_p + \sigma_\alpha + \sigma_{2n} + \sigma_f + ...$$ (8.1)

where σ_s, σ_i, σ_γ, σ_p, σ_α, σ_{2n}, and σ_f are, respectively, the cross sections for elastic scattering, inelastic scattering, (n, γ), (n, p), (n, α), (n, 2n), and (n, fission). Among the various types of interactions, σ_t and σ_s are in general the most easily measured ones. As such, an alternative expression of equation 8.1 is:

$$\sigma_t = \sigma_s + \sigma_{ne},$$ (8.2)

where σ_{ne} is the difference between σ_t and σ_s, and it is called the non-elastic cross section because it includes the cross sections of all types except that of the elastic scattering. σ_{ne} is further conveniently expressed as:

$$\sigma_{ne} = \sigma_i + \sigma_a,$$ (8.3)

where $\sigma_a = \sigma_\gamma + \sigma_p + \sigma_\alpha + \sigma_{2n} + \sigma_f + ...$ and it represents the absorption cross section, implying that the target nucleus first absorbs the incident neutron to form a compound nucleus, which then undergoes various types of decay: γ, p, α, 2n, fission, and so on.

As discussed in Chapter 7, the many types of nuclear reactions can be classified into two categories: direct interaction and interaction via compound-nucleus formation. This classification is based on the mechanistic model and time duration of the reaction process. Accordingly, a direct neutron interaction refers to a one-step process in that the core of the target nucleus is not involved in the process, and that the process takes less than 10^{-22} seconds. The major type of direct neutron interaction is potential scattering (also known as "shape scattering"), in which the neutron is scattered away from the target nucleus merely due to the presence of the strong nuclear force field. Potential scattering is elastic because the target nucleus stays at the same energy state throughout the scattering process. A neutron interaction via compound-nucleus reaction is a two-step process in that the neutron is first absorbed into the target nucleus to form an excited compound nucleus, which then decays by emitting one or more secondary particles. The process of a compound-nucleus reaction takes between 10^{-18} and 10^{-14} seconds. Figure 8.1 is an energy-level diagram showing the role of the compound nucleus in neutron interactions. As shown, the compound nucleus is instantly promoted to a highly excited state, mostly because of the Q-value ($\Delta Mc^2 \approx 7\text{-}8$ MeV) brought in by the neutron. The level of the excited state is even higher if the incident neutron also carries a significant amount of kinetic energy. As indicated in Figure 8.1, the total amount of excitation energy of the compound nucleus can be calculated using equation 7.19 as:

$$E_c' = E_c + Q = \left(\frac{M(^AX)}{m_n + M(^AX)} \right) E_n + \Delta Mc^2$$

$$\cong \left(\frac{A}{A+1} \right) E_n + \left[m_n + M(^AX) - M(^{A+1}X) \right] c^2 , \tag{8.4}$$

where E_n is the kinetic energy of the incident neutron.

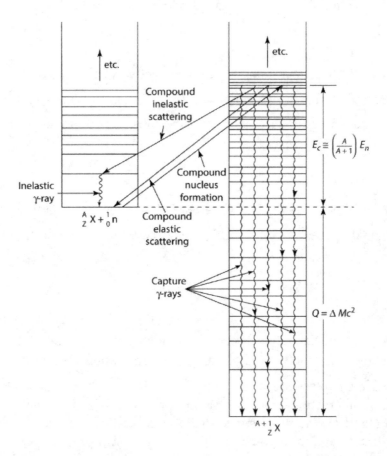

Figure 8.1. Energy diagram showing the role of the compound nucleus in neutron interactions.

Source: Lamarsh (1966)

From the interaction mechanism viewpoint, the expressions of equations 8.2 and 8.3 are somewhat misleading. This is because, according to Figure 8.1, both elastic scattering and inelastic scattering can take place via compound nucleus formation. Under such events, the incident neutron is first absorbed by the target nucleus to form an excited compound nucleus, which then decays by emitting a neutron. As such, the compound elastic scattering and inelastic scattering should both be considered as part of the absorption interaction. In practice, however, compound elastic scattering is included with potential elastic scattering in the term σ_s. In other words, mechanistically, σ_s is actually the sum of two terms:

$$\sigma_s = \sigma_{ps} + \sigma_{cs}, \tag{8.5}$$

where σ_{ps} and σ_{cs}, respectively, stand for potential elastic scattering and compound elastic scattering, and they differ from each other in that the former is often angular dependent in the center-of-mass (COM) system, whereas the latter is always isotropic. The angular dependency of σ_{ps} can be understood by the partial-wave analysis (see Section 3.11.2), and it will be further discussed Section 8.3. The reason why σ_{cs} is isotropic is because the compound nucleus by nature does not have any "memory" of the direction of the incident neutron. With this line of thought, all the particles emitted from the compound nucleus should be isotropic in the COM system. These would include the cross sections of σ_i, σ_γ, σ_p, σ_α, σ_{2n}, and σ_f. Mechanistically, one may define the cross section for compound nucleus formation as

$$\sigma_{cn} = \sigma_{cs} + \sigma_i + \sigma_a. \tag{8.6}$$

Further discussion of σ_{cn} is provided in Section 8.2.

8.2 Characteristics of Neutron Cross Sections

Figures 8.2 to 8.4 show, respectively, the neutron cross sections σ_s and σ_{ne} versus neutron energy for three nuclides of very different mass numbers: ^{12}C, ^{56}F, and ^{238}U. The first and most salient feature of neutron cross section is the presence of sharp maxima and minima (the resonances) at certain neutron energies. In general, for light nuclei ($A < 25$) the resonances begin to occur at neutron energies in the MeV region and the gap between the adjacent resonances is of the order of 1 MeV. For intermediate nuclei ($25 \le A \le 70$), the resonances begin to occur at neutron energies in the keV region and the gap between the adjacent resonances is of the order of 1 keV. For heavy nuclei ($A > 70$), the resonances begin to occur at neutron energies in the eV region and the gap between the adjacent resonances is of the order of 1 eV. In addition, the gap between adjacent resonances decreases as neutron energy increases. When neutron energy ascends into the MeV region, the resonances for intermediate and heavy nuclei can no longer be resolved and the cross sections appear to be a smooth continuum. The resonances correspond to the excited states of the compound nucleus. The quantum mechanical explanation of the resonance characteristics is provided in Section 8.3.

The second common feature in Figures 8.2 to 8.4 is the smooth increase of σ_{ne} as the neutron energy decreases. This is also known as the $1/v$ dependence of σ_{ne}. The quantum mechanical explanation of this $1/v$ behavior is provided in Section 8.4.

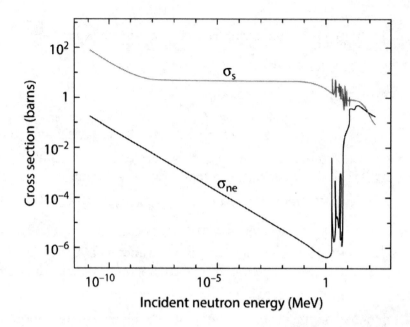

Figure 8.2. The evaluated neutron cross sections, σ_s and σ_{ne} , versus the neutron energy for ^{12}C (obtained from ENDF/B-VII).

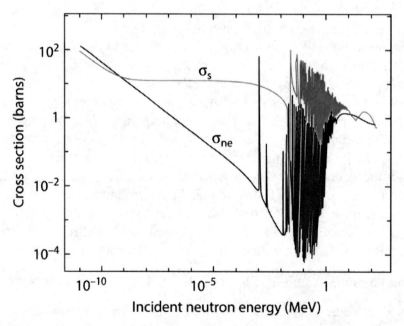

Figure 8.3. The neutron cross sections, σ_s and σ_{ne} , versus the neutron energy for ^{56}Fe (obtained from ENDF/B-VII).

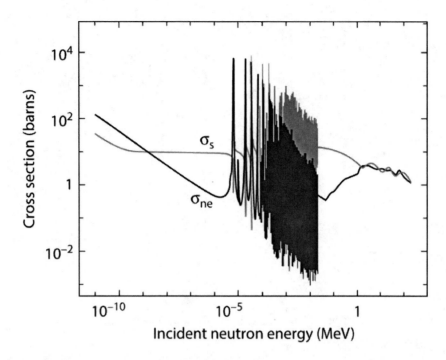

Figure 8.4. The neutron cross sections, σ_s and σ_{ne}, versus neutron energy for ^{238}U (obtained from ENDF/B-VII).

The third common feature in Figures 8.2 to 8.4 is that σ_s tends to be constant over a wide energy range for all three nuclides. This base value of σ_s is contributed from the potential scattering σ_{ps}, and it is in the order of $\pi(R+\lambda)^2$, where R is approximately the radius of the target nucleus ($\cong 1.2A^{1/3}$ fm) and $\lambda = \hbar / p \cong \hbar / \mu v$, which is the reduced wavelength of the incident neutron (μ is the reduced mass of neutron). More discussion on this is provided in Section 8.3.

The fourth feature that can be found in Figures 8.2 to 8.4 is the asymmetric resonances for σ_s (i.e., a minima occurs before each maxima). To depict this feature more clearly, the resonance region of σ_s in Figure 8.3 is re-plotted in Figure 8.5. This feature is attributed to the interference effect occurring between the neutron emerging from a compound elastic scattering and that from a potential elastic scattering. The phenomenon is caused by the slight time delay of the neutron emerging from a compound elastic scattering. Further discussion on this phenomenon is provided in Section 8.6.1.

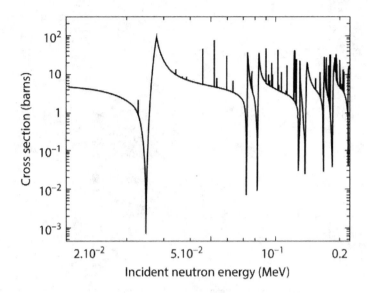

Figure 8.5. The asymmetric resonances of σ_s versus neutron energy for ^{56}Fe (obtained from ENDF/B-VII).

In addition to the energy dependency features of σ_s and σ_{ne} described above, σ_s can also be found to be highly dependent on the scattering angle. As mentioned in Section 8.1, the angular dependency of σ_s is characteristic of potential scattering, as the compound elastic scattering is usually isotropic in the COM system. Figures 8.6 and 8.7, respectively, show the differential scattering cross section ($d\sigma_s/d\Omega$) versus scattering angle for ^{12}C and ^{238}U for incident neutrons of various energies. As shown, $d\sigma_s/d\Omega$ is rather smooth and isotropic for low-energy neutrons and becomes oscillatory for high-energy neutrons. This oscillatory feature of $d\sigma_s/d\Omega$ can be explained by the partial-wave analysis method discussed in Section 8.4.

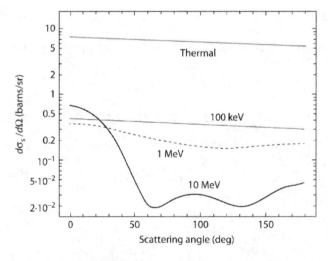

Figure 8.6. The differential scattering cross section versus scattering angle for ^{12}C for incident neutrons of various energies (obtained from ENDF/B-VII).

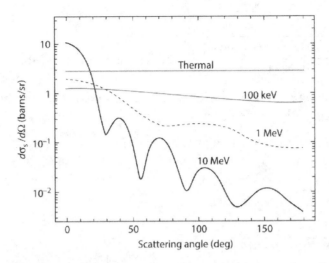

Figure 8.7. The differential scattering cross section versus scattering angle for ^{238}U for incident neutrons of various energies (obtained from ENDF/B-VII).

8.3 Partial-Wave Analysis on Total Neutron Cross Sections

In this section, we will use the partial-wave analysis method introduced in Section 3.11.2 to explain many of the features of neutron cross sections. The advantage of this method is that it is often sufficient to consider the effect of the nuclear potential on only a few of the lowest partial waves. Accordingly, we return to the scenario described in Figure 3.7, where the scattering potential is that of a nucleus. The incident neutron is represented by the plane wave (traveling in the +x direction), which in turn is expressed as a superposition of spherical partial waves (Krane, 1988):

$$\varphi_{in} = e^{ikx} = e^{ikr\cos\theta} = \sum_{\ell=0}^{\infty} (2\ell+1) i^{\ell} j_{\ell}(kr) p_{\ell}(\cos\theta). \tag{8.7}$$

This expression is significant in that, from a quantum-mechanical viewpoint of collision, the incident neutron can be broken into many partial neutrons, of which each carries a different angular momentum ($\ell\hbar$) and interacts separately with the nuclear potential. The number of partial waves that are involved in a neutron interaction can be estimated by equating the expression of the angular momentum of the classical form to that of the quantum-mechanical form. That is,

$$pR = \ell\hbar \quad \Rightarrow \quad \ell = \frac{pR}{\hbar} = \frac{R}{\lambda} = kR, \tag{8.8}$$

where R is the range of the nuclear potential, which can be approximated by $1.2(A^{1/3}+1)$ fm.

For example, if one considers a low-energy neutron of 0.1 MeV interacting with a small nucleus of ^{12}C, then the number of partial waves involved in such an interaction can be estimated as

$$\ell = kR = \frac{\sqrt{2m_n E_n}}{\hbar} R = \frac{\sqrt{2m_n c^2 E_n}}{\hbar c} R$$

$$= \frac{\sqrt{2(939.573 \text{ MeV})(0.1 \text{ MeV})}}{197.329 \text{ MeV} \cdot \text{fm}} \left[\left(1.25(12)^{1/3} + 1\right) \text{fm} \right] \cong 0.268.$$

Since ℓ must be an integer in quantum mechanics, this means that only the s-wave ($\ell = 0$) needs to be considered in this interaction.

On the other hand, if one considers a high-energy neutron of 10 MeV interacting with a large nucleus of ^{238}U, then

$$\ell = kR = \frac{\sqrt{2m_n E_n}}{\hbar} R = \frac{\sqrt{2m_n c^2 E_n}}{\hbar c} R$$

$$= \frac{\sqrt{2(939.573 \text{ MeV})(10 \text{ MeV})}}{197.329 \text{ MeV} \cdot \text{fm}} \left[\left(1.25(238)^{1/3} + 1\right) \text{fm} \right] \cong 6.08.$$

This means there are approximately 7 partial waves involved in the interaction, $\ell = 0, 1, 2, 3,$ 4, 5, and 6.

Neutrons with an angular momentum between $\ell \hbar$ and $(\ell + 1)\hbar$ are represented by the $\ell \hbar$ partial wave, and they will interact through impact parameters between $\ell \lambdabar$ and $(\ell + 1)\lambdabar$, which has a cross section area of

$$\sigma_\ell = \pi\left[(\ell + 1)\lambdabar\right]^2 - \pi(\ell \lambdabar)^2 = (2\ell + 1)\pi \lambdabar^2. \tag{8.9}$$

The total cross section is therefore the sum of all of the σ_ℓ that are involved. That is,

$$\sigma = \sum_{\ell=0}^{\ell_{max}} \sigma_\ell = \sum_{\ell=0}^{\ell_{max}} (2\ell + 1)\pi \lambdabar^2 = \pi \lambdabar^2 \sum_{\ell=0}^{\ell_{max}} (2\ell + 1) = \pi \lambdabar^2 (\ell_{max} + 1)^2, \tag{8.10}$$

where ℓ_{max} is the maximum value of ℓ that is involved in the interaction, and it can be approximated as $R / \lambdabar$. As such, equation 8.10 can be further reduced to

$$\sigma = \pi \lambdabar^2 (\ell_{max} + 1)^2 \cong \pi \lambdabar^2 \left[\left(\frac{R}{\lambdabar}\right)^2 + 2\frac{R}{\lambdabar} + 1 \right] = \pi(R^2 + 2\lambdabar R + \lambdabar^2) = \pi(R + \lambdabar)^2. \tag{8.11}$$

Accordingly, for $R \gg \lambdabar$ (i.e., $\ell_{max} \gg 1$), $\sigma \cong \pi R^2$, which is the classical cross section of interactions between two hard spheres. Oppositely, for $R \ll \lambdabar$ (i.e., $\ell_{max} \ll 1$), $\sigma \cong \pi \lambdabar^2$, which can be significantly larger than the classical cross section.

8.4 Partial-Wave Analysis on Elastic Neutron Scattering Cross Sections

Because the nuclear potential can either scatter or absorb the incident neutron, in analogy to equation 3.138, the total wave function of the interaction system can be expressed as

$$\varphi_t = \varphi_{in} + \varphi_{sc} = \sum_{\ell=0}^{\infty} \frac{(2\ell+1)}{2ikr} \left[\eta_\ell e^{ikr} - (-1)^\ell e^{-ikr} \right] p_\ell(\cos\theta), \tag{8.12}$$

where η_ℓ are general complex numbers that allow the outgoing waves to be modified by either elastic scattering or non-elastic scattering. Comparison of equations 8.12 and 3.135 yields

$$f(\theta) = \sum_{\ell=0}^{\infty} \frac{(2\ell+1)}{2ik} (\eta_\ell - 1) p_\ell(\cos\theta). \tag{8.13}$$

From equation 3.96, the differential scattering cross section can be obtained as

$$\frac{d\sigma_s}{d\Omega} = |f(\theta)|^2 = \left| \sum_{\ell=0}^{\infty} \frac{(2\ell+1)}{2ik} (\eta_\ell - 1) p_\ell(\cos\theta) \right|^2. \tag{8.14}$$

By using the orthogonality property

$$\int_{4\pi} p_\ell(\cos\theta) p_{\ell'}(\cos\theta)\, d\Omega = \frac{4\pi}{2\ell+1} \quad \text{for } \ell = \ell'$$

$$= 0 \qquad \text{for } \ell \neq \ell', \tag{8.15}$$

the total scattering cross section can then be obtained as

$$\sigma_s = \frac{\pi}{k^2} \sum_{\ell=0}^{\infty} (2\ell+1)|1 - \eta_\ell|^2 = \pi\lambda^2 \sum_{\ell=0}^{\infty} (2\ell+1)|1 - \eta_\ell|^2. \tag{8.16}$$

If we define

$$\sigma_{s,\ell} = \pi\lambda^2 (2\ell+1)|1 - \eta_\ell|^2, \tag{8.17}$$

then equation 8.16 can be rewritten as

$$\sigma_s = \sum_{\ell=0}^{\infty} \sigma_{s,\ell}. \tag{8.18}$$

Equation 8.14 shows that the different partial waves interfere with one another in producing the differential cross section, and it explains what was shown in Figures 8.6 and 8.7. Equation 8.18, however, shows that the contributions of the partial waves to the integral scattering cross section are simply added.

If elastic scattering is the only type of interaction that could occur, then the amplitude of the outgoing waves stays unchanged and the only change is the phase. Mathematically, this means $|\eta_\ell| = 1$. By comparing equation 8.12 with 3.138, one obtains

$$\eta_\ell = e^{2i\delta_\ell} , \tag{8.19}$$

where δ_ℓ is the phase shift of the ℓth partial wave. The problem of finding $d\sigma_s/d\Omega$ and σ_s is therefore reduced to one of finding δ_ℓ. As pointed out in Section 3.11.2, the phase shifts δ_ℓ can be obtained by solving the Schrödinger equation with the known $V(r)$. In the simplest case, where the total scattering is dominated by the s-wave ($\ell = 0$), equation 3.145 gives

$$\frac{d\sigma_s(\theta)}{d\Omega} = \frac{1}{k^2}\left[e^{-i\delta_0}\sin\delta_0 P_0(\cos\theta)\right]\left[e^{i\delta_0}\sin\delta_0 P_0(\cos\theta)\right] = \lambda^2 \sin^2\delta_0 . \tag{8.20}$$

Since δ_0 is a constant, equation 8.14 shows that an s-wave–dominated scattering is isotropic. Since the condition for an interaction to be s-wave dominated is $R/\lambda < 1$, where R and λ can be estimated as $R \cong 1.2(A^{1/3}+1)$ fm, and

$$\lambda = \frac{\hbar}{\sqrt{2\mu E_c}} \cong \frac{\hbar}{\sqrt{2\left(\frac{A}{A+1}\right)m_n\left(\frac{A}{A+1}\right)E_n}} = \frac{\hbar c}{\left(\frac{A}{A+1}\right)\sqrt{2m_n c^2 E_n}} = \frac{197.329 \text{ MeV}\cdot\text{fm}}{\left(\frac{A}{A+1}\right)\sqrt{2(939.573\text{ MeV})E_n}},$$

the neutron energy thresholds below which the condition of s-wave dominance is satisfied can then be obtained as follows: For $A = 1$, $E_n < 13.3$ MeV. For $A = 50$, $E_n < 0.63$ MeV. For $A = 200$, $E_n < 0.29$ MeV. The above calculation more or less confirms the plot of $d\sigma_s/d\Omega$ versus θ shown in Figures 8.6 and 8.7. Integration of equation 8.20 over the entire solid angle, 4π, yields

$$\sigma_s = 4\pi\lambda^2 \sin^2\delta_0 . \tag{8.21}$$

To illustrate how δ_0 can be calculated, we use the simple square-well potential as the nuclear potential. That is,

$$\begin{aligned} V(r) &= -V_0, \ r \leq R \\ &= 0, \ r > R, \end{aligned} \tag{8.22}$$

where R is the radius of the nuclear potential. The radial part of the Schrödinger equation for $\ell = 0$ can be deduced from equation 3.80 to be

$$-\frac{\hbar^2}{2\mu}\left(\frac{d^2\varphi}{dr^2} + \frac{2}{r}\frac{d\varphi}{dr}\right) + \left[V(r) - E\right]\varphi = 0, \tag{8.23}$$

where μ is the reduced mass of the neutron. If we define $u = \varphi/r$, then equation 8.23 can be rewritten as

$$\frac{d^2u}{dr^2} + \frac{2\mu}{\hbar^2}\left[E - V(r)\right]u = 0. \tag{8.24}$$

For $r \leq R$, we have $V(r) = -V_0$, and the general solution of equation 8.24 is

$$u(r) = A\sin k_0 r + B\cos k_0 r,$$

where $k_0 = \sqrt{2\mu(E + V_0)}/\hbar$ and A and B are constants. Because u needs to be zero at $r = 0$, B must be zero. Thus,

$$u(r) = A\sin k_0 r. \tag{8.25}$$

For $r > R$ we have $V(r) = 0$, and the general solution of equation 8.24 is

$$u(r) = C\sin kr + D\cos kr$$

or $\quad u(r) = F\sin(kr + \delta_0), \tag{8.26}$

where $k = \sqrt{2\mu E}/\hbar$. From the conditions of continuity for u and du/dr at $r = R$, one obtains

$$A\sin k_0 R = F\sin(kR + \delta_0)$$

and

$$Ak_0\cos k_0 R = Fk\cos(kR + \delta_0).$$

Division of the above two equations yields

$$\frac{k}{k_0}\tan k_0 R = \tan(kR + \delta_0) \quad \Rightarrow \quad \delta_0 = \tan^{-1}\left(\frac{k}{k_0}\tan kR\right) - kR. \tag{8.27}$$

By knowing δ_0, one may then proceed to calculate $d\sigma_s/d\Omega$ and σ_s. For an s-wave–dominated scattering, $E \ll V_0$, $kR \ll 1$, $k/k_0 \ll 1$. If one further assumes that $\tan k_0 R \ll k/k_0$ (which is quite true except for $k_0 R = \dfrac{\pi}{2}, \dfrac{3\pi}{2}, \dfrac{5\pi}{2}, \dots$ where $\tan k_0 R \to \infty$), then

$$\delta_0 \xrightarrow{\;E \ll V_0\;} \frac{k}{k_0}\tan k_0 R - kR = ka\left(\frac{\tan k_0 R}{k_0 R} - 1\right). \tag{8.28}$$

Equation 8.21 then becomes

$$\sigma_s \xrightarrow{\;E \ll V_0\;} 4\pi\lambda^2\sin^2\delta_0 \cong 4\pi\lambda^2\delta_0^2 = 4\pi a^2\left(\frac{\tan k_0 R}{k_0 R} - 1\right)^2. \tag{8.29}$$

Typically, $k_0 R \approx 2 - 10$. In the case that $k_0 R = \dfrac{\pi}{2}, \dfrac{3\pi}{2}, \dfrac{5\pi}{2}, \dots$ where $\tan k_0 R \to \infty$, it can be shown that equation 8.28 becomes $\delta_0 \cong k_0 R$, and therefore, from equation 8.21,

$$\sigma_s = 4\pi\lambda^2\sin^2\delta_0 \cong 4\pi\lambda^2\sin^2 k_0 R = 4\pi\lambda^2. \tag{8.30}$$

This value can be much larger than πR^2, the projected geometrical cross-section area. The above method of obtaining δ_0 can also be applied to obtain any other phase shift δ_ℓ. The calculation of δ_ℓ, however, becomes quite cumbersome when $kR \gg 1$, where too many partial waves (and therefore the corresponding δ_ℓ) must be analyzed. In those cases, it is easier to use the Born Approximation method, which is often of sufficient accuracy.

8.5 Partial-Wave Analysis on Non-Elastic Neutron Interaction Cross Sections

We now move to examine the non-elastic neutron interaction cross section, σ_{ne}, which by definition can be expressed as

$$d\sigma_{ne} = \left(\frac{J_{in} - J_{sc}}{J_{in}}\right) dA,$$ (8.31)

and

$$\sigma_{ne} = \frac{1}{J_{in}} \int (J_{in} - J_{sc}) \, dA.$$ (8.32)

By applying equation 3.28 and substituting φ with the total wave function given in equation 8.12 and carrying out the integration, 8.32 becomes

$$\sigma_{ne} = \frac{1}{J_{in}} \int (J_{in} - J_{sc}) \, dA = \frac{1}{J_{in}} \int_{4\pi} \frac{i\hbar}{2\mu}\left(\varphi^* \frac{d\varphi}{dr} - \varphi \frac{d\varphi^*}{dr}\right) r^2 d\Omega = \frac{\pi\hbar}{J_{in}\mu k} \sum_{\ell=0}^{\infty} (2\ell+1)\left(1 - |\eta_\ell|^2\right).$$ (8.33)

Since $J_{in} = \dfrac{\hbar k}{\mu}$ (see equation 3.112), equation 8.33 can be reduced to

$$\sigma_{ne} = \frac{\pi}{k^2} \sum_{\ell=0}^{\infty} (2\ell+1)\left(1 - |\eta_\ell|^2\right) = \pi\lambda^2 \sum_{\ell=0}^{\infty} (2\ell+1)\left(1 - |\eta_\ell|^2\right).$$ (8.34)

If we define

$$\sigma_{ne,\ell} = \pi\lambda^2 (2\ell+1)\left(1 - |\eta_\ell|^2\right),$$ (8.35)

then equation 8.34 can be rewritten as

$$\sigma_{ne} = \sum_{\ell=0}^{\infty} \sigma_{ne,\ell}.$$ (8.36)

From Equations 8.2, 8.16, and 8.34, we can then express the total cross section as

$$\sigma_t = \sigma_s + \sigma_{ne} = \pi\lambda^2 \sum_{\ell=0}^{\infty}(2\ell+1)\left(\left|1-\eta_\ell\right|^2 + 1 - \left|\eta_\ell\right|^2\right) = 2\pi\lambda^2 \sum_{\ell=0}^{\infty}(2\ell+1)(1 - \text{Re}\,\eta_\ell).$$

(8.37)

We can now make a few observations of the above results:

(a) The maximum possible value of $\sigma_{s,\ell}$ occurs when $\eta_\ell = -1$, and it is given as

$$\left(\sigma_{s,\ell}\right)_{\max} = 4\pi\lambda^2(2\ell+1).$$

(b) Since $\left|\eta_\ell\right|^2 \geq 0$, the maximum value of $\sigma_{ne,\ell}$ occurs when $\eta_\ell = 0$, and it is given as

$$\left(\sigma_{ne,\ell}\right)_{\max} = \pi\lambda^2(2\ell+1).$$

(c) Since $\sigma_{ne,\ell}$ cannot be negative, this means $\left|\eta_\ell\right|^2 \leq 1$.

(d) $\sigma_{s,\ell}$ is at its maximum value when $\eta_\ell = -1$, at which $\sigma_{ne,\ell} = 0$. Oppositely, $\sigma_{ne,\ell}$ is at its maximum value when $\eta_\ell = 0$, at which $\sigma_{s,\ell} = \left(\sigma_{ne,\ell}\right)_{\max} = \pi\lambda^2(2\ell+1)$, and the total cross section can be obtained from equation 8.10 as

$$\sigma_t = \sigma_s + \sigma_{ne} = \sum_{\ell=0}^{\ell_{\max}}\sigma_{s,\ell} + \sum_{\ell=0}^{\ell_{\max}}\sigma_{ne,\ell} = 2\pi\lambda^2 \sum_{\ell=0}^{\ell_{\max}}(2\ell+1) = 2\pi\lambda^2(\ell_{\max}+1)^2$$

$$\cong 2\pi\lambda^2\left[\left(\frac{R}{\lambda}\right)^2 + 2\frac{R}{\lambda} + 1\right] = 2\pi(R^2 + 2\lambda R + \lambda^2) = 2\pi(R+\lambda)^2.$$

(8.38)

(e) $\sigma_{s,\ell}$ is zero only when $\eta_\ell = +1$. In this case, $\sigma_{ne,\ell}$ is also zero. There is no case in which non-elastic reactions occur without elastic scattering.

In the case of $R \gg \lambda$, equation 8.38 shows that $\sigma_t \cong 2\pi R^2$, which is twice the classical value. This non-classical effect is a result of wave mechanics and is analogous to the absorption of light by a pure absorbing object where the diffraction of light appears at finite angles away from the direction of the incident beam.

8.6   Resonance Cross Sections via Compound Nucleus Formation

The characteristics of resonance cross sections can be understood by applying Fermi's Golden Rule (equation 3.110) to the compound nucleus formation model. That is, the probability of the incident neutron joining the target nucleus to form the compound nucleus is high only if there exists an excited state (of the compound nucleus) of which its energy and nuclear spin are both matched via the incorporation of the incident neutron. A single isolated resonance corresponds to the formation of an excited compound nucleus of which its energy level follows a Gaussian distribution centered around E_R with a width Γ. Accordingly, the neutron cross section near an isolated resonance can be expressed by

$$\sigma(E) = \frac{C}{(E - E_R)^2 + \Gamma^2/4},$$ (8.39)

where C is a constant. Figure 8.8 is the plot of equation 8.39, and it shows that $\sigma(E) = \sigma_{max}$ when $E = E_R$, and that $\sigma(E) = \sigma_{max}/2$ when $E = E_R \pm \Gamma/2$.

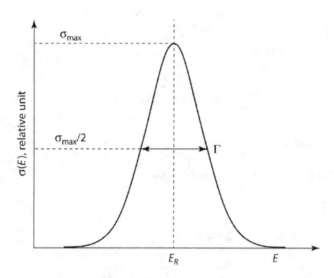

Figure 8.8. The neutron cross section as a function of energy near an isolated resonance.

Because the wave functions inside and outside the nucleus potential well must be matched smoothly, and because the degree of smooth matching is dependent on the phase shift δ_ℓ, the most relevant parameter to a resonance is δ_ℓ. A smooth matching of the wave functions at the nuclear boundary can result in significant variations between the relative amplitudes of the wave functions inside and outside the nucleus. A resonance occurs when the two amplitudes are identical, meaning the incident particle totally penetrates the nucleus.

From equations 8.17 and 8.34, a pure scattering resonance occurs when $\eta_\ell = -1$, because $\sigma_{ne} = 0$. According to equation 8.19, this corresponds to a phase shift $\delta_\ell = \pi/2$. As such, the shape of the resonance can be determined by carrying out the Taylor series expansion of δ_ℓ about $\pi/2$. Because $\cot \delta_\ell$ shows how fast the slope $d\delta_\ell/dE$ varies with E about E_R, it is even better if one carries out the Taylor series expansion with reference to $\cot \delta_\ell$. That is,

$$\cot\delta_\ell(E) = \cot\delta_\ell(E_R) + (E - E_R)\left(\frac{\partial\cot\delta_\ell}{\partial E}\right)_{E=E_R} + \frac{1}{2}(E - E_R)^2\left(\frac{\partial^2\cot\delta_\ell}{\partial E^2}\right)_{E=E_R} + \dots$$

$$(8.40)$$

where

$$\left(\frac{\partial\cot\delta_\ell}{\partial E}\right)_{E=E_R} = \left(\frac{\partial\cot\delta_\ell}{\partial\delta_\ell}\right)_{\delta_\ell=\pi/2}\left(\frac{\partial\delta_\ell}{\partial E}\right)_{E=E_R} = -\frac{1}{\sin^2(\pi/2)}\left(\frac{\partial\delta_\ell}{\partial E}\right)_{E=E_R} = -\left(\frac{\partial\delta_\ell}{\partial E}\right)_{E=E_R}.$$

If one ignores the second- and higher-order terms, equation 8.40 becomes

$$\cot\delta_\ell(E) \cong \cot\delta_\ell(E_R) - (E - E_R)\left(\frac{\partial\delta_\ell}{\partial E}\right)_{E=E_R} = \cot(\pi/2) - (E - E_R)\left(\frac{\partial\delta_\ell}{\partial E}\right)_{E=E_R}$$

$$= -(E - E_R)\left(\frac{\partial\delta_\ell}{\partial E}\right)_{E=E_R}.$$

$$(8.41)$$

Since equations 8.17 and 8.19 together show that $\sigma_{s,\ell} \propto \sin^2\delta_\ell$, which has a maximum value of 1.0 at $\delta_\ell = \pi/2$ (i.e., the resonance) and 0.5 at $\delta_\ell = \pi/4$ and $3\pi/4$, the resonance width Γ should correspond to δ_ℓ between $\pi/4$ and $3\pi/4$. Substitution of $\delta_\ell = \pi/4$ and $3\pi/4$ into equation 8.41 gives $E - E_R = -\left(\frac{\partial\delta_\ell}{\partial E}\right)^{-1}_{E=E_R}$ and $E - E_R = \left(\frac{\partial\delta_\ell}{\partial E}\right)^{-1}_{E=E_R}$, respectively. One may therefore conclude that

$$\Gamma = 2(E - E_R) = 2\left(\frac{\partial\delta_\ell}{\partial E}\right)^{-1}_{E=E_R}.$$

$$(8.42)$$

Equation 8.41 can then be rewritten as

$$\cot\delta_\ell(E) \cong -\frac{(E - E_R)}{\Gamma/2}.$$

$$(8.43)$$

It follows that

$$\cot^2\delta_\ell(E) \cong \frac{(E - E_R)^2}{(\Gamma/2)^2} = \frac{1 - \sin^2\delta_\ell}{\sin^2\delta_\ell} \quad \Rightarrow \quad \sin^2\delta_\ell = \frac{(\Gamma/2)^2}{(E - E_R)^2 + (\Gamma/2)^2}.$$

$$(8.44)$$

Accordingly, from equations 8.17, 8.19, and 8.44,

$$\sigma_{s,\ell} = 4\pi\lambda^2(2\ell + 1)\sin^2\delta_\ell = \pi\lambda^2(2\ell + 1)\frac{\Gamma^2}{(E - E_R)^2 + (\Gamma^2/4)}.$$

$$(8.45)$$

One may further generalize equation 8.45 in two ways:

(1) If one accounts for the effect of the spin carried by the incident neutron, the total angular momentum of the compound nucleus is expressed as

$$\vec{J} = \vec{s}_n + \vec{I} + \vec{\ell}, \tag{8.46}$$

where $\vec{s}_n, \vec{I}$, and $\vec{\ell}$ are, respectively, the spin of the incident neutron, the angular momentum of the target nucleus, and the orbital angular momentum carried by the incident neutron. There are $2s + 1, 2I + 1$, and $2\ell + 1$ equally probable orientations of the vectors $\vec{s}_n, \vec{I}$, and $\vec{\ell}$. Thus, there are a total of $(2s + 1)(2I + 1)(2\ell + 1)$ possible ways of making up $\vec{J}$. Since there are $2J + 1$ equally probable orientations of the vector $\vec{J}$, the probability of having the correct angular momentum of the compound nucleus would be

$$\frac{2J + 1}{(2s + 1)(2I + 1)(2\ell + 1)}. \tag{8.47}$$

Multiplying equation 8.45 with 8.47 yields

$$\sigma_{s,\ell} = \pi \lambdabar^2 g \frac{\Gamma^2}{(E - E_R)^2 + (\Gamma^2 / 4)}, \tag{8.48}$$

where $g = \dfrac{2J + 1}{(2s + 1)(2I + 1)}$, and it is referred to as the "statistical factor."

(2) If we let $\Gamma = \Delta E \cong \dfrac{\hbar}{\Delta t} = \hbar \lambda$, then the factor Γ^2 in the denominator of equation 8.48 can be generalized as being related to the lifetime (an analogy to radioactive decay) of the resonant state of the compound nucleus. Thus, Γ can be more specifically expressed as

$$\Gamma = \sum_j \Gamma_j, \tag{8.49}$$

where j represents the various decay channels, including elastic, inelastic, gamma, fission, and so on. The factor Γ^2 in the numerator of equation 8.48, on the other hand, can be expressed as the product of the probability of the formation of the resonant state (of the compound nucleus), and the probability for the compound nucleus to undergo a specific decay channel j. Therefore, equation 8.48 can be generalized for a non-elastic interaction type j as

$$\sigma_{j,\ell} = \pi \lambdabar^2 g \frac{\Gamma_n \Gamma_j}{(E - E_R)^2 + (\Gamma^2 / 4)}. \tag{8.50}$$

In the case that interactions are dominated by elastic scattering, equation 8.48 is reduced to

$$\sigma_{s,\ell} = \pi \lambdabar^2 g \frac{\Gamma_n^2}{(E - E_R)^2 + (\Gamma^2/4)}.$$ (8.51)

Equations 8.50 and 8.51 are referred to as the Breit-Wigner formula for the shape of a single, isolated resonance.

It is convenient to describe three experimentally observed rules of thumb for neutron resonance interactions:

(1) Three reaction types: neutron capture - (n, γ), compound elastic - (n, n'), and compound inelastic - $(n, n'\gamma)$, are widely found for resonance interactions for nuclei with relatively large mass numbers ($A \geq 20$).

(2) (n, n') is the only reaction type found for resonance reactions for nuclei with small mass numbers ($A < 20$).

(3) The resonance being dominated by an (n, γ) reaction typically has a width less than a few eV. The resonance being dominated by an (n, n') reaction typically has a much broader width of a few keV to a few tens of keV.

The above rules can be illustrated via the following two examples of nuclides ^{56}Fe and ^{12}C.

In the case of ^{12}C, the first resonance occurs at 2.078 MeV with $\Gamma \approx 6$ keV (from the zoomed-in version of Figure 8.2). The corresponding energy level (above the ground) of the excited state of ^{13}C can be calculated as

$$\left(\frac{A}{A+1}\right)E_n + \Delta Mc^2 = \left(\frac{12}{13}\right)(2.078 \text{ MeV}) + (0 + 8.071 - 3.125) \text{ MeV}$$

$$= 1.918 \text{ MeV} + 4.946 \text{ MeV} = 6.864 \text{ MeV}.$$

The above excited state at 6.864 MeV for ^{13}C can be confirmed via the Nuclear Structure and Decay Data (NuDat) link available at the National Nuclear Data Center website: www.nndc.bnl.gov. The NuDat shows that the nuclear spin for this state is $5/2^+$. Because the nuclear spins for the ground-state ^{12}C and the free incident neutron are, respectively, 0^+ and $1/2^+$, the only possible way for ^{13}C to gain a nuclear spin of $5/2^+$ is when the incident neutron brings in an orbital angular momentum of $\ell = 2$. As such, according to the partial-wave interpretation (equation 8.18), one may conclude that this resonance reaction is dominated by the d-wave neutron. In addition, the NuDat shows that (n, n') is the sole reaction type for this resonance reaction. The reaction cannot possibly be (n, γ) because a resonance width of $6\,\text{keV}$ corresponds to a mean lifetime of

$$t_m \approx \frac{\hbar}{\Gamma} = \frac{6.58217 \times 10^{-16}\,\text{eV} \cdot \text{sec}}{6\,\text{keV}} = 1.097 \times 10^{-19}\,\text{sec},$$

which is much shorter than the value estimated from equation 6.41 for the allowable gamma transition $M2$. That is,

$$\lambda(M2) \approx 2.2 \times 10^7 (13)^{2/3} (6.864)^5 \approx 1.85 \times 10^{12}\,\text{sec}^{-1} \Rightarrow t_m = \frac{1}{\lambda} \approx 5.4 \times 10^{-13}\,\text{sec}.$$

It is not possible to be $(n, n'\gamma)$ either because, according to NuDat, the first excited state of ^{12}C is 4.439 MeV (above the ground), which is higher than the 6.864 MeV state of ^{13}C (see illustration from Figure 8.9). As such, the best option is the compound elastic scattering (n, n') . Another way to argue for the (n, n') reaction is that, because there are so few nucleons in a ^{13}C nucleus, statistically it is likely for a neutron in a small nucleus ($A < 20$) to acquire enough energy to escape the compound nucleus. This option is less likely in a large nucleus ($A \geq 20$), because if (n, n') or $(n, n'\gamma)$ does not occur fast enough ($\approx 10^{-18}$ sec), most likely (n, γ) will take place. This can be shown in the example of ^{56}Fe below.

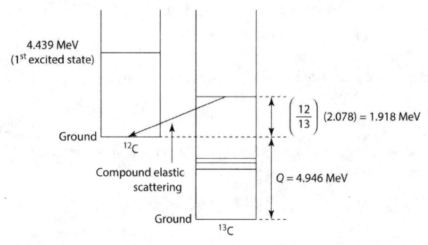

Figure 8.9. The energy levels of ^{12}C and ^{13}C that are essential to argue for the (n, n') reaction.

In the case of ^{56}Fe, the first resonance for σ_{ne} occurs at 1.1515 keV with $\Gamma \approx 4$ eV (from the zoomed-in version of Figure 8.3). The corresponding energy level (above the ground) of the excited compound state of ^{57}Fe can be calculated as

$$\left(\frac{A}{A+1}\right) E_n + \Delta Mc^2 = \left(\frac{56}{57}\right)(1.1515 \times 10^{-3}\,\text{MeV}) + (-60.606 + 8.071 + 60.181)\,\text{MeV}$$

$$= 1.1213 \times 10^{-3}\,\text{MeV} + 7.646\,\text{MeV} = 7.647\,\text{MeV}.$$

The existence of the excited state at 7.647 MeV for ^{57}Fe can also be confirmed via NuDat. The corresponding nuclear spin for this state is found to be $1/2^-$. Since the nuclear spins for the ground-state ^{56}Fe and the free incident neutron are, respectively, 0^+ and $1/2^+$, the only possible way for the ^{57}Fe to have the nuclear spin of $1/2^-$ is when the incident neutron brings in an orbital angular momentum of $\ell = 1$. As such, according to the partial-wave interpretation (equation 8.18), one may conclude that this resonance reaction is dominated by the p-wave neutron. In addition, the NuDat shows that (n, γ) is the sole reaction type for this resonance reaction, and that the gamma decays are dominated by $M1$ and $E2$ transitions to the lower state (14.4129 keV, $3/2^-$). This is consistent with the gamma-decay theory of Chapter 6 for a resonance width of $4\,\text{eV}$, because the corresponding mean lifetime can be calculated as

$$t_m \approx \frac{\hbar}{\Gamma} = \frac{6.58217 \times 10^{-16}\,\text{eV} \cdot \text{sec}}{4\,\text{eV}} = 1.6455 \times 10^{-16}\,\text{sec},$$

which falls right between the values obtained using equation 6.41 for $M1$ and $E2$ transitions to the lower state of (14.4129 keV, $3/2^-$) with $E_\gamma = 7.6467 - 0.0144 = 7.6323\,\text{MeV}$. That is,

$$\lambda(M1) \approx 3.1 \times 10^{13}(7.63)^3 \approx 1.4 \times 10^{16}\,\text{sec}^{-1} \Rightarrow t_m = \frac{1}{\lambda} = 7.1 \times 10^{-17}\,\text{sec}, \text{ and}$$

$$\lambda(E2) \approx 7.3 \times 10^7 (57)^{4/3}(7.63)^5 \approx 4.14 \times 10^{14}\,\text{sec}^{-1} \Rightarrow t_m = \frac{1}{\lambda} = 2.4 \times 10^{-15}\,\text{sec}.$$

8.6.1 Asymmetry in the Vicinity of a Resonance

To examine the asymmetry behavior of σ_s in the vicinity of a resonance (Figure 8.5), we rewrite equations 8.12, 8.17, and 8.35 for the s-wave dominated case ($\ell = 0$)(Buttlar, 1968):

$$\varphi_o = \frac{1}{2ikr}(\eta_o e^{ikr} + e^{-ikr}) \tag{8.52}$$

$$\sigma_{s,o} = \pi \lambda^2 |1 - \eta_o|^2 \tag{8.53}$$

$$\sigma_{ne,o} = \pi \lambda^2 \left(1 - |\eta_o|^2\right). \tag{8.54}$$

Equation 8.52 is the wave function external to the nucleus (i.e., for $r \geq R$). To obtain η_o, we refer back to equation 8.24 and take the simple case of a square-well potential described by equation 8.22. We again apply the conditions of continuity for u and du/dr at $r = R$:

$$u_i = u_o \text{ and } \frac{du_i}{dr} = \frac{du_o}{dr} \text{ at } r = R. \tag{8.55}$$

To assist the derivation of η_o, we define a dimensionless quantity, f:

$$f = \lim_{r \to R}\left(\frac{R}{u}\frac{du}{dr}\right). \tag{8.56}$$

Inserting $u_o = r\varphi_o = \frac{1}{2ik}(\eta_o e^{ikr} + e^{-ikr})$ into equation 8.56 yields

$$f = ikR\left(\frac{\eta_o e^{ikr} + e^{-ikr}}{\eta_o e^{ikr} - e^{-ikr}}\right), \tag{8.57}$$

which leads to

$$\eta_o = \left(\frac{f + ikR}{f - ikR}\right)e^{-2ikR}. \tag{8.58}$$

The problem of finding η_o is therefore reduced to the determination of f in terms of the properties of the wave function inside the potential well ($r < R$).

Since f in general is a complex number, it can be expressed with the following form:

$$f = kR(g + ih), \tag{8.59}$$

where g and h are real numbers. It follows that

$$\begin{aligned}
|1 - \eta_o|^2 &= \left|1 - \left(\frac{f + ikR}{f - ikR}\right)e^{-2ikR}\right| = \left|\frac{f(1 - e^{-2ikR}) - ikR(1 + e^{-2ikR})}{f - ikR}\right| \\
&= \left|\left(\frac{2if\sin kR - 2ikR\cos kR}{f - ikR}\right)e^{-2ikR}\right| = 4\left|\frac{(g + ih)\sin kR - \cos kR}{g + i(h - 1)}\right| \\
&= 4\left[\sin^2 kR + 2\sin kR\left(\frac{(h - 1)\sin kR + g\cos kR}{g^2 + (h - 1)^2}\right) + \frac{1}{g^2 + (h - 1)^2}\right],
\end{aligned} \tag{8.60}$$

and that

$$1 - |\eta_o|^2 = 1 - \left(\frac{g^2 + (h + 1)^2}{g^2 + (h - 1)^2}\right) = \frac{-4h}{g^2 + (h - 1)^2}. \tag{8.61}$$

From equations 8.53 and 8.54, the cross sections become

$$\sigma_{s,o} = 4\pi\lambdabar^2\left[\sin^2 kR + 2\sin kR\left(\frac{(h - 1)\sin kR + g\cos kR}{g^2 + (h - 1)^2}\right) + \frac{1}{g^2 + (h - 1)^2}\right] \tag{8.62}$$

and

$$\sigma_{ne,o} = 4\pi\lambdabar^2\left[\frac{-h}{g^2 + (h - 1)^2}\right]. \tag{8.63}$$

Equation 8.61 shows that h must be negative or $\sigma_{ne,o}$ becomes negative (which is nonphysical), and that $h = 0$ (or f is real) means $\sigma_{ne,o} = 0$. In other words, if $\sigma_{ne,o} \neq 0$, then f must be complex. Equation 8.62 can be used to explain the asymmetric resonances of σ_s mentioned in Section 8.2 and Figure 8.5. The first term on the right-hand side of equation 8.62 is simply the potential scattering cross section, σ_{ps} (see equations 8.21 and 8.30). Equations 8.62 and 8.63 both show that resonance takes place when $g^2 + (h-1)^2$ is minimized. This condition can be further examined below:

$$g^2 + (h-1)^2 = g^2 + h^2 + 1 - 2h = \frac{|f|^2}{(kR)^2} + 1 - 2h .$$

(8.64)

Equation 8.64 is minimized when $f = 0$ (or $g = h = 0$). This leads to $\left[g^2 + (h-1)^2\right]_{min} = 1$. Accordingly, the third term of equation 8.62 is reduced to $4\pi\lambdabar^2$, which corresponds to the compound elastic scattering cross section, σ_{cs}, and agrees with that of equation 8.30. The second term of equation 8.62 is reduced to $4\pi\lambdabar^2(-2\sin^2 kR)$, which causes a significant decrease in σ_s in the vicinity of the resonance and is responsible for its asymmetric shape.

The above finding is also consistent with equation 8.56, in that $f = 0$ corresponds to $\frac{du}{dr} = 0$ at $r = R$, meaning the two wave functions inside and outside the nucleus match perfectly at the nuclear boundary. In other words, resonance occurs when $f = 0$ at which the incident wave completely penetrates the nucleus. Oppositely, $f = \infty$ corresponds to $u = 0$ at $r = R$, meaning the incident wave cannot penetrate the nucleus at all, and therefore only potential scattering (i.e., the first term on the right-hand side of equation 8.60) contributes to the total cross section.

For low-energy neutrons of which $kR \ll 1$, and for the cases when $|g|$ and $|h|$ are sufficiently large (i.e., neutron energy is not in the vicinity of a resonance), the last two terms of equation 8.62 are negligible. The scattering cross section is therefore reduced to

$$\sigma_{s,o} = 4\pi\lambdabar^2 \sin^2 kR \cong 4\pi\lambdabar^2 k^2 R^2 = 4\pi R^2 ,$$

(8.65)

which is four times the geometrical cross section of the target nucleus.

8.6.2 The $1/v$ Behavior of σ_{ne}

To explain the $1/v$ behavior of σ_{ne} shown in Figures 8.2 to 8.4, we need to examine f from the wave function inside the compound nucleus. From the compound nucleus formation model, the incident neutron instantly exchanges energy with the nucleons, and therefore is lost from the entrance channel. Thus, the wave function inside the nucleus is an inward wave only, and it can be written as

$$u_i = Ce^{-iKr},$$ (8.66)

where C is a complex number, and K depends on the nuclear potential; for a simple square well with depth V_0, $K = \dfrac{\sqrt{2\mu(V_0 + E)}}{\hbar} \cong 1.6$ fm^{-1} for $V_0 = 50$ MeV. Then, from equation 8.56 we have

$$f = \lim_{r \to R}\left(\frac{R}{u_i}\frac{du_i}{dr}\right) = -iKR.$$ (8.67)

Substituting equation 8.67 into 8.58 yields

$$\eta_0 = \left(\frac{K-k}{K+k}\right)e^{-2ikR}.$$ (8.68)

Substituting equation 8.68 into 8.54 finally gives

$$\sigma_{ne,0} = 4\pi\lambdabar^2\frac{kK}{(k+K)^2} = 4\pi\frac{K}{k(k+K)^2} \cong \frac{4\pi}{kK}.$$ (8.69)

Since $k \propto \sqrt{E}$ and $K \cong$ const., equation 8.69 shows that $\sigma_{ne,0} \propto 1/\sqrt{E}$, or the "$1/v$" law. As an example, for a thermal neutron with kinetic energy of 0.025 eV,

$$k = \frac{\sqrt{2\mu E}}{\hbar} = \frac{\sqrt{2\mu c^2 E}}{\hbar c} \cong \frac{\sqrt{2(939.573\,\text{MeV})(2.5\times10^{-8}\,\text{MeV})}}{197.329\,\text{MeV}\cdot\text{fm}} = 3.473\times10^{-5}\,\text{fm}^{-1},\text{ and}$$

$$K = \frac{\sqrt{2\mu(V_0 + E)}}{\hbar} = \frac{\sqrt{2\mu c^2(V_0 + E)}}{\hbar c} \cong \frac{\sqrt{2(939.573\,\text{MeV})(50\,\text{MeV})}}{197.329\,\text{MeV}\cdot\text{fm}} = 1.553\,\text{fm}^{-1}.$$

Equation 8.69 then gives

$$\sigma_{ne,0} \cong \frac{4\pi}{kK} = \frac{4\pi\,(\text{fm})^2}{(3,473\times10^{-5})(1.553)} \cong 2.33\times10^{-21}\,\text{cm}^2 = 2.33\times10^3\,\text{barns}.$$

The "$1/v$" law is followed nicely for reactions well below the resonance region. While (n, γ) is the primary reaction that follows the "$1/v$" law, other reactions that also follow the "$1/v$" law include (n, p), (n, α), and (n, fission). Figures 8.10 and 8.11 show the $1/v$ behavior of neutron cross sections for two well-known reactions: ^{235}U(n, fission) and ^{10}B(n, α)^{7}Li, respectively. The symbol σ_{ne} shown in these two figures mainly refers to the neutron cross section for reactions ^{235}U(n, fission) and ^{10}B(n, α)^{7}Li, respectively. For ^{235}U(n, fission), the combination of a large cross section for low-energy neutrons and the large Q-value (~200 MeV) makes ^{235}U an excellent fuel material for nuclear reactors. The large cross section for the ^{10}B(n, α)^{7}Li reaction for low-energy neutrons makes ^{10}B an excellent neutron absorber, used in controlling neutron chain reactions in nuclear reactors.

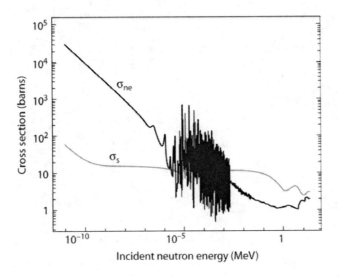

Figure 8.10. The neutron cross sections, σ_s and σ_{ne}, versus neutron energy for ^{235}U (obtained from ENDF/B-VII).

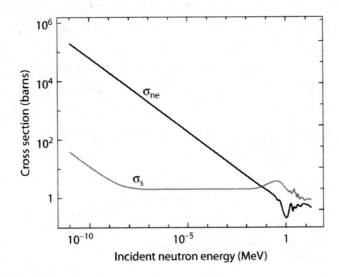

Figure 8.11. The neutron cross sections, σ_s and σ_{ne}, versus neutron energy for ^{10}B (obtained from ENDF/B-VII).

8.6.3 The Doppler Effect of (n,γ) Resonance Broadening

As mentioned earlier, the resonances corresponding to (n,γ) reactions usually have narrow widths of $\Gamma < 1.0$ eV. Figure 8.12 is a zoomed-in version of Figure 8.4 for the three lowest energy (n,γ) resonances located at 6.67 eV, 20.9 eV, and 36.7 eV. A closer examination shows that the corresponding widths of the resonances are approximately 0.1 eV, 0.19 eV, and 0.25 eV, respectively.

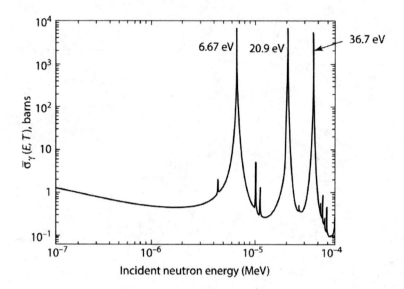

Figure 8.12. A zoomed-in version of Figure 8.4 for the three low-energy (n,γ) resonances located at 6.67 eV, 20.9 eV, and 36.7 eV (obtained from ENDF/B-VII).

Because these resonance cross sections are based on the relative speed between the incident neutron and the target nucleus, and because the target nuclei are in constant motion due to their thermal energy, the actual (n,γ) reaction rate over a resonance will deviate somewhat from that based on Figure 8.4. In other words, the uncertainty of the relative speed due to thermal motion of the target nuclei appears to broaden the width of each resonance. This resonance broadening is referred to as the Doppler Effect, and it has significant impact on the resonance escape probability as neutrons slow down in a nuclear reactor. To quantitatively evaluate this effect, we denote the velocity of the incident neutron as $\vec{v}$ and that of the target nucleus as $\vec{V}$. The relative velocity and neutron energy can then be, respectively, expressed as $\vec{v}_r = \vec{v} - \vec{V}$ and

$$E_r = \frac{1}{2}\mu\left|\vec{v} - \vec{V}\right|^2 = \frac{1}{2}\mu v^2 + \frac{1}{2}\mu V^2 - \mu\vec{v} \cdot \vec{V}. \tag{8.70}$$

Substituting $\mu = \dfrac{mM}{m+M}$ into equation 8.70 yields

$$E_r = \frac{M}{m+M}E + \frac{m}{m+M}E_A - \mu\left(\sqrt{\frac{2E}{m}}\right)V_x, \tag{8.71}$$

where E and E_A are, respectively, the kinetic energies of the neutron and the target nucleus in the laboratory system (i.e., $E = \frac{1}{2}mv^2$ and $E_A = \frac{1}{2}MV^2$), and V_x is the projected magnitude of $\vec{V}$ on the direction of the incident neutron. For heavy nuclei such as ^{238}U, $m \ll M$ and $V \ll v$, and equation 8.71 is reduced to

$$E_r \approx E - \left(\sqrt{2mE}\right)V_x \quad \Rightarrow \quad V_x \approx \frac{E_r - E}{\sqrt{2mE}}. \tag{8.72}$$

We now express the temperature-dependent reaction rate per unit volume as

$$\frac{\text{reactions}}{\text{cm}^3} = \phi\, N \bar{\sigma}_\gamma(E, T). \tag{8.73}$$

To compute $\bar{\sigma}_\gamma(E, T)$, let $N(\vec{V})d\vec{V}$ be the number of atoms per unit volume (atoms cm^{-3}, of the target medium) moving with a velocity between $\vec{V}$ and $\vec{V} + d\vec{V}$. Since N is the total number of atoms per unit volume of the target medium, $N = \int N(\vec{V})d\vec{V}$. Equation 8.73 can then be expressed as

$$\phi\, N \bar{\sigma}_\gamma(E, T) = \int n v_r \sigma_\gamma(E_r) N(\vec{V})d\vec{V}, \tag{8.74}$$

where n is the neutron density (neutrons cm^{-3}). Substituting $\phi = nv$ into equation 8.74 yields

$$\bar{\sigma}_\gamma(E, T) = \frac{1}{Nv} \int v_r \sigma_\gamma(E_r) N(\vec{V})d\vec{V} = \frac{1}{Nv} \int v_r \sigma_\gamma(E_r) N(V_x) dV_x. \tag{8.75}$$

If the target medium is a gas, $N(V_x)$ is given by the Maxwell-Boltzmann distribution function:

$$N(V_x) = N\left(\frac{M}{2\pi kT}\right)^{1/2} e^{-MV_x^2/2kT}, \tag{8.76}$$

where k is the Boltzmann's constant $(8.617 \times 10^{-5}$ eV $^\circ$K$^{-1})$ and T is the absolute temperature in $^\circ$K. The formula is not very different for solids for temperatures above 300 $^\circ$K. Substituting equations 8.50 and 8.76 into 8.75, and assuming $v_r \approx v$, yields

$$\bar{\sigma}_\gamma(E, T) = \frac{4\pi \lambda^2 g \Gamma_n \Gamma_\gamma}{\Gamma^2}\left(\frac{M}{2\pi kT}\right)^{1/2} \int \frac{e^{-MV_x^2/2kT}}{\left[2(E_r - E_R)/\Gamma\right]^2 + 1} dV_x, \tag{8.77}$$

where $V_x^2 = (E_r - E)^2/2mE$ and $dV_x = dE_r/\sqrt{2mE}$. To simplify the formula, we define the following variables: $\chi = \frac{2}{\Gamma}(E - E_R)$, $y = \frac{2}{\Gamma}(E_r - E_R)$, $\zeta = \frac{\Gamma}{\Gamma_D}$, and $\Gamma_D = \left(4E_R kT/A\right)^{1/2}$, where $A = M/m$, and Γ_D is known as the Doppler width. Equation 8.77 then becomes

$$\bar{\sigma}_\gamma(E, T) = \frac{\sigma_o \Gamma_\gamma}{\Gamma} \psi(\zeta, \chi), \tag{8.78}$$

where $\sigma_o = \dfrac{4\pi \lambdabar^2 g \Gamma_n}{\Gamma}$ and $\psi(\zeta, \chi) = \dfrac{\zeta}{2\sqrt{\pi}} \displaystyle\int_{-\infty}^{\infty} \dfrac{e^{-\frac{1}{4}\zeta^2(\chi-y)^2}}{1+y^2} dy$. The function $e^{-\frac{1}{4}\zeta^2(\chi-y)^2}$ is a

Gaussian distribution centered around $y = \chi$, whose width is proportional to $1/\zeta$. As can be seen in Figure 8.13, as temperature increases, $1/\zeta$ increases, and the Gaussian broadens. This is the so-called Doppler broadening, which will cause an increase in the absorption rate of neutrons (i.e., the resonance escape probability) as they slow down, passing through the resonances in a nuclear reactor.

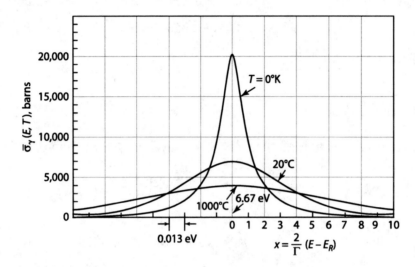

Figure 8.13. The Doppler broadening of the (n,γ) cross section at the 6.67 eV resonance.

It should be noted that the Doppler broadening effect is negligible for scattering resonances because Γ_n is typically more than a few keV, which is much greater than the thermal energy (< 1 eV) of the target nuclei.

8.7   Inelastic Scattering and (n, 2n) Reactions

As indicated in Figure 8.1, inelastic scattering occurs when the excited compound nucleus ($^{A+1}X^*$) undergoes a transition to an excited nucleus, $^{A}X^*$, by emitting a neutron of less kinetic energy than that of the incident neutron. The excited nucleus, $^{A}X^*$, then promptly undergoes gamma decay(s) to the ground level. Because of the extra energy needed for $^{A}X^*$, there exists an energy threshold for σ_i. Figure 8.14 shows many possible inelastic-scattering transitions for $^{238}U + {}^{1}n \rightarrow {}^{239}U^* \rightarrow {}^{238}U^* + {}^{1}n$, and the energy threshold corresponding to the first excited state of ^{238}U.

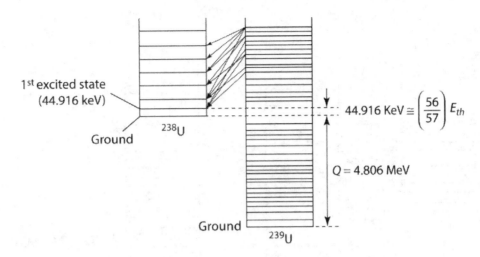

Figure 8.14. The energy levels of ^{238}U and ^{239}U, and the many possible inelastic-scattering transitions.

Since the first excited state of ^{238}U is 44.916 keV, the neutron energy threshold can be calculated as

$$E_{th} \cong \left(\frac{A+1}{A}\right)(44.916\,\text{keV}) = \left(\frac{238+1}{238}\right)(44.916\,\text{keV}) \cong 45.1\,\text{keV}.$$

Because the energy level of the first excited state of a nucleus generally is lower for nuclides with mass number in the regions $150 < A < 190$ and $A > 230$ (see Section 4.10), the neutron energy threshold for inelastic scattering is higher for nuclides with a mass number in the regions $A < 150$ and $190 < A < 230$. In addition, because the energy density generally decreases as the mass number decreases, σ_i also decreases as the mass number decreases. As a result, inelastic scattering is most important for large nuclei (e.g., ^{238}U) and is least important for small nuclei for fission neutrons that have energies of a few MeV. That is, a fission neutron with energy of a few MeV can lose a large fraction of its energy in a single inelastic scattering event. Practically, this is important in a thermal nuclear reactor, where fission neutrons need to first slow down and then be preferentially absorbed by the fissile material (i.e., ^{235}U) in the fuel to maintain fission chain reactions.

The (n,2n) reaction can be considered as a sister reaction to inelastic scattering in that the excited compound nucleus throws out two neutrons instead of one, and that it also has an energy threshold. Figure 8.15 shows many possible (n,2n) transitions for $^{238}\text{U} + \text{n} \rightarrow {}^{239}\text{U}^* \rightarrow {}^{237}\text{U} + 2\text{n}$. Because the neutron separation energy for ^{238}U is 6.153 MeV, the energy threshold for the incident neutron for this (n,2n) reaction can be calculated as

$$E_{th} \cong \left(\frac{A+1}{A}\right)(6.153\,\text{MeV}) = \left(\frac{238+1}{238}\right)(6.153\,\text{MeV}) \cong 6.18\,\text{MeV}.$$

Because of the high threshold energies, the (n,2n) reactions are generally not important when dealing with neutrons having energies less than 10 MeV. One exception is for ^{9}Be, of which the neutron separation energy is only 1.665 MeV and the neutron threshold energy for (n,2n)

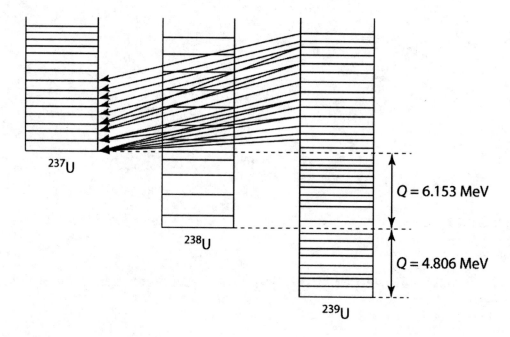

Figure 8.15. The energy levels of ^{237}U, ^{238}U, and ^{239}U, and the many possible (n,2n) transitions for ^{238}U + n $\rightarrow$ ^{239}U* $\rightarrow$ ^{237}U + 2n.

reaction is 1.85 MeV. This makes ^{9}Be a neutron multiplying medium in a nuclear reactor, although not via fission.

Figure 8.16 shows the experimentally obtained neutron cross sections versus neutron energy for σ_i and $\sigma(n, 2n)$ for ^{238}U. As shown, the energy thresholds for both σ_i and $\sigma(n, 2n)$ agree well with the above calculations. It is worth pointing out that the cross section versus neutron energy data for σ_i and $\sigma(n, 2n)$ do not show resonances. This is because the state density of ^{239}U is so high (as indicated in Figures 8.14 and 8.15) that each resonance significantly overlaps with the neighboring ones.

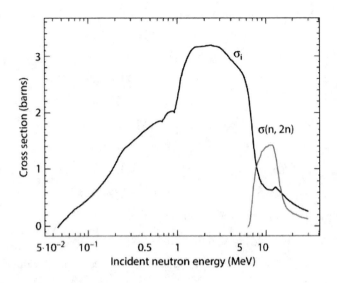

Figure 8.16. The neutron cross sections versus neutron energy for σ_i and $\sigma(n, 2n)$ for ^{238}U (obtained from ENDF/B-VII).

8.8 The Neutron Cross Section Data

The microscopic neutron cross section data for various isotopes are available at the National Nuclear Data Center website: www.nndc.bnl.gov/sigma/. These data files are intended to be used for radiation transport calculations. As such, the data must be "complete" in some sense; for example, all energies must be represented, even if the experimental data do not cover them all. Otherwise, radiation transport calculation would not be possible. Accordingly, a specific data format, the ENDF (Evaluated Nuclear Data File), was developed. A computer readable data file of neutron cross sections is produced by combining the experimental data with nuclear model code calculations to extend or interpolate the available data. The ENDF format was originally developed for use in the US national nuclear data files called ENDF/B, but is now widely adopted around the world. The latest version of ENDF is called ENDF/B-VII. The neutron cross section data shown in many of the figures in this chapter were obtained from ENDF/B-VII.

Bibliography

Krane, Kenneth S. *Introductory Nuclear Physics*. New York: John Wiley & Sons, 1988.

Lamarsh, John R. *Introduction to Nuclear Reactor Theory*. Reading, MA: Addison-Wesley Publishing Company, Inc., 1966.

Buttlar, Haro V. *Nuclear Physics: An Introduction*. New York: Academic Press, Inc., 1968.

Credits

Problems

1. The thermal neutron ($E_n \cong 0.025$ eV) cross-sections in ^{235}U are:

   $\sigma_e \cong 14.7$ b – elastic cross-section

   $\sigma_f \cong 538.6$ b – fission cross-section

   $\sigma_\gamma \cong 79.9$ b – neutron capture cross-section

   $\sigma_i \cong$ negligible – inelastic cross-section

   Neglecting (for the sake of the solving this problem) other interaction processes:
   (a) Compute the total thermal neutron interaction cross-section (σ_t) in ^{235}U.
   (b) Compute the total macroscopic cross-section (Σ_t)
   (c) Compute the mean free path (λ) of a thermal neutron in ^{235}U.
   (d) For thermal neutrons, what is the probability of neutron induced fission, neutron elastic scattering and neutron capture in ^{235}U ?

2. Using the neutron cross-section data available from www.nndc.bnl.gov/sigma/ display for lead ($^{207}_{82}$Pb) and neutron energies in the range 10^{-5} eV $\leq E_n \leq 10^7$ eV, the:
   a) neutron total cross-section (σ_t),
   b) neutron elastic scattering cross-section (σ_e)
   c) neutron radiative capture cross-section (σ_γ)

   Explain succinctly if lead is a good material for shielding neutrons.

3. Using the neutron cross-section data available from www.nndc.bnl.gov/sigma/ display for cadmium ($^{113}_{48}$Cd) and neutron energies in the range 10^{-5} eV $\leq E_n \leq 10^7$ eV, the:
   (a) neutron total cross-section (σ_t),
   (b) neutron radiative capture cross-section (σ_γ)

   Considering these cross-section data, explain succinctly the applications of $^{113}_{48}$Cd in neutron experiments and detection.

4. Using the neutron cross-section data repository at www.nndc.bnl.gov/sigma/ display for helium ($^3_2$He) and neutron energies in the range 10^{-5} eV $\leq E_n \leq 10^7$ eV, the:
   (a) neutron total cross-section (σ_t),
   (b) (n,p) cross-section (σ_p),

   Considering the previously determined cross-section data, explain succinctly the applications of ($^3_2$He) in neutron detection.

5. Consider a neutron with kinetic energy $E_n = 2$ MeV incident on a ^{238}U nucleus. Assume that the nuclear reaction proceeds via compound nucleus formation. Determine:
   (a) The total kinetic energy in the COM frame, before the nuclear reaction occurs;

(b) The total kinetic energy in the COM frame, immediately after compound nucleus formation;

(c) The energy of the excited state $\left(^{239}\mathrm{U}\right)^{*}$ above the ground state $^{239}\mathrm{U}$.

(d) Give examples of four possible final states for this reaction and quantify the corresponding cross-sections.

6. Resonances are observed in the neutron total cross section for $^{1}_{0}\mathrm{n} + {}^{10}\mathrm{B} \rightarrow {}^{11}\mathrm{B}$ at the following (laboratory) energies: 0.53 MeV, 1.9 MeV, 2.8 MeV, 3.4 MeV, and 4.2 MeV. At what energies, measured from the ground state, are the excited states that give rise to the above resonances?

7. In the following scenarios of elastic scattering between neutrons and various types of nuclei, use partial-wave analysis to predict the characteristics of $d\sigma(\theta)/d\Omega$ in the center-of-mass system. Are your answers for each scenario the same for the laboratory system? Why?
   Scenarios: (a) A 10-keV neutron interacting with a $^{1}\mathrm{H}$ nucleus.
   (b) A 10-keV neutron interacting with a $^{12}\mathrm{C}$ nucleus.
   (c) A 10-MeV neutron interacting with a $^{12}\mathrm{C}$ nucleus.
   (d) A 10-MeV neutron interacting with a $^{238}\mathrm{U}$ nucleus.

8. Which of the following two nuclei would you expect to have a larger cross section for thermal neutron-induced fission: $^{240}\mathrm{Pu}$ or $^{241}\mathrm{Pu}$? Why?

9. In low-energy neutron capture by $^{55}\mathrm{Mn}$, what are the possible I^{π} assignments of the $^{56}\mathrm{Mn}$ excited states?

10. Following thermal neutron capture by $^{143}\mathrm{Nd}$, would you expect to see a strong primary transition from capture state to the $^{144}\mathrm{Nd}$ ground state? Would you expect the same in the case of thermal neutron capture by $^{119}\mathrm{Sn}$?

11. An s-wave ($l = 0$) resonance in the total cross section for neutrons incident on $^{238}\mathrm{U}$ is observed at a COM energy $E_n = 115$ eV. The total width of the resonance is 9.4×10^{-2} eV and the peak cross section is 19,200 barns. Calculate the partial widths Γ_n and Γ_γ for neutron and γ emission (assuming that these are the only exit channels) and the peak cross section for the (n, γ) capture reaction.

12. What is "the Doppler broadening effect (DBE)" in neutron interactions? What type of neutron interaction, e.g., (n, γ), (n, elastic), (n, inelastic), ..etc, to which DBE is most important? Why?

13. Choose the proper neutron interaction type for each of the following scenarios and explain why.
   Scenarios: (a) 10-MeV neutrons interacting with lead.
   (b) Thermal neutrons interacting with gold.
   (c) 1-MeV neutrons interacting with hydrogen in water.
   (d) Thermal neutrons interacting with boron-10.
   (e) 6- MeV neutrons interacting with beryllium.
   Interaction types: elastic, inelastic, (n, γ), (n, 2n), and (n, α).

14. Estimate the neutron energy needed to produce fission of $^{208}\mathrm{Pb}$. Is it likely that such neutrons would be released in the fission, making possible a self-sustaining reaction?

15. Given that the activation energy of ^{236}U is 6.2 MeV, what is the minimum energy of an alpha particle that can produce fission following bombardment of a ^{232}Th target?

16. Write down the equations explaining the kinematics of elastic scattering of a neutron of mass m crossing a medium with atoms of mass M.

    (a) Use the variable $A \cong \frac{M}{m}$ to determine the maximum and minimum value of the energy transferred from the incoming neutron to the recoil nucleus. How does this vary with A?

    (b) Use the previous findings to explain the process of neutron moderation and justify the choice of materials to attain such objective.

CHAPTER 9: INTERACTIONS OF CHARGED PARTICLES WITH MATTER

Charged particles such as electrons, protons, alpha particles, and heavy ions mainly interact with atoms and molecules instead of nuclei. This is because most of the space of matter (being made of atoms and molecules) is occupied by electrons with which a charged particle can exert Coulomb forces. The interactions usually result in ionizations and excitations of the atoms and molecules, and therefore they are referred to as inelastic collisions. Charged particles can also undergo elastic collisions with atoms and atomic nuclei (see Section 1.8). But the cross sections for elastic collisions are in general much smaller than those for inelastic collisions. Lastly, a charged particle can also undergo inelastic scattering with the nuclear Coulomb field via the so-called the "bremsstrahlung process." This process is well known in classical electrodynamics for electrons undergoing acceleration (or deceleration) in a Coulomb field. As will be discussed in Section 9.3, the bremsstrahlung process only becomes important for energetic electrons interacting with materials made of atoms of high atomic numbers (i.e., the high-Z materials).

It should be noted that a charged particle mainly loses its energy in materials via inelastic collisions. However, inelastic collisions have little effect on a charged particle's traveling direction. It is the elastic collisions with the atomic nuclei (i.e., the Rutherford scattering) that affect the direction of a charged particle the most. The various types of charged-particle interaction mechanisms and cross sections are discussed in the following sections.

9.1 Semi-Classical Theory of Inelastic Collision Between a Charged Particle and Atomic Electrons

The inelastic collision between a charged particle and the atoms along the particle track is complicated by the fact that the incident particle can simultaneously interact with many atoms and that each atom has many electrons. The approach by Niels Bohr was to simplify the process by considering just the Coulomb interaction between two point charges: the incident charged particle and a resting electron (see Figure 9.1). This classical model, in theory, is only valid if the particle's kinetic energy is much greater than the electron's binding energy. But with some simple arguments of quantum mechanics, the classical model can be used to illustrate the energy loss mechanism and to derive the stopping-power formula for charged particles.

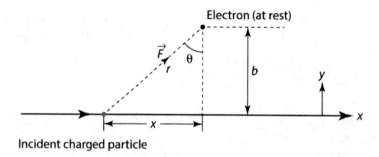

Figure 9.1. The classical approach of the Coulomb interaction between two point charges: the incident charged particle and a free resting electron.

As shown in Figure 9.1, the Coulomb force between the incident charged particle and the resting electron can be expressed as

$$\left|\vec{F}\right| = \frac{k_c ze^2}{r^2} = \frac{k_c ze^2 \cos^2 \theta}{b^2}, \tag{9.1}$$

where $k_c = 1/4\pi\varepsilon_0$, ε_0 is the dielectric constant in a vacuum, $k_c e^2 = 1.44 \times 10^{-15}$ MeV·m, and r, b, and θ are those described in Figure 9.1. From Figure 9.1 and equation 9.1, the magnitude of $\vec{F}$ in the y direction can be expressed as

$$\left|\vec{F}_y\right| = F_y = \frac{zk_c e^2 \cos^3 \theta}{b^2}. \tag{9.2}$$

The transfer of momentum from the incident particle to the electron is then

$$\Delta p = \sqrt{(\Delta p_x)^2 + (\Delta p_y)^2} = \Delta p_y = \int F_y \, dt = \int \frac{zk_c e^2 \cos^3 \theta}{b^2} \, dt. \tag{9.3}$$

$\Delta p_x = 0$ because F_x is symmetric with reference to the electron as the incident particle passes by. To carry out the above integral, we use the following relationships:

$$\frac{d\tan\theta}{dt} = \frac{d(x/b)}{dt} = \frac{1}{b}\frac{dx}{dt} = \frac{v}{b} \tag{9.4}$$

and

$$\frac{d\tan\theta}{dt} = \frac{d\tan\theta}{d\theta}\frac{d\theta}{dt} = \frac{1}{\cos^2\theta}\frac{d\theta}{dt}. \tag{9.5}$$

Equations 9.4 and 9.5 together give the following relationship:

$$dt = \frac{b}{v}\cos^{-2}\theta \, d\theta. \tag{9.6}$$

Substituting equation 9.6 into 9.3 results in

$$\Delta p = \Delta p_y = \frac{zk_c e^2}{bv} \int_{-\pi/2}^{+\pi/2} \cos\theta \, d\theta = \frac{2zk_c e^2}{bv}. \tag{9.7}$$

The energy transferred from the charged particle to the electron per collision can be obtained as

$$Q = \frac{(\Delta p)^2}{2m} = \frac{2z^2 k_c^2 e^4}{mv^2 b^2}. \tag{9.8}$$

We now consider a charged particle moving through a homogeneous medium having an electron density of NZ, electrons cm⁻³, where N is the atomic number density in atoms cm⁻³ and Z is the atomic number of the atom. As shown in Figure 9.2, the number of collisions in a path length dx at an impact parameter lying between b and $b+db$ equals the number of electrons contained in the annualar cylindrical ring dV, and that number is

$$NZ \, dV = NZ \, dA \, dx = NZ(2\pi b \, db)dx = 2\pi NZb \, dbdx. \tag{9.9}$$

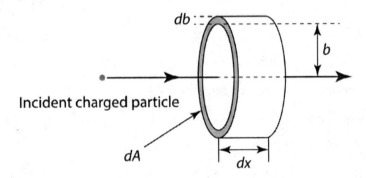

Figure 9.2. Annular cylinder of length dx centered around path of the incident charged particle.

Thus, the energy transfer from the incident charged particle to the electrons surrounding the particle track in a distance dx can be obtained as

$$dE = NZ \int Q \, dV = NZ \int Q \, dA \, dx = NZ \int_{b_{min}}^{b_{max}} \left(\frac{2z^2 k_c^2 e^4}{mv^2 b^2} \right)(2\pi b \, db)dx$$

$$= \frac{4\pi z^2 k_c^2 e^4 NZ}{mv^2} \int_{b_{min}}^{b_{max}} \frac{db}{b} \, dx. \tag{9.10}$$

The energy loss rate of the charged particle can therefore be expressed as

$$\frac{dE}{dx} = \frac{4\pi z^2 k_c^2 e^4 NZ}{mv^2} \int_{b_{min}}^{b_{max}} \frac{db}{b} = \frac{4\pi z^2 k_c^2 e^4 NZ}{mv^2} \ln \frac{b_{max}}{b_{min}} .$$ (9.11)

The question remains: How does one obtain the appropriate values for b_{max} and b_{min}? The clue for the answer comes from the following arguments of quantum mechanics. First, in order for a charged particle to cause a quantum transition in an atom (i.e., an ionization or excitation event), the interaction impulse on an electron of the atom must be sharp. If the time of passage of the charged particle $\approx (b/v)$ is longer than the orbital period of an atomic electron $\approx (1/\bar{v})$, then the probability of a transition is small. This restricts the maximum value of the impact parameter b. That is,

$$\frac{b}{v} \le \frac{1}{\bar{v}} \quad \text{or} \quad b_{max} \le \frac{v}{\bar{v}} ,$$ (9.12)

where $\bar{v}$ is the average vibration frequency of the atomic electrons. To set the value for b_{min}, one argues that the classical treatment has meaning only when the Coulomb field of the charged particle varies negligibly over the dimensions of the wave packet representing the electron. That is,

$$b \ge \lambdabar \quad \text{or} \quad b_{min} \approx \lambdabar = \frac{\hbar}{mv} .$$ (9.13)

By substituting equations 9.12 and 9.13 back into 9.11, one obtains

$$\left(\frac{dE}{dx}\right)_c = \frac{4\pi z^2 k_c^2 e^4 NZ}{mv^2} \ln \frac{mv^2}{\hbar \bar{v}} .$$ (9.14)

We add a subscript c to indicate that this energy loss formula is for "collisional loss," as opposed to "radiative loss," which is caused by the emission of bremsstrahlung X rays (see Section 9.4). Equation 9.14 is the semi-classical formula of collision stopping power derived by Niels Bohr.

An alternative way of obtaining the expression of $(dE/dx)_c$ is to use equation 9.8 to express the differential cross section as a function of Q; that is,

$$d\sigma(Q) = 2\pi b \, db = \pi \, db^2 = \pi \, d\left(\frac{2z^2 k_c^2 e^4}{mv^2 Q}\right) = \frac{2\pi z^2 k_c^2 e^4}{mv^2} d(Q^{-1}) = -\frac{2\pi z^2 k_c^2 e^4}{mv^2} \frac{dQ}{Q^2} .$$ (9.15)

It then follows that

$$\left(\frac{dE}{dx}\right)_c = NZ \int_{Q_{min}}^{Q_{max}} Q \, d\sigma(Q) = -\frac{2\pi z^2 k_c^2 e^4 NZ}{mv^2} \int_{Q_{min}}^{Q_{max}} Q^{-1} \, dQ .$$ (9.16)

Equation 9.16 then leads to an alternative form of 9.11; that is,

$$\left(\frac{dE}{dx}\right)_c = \frac{2\pi z^2 k_c^2 e^4 NZ}{m v^2} \ln\frac{Q_{max}}{Q_{min}}, \tag{9.17}$$

where Q_{max} corresponds to the energy transfer of the head-on collision between the incident particle and the atomic electron. To find Q_{max}, one first uses equation 7.28 to obtain the maximum speed of the knocked-out electron. That is,

$$\left(v_e\right)_{max} = v_0 + v_c = \left(\frac{M}{m+M}\right)v + \left(\frac{M}{m+M}\right)v = \left(\frac{2M}{m+M}\right)v, \tag{9.18}$$

where v is the speed of the incident charged particle in the LAB frame, v_e is the speed of the knocked-out electron in the LAB frame, v_0 is the speed of the COM with reference to the LAB frame, v_c is the speed of the knocked-out electron in the COM frame, m is the rest mass of the electron, and M is the rest mass of the incident charged particle. For charged particles other than electrons and positrons, $M >> m$, and $\left(v_e\right)_{max} \cong 2v$. In other words, the maximum speed of the knocked-out electron is twice the speed of the incident charged particle. The maximum kinetic energy of the knocked-out electron can then be obtained from the classical formula as

$$Q_{max} = \frac{1}{2}m\left(v_e\right)_{max}^2 \cong \frac{1}{2}m(2v)^2 = 2mv^2 = 2mc^2\beta^2. \tag{9.19}$$

One can also use equation 9.19 to obtain the maximum fraction of energy that can be transferred from the incident particle to an atomic electron as

$$\frac{Q_{max}}{E} = \frac{2mv^2}{\frac{1}{2}Mv^2} = \frac{4m}{M}. \tag{9.20}$$

For example, the maximum amount of energy that can be transferred from a 5-MeV alpha particle to an atomic electron is

$$(5\,\text{MeV})(4)\left(\frac{0.511\,\text{MeV}}{3727.4\,\text{MeV}}\right) = 2.74\,\text{keV}.$$

An energetic knocked-out electron that is capable to causing further ionization is called a delta ray (δ ray).

If one takes relativistic effect into consideration, the exact expression of Q_{max} is

$$Q_{max} = \frac{2\gamma^2 mv^2}{1 + \frac{2\gamma m}{M} + \frac{m^2}{M^2}}, \tag{9.21}$$

where $\gamma = \dfrac{1}{\sqrt{1-\beta^2}}$ and $\beta = \dfrac{v}{c}$. It can be easily shown that under the conditions that $\gamma \to 1$ and $M \gg m$, equation 9.21 is reduced to the classical formula of 9.19.

If the incident charged particle is an electron, then equation 9.18 shows that the maximum speed of the knocked-out electron is the same as that of the incident electron. In other words, the maximum energy of the knocked-out electron is the same as the energy of the incident electron. In reality, however, because there is no way to distinguish the incident electron from the knocked-out electron, one can only attribute the more energetic one as the primary electron and the less energetic one as the knocked-out electron. This argument leads to the notion that the maximum energy of the knocked-out electron is half that of the incident electron (i.e., $Q_{max} = E/2$). Consequently, if the incident particle is a positron, then the maximum energy of the knocked-out electron is indeed the same as the energy of the incident positron (i.e., $Q_{max} = E$).

From the quantum mechanical argument, Q_{min} corresponds to the minimum amount of energy needed to bring an atom from its ground state to an excited state. Since there are many excited states in an atom, Q_{min} should correspond to the mean excitation potential, i.e. the geometric-mean value of all the ionization and excitation potentials of an atom of the absorbing midium. A more rigorous quantum mechanical treatment of Q_{min} will be given in Section 9.2. For now, we simply give a new notation I for the mean excitation potential. For non-relativistic charged particles other than electrons and positrons (referred to as "heavy charged particles" hereafter), it can be shown that

$$\frac{Q_{max}}{Q_{min}} \cong \left(\frac{2mv^2}{I}\right)^2 \tag{9.22}$$

Substituting equation 9.22 into 9.17 yields

$$\left(\frac{dE}{dx}\right)_c = \frac{2\pi z^2 k_c^2 e^4 NZ}{mc^2 \beta^2} \ln\left(\frac{2mv^2}{I}\right)^2 = \frac{4\pi z^2 k_c^2 e^4 NZ}{mv^2} \ln\frac{2mv^2}{I}, \tag{9.23}$$

The similarity between equations 9.14 and 9.23 is obvious. The more accurate formula based on quantum mechanics and with equation 9.21 for relativistic mass correction is given below (see Section 9.2 for derivation):

$$\left(\frac{dE}{dx}\right)_c = \frac{4\pi z^2 k_c^2 e^4 NZ}{mc^2 \beta^2}\left[\ln\left(\frac{2mc^2 \beta^2}{I}\right) - \ln\left(1-\beta^2\right) - \beta^2\right]. \tag{9.24}$$

where $\beta = v/c$. The above formula is referred to as the Bethe stopping power formula. The last two terms in the bracket of the right-hand side of equation 9.23 are the relativistic mass correction terms. The values of I can be obtained with the following empirical formula:

$$I = 19.0 \text{ eV}, \text{ for } Z = 1$$
$$= 11.2 + 11.7Z \text{ eV}, \text{ for } 2 \leq Z \leq 13$$
$$= 52.8 + 8.81Z \text{ eV}, \text{ for } Z > 13. \tag{9.25}$$

Conventionally, equation 9.24 can be conveniently expressed in terms of the classical electron radius, $r_0 = \dfrac{k_c e^2}{mc^2} = 2.818 \times 10^{-13}$ cm. That is,

$$\left(\frac{dE}{dx} \right)_c = 4\pi z^2 r_0^2 mc^2 \beta^{-2} NZ \left[\ln\left(\frac{2mc^2\beta^2}{I} \right) - \ln\left(1 - \beta^2\right) - \beta^2 \right] \tag{9.26}$$

Because $Q_{\max}$ for electrons and positrons is quite different from that for heavy charged particles, the collision stopping power formula for electrons and positrons is derived separately in Section 9.2.

It should be noted that $(dE / dx)_c$ is proportional to β^{-2} in equation 9.26, and that the mass of the incident charged particle never appears in either of the equations.

Example 9.1.1

Use equation 9.26 to calculate the collision stopping power in water for a 1-MeV proton.

Solutions

$$1 \text{ MeV} = (\gamma - 1)m_p c^2 = \left(\frac{1}{\sqrt{1-\beta^2}} - 1 \right)(938.28 \text{ MeV}) \quad \Rightarrow \quad \beta^2 \cong 0.00213 \ll 1. \text{ The electron}$$

densities associated with hydrogen and oxygen in water can be obtained, respectively, as

$$(NZ)_H = \left(\frac{1 \text{ g/cm}^3}{18 \text{ g/mole}} \right)\left(6.023 \times 10^{23} \frac{\text{molecules}}{\text{mole}} \right)\left(2 \frac{\text{electrons}}{\text{molecule}} \right) = 6.692 \times 10^{22} \frac{\text{electrons}}{\text{cm}^3},$$

and

$$(NZ)_O = \left(\frac{1 \text{ g/cm}^3}{18 \text{ g/mole}} \right)\left(6.023 \times 10^{23} \frac{\text{molecules}}{\text{mole}} \right)\left(8 \frac{\text{electrons}}{\text{molecule}} \right) = 2.6768 \times 10^{23} \frac{\text{electrons}}{\text{cm}^3}.$$

From equation 9.25, $I_H = 19$ eV and $I_O = 11.2 + 11.7(8) = 104.8$ eV.

Since $z = 1$, $r_0 = 2.818 \times 10^{-13}$ cm, and $mc^2\beta^2 = (0.511 \text{ MeV})(0.00213) \cong 0.0011 \text{ MeV}$,

equation 9.26 can t be applied for water as

$$\left(\frac{dE}{dx}\right)_c^{H_2O} = \left(\frac{dE}{dx}\right)_c^{H} + \left(\frac{dE}{dx}\right)_c^{O}$$

$$\cong \frac{4\pi\left(2.818\times10^{-13}\ \text{cm}\right)^2 (0.511\,\text{MeV})\left(6.692\times10^{22}\ \text{cm}^{-3}\right)}{0.00213}\ln\left(\frac{2(0.0011\times10^6\ \text{eV})}{19\,\text{eV}}\right)+$$

$$\frac{4\pi\left(2.818\times10^{-13}\ \text{cm}\right)^2 (0.511\,\text{MeV})\left(2.676\times10^{23}\ \text{cm}^{-3}\right)}{0.00213}\ln\left(\frac{2(0.0011\times10^6\ \text{eV})}{104.8\,\text{eV}}\right)$$

$$\cong 76.13\ \text{MeV cm}^{-1} + 195.02\ \text{MeV cm}^{-1} \cong 27.2\ \text{keV}\ \mu\text{m}^{-1}.$$

A slightly different but more convenient way to carry out the above calculation is to calculate the I value for water using the formula for chemical compound:

$$n\ln I = \sum_i N_i Z_i \ln I_i \qquad (9.27)$$

where n is the total number of electrons cm-3 in the absorbing medium, i.e. $n = \sum_i N_i Z_i$.

Since $n_{H_2O} = (NZ)_H + (NZ)_O = 6.692\times10^{22} + 2.6768\times10^{23} = 3.346\times10^{23}\ \dfrac{\text{electrons}}{\text{cm}^3}$, from equation 9.27 one obtains

$$\ln I_{H_2O} = \frac{1}{n_{H_2O}}\left[(NZ)_H\left(\ln I_H\right) + (NZ)_O\left(\ln I_O\right)\right]$$

$$= \frac{1}{3.346\times10^{23}}\left[\left(6.692\times10^{22}\right)\left(\ln(19\ \text{eV})\right) + \left(2.6768\times10^{23}\right)\left(\ln(104.8\ \text{eV})\right)\right]$$

$$= (0.2)\ln(19\ \text{eV}) + (0.8)\ln(104.8\ \text{eV})$$

$$\Rightarrow\ I_{H_2O} = e^{(0.2)\ln(19)+(0.8)\ln(104.8)} = 74.4\ \text{eV}$$

It then follows that

$$\left(\frac{dE}{dx}\right)_c^{H_2O} = \frac{4\pi\left(2.818\times10^{-13}\ \text{cm}\right)^2 (0.511\,\text{MeV})\left(3.346\times10^{23}\ \text{cm}^{-3}\right)}{0.00213}\ln\left(\frac{2(0.0011\times10^6\ \text{eV})}{74.4\,\text{eV}}\right)$$

$$\cong 272\ \text{MeV cm}^{-1}\ \text{or}\ 27.2\ \text{keV}\ \mu\text{m}^{-1}.$$

9.2 Quantum Mechanical Treatment of Inelastic Collision Between a Charged Particle and Atomic Electrons

As mentioned in the previous section, the mean excitation energy I that appears in the collisional stopping power formula is an average value of the excitation energy of all the available excited states of the atom. To properly estimate I, one needs to know the transition probability for the atom to go from the ground state to all other excited states during the collision process. As discussed in Section 3.11.1, this probability for the atom to undergo a transition from the initial ground state "o" to the final excited state "n" can be obtained using the model of the Born Approximation. According to equation 3.123,

$$\frac{d\sigma_n}{d\Omega} = \frac{k^2}{4\pi^2\hbar^2 v^2}\left[\int e^{i\vec{K}\cdot\vec{r}}\varphi_n *(\vec{r})V(\vec{r})\varphi_o(\vec{r})d\vec{r}\right]^2, \tag{9.28}$$

where $V(\vec{r}) = -\displaystyle\sum_{j=1}^{Z}\frac{zk_c e^2}{\left|\vec{r}-\vec{r}_j\right|}+\frac{zZk_c e^2}{r}$, z is the charge of the incident particle, $\vec{r}$ is the position

vector of the incident charged particle, $\vec{r}_j$ is the position vector of the atomic electron j, and $\vec{K} = \vec{k} - \vec{k}'$, where $\vec{k}$ and $\vec{k}'$ are, respectively, the wave number vectors of the incoming and outgoing charged particle. The integration of equation 9.28 can be performed by using the relation of the Fourier integral:

$$\int \frac{e^{i\vec{K}\cdot\vec{r}}}{\left|\vec{r}-\vec{r}_j\right|}d\vec{r} = \frac{4\pi}{K^2}e^{i\vec{K}\cdot\vec{r}_j}. \tag{9.29}$$

Equation 9.28 can then be expressed as

$$\frac{d\sigma_n}{d\Omega} = \frac{4z^2 k_c^2 e^4 k^2 Z}{K^4\hbar^2 v^2}\left|F_n\left(\vec{K}\right)\right|^2, \tag{9.30}$$

where $F_n(\vec{K})$ is referred to as the "inelastic form factor," and is defined as

$$F_n(\vec{K}) = \frac{1}{\sqrt{Z}}\sum_{j=1}^{Z}\int \varphi_n *(\vec{r})e^{i\vec{K}\cdot\vec{r}_j}\varphi_o(\vec{r})\,d\vec{r}. \tag{9.31}$$

The factor $\left|F_n(\vec{K})\right|^2$ in equation 9.30 gives the conditional probability that the atom makes the transition to a particular excited state "n" upon receiving a momentum transfer $\hbar\vec{K}$. The nuclear interaction represented by the second term of $V(\vec{r})$ gives no contribution, owing to the orthogonality of states "o" and "n".

Since $\left|\vec{k}'\right| \cong \left|\vec{k}\right| = k$, it can be seen from Figure 9.3 that

$$\left|\vec{K}\right| = K \cong 2k\sin\frac{\theta}{2}. \tag{9.32}$$

It follows that

$$\sin\frac{\theta}{2} = \frac{K}{2k} \quad \Rightarrow \quad \sin^2\frac{\theta}{2} = \frac{K^2}{4k^2} \tag{9.33}$$

and that

$$d\Omega = 2\pi \sin\theta\, d\theta = -2\pi\, d\cos\theta = -2\pi\, d\left(1 - 2\sin^2\frac{\theta}{2}\right) = 2\pi\left(\frac{dK^2}{2k^2}\right) = \frac{\pi}{k^2}dK^2. \tag{9.34}$$

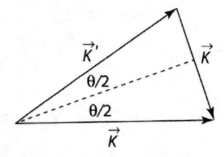

Figure 9.3. The geometric relationship of $\vec{k}$ and $\vec{k}'$ and $\vec{K}$.

Substituting equation 9.34 into 9.31 gives

$$d\sigma_n = \frac{4\pi z^2 k_c^2 e^4 Z}{K^4 \hbar^2 v^2}\left|F_n\left(\vec{K}\right)\right|^2. \tag{9.35}$$

It can also be shown from Figure 9.3 that

$$\Delta\vec{p} = \hbar\vec{k} - \hbar\vec{k}' = \hbar\vec{K}. \tag{9.36}$$

We now define the quantity Q as the kinetic energy of a free electron having the momentum $\hbar\vec{K}$; that is,

$$Q = \frac{(\Delta p)^2}{2m} = \frac{\left|\hbar\vec{K}\right|^2}{2m} = \frac{\hbar^2 K^2}{2m}. \tag{9.37}$$

Equation 9.37 can then be expressed in terms of Q as:

$$d\sigma_n = \frac{2\pi k_c^2 e^4 z^2 Z}{mv^2}\left|F_n\left(\vec{K}\right)\right|^2 \frac{dQ}{Q^2}. \tag{9.38}$$

In equation 9.38, $d\sigma_n$ is the cross section for an atom to receive an energy transfer of dQ from the incident particle. The product of $\dfrac{2\pi k_c^2 e^4 z^2 Z}{mv^2}$ and $\dfrac{dQ}{Q^2}$ is the cross section obtained with the classical treatment for a scattering with a free electron (see equation 9.15). The inelastic form factor, $F_n(\vec{K})$, represents the probability for an atom to go from its ground state "o" to an excited state "n," if one of its electrons receives a recoil momentum $\hbar\vec{K}$. The stopping power formula for soft collisions can then be obtained as:

$$\left(\frac{dE}{dx}\right)_c = N\sum_n (E_n - E_o)\int_{Q_{min}}^{Q_{max}} d\sigma_n$$

$$= \frac{2\pi k_c^2 e^4 z^2 NZ}{mv^2}\sum_n (E_n - E_o)\int_{Q_{min}}^{Q_{max}} \left|F_n(\vec{K})\right|^2 \frac{dQ}{Q^2}. \tag{9.39}$$

To carry out the integral in equation 9.39, we divide the integral over Q into two parts, one going from Q_{min} to an intermediate value Q_c, and the second going from Q_c to Q_{max}. The first part corresponds to the soft collisions where the atomic electrons are not free and the transition probability factor $\left|F_n(\vec{K})\right|^2$ plays a significant role. The second part corresponds to the hard collisions, where atomic electrons can be treated as free electrons and the classical approach of equation 9.22 is valid. In other words, we artificially introduce the quantity Q_c to conveniently separate the inelastic collisions into two groups. Accordingly, equation 9.39 is rewritten as

$$\left(\frac{dE}{dx}\right)_c = \left(\frac{dE}{dx}\right)_c^{soft} + \left(\frac{dE}{dx}\right)_c^{hard}, \tag{9.40}$$

where

$$\left(\frac{dE}{dx}\right)_c^{hard} = \frac{2\pi k_c^2 e^4 z^2 NZ}{mv^2}\int_{Q_c}^{2mv^2} \frac{dQ}{Q} = \frac{2\pi k_c^2 e^4 z^2 NZ}{mv^2}\ln\frac{2mv^2}{Q_c} \tag{9.41}$$

and

$$\left(\frac{dE}{dx}\right)_c^{soft} = \frac{2\pi k_c^2 e^4 z^2 NZ}{mv^2}\sum_n (E_n - E_0)\int_{Q_{min}}^{Q_c} \left|F_n(\vec{K})\right|^2 \frac{dQ}{Q^2}. \tag{9.42}$$

To carry out the integral in equation 9.42, one needs to first determine Q_{min}. To do so, we apply the soft collision condition that $p_o \cong p_n = p$, and that ΔE and Δp are related as

$$\Delta E = \frac{p_o^2 - p_n^2}{2m} = \frac{(p_o + p_n)(p_o - p_n)}{2m} \cong \frac{2p(p_o - p_n)}{2m} = v\Delta p. \tag{9.43}$$

Thus,

$$Q_{min} = \frac{(\Delta p)_{min}^2}{2m} = \frac{(\Delta E)_{min}^2}{2mv^2} = \frac{(E_n - E_o)^2}{2mv^2}. \tag{9.44}$$

Equation 9.42 can then be written as

$$\left(\frac{dE}{dx}\right)_c^{soft} = \frac{2\pi k_c^2 e^4 z^2 NZ}{mv^2} \sum_n \left((E_o - E_n) \int_{\frac{(E_n-E_o)^2}{2mv^2}}^{Q_c} \left|F_n(\vec{K})\right|^2 \frac{dQ}{Q^2} \right)$$

$$= \frac{2\pi k_c^2 e^4 z^2 NZ}{mv^2} \ln \frac{2mv^2 Q_c}{I^2}, \tag{9.45}$$

where I is the mean excitation energy, which is related to $F_n(\vec{K})$ via the following formula:

$$\ln I = \sum_n f_n \ln(E_n - E_o), \tag{9.46}$$

where f_n is the optical dipole oscillator strength, which is obtained by keeping only the first-order term in the Taylor series expansion of $e^{i\vec{K}\cdot\vec{r}_j} \cong 1 + iKx_j + \dots$ in $F_n(\vec{K})$:

$$f_n = \frac{2m}{\hbar} \frac{\left| \int \varphi_n{}^*(\vec{r}) \sum_{j=1}^Z x_j \varphi_0(\vec{r}) d\vec{r} \right|^2}{Z} (E_n - E_o). \tag{9.47}$$

Combining equations 9.41 and 9.45, 9.40 now becomes

$$\left(\frac{dE}{dx}\right)_c = \left(\frac{dE}{dx}\right)_c^{soft} + \left(\frac{dE}{dx}\right)_c^{hard} = \frac{2\pi k_c^2 e^4 z^2 NZ}{mv^2} \left(\ln \frac{2mv^2 Q_c}{I^2} + \ln \frac{2mv^2}{Q_c} \right)$$

$$= \frac{2\pi k_c^2 e^4 z^2 NZ}{mv^2} \ln \left(\frac{2mv^2}{I} \right)^2 = \frac{4\pi k_c^2 e^4 z^2 NZ}{mv^2} \ln \left(\frac{2mv^2}{I} \right). \tag{9.48}$$

The above concludes the quantum-mechanical derivation of equation 9.23 (i.e. equation 9.48), which is the collisional stopping power formula for heavy charged particles. It is instructive to compare equation 9.48 with the semi-classical formula in equation 9.14. As shown, Bohr's descriptive argument of the average atomic constant $\hbar v$ in equation 9.14 is now more rigorously defined as the mean excitation energy I in equations 9.46 and 9.47.

For electrons and positrons, $Q_{max} = E/2$. From equation 9.12, the "hard collision" term of the collision stopping power can be expressed as

$$\left(\frac{dE}{dx}\right)_c^{hard} = NZ \int_{Q_c}^{E/2} Q \left(\frac{d\sigma}{dQ}\right)_{hard} dQ \tag{9.49}$$

where $\left(\frac{d\sigma}{dQ}\right)_{hard}$ has been derived by Møller, assuming the atomic electrons are free, and is given below (ICRU, 1984):

$$\left(\frac{d\sigma}{dQ}\right)_{hard} = \left(\frac{2\pi k_c^2 e^4}{mc^2\beta^2}\right)Q^{-2}\left[1 + \frac{Q^2}{(E-Q)^2} + \frac{\tau^2}{(\tau+1)^2}\left(\frac{Q}{E}\right)^2 - \frac{(2\tau+1)}{(\tau+1)^2}\frac{Q}{(E-Q)}\right] \quad (9.50)$$

where $\tau = \dfrac{E}{mc^2}$. The "soft collision" term of the collision power (i.e. equation 9.45) after the relativistic mass correction can be shown as

$$\left(\frac{dE}{dx}\right)_c^{soft} = \frac{2\pi k_c^2 e^4 NZ}{mc^2\beta^2}\left[\ln\left(\frac{2mc^2\beta^2 Q_c}{I^2(1-\beta^2)}\right) - \beta^2\right] \quad (9.51)$$

By combining equations 9.49, 9.50, and 9.51, one can then obtain the collision stopping power formula for electron and positron below:

$$\left(\frac{dE}{dx}\right)_c = \left(\frac{dE}{dx}\right)_{soft} + \left(\frac{dE}{dx}\right)_{hard} = \frac{2\pi k_c^2 e^4 NZ}{mc^2\beta^2}\left[\ln\left(\frac{\tau^2(\tau+2)}{2(I/mc^2)^2}\right) + F^{\pm}(\tau)\right]$$

$$= 2\pi r_0^2 mc^2\beta^{-2}NZ\left[\ln\left(\frac{\tau^2(\tau+2)}{2(I/mc^2)^2}\right) + F^{\pm}(\tau)\right] \quad (9.52)$$

where

$$F^-(\tau) = 1 - \beta^2 + \frac{\dfrac{\tau^2}{8} - (2\tau+1)\ln 2}{(\tau+1)^2}, \quad (9.53)$$

which is to be used for electrons, and

$$F^+(\tau) = 2\ln 2 - \frac{\beta^2}{12}\left[23 + \frac{14}{\tau+2} + \frac{10}{(\tau+2)^2} + \frac{4}{(\tau+2)^3}\right], \quad (9.54)$$

which is to be used for positrons.

Example 9.2.1
Use equations 9.52 and 9.53 to calculate the collision stopping power in water for a 1-MeV electron.

Solutions

$$1\,\mathrm{MeV} = (\gamma-1)mc^2 = \left(\frac{1}{\sqrt{1-\beta^2}} - 1\right)(0.511\,\mathrm{MeV}) \implies \beta^2 \cong 0.8856$$

From example 9.1.1, the electron density and the I value for water are, respectively,

$$n_{H_2O} = 3.346 \times 10^{23} \, \frac{\text{electrons}}{\text{cm}^3} \quad \text{and} \quad I_{H_2O} = 74.4 \, \text{eV}.$$

Since $mc^2\beta^2 = (0.511)(0.8856) \cong 0.453$ MeV, $\tau = \dfrac{E}{mc^2} = \dfrac{1}{0.511} \cong 1.96$, and from equation

9.50, $F^-(\tau) = 1 - 0.8856 + \dfrac{\dfrac{(1.96)^2}{8} - (4.92)\ln 2}{(2.96)^2} \cong -0.22$, one may then apply equation 9.52

to obtain the collision stopping power for a 1-MeV electron as:

$$\left(\frac{dE}{dx}\right)_c^{H_2O} = \frac{2\pi(2.818 \times 10^{-13} \text{ cm})^2 (0.511 \text{ MeV})(3.346 \times 10^{23} \text{ cm}^{-3})}{0.8856} \left[\ln\left(\frac{(1.96)^2(3.96)}{2\left(\dfrac{74.4 \text{ eV}}{511 \times 10^3 \text{ eV}}\right)^2} \right) - 0.22 \right]$$

$$\cong 1.88 \text{ MeV cm}^{-1} \quad \text{or} \quad 0.188 \text{ keV } \mu\text{m}^{-1}.$$

Comparison of the above result with that of example 9.1.1 shows that the collision stopping power for a 1-MeV proton is more than two orders of magnitude greater than that for a 1-MeV electron. This huge difference is mainly due to the difference in β^2 of the two particles.

9.3 Energy Loss of Charged Particles via Bremsstrahlung

As mentioned at the beginning of this chapter, a charged particle (mainly an electron or a position) can lose energy in matter via inelastic scattering with the Coulomb field of the atomic nucleus in the process called "bremsstrahlung," meaning "braking radiation." Figure 9.4 illustrates the bremsstrahlung process as an electron comes near an atomic nucleus and gets deflected. The incident electron decelerates (i.e., loses energy) when it is deflected, and the amount of energy lost is converted into a photon. As such, unlike the process of the collision loss, where the energy is locally transferred to the atoms and molecules in the matter, the energy lost by the incident charged particle in a bremsstrahlung process is not locally deposited.

This bremsstrahlung process is well studied in classical electrodynamics for electrons being deflected by a Coulomb field. The most general formula for radiated power as a function of angle is (Jackson, 1975):

$$\frac{dP}{d\Omega} = \frac{z^2 e^2}{16\pi^2 \varepsilon_0 c} \frac{\left| \vec{n} \times \left((\vec{n} - \vec{\beta}) \times \dot{\vec{\beta}} \right) \right|^2}{(1 - \vec{n} \cdot \vec{\beta})^5}, \tag{9.55}$$

where $\vec{\beta} = \vec{v}/c$, z is the charge of the incident particle, $\vec{n}$ is a unit vector pointing from the particle towards the observer, and $d\Omega$ is the differential solid angle.

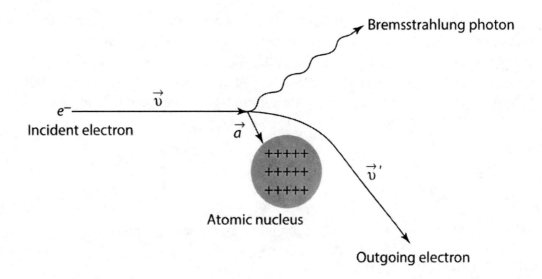

Figure 9.4. The bremsstrahlung process of a photon production as an electron comes near an atomic nucleus and gets deflected by the Coulomb force, and $\vec{a} = \vec{v} - \vec{v}'$.

In the case where velocity is parallel to acceleration, equation 9.55 is reduced to

$$\left(\frac{dP}{d\Omega}\right)_{/\!/} = \frac{z^2 e^2 a^2}{16\pi^2 \varepsilon_0 c^3} \frac{\sin^2 \theta}{(1 - \beta \cos\theta)^5}, \tag{9.56}$$

where θ is the angle between $\vec{a}$ and the direction of observation (see Figure 9.4). By integrating equation 9.55 over Ω, one obtains the general formula for total radiated power:

$$P = \frac{z^2 e^2 \gamma^4}{6\pi\varepsilon_0 c}\left(\dot{\beta}^2 + \frac{\left(\vec{\beta}\cdot\dot{\vec{\beta}}\right)^2}{1 - \beta^2}\right), \tag{9.57}$$

where $\gamma = 1/\sqrt{1 - \beta^2}$. In the case where velocity is parallel to acceleration, equation 9.57 is reduced to

$$P_{/\!/} = \frac{z^2 e^2 a^2 \gamma^6}{6\pi\varepsilon_0 c^3}, \tag{9.58}$$

where $a = \dot{v} = \dot{\beta}c$ is the acceleration. For the case where velocity is perpendicular to acceleration $(\vec{\beta}\cdot\dot{\vec{\beta}} = 0)$, equation 9.57 is reduced to

$$P_\perp = \frac{z^2 e^2 a^2 \gamma^4}{6\pi\varepsilon_0 c^3}. \tag{9.59}$$

Equations 9.58 and 9.59 show that, in general, the total radiated power is proportional to $\gamma^4 - \gamma^6$. Because electrons (or positrons) and protons have the same charge, they are subject to the same Coulomb force as they travel near an atomic nucleus. However, because the mass of a proton is much greater than that of an electron (or a positron), and because $\vec{F} = \gamma m \vec{a}$, the acceleration of a proton is much smaller than that of an electron (or a positron). From equation 9.59, for a proton and an electron (or a positron) having the same kinetic energy, the ratio of their radiative power can be estimated as

$$\frac{a_p^2 \gamma_p^4}{a_e^2 \gamma_e^4} = \left(\frac{\gamma_e m_e}{\gamma_p m_p}\right)^2 \left(\frac{\gamma_p}{\gamma_e}\right)^4 = \left(\frac{\gamma_p m_e}{\gamma_e m_p}\right)^2 < \left(\frac{m_e}{m_p}\right)^2 = \left(\frac{0.511}{938.28}\right)^2 = 2.97 \times 10^{-7}. \tag{9.60}$$

As such, radiative loss can be totally ignored for heavy charged particles.

9.3.1 Radiative Stopping Power

The above discussion is based on classical electrodynamics showing that the bremsstrahlung radiation is emitted whenever an electron is being deflected in a Coulomb field. According to quantum mechanics, however, the production of a photon in a bremsstrahlung process is similar to the process of a pair production, in that both involve an electron that, upon being deflected in a Coulomb field, only has a small chance of producing bremsstrahlung radiation. This is because the radiative process involves intermediate states (i.e., virtual negative energy states) so that the cross section for bremsstrahlung is of the order of 1/137 (the fine structure constant) times the cross section for elastic scattering. In other words, most of the individual deflections of incident electrons by atomic nuclei are elastic and do not produce bremsstrahlung. The above quantum-mechanical prediction of bremsstrahlung emission has been confirmed by experiments. In other words, the classical electrodynamics incorrectly predicted the emission of radiation in every collision in which an electron is deflected. Yet for the averages over a large number of collisions, both classical theory and quantum mechanics give a similar differential bremsstrahlung production cross section (Evans, 1955), shown below:

$$\frac{d\sigma_r}{d(h\nu)} = \alpha \, r_0^2 Z^2 \left(\frac{E + mc^2}{E}\right)\left(\frac{1}{h\nu}\right) B, \quad \text{cm}^2 \text{ nucleus}^{-1} \text{ eV}^{-1}, \tag{9.61}$$

where $\alpha \cong 1/137$ (the fine structure constant), $r_0 = 2.818 \times 10^{-13}$ cm (the classical electron radius), E is the kinetic energy of the incident electron, and B is a function of $h\nu$ shown in Figure 9.5. The stopping power of an electron due to radiative loss can be obtained by integrating equation 9.61 over $h\nu$ and multiplying it by the atomic number density. That is,

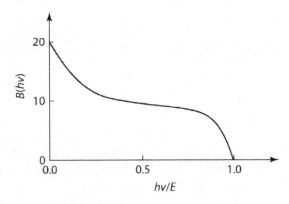

Figure 9.5. The parameter B versus $h\nu/E$.

$$\left(\frac{dE}{dx}\right)_r = N\int_0^E h\nu \, d\sigma_r = N\alpha \, r_o^2 Z^2 \left(E + mc^2\right)\int_0^1 B \, d\left(\frac{h\nu}{E}\right)$$

$$= N\alpha \, r_o^2 Z^2 \left(E + mc^2\right)\overline{B}, \tag{9.62}$$

where $\overline{B} = \displaystyle\int_0^1 B \, d\left(\frac{h\nu}{E}\right) \cong 10$. The total stopping power for an electron can then be expressed as the sum of the collision stopping power and the radiative stopping power. That is,

$$\left(\frac{dE}{dx}\right)_t = \left(\frac{dE}{dx}\right)_c + \left(\frac{dE}{dx}\right)_r. \tag{9.63}$$

Figure 9.6 shows the collision stopping power, radiative stopping power, and total stopping power of an electron in tungsten as a function of electron energy. The numerical values of these quantities for electrons, protons, and helium ions in various materials are available from the following website: www.nist.gov/pml/data/star.

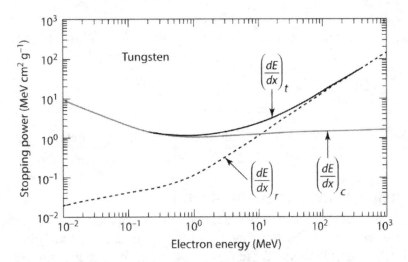

Figure 9.6. The collision stopping power, radiative stopping power, and total stopping power of electron in tungsten as a function of electron energy.

9.3.2 Radiation Yield

Empirically, the ratio of the radiative stopping power to the collision stopping power can be shown as

$$\frac{(dE/dx)_r}{(dE/dx)_c} \approx \frac{ZE}{750}, \tag{9.64}$$

where E is the numerical value of the electron energy when its unit is in MeV. For example, for a 10-MeV electron traveling in tungsten ($Z = 74$), equation 9.64 shows that the ratio of the radiative stopping power to the collision stopping power is about 1, which means the two mechanisms are equally responsible for slowing down the electron. Similarly, for a 1-MeV electron traveling in aluminum ($Z = 13$), equation 9.64 shows that the ratio of the radiative stopping power to the collision stopping power is about 0.017, which means the energy loss of the electron is almost entirely due to inelastic collisions. It should be noted, however, that the collision stopping power is made of a large number of energy-transfer events, of which each gives a small contribution, whereas the radiative stopping power is made of a few energy-transfer events, of which each gives a major contribution. In addition, the energy loss due to inelastic collisions is locally deposited, whereas the energy loss due to bremsstrahlung production is not deposited locally.

Equation 9.64 can be used to derive the radiation yield for an electron of kinetic energy E passing through a thin target. That is,

$$y(E) = \frac{(dE/dx)_r}{(dE/dx)_t} = \frac{(dE/dx)_r}{(dE/dx)_c + (dE/dx)_r} \cong \frac{1}{\frac{750}{ZE}+1} = \frac{ZE}{ZE+750}. \tag{9.65}$$

The radiation yield for an electron with an initial energy E_0 to be fully stopped in a thick target can be obtained by taking the average value of $y(E)$ over the range between 0 and E_0. That is,

$$Y(E_0) = \frac{1}{E_0} \int_0^{E_0} y(E)\, dE. \tag{9.66}$$

Specifically, for a relativistic electron when $E_0 \gg mc^2$, the following empirical formula is available:

$$Y(E_0, Z) \cong \frac{CE_0 Z}{1+CE_0 Z}, \tag{9.67}$$

where E_0 is the numerical value of the initial electron energy when its unit is in MeV, and $C \approx 6.0 \times 10^{-4}$.

9.3.3 Photon Spectrum from X-ray Machines

Bremsstrahlung-based X ray machines are commonly used in industry, medicine, and research. Depending on the application, these X ray machines produce X rays with energy ranges from a few tenths of keV to greater than 10 MeV. Regardless of their energy ranges, these machines are all based on bombarding a high-Z metal target, typically made of tungsten, with a beam of electrons. While the incident electrons are monoenergetic, the bremsstrahlung X rays emitted from the target have a broad energy spectrum. In general, the energy range of the bremsstrahlung X rays is proportional to the incident energy of the bombarding electrons. Theoretically, it is shown in equation 9.61 that when E and Z are fixed, the probability of a photon of energy hv being produced via bremsstrahlung is proportional to B, and inversely proportional to hv. As such, the bremsstrahlung X ray spectrum can be obtained by multiplying Figure 9.5 by hv^{-1} (Attix, 2004). A typical spectrum should look like Figure 9.7, which corresponds to the energy distribution of bremsstrahlung X rays emitted from a monoenergetic electron beam bombarding a very thin target, where the energy loss of the incident electrons is negligible.

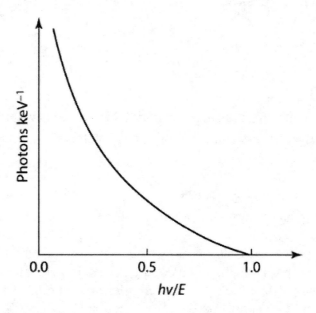

Figure 9.7. A typical thin-target bremsstrahlung photon spectrum.

In reality, however, because the target of most X-ray machines are thick enough to fully stop the electrons, most bremsstrahlung X-ray spectra look quite different from that shown in Figure 9.7. There are three aspects of spectrum shifting in a thick target. First, bremsstrahlung X rays are continuously produced as the electrons slow down and fully stop in the target. As such, the X-ray spectrum is the sum of the partial spectra produced by electrons with energies from its initial energy all the way down to zero. This makes the spectrum even more skewed towards the low-energy side than that shown in Figure 9.7. The second aspect has to do with self-absorption of the X rays by the target via photoelectric absorption. This preferentially knocks down the low-energy portion of the X-ray spectrum. The third aspect has to do with some K-shell electrons of the target atoms being knocked out by the incident electrons. The emission of characteristic X rays following the removal of the K-shell electrons thus adds to the overall X-ray spectrum emitted from a thick target. This third aspect, however, is only important for kilo-voltage X-ray machines (e.g., those used for diagnostic imaging in medicine). For mega-voltage X-ray machines (e.g., those used for cancer treatment and food irradiation), the low-energy portion of the spectrum (including the characteristic X rays) is purposely filtered out with an extra thick target. Figures 9.8a and 9.8b, respectively, show the spectra of the X rays emitted from a typical kilo-voltage X-ray machine and a typical mega-voltage X-ray machine.

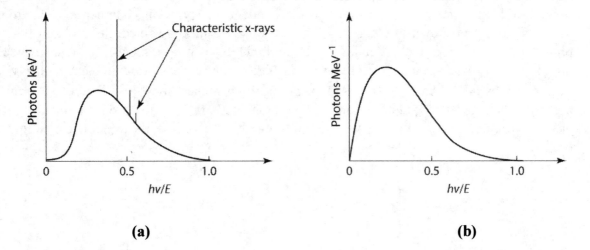

Figure 9.8. (a) A typical photon spectrum emitted from a kilo-voltage X-ray machine, and **(b)** a typical photon spectrum emitted from a mega-voltage X-ray machine.

9.4   Range of Charged Particles

Unlike neutrons and gamma rays that can travel freely in matter for quite some distance (centimeters to meters) without any interactions, charged particles continuously lose their energies via inelastic collisions. As such, unlike neutrons and gamma rays, of which the path lengths vary greatly, the path lengths of charged particles in general are much more defined. The distance a charged particle travels in matter before coming to rest is called the "range." Accordingly, the range of a charged particle is a function of its energy as well as the density of the matter, and in theory it can be calculated as

$$R(E) = \int_0^E \left(\frac{dE}{dx}\right)_t^{-1} dE,\qquad(9.68)$$

where $(dE/dx)_t$ is the total stopping power defined in equation 9.63. Since it is not easy to analytically carry out the integral in equation 9.68, the integral is usually carried out numerically using discretized values of stopping powers. As a first-order approximation, one can assume that the stopping power is constant throughout the particle track. The range can then be easily estimated by dividing the particle's energy with the stopping power. For example, the stopping powers of a 1-MeV proton and a 1-MeV electron in water are known from Examples 9.1.1 and 9.2.1 to be $272\,\text{MeV cm}^{-1}$ and $1.88\,\text{MeV cm}^{-1}$, respectively (see the examples in Sections 9.1 and 9.2). The ranges for a 1-MeV proton and a 1-MeV electron in water are therefore estimated to be $\dfrac{1\,\text{MeV}}{272\,\text{MeV cm}^{-1}} \cong 36.8\,\mu\text{m}$ and $\dfrac{1\,\text{MeV}}{1.88\,\text{MeV cm}^{-1}} \cong 5.3\,\text{mm}$, respectively. One must bear in mind that the results thus obtained are overestimates of the actual ranges, because the stopping power increases as the particle slows down.

The range obtained using the stopping power, however, is only an average quantity. In reality, the range of every particle (even if it is of the same type and with the exact same energy) is different due to the randomness of energy-transfer events occurring along each particle track. Generally speaking, the ranges for heavy charged particles are much better defined than the ranges for electrons and positrons, for two reasons: First, heavy charged particles are much more massive than the electrons, and therefore, they mostly travel in straight lines. Second, heavy charged particles lose their energies in smaller steps compared to electrons and positrons, and therefore, the degree of variation in energy loss is less for heavy charged particles. In other words, electrons and positrons not only continuously change their traveling directions via the numerous inelastic collisions, they also lose sizable amounts of energy via a few hard inelastic collisions or bremsstrahlung production events, which results in a large degree of variation in energy loss over each particle's track. For these reasons, the range defined in equation 9.68 (which is based on the stopping power) is strictly referred to as the continuous slowing down approximation (CSDA) range. Figure 9.9 shows the CSDA ranges versus energy for protons, alpha particles, and electrons in various materials. The numerical values of stopping powers, CSDA ranges, and radiation yield for electrons, positrons, and helium ions in various materials are available from the following website: www.nist.gov/pml/data/star.

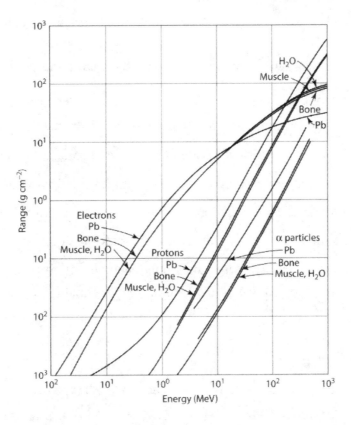

Figure 9.9. CSDA ranges versus energy for protons, alpha particles, and electrons in water, muscle, bone, and lead, expressed in $g\,cm^{-2}$.
Source: Turner (2007)

9.5   Characteristics of Charged Particle Tracks

The detailed structures of charged particle tracks are important in explaining the biological effectiveness of various types of ionizing radiations. In addition to the stopping power, the parameters depicting the structure of a charged particle include the mean free path (i.e., the average distance between two consecutive energy-transfer events), the average energy and range of secondary electrons (referred to as δ-rays), and the average direction change throughout the track length. The mean free path (MFP) for various types of interactions can be obtained from their corresponding cross sections. The total cross section for a charged particle can be expressed as the sum of the cross sections for the various types of interactions. That is,

$$\sigma_t = \sigma_c + \sigma_{el} + \sigma_r + \sigma_n, \tag{9.69}$$

where σ_t = the total cross section

σ_c = the cross section for inelastic collisions with atoms and molecules via the Coulomb force fields

σ_{el} = the cross section for elastic collisions with atoms and atomic nuclei via the Coulomb force fields

σ_r = the cross section for bremsstrahlung production via the Coulomb force fields of atomic nuclei

σ_n = the cross section for nuclear reactions via the strong force fields of atomic nuclei

The units of all the cross sections above are in cm^2 $atom^{-1}$. For practical reasons, we will ignore σ_n, as it is in general much smaller than other types of interactions. As discussed in Sections 9.1 and 9.2, σ_c can be further divided into two categories; one being associated with soft collisions, σ_c^s, and the other being associated with hard collisions, σ_c^h. As indicated, σ_{el} is associated with the elastic collisions with either atoms or atomic nuclei. For practical reasons, however, one may refer σ_{el} as the cross section for Rutherford scattering (i.e., elastic collision with the nucleus), as σ_{el} with atoms only becomes significant for charged particles with very low speed (or energy), where they are no longer capable of causing ionizations and excitations. Equation 9.69 can then be expressed as

$$\sigma_t = \sigma_c^s + \sigma_c^h + \sigma_{el} + \sigma_r. \tag{9.70}$$

Since MFP is inversely proportional to the cross section, each type of cross section in equation 9.64 has its own corresponding MFP (i.e., $\lambda_t, \lambda_c^s, \lambda_c^h, \lambda_{el},$ and λ_r). One useful rule of thumb is that inelastic soft collisions with small energy transfers represent an overwhelming majority of the events, that inelastic hard collisions with large energy transfers are rare, and that Rutherford scattering and bremsstrahlung production events are even less frequent. In other words,

$$\sigma_c^s \gg \sigma_c^h > \sigma_{el} > \sigma_r, \text{ which translates to } \lambda_c^s \ll \lambda_c^h < \lambda_{el} < \lambda_r. \tag{9.71}$$

The average kinetic energy of the δ rays can be estimated by multiplying the energy transfer, Q, with its corresponding differential cross sections, $d\sigma(Q)$ (given in equation 9.15), and then integrating over the range of Q for hard collisions. That is,

$$\overline{E}_\delta \approx \frac{1}{\sigma} \int_{Q_c}^{Q_{max}} Q \, d\sigma(Q).$$ (9.72)

where $\sigma = \int_{Q_c}^{Q_{max}} d\sigma(Q).$ As far as traveling direction goes, the general rule is that heavy charged particles mostly travel in straight lines, whereas electrons and positrons change directions continuously throughout the track length. Figure 9.10 shows two charged particle tracks in water: a 0.7-MeV proton track and a 20-MeV α particle track. Each dot represents an energy transfer event (i.e., excitation or ionization). The results were obtained from computer simulations based on the Monte Carlo method.

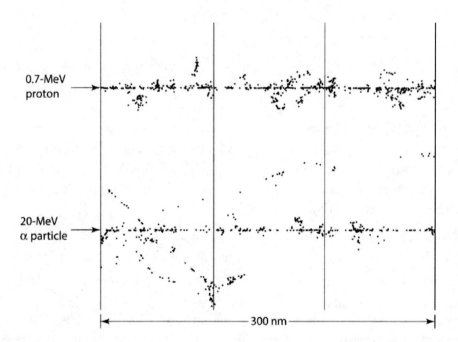

Figure 9.10. Two charged particle tracks in water: a 0.7-MeV proton track and a 20-MeV α particle track. While both particles have the same stopping power (≈ 33 keV μm^{-1}), the track structures appear to be quite different.

While both particles have the same stopping power (≈ 33 keV μm^{-1}), the track structures appear to be quite different, in that the energy transfer events are more densely packed at the nanometer scale along the 0.7-MeV proton track than the 20-MeV α particle track. This difference is mainly caused by the energetic δ rays along the 20-MeV α particle track, which form their own tracks away from the primary particle track. As discussed in Section 9.1, the maximum energy of a δ ray of a heavy charged particle track can be estimated by $2mc^2\beta^2$ (equation 9.19), where m is the electron rest mass. For a 0.7-MeV proton, β^2 can be calculated as

$$0.7\,\text{MeV} = (\gamma - 1)m_p c^2 = \left(\frac{1}{\sqrt{1-\beta^2}} - 1\right)(938.28\,\text{MeV}) \quad \Rightarrow \quad \beta^2 \cong 0.00149.$$

As such, the δ ray along a 0.7-MeV proton track has a maximum energy of

$$2(511\,\text{keV})(0.00149) = 1.52\,\text{keV}.$$

Further calculation using equation 9.72 shows that the average δ-ray energy is about 230 eV, which has a range of about 10 nm.

Similarly, for a 20-MeV α particle, β^2 can be calculated as

$$20\,\text{MeV} = (\gamma - 1)m_\alpha c^2 = \left(\frac{1}{\sqrt{1-\beta^2}} - 1\right)(3727.409\,\text{MeV}) \quad \Rightarrow \quad \beta^2 \cong 0.01065.$$

As such, the δ ray along a 20-MeV α particle track has a maximum energy of

$$2(511\,\text{keV})(0.01065) = 10.9\,\text{keV}.$$

Further calculation using equation 9.72 shows that the average δ-ray energy is about 395 eV, which has a range of about 20 nm, being twice as long as an average δ ray of the 0.7-MeV proton. It has been shown experimentally that the denser track structure of the 0.7-MeV proton makes it more effective than the 20-MeV α particle in causing biological damage (e.g., DNA double strand breaks, or DSBs).

The collision stopping power $(dE/dx)_c$ discussed in Sections 9.1 and 9.2 is also referred to as LET (linear energy transfer). In general, a radiation is called a high-LET radiation if $(dE/dx)_c > 10\,\text{keV}\,\mu\text{m}^{-1}$. Oppositely, it is called a low-LET radiation if $(dE/dx)_c < 1\,\text{keV}\,\mu\text{m}^{-1}$. As such, the 1-MeV proton of the example shown in Section 9.1 is a high-LET radiation, whereas the 1-MeV electron in that same example is a low-LET radiation. Electrons, gamma rays, and X rays are usually referred to as low-LET radiations. An alpha particle is a high-LET radiation. Depending on the energy, a proton is high-LET if its energy is < 5 MeV, and low-LET if its energy is > 50 MeV. In general, high-LET radiations are more effective in causing harmful biological effects because the dense ionization track is more capable of producing DNA DSBs, which may lead to chromosome aberrations, and cell death. Table 9.1 provides the track structure data for several charged particle types of different energies. These data include LET_∞, LET_{100}, and λ_c, as well as the average energy and range of the δ rays, where LET_{100} is the collision stopping power that excludes energy transferred to δ rays with energies > 100 eV, whereas LET_∞ is the collision stopping power that includes energy transferred to all δ rays.

Table 9.1. The track structure data for several charged particle types of different energies, where $\overline{E}_\delta$ and $\overline{R}_\delta$ are respectively the average energy and range of the δ rays. **Source:** Watt (1996)

Particle type/energy	LET_∞ (keV μm^{-1})	LET_{100} (keV μm^{-1})	λ_c (nm)	$\overline{E}_\delta$ (eV)	$\overline{R}_\delta$ (nm)
Proton					
0.1 MeV	81.5	67.97	1.62	106.4	4.4
0.3 MeV	55.0	33.05	3.54	174.5	7.5
0.5 MeV	41.3	23.85	5.64	207.2	9.2
0.7 MeV	33.3	18.92	7.69	230.7	10.4
1.0 MeV	26.1	14.74	10.71	257.2	11.8
1.5 MeV	19.6	11.17	15.39	289.2	13.5
2.0 MeV	15.9	8.78	21.02	313.1	14.9
4.0 MeV	9.4	5.11	42.08	374.2	18.5
Alpha					
1.2 MeV	208.0	150.5	0.95	163.0	7.0
2.0 MeV	162.5	92.94	1.44	207.2	9.2
3.0 MeV	125.7	71.93	2.08	235.5	10.6
4.0 MeV	103.5	58.63	2.74	257.2	11.8
5.0 MeV	88.6	51.54	3.35	273.2	12.6
6.0 MeV	77.8	44.44	3.97	289.2	13.5
8.0 MeV	63.1	34.94	5.38	313.1	14.9
10.0 MeV	53.4	30.52	6.58	330.7	15.9
16.0 MeV	37.5	20.31	10.66	274.2	18.5
20.0 MeV	31.5	16.93	13.37	394.8	19.7
Electron					
100 eV	27.8	27.8	1.41		
200 eV	22.2	22.2	1.78		
300 eV	19.6	19.3	2.16		
400 eV	17.9	16.9	2.54		

500 eV	16.5	14.8	2.92		
700 eV	14.3	11.8	3.67		
1 keV	12.0	9.23	4.75		
2 keV	7.75	5.46	8.25		
5 keV	3.82	2.59	18.1		
10 keV	2.32	1.47	33.1		
50 keV	0.657	0.412	123.4		
100 keV	0.418	0.251	200.0		
1 MeV	0.184	0.106	532.4		

Bibliography

Attix, Frank H. *Introduction to Radiological Physics and Radiation Dosimetry*. Weinheim, Germany: WILEY-VCH, Verlag GmbH & Co. KGa, 2004.

Evans, Robley D. *The Atomic Nucleus*. New York: McGraw-Hill, Inc., 1955.

Internaional Commision on Radiation Units and Measurements, *Stopping Powers for Electrons and Positrons*, ICRU Report 37, 1984.

Jackson, John D. *Classical Electrodynamics*, 2nd edition, New York: John Wiley & Sons, Inc., 1975.

Turner, James E. *Atoms, Radiation, and Radiation Protection*. Weinheim, Germany: WILEY-VCH, Verlag GmbH & Co. KGa, 2007.

Watt, D. E. *Quantities for Dosimetry of Ionizing Radiations in liquid Water*. Bristol, PA: Taylor & Francis Inc., 1996.

Credits

Problems

1. Use Bethe stopping power formula to calculate the collisional stopping power (in keV/μm) of a 1-MeV proton slowing down in aluminum (Z = 13, ρ = 2.7g cm⁻³).

2. Repeat the same calculation of problem 1 for a 1-MeV electron.

3. Consider a proton and an alpha particle with the same energy, which particle can transfer more energy to an electron in a single collision?

4. Consider a proton and an alpha particle with the same velocity incident on a water target, which will penetrate deeper into the target? Justify your answer in a quantitative manner.

5. Use the Bethe's collision stopping power to estimate the CSDA range for 1.7-MeV beta particle in silicon. Assume that the radiative contribution to the total stopping power is negligible.

6. Astatine-211 (^{211}At) is an alpha-emitting isotope that is used in radiation therapy by attaching it to a monoclonal anibody. The energy of the ^{211}At alpha particle is 6.87 MeV.
   (a) Compute the stopping power (-dE/dx) of water for the ^{211}At alpha particle.
   (b) What is its range in water.

7. Estimate kinetic energy at which the collisional and radiative stopping powers are equal for electrons in (a) Al and (b) W.

8. Estimate the radiation yields for electrons with initial energies of 100 keV and 10 MeV, respectively, to be fully stopped in tungsten.

9. If the mass collision stopping power for 25-MeV electrons in tungsten is approximately 1.3 MeV cm² g⁻¹, (a) use the empirical formula (equation 9.58) to estimate the total stopping power for 25-MeV electrons, and (b) what is the radiation yield in tungsten?

10. Inhalation of alpha-emitting radionuclides is a cause of concern, due to their potential for causing lung cancer in exposed individuals. Explain succinctly why alpha particles can cause significant biological damage using, among others, concepts such as the linear energy transfer (LET) and the particle track structure.

11. As shown, a 1 μA 10-MeV electron beam is brought to perpendicularly impinge on a thin (20 μm) lead foil with $Z = 82$ and $\rho = 11.3$ g cm⁻³.

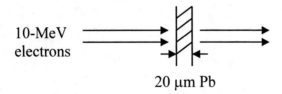

10-MeV electrons

20 μm Pb

Both soft and hard collisions are responsible for the collisional energy loss of a 10-MeV electron. That is,

$$\left(\frac{dE}{dx}\right)_c = \left(\frac{dE}{dx}\right)_{soft} + \left(\frac{dE}{dx}\right)_{hard},$$

(a) Assuming $Q_c = 1\,\text{keV}$, use equations 9.50 and 9.51 to calculate $\left(\dfrac{dE}{dx}\right)_{hard}$ and $\left(\dfrac{dE}{dx}\right)_{soft}$, respectively.

(b) Since the total stopping power is the sum of the collisional stopping power and the radiative stopping power; i.e. $\left(\dfrac{dE}{dX}\right)_t = \left(\dfrac{dE}{dX}\right)_c + \left(\dfrac{dE}{dX}\right)_r$, use equation 9.64 to estimate the average power (in watts) of the bremsstrahlung radiation produced in the lead foil.

CHAPTER 10: INTERACTIONS OF GAMMA PHOTONS WITH MATTER

Photons of interest to our studies have energies in the range of 10 eV to 10 MeV. Specifically, photons with energies in the range of 10 keV to 10 MeV are highly penetrating in materials. Interactions of these photons with matter are of great importance in radiation shielding design, medical and industrial imaging, medical radiotherapy dosimetry, and radiation protection dosimetry. Because photons are electromagnetic in nature, they mainly interact with atoms and atomic electrons via electromagnetic forces. But when the energy of a photon is sufficiently high ($\geq$ ~7 MeV, the nucleon binding energy), it is also possible to undergo the so-called photonuclear reactions; for example, (γ, n), (γ, p), and $(\gamma, \text{fission})$.

In the energy range of our concern (10 eV to 10 MeV), the major types of photon interactions with matter include elastic scattering, inelastic scattering, photoelectric effect, and pair production. Elastic scattering occurs when an incident photon is bounced off from an atom or an atomic electron with no energy loss. Inelastic scattering occurs when an incident photon transfers some of its energy to an atomic electron and scatters off as a lower-energy photon. Photoelectric effect occurs when the energy of an incident photon is completely transferred to an atomic electron, ejecting it from the atom. Pair production occurs when an incident photon disappears in the vicinity of an atomic nucleus, and its energy is converted into an electron and a positron.

There are two types of elastic scattering. The first type is called Rayleigh scattering, which occurs between the incident photon and many electrons of an atom collectively, and is therefore a type of coherent scattering. The second type is called Thomson scattering, which occurs between the incident photon and an individual free electron, and is therefore a type of incoherent elastic scattering. Inelastic scattering, on the other hand, can only be a type of incoherent scattering because it mainly occurs between the incident photon and an individual electron. In other words, incoherent scattering that occurs between the incident photon and an individual electron can be either elastic or inelastic. The elastic one is called Thomson scattering. As a rule of thumb, photoelectric effect is the predominant interaction mechanism for low-energy photons; Compton scattering (the main type of inelastic scattering) is the predominant interaction mechanism for the intermediate energy range; and pair production is the predominant interaction mechanism for high-energy photons. The above rule of thumb is shown in Figure 10.1 in terms of cross sections versus incident photon energy for various interaction types for lead. Also shown in Figure 10.1 is that elastic scattering is of little importance, because its cross section is much smaller than that of photoelectric effect for the same energy range. As such, in the sections below we will only discuss the three major types of interaction mechanisms: photoelectric effect, Compton scattering, and pair production.

10.1 Photoelectric Effect

As shown in Figure 10.2, the photoelectric effect is a process where the incident photon is absorbed by an atom and an electron is ejected as a result. The ejected electron is referred to as the photoelectron. Since the electrons are bound in an atom, from an energy conservation standpoint the energy of the incident photon must be greater than the electron's binding energy in order to knock it out. From a momentum conservation viewpoint, the process must involve three particles: the incident photon, the photoelectron, and the recoil ion. That is, the linear momentum carried by the incident photon cannot be fully conserved unless the ion takes some momentum.

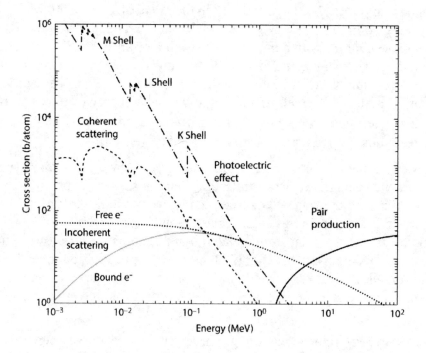

Figure 10.1. Atomic cross sections versus incident photon energy for various interaction types for lead.
Source: Cullen (1994).

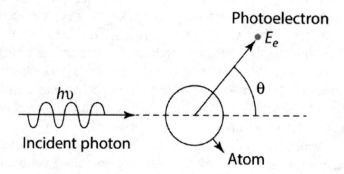

Figure 10.2. A schematic representation of the photoelectric effect process.

Because the mass of the ion is far greater than the mass of the electron, the kinetic energy of the ion can be ignored in the energy conservation equation. As such, the kinetic energy of the photoelectron can be obtained as

$$E_e = hv - B_e,\tag{10.1}$$

where hv is the energy of the incident photon and B_e is the binding energy of the electron.

Figure 10.1 shows that the cross section of photoelectric effect has several discontinuities (or edges) corresponding to the binding energies $(B_e)_K$, $(B_e)_L$, and $(B_e)_M$, for K-shell, L-shell, and M-shell electrons, respectively. The total photoelectric cross section per atom includes contributions from electrons in all atomic shells. That is, $\sigma_{pe} = (\sigma_{pe})_K + (\sigma_{pe})_L + (\sigma_{pe})_M + \ldots$ where $(\sigma_{pe})_K$, $(\sigma_{pe})_L$, and $(\sigma_{pe})_M$ are, respectively, the photoelectric cross sections contributed from electrons in K shell, L shell, and M shell. From an energy conservation viewpoint, however, only the electrons with binding energies less than the incident photon energy can participate in the photoelectric effect. As such, $(\sigma_{pe}) = (\sigma_{pe})_K$ if $hv > (B_e)_K$, $\sigma_{pe} = (\sigma_{pe})_K + (\sigma_{pe})_L$ if $(B_e)_L < hv < (B_e)_K$, $\sigma_{pe} = (\sigma_{pe})_K + (\sigma_{pe})_L + (\sigma_{pe})_M$, if $(B_e)_M < hv < (B_e)_L$, and so on. The ratio of the total photoelectric cross section of the entire atom to the photoelectric cross section for the two K-shell electrons has been evaluated for photon energies just above the K-shell binding energy. This ratio is given by the following empirical formula:

$$\frac{\sigma_{pe}}{(\sigma_{pe})_K} = 1 + 0.01481(\ln Z)^2 - 0.00079(\ln Z)^3.\tag{10.2}$$

For most elements, this ratio is less than 1.2. This means that for $hv > (B_e)_K$, photoelectric interactions mainly occur with the two K-shell electrons, even though there are many more electrons on the outer shells in an atom. Similarly, for $(B_e)_L < hv < (B_e)_K$, photoelectric interactions mainly occur with the L-shell electrons; and for $(B_e)_M < hv < (B_e)_L$, photoelectric interactions mainly occur with the M-shell electrons. The photoelectric cross section for the K-shell electrons has been evaluated using quantum mechanical techniques to be a strong function of hv and Z, and can be expressed by the empirical formula below:

$$(\sigma_{pe})_K = C\frac{Z^n}{(hv)^m},\tag{10.3}$$

where C is a constant, n varies between 4 and 5 for $0.1\,\mathrm{MeV} < hv < 3\,\mathrm{MeV}$, and m varies between 3.5 and 1 for $0.1\,\mathrm{MeV} < hv < 5\,\mathrm{MeV}$.

The angular distribution of the K-shell photoelectrons has also been evaluated by quantum mechanical techniques, and it is shown below in terms of the differential cross section per unit solid angle:

$$\frac{d(\sigma_{pe})_K(hv,\theta)}{d\Omega} = C\frac{Z^n}{(hv)^m}\frac{\sin^2\theta}{\left[1 - \left(\dfrac{p_e c}{mc^2}\right)\cos\theta\right]^4},\tag{10.4}$$

where *C*, *n*, *m*, are the same as that for equation 10.3, and p_e is the momentum of the photoelectron; it can be obtained from equation 1.10: $p_e = \frac{1}{c}\sqrt{E_e^2 + 2mc^2 E_e}$. Equation 10.4 is graphically shown in Figure 10.3 for $n = 5$ and $m = 3.5$. As shown, photoelectrons are preferably emitted into the directions that are perpendicular to the incident photon, and their chance of moving in forward and backward directions (i.e., $\theta = 0°$ and $180°$) approaches zero.

Techniques that take advantage of the strong dependence of $(\sigma_{pe})_K$ on *hv* and *Z* have been developed in both medicine and industry for obtaining images with good contrast. For example, the good contrast between bones and soft tissues shown in the traditional planar X ray images is

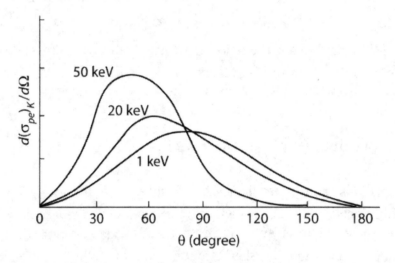

Figure 10.3. The angular distribution of photoelectrons for incident photons of various energies in low-Z materials.
Source: Anderson (1984)

mainly due to the high content of calcium ($Z = 20$) in the bone. The value of $(\sigma_{pe})_K$ for calcium is much higher than that for soft tissues ($Z < 8$) for photons with energies above $(B_e)_K$ for calcium, which is about 4 keV. As such, incident photons with energies above 4 keV (but not too much greater) will be preferentially absorbed by the bone and thus produce an image with good contrast between bones and soft tissues. Photons with energies too much greater ($hv > 100\,\text{keV}$) are less useful because $(\sigma_{pe})_K$ decreases rapidly as *hv* increases.

Example 10.1.1

A 200-keV photon undergoes the photoelectric effect in lead with a K-shell electron. What is the kinetic energy and momentum of the ejected photoelectron? How is the electron's momentum compared to that of the incident photon?

Solution

From www.nist.gov/pml/data/xraycoef/index.cfm, it can be found that $(B_e)_K \cong 88\,keV$ for lead. From equation 10.1, the kinetic energy of the photoelectron can be calculated as $E_e = h\nu - B_e = 200\,keV - 88\,keV = 112\,keV$. The momentum of the electron can be obtained as

$$p_e = \frac{1}{c}\sqrt{E_e^2 + 2mc^2 E_e} = \frac{1}{c}\sqrt{(112\,keV)^2 + 2(511\,keV)(112\,keV)} \cong \frac{356.4\,keV}{c}.$$

The momentum of the incident photon is $p_\gamma = \dfrac{E_\gamma}{c} \cong \dfrac{200\,keV}{c}$. So the momentum of the ejected photoelectron is greater than the momentum of the incident photon!

10.2 Compton Scattering

Compton scattering is a scattering interaction between the incident photon and a free electron during which the photon transfers a fraction of its energy to the electron. It is the main type of inelastic scattering, and becomes predominant as the photon's energy significantly exceeds the material's K-shell electron binding energy. As shown in Figure 10.4, the incident photon with energy $h\nu$ transfers some of its energy to the electron and then scatters off with a lower energy $h\nu'$. The kinematics of Compton scattering will be treated in detail below by using the conservation laws of energy and linear momentum, and by assuming the electron is at rest before the collision (Podgorsak, 2010). To obtain the differential cross sections for Compton scattering, however, requires the treatment of relativistic quantum electrodynamics, which is beyond the scope of this book, and therefore will only be treated phenomenologically below.

10.2.1 Kinematics of Compton Scattering

Because the binding energy of the electron is negligible, the law of energy conservation of the Compton scattering can be written as

$$h\nu = h\nu' + E_e. \tag{10.5}$$

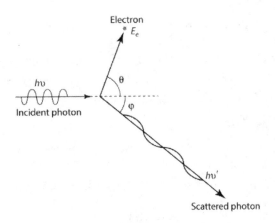

Figure 10.4. A schematic representation of the Compton scattering process.

By applying the conservation of momentum before and after the collision, one obtains the following two equations for x-direction and y-direction, respectively:

$$p_\gamma = \frac{hv}{c} = \frac{hv'}{c}\cos\varphi + p_e\cos\theta \quad \Rightarrow \quad p_e c\cos\theta = hv - hv'\cos\varphi \tag{10.6}$$

and

$$p_e\sin\theta = \frac{hv'}{c}\sin\varphi \quad \Rightarrow \quad p_e c\sin\theta = hv'\sin\varphi, \tag{10.7}$$

where p_γ and p_e are, respectively, the momenta of the incident photon and the recoil electron, θ and φ are, respectively, the scattering angles of the recoil electron and the scattered photon. By squaring equations 10.6 and 10.7 and then adding them together, one obtains

$$(p_e c)^2 = (hv)^2 - 2(hv)(hv')\cos\varphi + (hv')^2, \tag{10.8}$$

where $(p_e c)^2$ also has a relativistic relationship with E_e, expressed by

$$(p_e c)^2 = (E_e)^2 + 2E_e mc^2. \tag{10.9}$$

Replacing E_e with $hv - hv'$ in equation 10.9 gives:

$$(p_e c)^2 = (hv)^2 - 2(hv)(hv') + (hv')^2 + 2(hv - hv')mc^2. \tag{10.10}$$

Subtraction of equation 10.8 from 10.10 then gives $0 = 2(hv)(hv')(1 - \cos\varphi) - 2(hv - hv')mc^2$, which leads to

$$hv' = \frac{hv}{1 + \tau(1 - \cos\varphi)}, \tag{10.11}$$

where $\tau = hv/mc^2$. Equation 10.11 is a powerful formula showing that the relationship between hv' and hv is solely a function of the scattering angle φ. Substituting equation 10.11 into 10.5, one obtains a similar formula for the recoil electron; that is,

$$E_e = hv - hv' = hv - \frac{hv}{1 + \tau(1 - \cos\varphi)}. \tag{10.12}$$

According to equation 10.11, $hv' = hv$ for $\varphi = 0$, which is consistent with the limit that there is no interaction between the incident photon and the target electron. On the other hand, for a head-on collision (i.e., $\varphi = \pi$), equation 10.11 is reduced to

$$hv'\Big|_{\varphi=\pi} = \frac{hv}{1 + 2\tau}, \tag{10.13}$$

which corresponds to the minimum value of hv'. In other words, $\dfrac{hv}{1 + 2\tau} \leq hv' \leq hv$. The maximum energy for E_e can then be obtained as

$$\left(E_e\right)_{max} = E_e\big|_{\varphi=\pi} = h\nu - h\nu'\big|_{\varphi=\pi} = h\nu - \frac{h\nu}{1+2\tau} = \left(\frac{2\tau}{1+2\tau}\right)h\nu. \qquad (10.14)$$

In other words, $0 \le E_e \le \left(\dfrac{2\tau}{1+2\tau}\right)h\nu$. Equations 10.12 and 10.14 show that the fraction of energy of an incident photon that can be transferred to a free electron during a Compton scattering process increases as the incident photon's energy increases. This can be appreciated from the concept of the virtual mass of a photon. That is, while a photon is massless, it does have a linear momentum, $h\nu/c$. The virtual mass of a photon (m') can be obtained by making $p_\gamma = m'c$, the momentum of a particle with rest mass m' traveling at the speed c. Since $p_\gamma = h\nu/c$, this leads to $m' = h\nu/c^2$. As such, for low-energy photons with $h\nu \ll mc^2$, it translates to $m' \ll m$. And for high-energy photons with $h\nu \gg mc^2$, it translates to $m' \cong \gamma m$. This makes equations 10.12 and 10.14 consistent with the phenomenon in classical collisions where an incident lightweight particle can only transfer a very small fraction of its energy to a heavyweight target particle, whereas an incident particle can transfer all of its energy to the target particle when both particles have the same weight (see equations 7.28 and 9.18). A subtle difference shown in equation 10.14, however, is that a massless photon can never completely transfer all of its energy to a target electron (which has a rest mass), as in a classical collision between two particles of equal mass.

Example 10.2.1

A 0.662-MeV gamma photon from a ^{137}Cs source is Compton scattered at an angle of 60°. Calculate the energy, momentum, and direction of the recoil electron. How does the momentum of the electron compare to that of the incident photon?

Solution

From equation 10.12, $E_e = h\nu - \dfrac{h\nu}{1+\tau(1-\cos\varphi)}$, where $\tau = \dfrac{h\nu}{mc^2} = \dfrac{0.662\,\text{MeV}}{0.511\,\text{MeV}} = 1.2955$

$$\Rightarrow E_e = h\nu - \frac{h\nu}{1+\tau(1-\cos\varphi)} = 0.662 - \frac{0.662}{1+(1.2955)(1-\cos 60°)} \cong 0.26\,\text{MeV}$$

$$\Rightarrow p_e = \frac{1}{c}\sqrt{E_e^2 + 2mc^2 E_e} = \frac{1}{c}\sqrt{(260\,\text{keV})^2 + 2(511\,\text{keV})(260\,\text{keV})} \cong \frac{577\,\text{keV}}{c}.$$

From equation 10.7,

$$p_e \sin\theta = p_\gamma' \sin\varphi \quad \Rightarrow \quad \sin\theta = \left(\frac{p_\gamma'}{p_e}\right)\sin\varphi, \text{ where } p_\gamma' = \frac{E_\gamma'}{c} = \frac{E_\gamma - E_e}{c} = \frac{0.402\,\text{MeV}}{c}$$

$$\Rightarrow \quad \sin\theta = \left(\frac{p_\gamma^{'}}{p_e}\right)\sin\varphi = \left(\frac{402\text{ keV}}{577\text{ keV}}\right)\sin 60^\circ = 0.6034 \Rightarrow \theta = 37.1^\circ.$$

The momentum of the incident photon is $p_\gamma = \dfrac{E_\gamma}{c} \cong \dfrac{662\text{ keV}}{c}$. So the momentum of the ejected Compton electron is less than the momentum of the incident photon.

10.2.2 The Klein-Nishina Cross Section

Klein and Nishina in 1929 applied the methods of quantum electrodynamics and obtained the differential cross section for Compton scattering as

$$\frac{d\sigma_{KN}(hv,\varphi)}{d\Omega} = \frac{r_o^2}{2}\left\{\frac{1+\cos^2\varphi}{\left[1+\tau(1-\cos\varphi)\right]^2} + \frac{\tau^2(1-\cos\varphi)^2}{\left[1+\tau(1-\cos\varphi)\right]^3}\right\}, \tag{10.15}$$

where τ and φ are the same as that defined in equation 10.11, and r_o = the classical electron radius = 2.818×10^{-13} cm. For low-energy photons, of which $\tau \to 0$, equation 10.15 is reduced to

$$\frac{d\sigma_{KN}(hv,\varphi)}{d\Omega} = \frac{r_o^2}{2}\left(1+\cos^2\varphi\right), \tag{10.16}$$

which is exactly the same formula as that derived by Thomson using the methods of classical electrodynamics for non-polarized electromagnetic waves. Figure 10.5 is a plot of the Klein-Nishina (KN) cross section (i.e., equation 10.15) for photons with various energies. As shown, the cross section is highly forwardly directed for high-energy photons, and becomes more symmetric in forward and backward directions for low-energy photons.

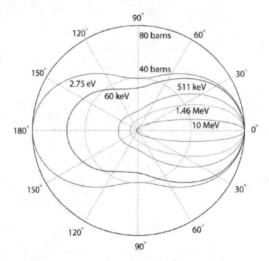

Figure 10.5. The Klein-Nishina cross section plotted in the polar coordinate for photons with various energies.

By replacing $d\Omega$ with $2\pi \sin\varphi \, d\varphi$ and then integrating equation 10.15 for φ from 0 to π, one obtains the total cross section for Compton scattering per electron. That is,

$$\sigma_{KN}(hv) = \int_0^\pi \frac{d\sigma_{KN}(hv,\varphi)}{d\Omega} d\Omega = \int_0^\pi \frac{r_0^2}{2} \left\{ \frac{1+\cos^2\varphi}{\left[1+\tau(1-\cos\varphi)\right]^2} + \frac{\tau^2(1-\cos\varphi)^2}{\left[1+\tau(1-\cos\varphi)\right]^3} \right\} 2\pi \sin\varphi \, d\varphi$$

$$= \pi r_0^2 \int_0^\pi \left\{ \frac{1+\cos^2\varphi}{\left[1+\tau(1-\cos\varphi)\right]^2} + \frac{\tau^2(1-\cos\varphi)^2}{\left[1+\tau(1-\cos\varphi)\right]^3} \right\} \sin\varphi \, d\varphi$$

$$= 2\pi r_0^2 \left\{ \left(\frac{1+\tau}{\tau^2} \right) \left[\frac{2(1+\tau)}{1+2\tau} - \frac{\ln(1+2\tau)}{\tau} \right] + \frac{\ln(1+2\tau)}{2\tau} - \frac{1+3\tau}{(1+2\tau)^2} \right\}.$$

$$(10.17)$$

The KN free-electron formula (equation 10.15) is usually valid for valence electrons. For inner-shell electrons (especially those of high-Z elements), this formula needs to be corrected for the effects of electron binding. This is done by multiplying equation 10.15 by the so-called incoherent scatter function, $S(hv,\varphi,Z)$. The corrected incoherent KN scattering cross section, $d\sigma_{is} = d\sigma_{KN}(hv,\varphi)S(hv,\varphi,Z)$, decreases at low incoming photon energies. Figure 10.6 shows both σ_{KN} and σ_{is} as functions of the incident photon energy for lead. Obviously this correction factor can be ignored for low-Z materials as the electron binding energies are negligible.

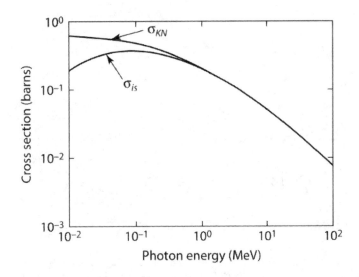

Figure 10.6 The total KN cross sections σ_{KN} and σ_{is} as functions of the incident photon energy for lead.
Source: Anderson (1984)

If one assumes that all the atomic electrons are free and each has the same σ_{KN} as that given by equation 10.17, then the total Compton scattering cross section per atom would be the atomic number times σ_{KN}. That is,

$$\sigma_{cs} \cong Z\sigma_{KN}. \tag{10.18}$$

The results of $Z\sigma_{KN}$ obtained this way agree well with the measured results for photons interacting with low-Z materials. However, $Z\sigma_{KN}$ greatly overestimates σ_{cs} for low-energy photons interacting with high-Z materials. This is because the inner-shell electrons of high-Z atoms are tightly bound and therefore are not available as free electrons for Compton scattering. This overestimation is clearly shown in Figure 10.1.

Example 10.2.2

Assume the Klein-Nishina (KN) formula of Compton scattering for all gamma-ray energies can be approximated by

$$\frac{d\sigma}{d\Omega} = \frac{r_o^2}{2}(1 + \cos\varphi)^2.$$

Calculate (a) the Compton scattering cross section per atom, σ_{cs} (in cm^2 atom^{-1}), and (b) the linear attenuation coefficient, μ_{cs} (in cm^{-1}), for a 1-MeV photon interacting with aluminum ($A = 27, Z = 13$, and $\rho = 2.7$ g cm^{-3}).

Solution

(a) $\sigma_{KN} = \int \frac{d\sigma}{d\Omega} d\Omega = \frac{r_o^2}{2} \int_0^\pi (1 + \cos\varphi)^2 (2\pi \sin\varphi d\varphi)$

$\quad = -\pi r_o^2 \int_0^\pi u^2 du$ (where $u = 1 + \cos\varphi$ and $du = -\sin\varphi d\varphi$)

$\quad = \frac{8}{3}\pi r_o^2 = \frac{8}{3}\pi(2.818 \times 10^{-13} \text{ cm})^2 \cong 6.653 \times 10^{-25} \text{ cm}^2$

From equation 10.18, $\sigma_{cs} \cong Z\sigma_{KN} = (13)(6.653 \times 10^{-25} \text{ cm}^2) \cong 8.65 \times 10^{-24} \text{ cm}^2 \text{ atom}^{-1}$.

(b) $N = \frac{\rho}{A}N_a = \frac{2.7 \text{ g cm}^{-3}}{27 \text{ g mole}^{-1}}(6.02 \times 10^{23} \text{ atoms mole}^{-1}) = 6.02 \times 10^{22} \text{ atoms cm}^{-3}$

$\mu_{cs} = N\sigma_{cs} = (6.02 \times 10^{22} \text{ atoms cm}^{-3})(8.65 \times 10^{-24} \text{ cm}^2 \text{ atom}^{-1}) \cong 0.52 \text{ cm}^{-1}$

10.3 Pair Production

As mentioned in Section 1.5, a pair of an electron and a positron can be created by bombarding a thin piece of high-Z material (e.g., lead or tungsten) with high-energy gamma photons. The pair-production process cannot take place in a vacuum. As shown in Figure 10.7, it mainly occurs in the vicinity of an atomic nucleus, where the incident photon disappears and in its place an electron and a positron are created. Without the nucleus, the conservation of energy and momentum cannot be held simultaneously. One can prove this by simply applying the conservation equations of energy and momentum before and after the process, without the involvement of a nucleus. That is,

Energy conservation: $hv = \sqrt{p_-^2 c^2 + m^2 c^4} + \sqrt{p_+^2 c^2 + m^2 c^4} \quad \Rightarrow \quad hv > p_- c + p_+ c$ (10.19)

Momentum conservation: $p_\gamma = \dfrac{hv}{c} = p_- \cos\theta_- + p_+ \cos\theta_+ \quad \Rightarrow \quad hv < p_- c + p_+ c$, (10.20)

where p_γ, p_- and p_+ are, respectively, the momenta of the incident photon, the electron, and the positron. Obviously, equations 10.19 and 10.20 cannot be held simultaneously. With the presence of a nucleus, these two equations , respectively, become

$$hv > p_- c + p_+ c + E_N \qquad (10.21)$$

and

$$hv < p_- c + p_+ c + p_N c, \qquad (10.22)$$

where E_N and p_N are, respectively, the kinetic energy and momentum of the recoil nucleus. Equations 10.21 and 10.22 can now be held simultaneously as long as $p_N c > E_N$. In fact, pair production is also possible in the vicinity of an atomic electron, but its probability is negligible compared to that in the vicinity of a nucleus.

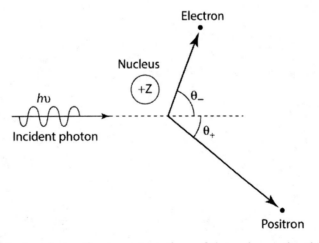

Figure 10.7. A schematic representation of the pair-production process.

Because the mass of the nucleus is far greater than the masses of the electron and positron, the kinetic energy of the recoil nucleus is negligible (i.e., $E_N \cong 0$) compared to that of the electron and positron. As such, the energy conservation equation can be written as:

$$hv \cong \sqrt{p_-^2 c^2 + m^2 c^4} + \sqrt{p_+^2 c^2 + m^2 c^4} = 2mc^2 + E_- + E_+, \qquad (10.23)$$

where E_- and E_+ are the kinetic energies of the electron and positron, respectively. From equation 10.23, it is obvious that the energy of the incident photon must exceed the threshold energy (i.e., $2mc^2$ or 1.022 MeV) in order for pair production to occur. The excess amount of energy ($hv - 1.022$ MeV) is shared by the electron and the positron as their kinetic energies. The probability of how this amount of energy is distributed between the electron and the positron is determined by a quantum mechanical method in which the atomic differential cross section for pair production is shown to be

$$\frac{d\sigma_{pp}}{dT_+} = \frac{\alpha \, r_o^2 Z^2 f}{hv - 2mc^2}, \qquad (10.24)$$

where $\alpha \cong 1/137$ (the fine structure constant), $r_o = 2.818 \times 10^{-13}$ cm (the classical electron radius), and f is a function of $hv, E_+,$ and Z shown in Figure 10.8. As shown, the probability tends to be in favor of equally splitting the available amount of energy between the electron and the positron. The quantum mechanical method also showed that the angular distributions of the positrons and electrons are generally forwardly directed. Figure 10.9 shows the angular distribution per unit solid angle for positrons. As shown, the distribution becomes even more forwardly directed as the kinetic energy of the positron increases. Because of the symmetry between positrons and electrons in the pair-production process, Figure 10.9 also applies to electrons.

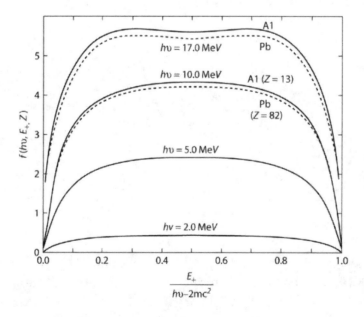

Figure 10.8. The function f in equation 10.24, plotted as a function of $hv, E_+,$ and Z.
Source: Anderson (1984)

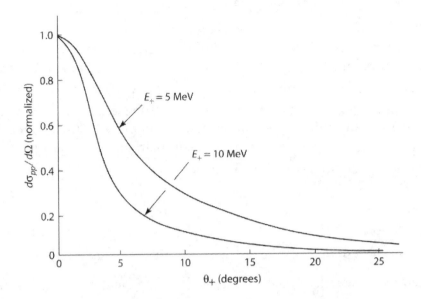

Figure 10.9. The angular distribution per unit solid angle for positrons of two different energies.
Source: Anderson (1984)

The atomic cross section for pair production can be obtained by integrating the differential cross section of 10.24 over E_+ as

$$\sigma_{pp}(h\nu, Z) = \alpha\, r_0^2 Z^2 \int_0^1 f(h\nu, E_+, Z)\, d\left(\frac{E_+}{h\nu - 2mc^2}\right) = \alpha\, r_0^2 Z^2 g(h\nu, Z), \qquad (10.25)$$

where $g(h\nu, Z)$ is shown in Figure 10.10 as monotonically increasing as $h\nu$ increases. Accordingly, the atomic cross section for pair production is most important for high-energy photons interacting with high-Z materials.

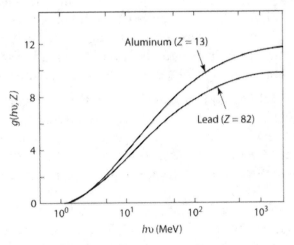

Figure 10.10 The function g in equation 10.25, plotted as a function of $h\nu$ and Z.
Source: Anderson (1984)

10.4 The Gamma-Ray Attenuation Coefficients

Conventionally, the probability of a gamma photon undergoing a collision per unit distance as it travels through material is called the "linear attenuation coefficient" (instead of the "macroscopic cross section" for neutrons), which has the symbol μ (instead of Σ for neutrons). Experimentally, μ is obtained via two measurements made with the setup of a narrow-beam geometry described in Figure 1.4. One measurement is made without the material and the second measurement is made with the material in place. If the two recordings of the radiation detector are C_o and C, respectively, then the ratio of C to C_o is the attenuation factor. Equation 1.24 can then be used to obtain μ. That is,

$$\frac{C}{C_o} = e^{-\mu\ell} \quad \Rightarrow \quad \mu = -\frac{1}{\ell}\ln\left(\frac{C}{C_o}\right), \tag{10.26}$$

where ℓ is the thickness of the material in cm, and μ therefore has a unit of cm^{-1}.

Since there are three major types of interactions involved, μ is often expressed as the sum of the contributions from all three interaction types. That is,

$$\mu = N(\sigma_{pe} + \sigma_{cs} + \sigma_{pp}) = \mu_{pe} + \mu_{cs} + \mu_{pp}, \tag{10.27}$$

where N is the atomic number density of the material, and σ_{pe}, σ_{cs}, and σ_{pp} are, respectively, the atomic cross sections for photoelectric effect, Compton scattering, and pair production. More common in data presentation is to divide 10.27 by the physical density of the material to obtain the mass attenuation coefficient:

$$\frac{\mu}{\rho} = \frac{N}{\rho}(\sigma_{pe} + \sigma_{cs} + \sigma_{pp}) = \frac{\mu_{pe}}{\rho} + \frac{\mu_{cs}}{\rho} + \frac{\mu_{pp}}{\rho}. \tag{10.28}$$

Figure 10.11 shows the various components of μ/ρ versus the incident photon energy for a low-Z material (carbon) and a high-Z material (lead), respectively. The curves shown in Figure 10.11 are consistent with those shown in Figure 10.1 in that photoelectric effect prevails for low-energy photons; that Compton scattering prevails for the intermediate energy range; and that pair production prevails for high-energy photons. It should be noted, however, that the intermediate energy range (where Compton scattering prevails) is much broader in low-Z materials than in high-Z materials. This point is further stressed in Figure 10.12, which shows the equal reaction probability lines for the three types of photon interactions.

We now use Figure 10.12 to explain some important points in gamma-ray shielding. First, photons with energies between 1 MeV and 5 MeV are most difficult to be shielded against. The reason is not only because Compton scattering is the only available interaction type in this energy range, but also because a Compton scattering event does not remove the incident photon and it often takes multiple Compton scattering events to reduce the energy of a photon in this energy range to below 0.5 MeV, where absorption by photoelectric effect can take place. Second, high-Z materials (e.g., lead and tungsten) in general provide much better shielding against gamma rays than do the low-Z materials. This is because for high-Z materials the photoelectric cross section is fairly high up to photon energy of ~0.5 MeV, and at the same time the pair production cross section is significantly large for photon energy above ~5 MeV.

It should be noted that, unlike the situation in Compton scattering, the incident photon is completely removed by either photoelectric effect or pair production. While there are characteristic X rays and 0.511-MeV photons (from positron-electron annihilation) reemitted after photoelectric effect and pair production, these low-energy secondary photons can be stopped by a relatively small thickness of high-Z material. The numerical values of linear attenuation coefficients for various materials are available from the following website: www.nist.gov/pml/data/xraycoef/.

Example 10.4.1

A 1-MeV photon beam is brought to perpendicularly impinge on a 1-cm thick lead plate. Given that $\mu = \mu_{pe} + \mu_{cs}$, and that $\mu_{pe} = 0.5$ cm^{-1} and $\mu_{cs} = 0.7$ cm^{-1}, calculate the percentage of the incident photons that would undergo photoelectric effect and Compton scattering, respectively.

Solution

The probability of an incident photon penetrating the lead plate can be obtained as

$$e^{-\mu\ell} = e^{-(\mu_{pe} + \mu_{cs})\ell} = e^{-(0.5+0.7)(1.0)} = e^{-1.2} = 0.301.$$

The probability of the photon to undergo an interaction would be $1 - e^{-\mu\ell} = 1 - 0.301 = 0.699$, of which photoelectric effect represents $0.699\left(\dfrac{\mu_{pe}}{\mu}\right) = 0.699\left(\dfrac{0.5}{0.5+0.7}\right) = 0.291$, or 29.1%,

and the rest (40.8%) goes to Compton scattering.

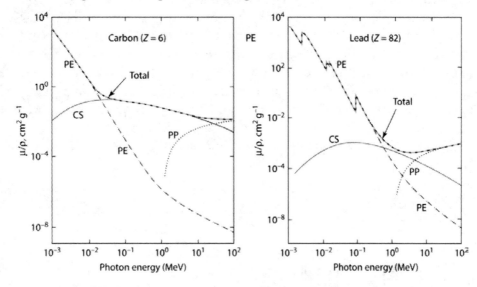

Figure 10.11. The various components of μ/ρ versus the incident photon energy for a low-Z material (carbon) and a high-Z material (lead).
Source: Cullen et al. (1989a and 1989b).

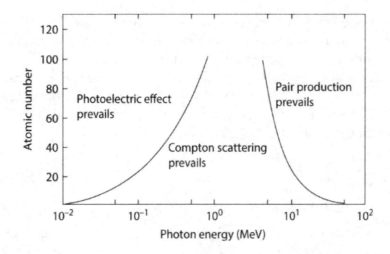

Figure 10.12. Equal probability lines for the three types of photon interactions.

10.5 Absorbed Dose, Kerma, Energy Transfer and Energy Absorption Coefficients

As mentioned in Section 1.7, the most basic radiation quantity in health and medical physics applications is the absorbed dose. It is defined as the energy absorbed per unit mass of the object of concern (e.g., a human organ). It is quite difficult to calculate the absorbed gamma dose in an object because one must know the radiation field in great detail, including the fluence and energy spectrum of the gamma rays as well as that of the electrons released from gamma-ray interactions in that object. The calculation, however, can be greatly simplified if one assumes that the energy of the electrons is absorbed in the immediate vicinity of their release. This assumption is valid for most applications because the electrons released from gamma-ray interactions usually dissipate all their energies within a few millimeters, which is much smaller than the object of concern (e.g., a human organ). Under such a condition, the absorbed dose can be approximated by a quantity called "kerma," the <u>k</u>inetic <u>e</u>nergy of charged particles <u>r</u>eleased per unit <u>ma</u>ss of a material (Attix, 2004). This quantity can be calculated by multiplying the number of gamma interactions per unit mass, which is $\mu\phi/\rho$, with the fraction of the gamma-photon energy that is transferred (or converted) into the kinetic energy of the electrons. That is,

$$D \cong K = \frac{1}{\rho}\mu\phi f E_\gamma, \tag{10.29}$$

where D, K, ϕ, E_γ are, respectively, the absorbed dose, kerma, photon fluence, and gamma photon energy, and f is the fraction of the photon energy that is transferred (or converted) into the kinetic energy of the electrons. Depending on the complexity of the geometric configuration involved in the problem, the photon fluence ϕ can be calculated either by analytical equations or by solving the photon transport equation using computers. The coefficient f is less straightforward because the energy transfer fraction is different for different types of gamma-ray interaction, and because μ is made of different types of interactions. To obtain f one must separately examine the energy transfer fraction for each type of gamma-ray interaction. The energy transfer fraction for photoelectric effect can be obtained as

$$f_{pe} = \frac{hv - p_K Y_K \overline{(hv)}_K - p_L Y_L \overline{(hv)}_L - \cdots}{hv} \cong \frac{hv - p_K Y_K \overline{(hv)}_K}{hv},$$

(10.30)

where

$hv = $ the energy of the incident photon

$p_K = $ the fraction of the photoelectric-effect interactions that occur in the K-shell

$Y_K = $ the yield of characteristic X ray due to the ejection of a K-shell electron

$p_L = $ the fraction of the photoelectric-effect interactions that occur in the L-shell

$Y_L = $ the yield of characteristic X ray due to the ejection of a K-shell electron

$\overline{(hv)}_K = $ the mean energy of characteristic X rays resulting from the ejection of a K-shell electron

$\overline{(hv)}_L = $ the mean energy of characteristic X rays resulting from the ejection of an L-shell electron

The energy transfer fraction for Compton scattering can be expressed as

$$f_{cs} = \frac{\overline{E}_e}{hv},$$

(10.31)

where $\overline{E}_e$ is the mean energy of the recoil electron in a Compton scattering event, and it can be calculated by multiplying equation 10.12 by equation 10.15 (the Klein-Nishina formula), and integrating over the entire solid angle of 4π. That is,

$$\overline{E}_e = \frac{1}{\sigma_{KN}(hv)} \int_{4\pi} E_e \frac{d\sigma_{KN}(hv,\varphi)}{d\Omega} d\Omega$$

$$= \frac{1}{\sigma_{KN}(hv)} \int_0^\pi \left(hv - \frac{hv}{1+\tau(1-\cos\varphi)} \right) \frac{d\sigma_{KN}(hv,\varphi)}{d\Omega} 2\pi \sin\varphi \, d\varphi,$$

(10.32)

where $\sigma_{KN}(hv)$ is that shown in equation 10.17.

The energy transfer fraction for pair production is the simplest of the three, and it can be obtained as

$$f_{pp} = \frac{E_- + E_+}{hv} = \frac{hv - 2mc^2}{hv}.$$

(10.33)

We now define the energy transfer coefficient as

$$\mu_{tr} = \mu f = (\mu_{pe} + \mu_{cs} + \mu_{pp}) f = \mu_{pe} f_{pe} + \mu_{cs} f_{cs} + \mu_{pp} f_{pp},$$

(10.34)

which leads to $f = \dfrac{\mu_{pe} f_{pe} + \mu_{cs} f_{cs} + \mu_{pp} f_{pp}}{\mu_{pe} + \mu_{cs} + \mu_{pp}}$. (10.35)

Equation 10.29 can then be written as

$$D \cong K = \frac{1}{\rho} \mu \, \phi \, E_\gamma f = \frac{\mu_{tr}}{\rho} \phi \, E_\gamma .$$ (10.36)

Equation 10.36 works well overall, except for high-energy photons interacting with high-Z materials. This is because, in high-Z materials, high-energy photons may undergo pair production and high-energy recoil electrons may undergo bremsstrahlung production. In either case, some of the kinetic energy of the electron (or positron) will be converted back to photons and thus will not be locally absorbed. To compensate for this error, another quantity called the energy absorption coefficient was introduced. It is defined as

$$\mu_{en} = \mu_{tr}(1-g),$$ (10.37)

where g is the average fraction of the kinetic energy of secondary charged particles (produced in all the types of interactions) that is subsequently lost in radiative (photon-emitting) energy-loss processes as the particles slow to rest in the medium. The evaluation of g is accomplished by integrating the cross section for the radiative process of interest over the differential track-length distribution established by the particles in the course of slowing down. Accordingly, the kerma K of equation 10.36 can be divided into two parts, the collision kerma K_c and the radiative kerma K_r. That is,

$$K = K_c + K_r ,$$ (10.38)

where $K_c = K(1-g) = \dfrac{\mu_{tr}}{\rho}(1-g)\phi \, E_\gamma$, and $K_r = Kg = \dfrac{\mu_{tr}}{\rho}\phi \, E_\gamma g$. Collision kerma is most closely related to the absorbed dose, as it corresponds to the portion of the electron's energy that is locally dissipated via the collisional loss (i.e., as ionization and excitation of nearby atoms). As such, equation 10.36 is further modified as

$$D \cong K_c = \frac{\mu_{tr}(1-g)}{\rho} \phi \, E_\gamma = \frac{\mu_{en}}{\rho} \phi \, E_\gamma .$$ (10.39)

The numerical values of μ_{en}/ρ as a function of photon energy for various materials are available from the following website: www.nist.gov/pml/data/xraycoef.

Example 10.5.1

A mouse is being irradiated with a 1-Ci ^{137}Cs gamma source. Assuming the source is a point source and the mouse is 30 cm away from the source, calculate the collision kerma rate $\dot{K}_c$ received by the mouse. Is $\dot{K}_c$ a good approximation of the absorbed dose rate $\dot{D}$ in this case?

Solution

Figure 6.13(b) shows that the gamma yield is 0.85 for each decay of ^{137}Cs and the gamma photon energy is 0.662 MeV. Since $1 \text{ Ci} = 3.7 \times 10^{10}$ decays/s, the gamma fluence rate at the mouse can be calculated as

$$\dot{\phi}_\gamma = \frac{3.7 \times 10^{10} \text{ decays s}^{-1}(0.85 \text{ photon decay}^{-1})}{4\,\pi(30\,\text{cm})^2} = 2.78 \times 10^6 \frac{\text{photons}}{\text{cm}^2\,\text{s}}.$$

The value of μ_{en}/ρ for tissue is found to be 0.0324 cm^2 g^{-1}. The collision kerma rate can then be obtained from equation 10.39:

$$\dot{K}_c = \frac{\mu_{en}}{\rho}\dot{\phi}_\gamma E_\gamma = (0.0324\,\text{cm}^2\,\text{g}^{-1})\left(2.78 \times 10^6 \frac{\text{photons}}{\text{cm}^2\,\text{s}}\right)(0.662\,\text{MeV photon}^{-1})$$

$$= 5.96 \times 10^4 \text{ MeV g}^{-1}\,\text{s}^{-1}(1.6 \times 10^{-13} \text{ joules MeV}^{-1})(10^3 \text{ g kg}^{-1})(3600 \text{ s hr}^{-1})$$

$$= 3.43 \times 10^{-2} \text{ joules kg}^{-1}\,\text{hr}^{-1} \text{ or } 0.0343 \text{ Gy hr}^{-1}.$$

The $\dot{K}_c$ calculated above is a good approximation of the $\dot{D}$ received by the mouse for two reasons. First, the electrons released from the interactions of 0.662-MeV photons have ranges less than 2 mm, which is much smaller than the size of the mouse. On the other hand, the mean free path (MFP) of a 0.662-MeV photon is approximately 10 cm, which is much greater than the size of a mouse. As such, the value of $\dot{\phi}_\gamma$ calculated above is relatively uniform across the entire body of the mouse. Should the MFP of the photon be comparable or smaller then the size of the mouse, there will be significant attenuation of the incident photons rendering a nonuniform distribution of $\dot{\phi}_\gamma$ (and thus $\dot{D}$) in the mouse body.

10.6 Characteristic X Ray and Auger Emission

We mentioned in Section 2.6 that characteristic X rays can be produced by bombarding atoms with electrons of energy greater than the binding energies of the inner-shell electrons of the atom. The creation of a vacancy in an atomic subshell brings the atom to a highly excited state. It then follows with a series of complex transitions as the vacancy moves to outer subshells and the atom relaxes back to its stable state. Because photoelectric effect creates a vacancy in an inner atomic subshell, it is accompanied by this atomic relaxation process. It turns out that there are two types of transitions, radiative and non-radiative, that are involved in the relaxation process. The emission of characteristic X rays is a part of radiative transition.

Non-radiative transition is also called the Auger emission, named after the physicist P. Auger. It refers to the process that the initial vacancy is filled by an electron from an outer subshell and the available energy (due to the difference in the binding energies of the two subshells) results in the removal of another electron from either the same subshell or one further out. This process produces two electron vacancies. The kinetic energy of the Auger electron can be calculated using the example of lead ($Z = 82$) shown in Figure 10.13. In this case, the transition starts from a vacancy in the K shell, which results in two vacancies in the subshells L1 and L2. The kinetic energy of the electron ejected from subshell L2 can be calculated as

$$E_{K-L1-L2} = (88.29 - 15.847) - 15.251 = 57.192 \text{ keV.}$$

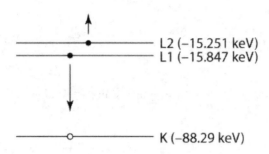

Figure 10.13. An Auger emission starting with a vacancy in K shell, which results in two vacancies in the subshells L1 and L2.

As a rule of thumb, the transition that starts with a vacancy in the K shell of a high-Z element is strongly in favor of the radiative process. That is, the radiative transition probabilities are significantly greater than the non-radiative transition probabilities. The transition probability data for various transition processes and elements are available via the US government report (Perkins, 1991). In addition to the photoelectric effect, the two radioactive decay modes, electron capture (EC) and internal conversion (IC), also create a vacancy in an inner atomic subshell, and therefore, are also accompanied by the emission of characteristic X rays and Auger electrons.

Bibliography

Anderson, David W. *Absorption of Ionizing Radiation.* Baltimore: University Park Press, International Publishers in Medicine and Human Services, 1984.

Attix, Frank H. *Introduction to Radiological Physics and Radiation Dosimetry.* Weinheim, Germany: WILEY-VCH, Verlag GmbH & Co. KGa, 2004.

Cullen, D. E. *A Computer Program to Allow Viewing of EPIC Data Libraries.* Report UCRL-ID-116819. Livermore, CA: Lawrence Livermore National Laboratory, 1994.

Cullen, D. E., Chen, M. H., Hubbell, J. H., Perkins, S. T., Plechaty, E. F. et al. *Tables and Graphs of Photon-Interaction Cross Sections from 10 eV to 100 GeV Derived from the LLNL Evaluated Photon Data Library (EPDL), Part A: Z=1 to 50.* Report UCRL-50400, Vol. 6, Part A, Rev. 4. Livermore, CA: Lawrence Livermore National Laboratory, 1989a.

Cullen, D. E., Chen, M. H., Hubbell, J. H., Perkins, S. T., Plechaty, E. F. et al. *Tables and Graphs of Photon-Interaction Cross Sections from 10 eV to 100 GeV Derived from the LLNL Evaluated Photon Data Library (EPDL), Part A: Z=51 to 100.* Report UCRL-50400, Vol. 6, Part B, Rev. 4. Livermore, CA: Lawrence Livermore National Laboratory, 1989b.

Evans, Robley D. *The Atomic Nucleus*. New York: McGraw-Hill, Inc., 1955.

Perkins, S. T., Cullen, D. E., Chen, M. H., Hubbell, J. H., Rathkopf, J. et al. *Tables and Graphs of Atomic Subshell and Relaxation Data Derived from the LLNL Evaluated Atomic Data Library (EADL), Z=1-100*. Report UCRL-50400, Vol. 30. Livermore, CA: Lawrence Livermore National Laboratory, 1991.

Podgorsak, Ervin B. *Radiation Physics for Medical Physicists*, 2nd ed. Berlin Heidelberg: Springer-Verlag, 2010.

Turner, James E. *Atoms, Radiation, and Radiation Protection*, 3rd ed. Weinheim, Germany: Wiley-VCH Verlag GmbH & Co. KGa, 2007.

Credits

Problems

1. Which is the predominant type of photon interactions in a material, for:
   (a) low-energy (below a few tens of keV) photons?
   (b) intermediate-energy (from a few tens of keV to a few MeV) photons?
   (c) high-energy (above a few MeV) photons?

2. What type of dependence with Z (atomic number of the material) is observed for:
   (a) the pair production cross-section of photons?
   (b) the photoelectric cross-section?

3. A 1-MeV photon is scattered at an angle of 60°, with respect to its incident direction.
   (a) What is the energy of the scattered electron?
   (b) What is the angle between the paths of the scattered electron and the incident photon?

4. Consider photons of different energies, incident on soft tissue (density 1 g cm^{-3}). Use the values of mass attenuation coefficients at http://www.nist.gov/pml/data/xraycoef/ to determine the mean free path (λ) in soft tissue for: (a) 10-keV photons, (b) 100-keV photons, and (c) 6-MeV photons. In view of the results, discuss which energy you would use for medicl imaging.

5. Assume that the Klein-Nishina (KN) formula of Compton scattering can be approximated by

   $$\frac{d\sigma}{d\Omega} = \frac{r_o^2}{2}(1+\cos\varphi)^2,$$

   where r_o = the classical electron radius = 2.818 x 10^{-13} cm, and φ is the scattering angle.
   (a) Calculate the average energy of the recoil electron in a single Compton scattering event.
   (b) Calculate the average scattering angle (φ) of the scattered photon in a single Compton scattering event.
   (c) Calculate, on average, how many Compton scattering events are needed for a 1-MeV photon to lose its energy to below 0.1 MeV.

6. A 5-MeV photon creates an electron-positron pair in the field of a nucleus. What is the total kinetic energy of the pair?

7. Use Appendix B to calculate the threshold energy for this photonuclear reaction: $^{12}C(\gamma,n)^{11}C$.

8. An experiment is carried out with monoenergetic photons in the "narrow beam" geometry (similar to Figure 1.4) to measure the attenuation coefficients of a metal. Assuming that the background and scattered radiation are negligible, that the thickness of the metal sheet is 1 cm, and that the count rates of the detector (with and without the metal sheet placed between the photon source and the detector) are 8,119 counts sec^{-1} and 10,000 count sec^{-1}, what is the linear attenuation coefficient of the metal?

9. A beam of 500-keV photons is incident on a slab of iron (density 7.8 g cm^{-3}) of 5 cm thickness. The mass attenuation coefficient for photons of this energy in iron is 0.08414 cm^2 g^{-1}.

   (a) What fraction of the incident photons will transmit through the slab?
   (b) What is the mean free path of the incident photons in iron?

(c) What will be the predominant type of photon interaction inside the slab?

10. A 250-keV photon beam is normally incident on a 2-cm thick sheet of aluminum pressed against a 2-mm thick sheet of lead behind it. The densities of aluminum and lead are 2.7 g cm^{-3} and 11.3 g cm^{-3}, respectively. Use the values of mass attenuation coefficients available from http:/www.nist.gov/pml/data/xraycoef/ and answer the following questions:
    (a) What fraction of incident photons interacts with aluminum?
    (b) What fraction of incident photons interacts with lead?
    (c) What will be the answers for (a) and (b) if the order of aluminum and lead is switched?

11. For problem 10, if the photon beam fluence rate is 1.0x10^8 photons cm^{-2} s^{-1}, use the values of the mass absorption coefficients available from the same website to answer the following questions.
    (a) What fraction of the incident photon energy is absorbed in aluminum?
    (b) What fraction of the incident photon energy is absorbed in lead?
    (c) What are the absorbed dose rates in aluminum and lead?

12. The electron binding energies of K, L1, and L2 shells in tungsten are given to be 69.69 keV, 12.08 KeV, and 11.57 keV, respectively. A transition starting from a vacancy in the K shell results in the emission of a characteristic X ray photon and the emission of an Auger electron. The X ray photon is due to the electron transition from L1 to K, and the Auger electron is emitted from the L2 shell. What are the energies of the photon and electron, respectively?

CHAPTER 11: APPLICATIONS OF IONIZING RADIATION

This final chapter is dedicated to making connections between the physics learned from the previous chapters and the real-world practices in three closely related fields: nuclear engineering, medical physics, and health physics. Nuclear engineering, as a profession, particularly involves the design, fabrication, construction, operation, and maintenance of systems and components like nuclear reactors, nuclear power plants, and/or nuclear weapons. Medical physics, as a profession, particularly involves the use of ionizing radiation for diagnosis and treatment of human diseases. Health physics, as a profession, particularly concerns with the recognition, evaluation, and control of health hazards due to the use of ionizing radiation. The first two sections are related to nuclear engineering. The next two sections are related to medical physics. The last section is related to health physics.

11.1 Nuclear Fission Reactor-Based Systems

As of January 2016, there are about 440 commercial electricity-generating nuclear power reactors operable in thirty-one countries, with over 380 GWe of total capacity. About sixty-five or more new reactors are being built in fifteen countries. They provide approximately eleven percent of the world's electricity as continuous, reliable, base-load power, without carbon dioxide emissions. There are about 240 research reactors in operation. These reactors are of a much smaller scale in both size and power level compared to the commercial power reactors, and are mainly used as high-intensity neutron sources for research purposes, or occasionally for isotopes production. Lastly, there are about 180 reactors in operation to power some 140 ships and submarines. These reactors are mostly referred to as thermal reactors, because the energy produced is mainly from thermal neutron-induced fission reactions.

Nuclear power plants work in a similar way as those powered by fossil fuels, in that they both use their fuels to produce thermal energy, which converts water into steam, which in turn drives turbines and electric generators. The difference is how they produce the thermal energy. A nuclear power plant produces thermal energy in the nuclear reactor core, which resides inside a pressure vessel. This difference, however, makes the construction cost of a nuclear power plant far greater than that of a plant based on fossil fuel. The reason is because, in addition to the thermal power, a nuclear reactor also produces huge amounts of ionizing radiation and radioactivity, which can cause a tremendous human health hazard if not properly dealt with. Figure 11.1 shows a schematic diagram of a nuclear power plant.

There are two major types of commercial thermal power reactors—the pressurized water reactor (PWR) and the boiling water reactor (BWR). The PWR is the most widely used type, and it employs two water loops. The water in the primary loop is pumped through the reactor to remove the thermal energy produced in the reactor. The primary water is held at sufficiently high pressure (~2200 psia) that it stays in the liquid form while passing through the reactor. The pressurized hot water is then passed through a steam generator, which converts the water in the secondary loop into steam, which is in turn sent to the turbine. The reactor shown in Figure 11.1 is a PWR. The BWR, on the other hand, has only one water loop. The pressure in the loop is much lower than that of the PWR, so it allows water to boil into steam as it passes through the reactor. The steam is then directly sent to the turbine.

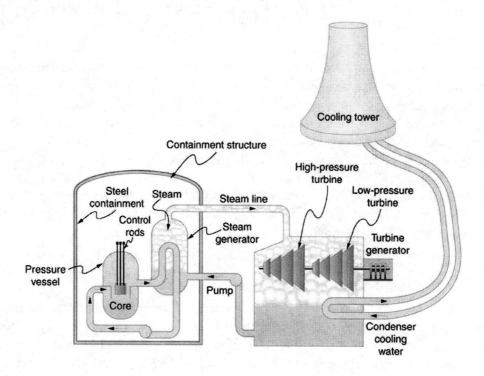

Figure 11.1. Schematic diagram of a nuclear power plant based on a pressurized water reactor.

11.1.1 Thermal Reactors

Depending on the design, the core of a PWR or BWR may contain dozens of fuel assemblies (also known as fuel bundles), each of which in turn may contain two hundred or more fuel rods. Each fuel rod is a sealed metal tube inside which a large number of fuel pellets (made of uranium oxide) are stacked together. The fuel rod is approximately 3.7 m (or 12 ft) long and 1 cm in diameter. Figure 11.2 shows a typical fuel rod, along with a fuel assembly. An overwhelming majority of the radioactivity produced by a nuclear reactor comes from the fission products (see Section 7.3.2) that are produced in the fuel rods. There are at least three engineered barriers (shown in Figures 11.1 and 11.2) included in a nuclear power plant to prevent the radioactivity from being released into its surroundings in case an accident occurs. These barriers include the fuel rod cladding, the reactor pressure vessel, and the containment structure.

Similarly, there are two layers of radiation shielding built around the reactor to stop the huge amount of neutrons and gamma rays from escaping. The first layer is called "thermal shielding", and the second "biological shielding." The thermal shielding is located inside the reactor vessel. It is made of heat-resistant material (e.g., steel or cast iron). The biological shielding is located outside the reactor vessel, and it is made of reinforced concrete. The purpose of the thermal shield is to significantly reduce the neutron and gamma-ray fluxes to levels that are acceptable to the biological shielding. Without it, the biological shielding cannot withstand the elevated temperatures caused by the high fluxes of neutrons and gamma rays.

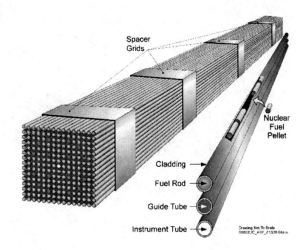

Figure 11.2. Geometric description of nuclear fuel pellet, fuel rod, and fuel assembly.

During normal operation, water enters the reactor from the bottom of the fuel assembly and rises up in the direction parallel to the axis of the assembly. Water not only serves as the coolant carrying out the thermal energy produced in the fuel rods, it also serves as the neutron moderator, which slows down the fission neutrons from an average energy of ~2 MeV to the thermal-equilibrium range of ~0.025 eV. As discussed in Section 8.6.2, the neutron-induced fission cross section for ^{235}U is inversely proportional to the neutron speed. Effectively slowing neutrons down to the thermal range, therefore, significantly increases the chance for neutrons to cause fissions. This, in turn, would allow a system with relatively low concentrations of fissile materials to achieve self-sustaining nuclear chain reactions.

Figure 11.3 illustrates the schematic details as to how energy released from a fission reaction is converted to heat and how the accompanied neutrons and gamma rays escape from the fuel rod and deposit their energy in water. As shown, when a fission reaction occurs inside a fuel rod, the energy released is mostly in the form of the kinetic energy of the two fission fragments. According to Section 7.4.2, for a thermal neutron-induced fission of ^{235}U, the two fission fragments carry approximately 170 MeV, which represents 93% of the total prompt energy release per fission reaction. The remaining 7% is carried by neutrons and gamma rays. Since the fission fragments are massive charged ions, their traveling ranges in the fuel pellet are less than 1 micrometer. Consequently, the 170 MeV carried by the fission fragments is instantly and locally converted to heat in the fuel rod. While Figure 11.3 only shows one neutron and one gamma photon coming out of a fission, in reality there are on average 2.4 neutrons and 10 gamma photons emitted in each fission, and they carry approximately 5 MeV and 7 MeV, respectively. The average energy of a prompt fission neutron is therefore about 2.1 MeV, and that of a gamma photon about 0.7 MeV. Because of their long mean free paths, these neutrons and gamma photons can easily wander out of the original fuel rod and undergo multiple interactions with the surrounding water or other fuel rods. As such, the energy carried by neutrons and gamma rays is converted to heat quite some distance away from the original fuel rod.

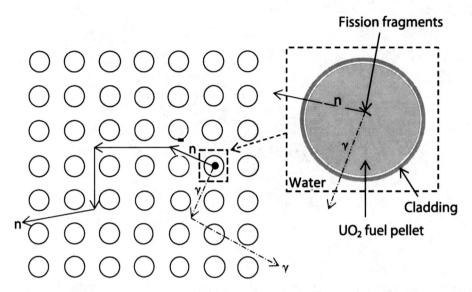

Figure 11.3. A simplified 2-D view of a 7 x 7 fuel assembly and an enlarged fuel rod, illustrating how the energy released from a fission reaction is converted to heat and how the accompanied fission neutrons and gamma photons escape from the fuel rod and interact with water.

For a nuclear reactor to be able to generate a constant power level, it must be operated under a condition called "self-sustained nuclear chain reaction." This is possible because each fission reaction produces two or more neutrons. If one of these neutrons can be used to trigger another fission reaction, then the neutron-induced fission reactions are self-sustained (and thus the constant power level is maintained). Since the fission reactions in a thermal reactor are mostly triggered by thermal neutrons, a newly born 2.1-MeV fission neutron must undergo a "slowing-down" process to become "thermalized" before it is used to trigger another fission reaction. The most effective process for slowing down a neutron is via a score of elastic collisions with hydrogen in water. It can be shown (using the nuclear kinematics discussed in Section 7.3) that a neutron on average loses half of its energy in an elastic collision with a hydrogen nucleus. Thus, for a 2.1 MeV to slow down to 0.025 eV (i.e., a factor of $\sim 1.2 \times 10^{-8}$) it would undergo on average 26.3 elastic collisions with hydrogen nuclei in water as $\left(\frac{1}{2}\right)^{26.3} \cong 1.2 \times 10^{-8}$. One can then estimate the total slowing-down path length of a neutron by multiplying its mean free path (MFP) by the number of collisions. This path length is the total distance the neutron travels from its birth until it is thermalized. It can be found from the nuclear data library that the neutron elastic scattering cross section for hydrogen is between ~ 3 barns (at 2 MeV) and ~ 20 barns (at 0.025 eV). If one takes an intermediate value of 10 barns for a hydrogen nucleus and assumes the cross section of the oxygen nucleus is negligible, then the macroscopic cross section of neutron in water can be estimated as

$$\Sigma_{H_2O} \cong N_H \sigma_H = \left(\frac{2}{18}\right)\left(\frac{g}{cm^3}\right)\left(\frac{mole}{1\,g}\right)\left(6.02 \times 10^{23}\,\frac{atoms}{mole}\right) \cong 0.67\,cm^{-1}.$$

The neutron mfp is then estimated to be $\dfrac{1}{\Sigma_{H_2O}} = \dfrac{1}{0.67\,\text{cm}^{-1}} \cong 1.5\,\text{cm}$. The total slowing-down path length for a neutron is therefore a whopping 39.45 cm (i.e., $26.3 \times 1.5\,\text{cm}$)! After being thermalized, the neutron may diffuse an additional few centimeters before it has a chance to encounter a ^{235}U nucleus and trigger another fission reaction.

The long journey of a neutron brings up a concept called "neutron economy", which is a big part of nuclear reactor design. It refers to how to best utilize every fission neutron to trigger another fission reaction. Since in a neutron's lifetime it typically travels through many fuel rods and water channels, there exist many competing reactions that would "kill" the neutron before it has a chance to trigger another fission reaction. For example, a neutron can be absorbed by ^{238}U via the resonance absorption reaction, $^{238}U(n, \gamma)^{239}U$, in the fuel rods, or via the capture reaction $^{1}H(n, \gamma)^{2}H$ in the water. In addition, even if a thermal neutron is absorbed by ^{235}U, it may not trigger a fission reaction. In fact, there is a 20% chance that the neutron will undergo the capture reaction $^{235}U(n, \gamma)^{236}U$ rather than fission. Lastly, a neutron may simply "leak" out of the reactor. Obviously the neutron leakage probability has to do with the surface-to-volume ratio of the reactor. That is, a small reactor has a larger neutron leakage probability than a large reactor; and a cylinder- or rod-shaped reactor has a larger neutron leakage probability than a ball-shaped reactor.

Accordingly, there are many ways to improve the neutron economy in a nuclear reactor. Descriptions of four obvious ones follow. First, one can make the large size reactor and with a ball-like shape to minimize the neutron leakage probability. A large size reactor, however, will significantly increase the radiation shielding requirement. Second, one can use enriched uranium as fuel to increase the quantity of fissile material in the reactor. In natural uranium, the ^{235}U concentration is about 0.711%. The fuels used in today's PWRs and BWRs contain enriched uranium having a ^{235}U concentration of 3%–5%. Third, one can use heavy water (D_2O) instead of light water (H_2O) as the neutron moderator to reduce the chance for a neutron to be absorbed via the $^{1}H(n, \gamma)^{2}H$ reaction. In fact, a Canadian-developed reactor type called CANDU (short for <u>Can</u>ada <u>d</u>euterium <u>u</u>ranium) uses natural uranium as the fuel and D_2O as the neutron moderator. Fourth, one can surround the reactor with a shell of neutron-reflecting material, the so-called "neutron reflector." Its purpose is to return some of the leaking neutrons back to the reactor. The most effective neutron reflector is made of beryllium, because it has a large elastic scattering cross section and small absorption cross section. The beryllium plays a significant role in a uniquely built research reactor called the High Flux Isotope Reactor (HFIR) at the Oak Ridge National Laboratory. The HFIR uses light water as the neutron moderator, but the beryllium reflector allows the HFIR to have an unusually small core. The core of HFIR is cylindrical, approximately 2 ft (61 cm) high and 15 inches (38 cm) in diameter. It is a trash can–sized reactor, which routinely produces a whopping 86 MW of power! The thermal neutron flux level at the center of the core is approximately 2×10^{15} neutrons $\text{cm}^2\,\text{s}^{-1}$, which is about two orders of magnitude greater than that in a commercial PWR or BWR. Readers who are interested in learning more details on the HFIR are referred to the following website: https://neutrons.ornl.gov/hfir.

11.1.2 Design Concerns of a Thermal ReactorlIet

One safety-related issue regarding the design of a nuclear reactor is how to properly maintain, control, and operate the reactor at different power levels. A reactor is referred to as being "critical" when its neutron population (or power level) stays constant with time. It simply means that, on average, one neutron is produced for every neutron that disappears. A reactor is "super-critical" when its neutron population is increasing with time, or, on average, more than one neutron is produced for every neutron that disappears. A reactor is "sub-critical" when its neutron population is decreasing with time, or, on average, less than one neutron is produced for every neutron that disappears. Because the power produced by a reactor is directly proportional to the neutron population in the reactor, to change the power level the reactor must be able to safely undergo a transient among the various states (i.e., critical, super-critical, and sub-critical). The typical way (used by PWRs and BWRs) is to simply withdraw or insert "control rods" from or into a reactor. The control rods are made of strong thermal neutron absorption materials (that contain high concentrations of ^{10}B or natural gadolinium), and therefore, by withdrawing or inserting the control rods, one makes the reactor super- or sub-critical. A less popular way (used by the HFIR) is to insert or withdraw the reflector into or from the reactor. Because the reflector returns some of the leaking neutrons back to the reactor, inserting or withdrawing the reflector accordingly makes the reactor super- or sub-critical.

The above description, however, overlooks a very important player—the delayed neutrons. As mentioned in Sections 5.3.5 and 7.4.3, in a thermal reactor approximately 99.3% of the neutrons are prompt (i.e., instantly emitted from fissions) and 0.7% are delayed (i.e., emitted at a certain time after fissions). These delayed neutrons are mainly emitted from a few indirect fission products (e.g., ^{87}Kr and ^{137}Xe), which have average delays of 78.6 s and 35.2 s, respectively. Because the neutron lifetime in a thermal reactor is so short ($\sim 10^{-4}$ sec), without the delayed neutrons a change of the reactor from critical state to a slightly super-critical state would cause a nuclear excursion. For example, if there are 1.001 neutrons produced for every neutron that disappears, then in one second the neutron population (i.e., the power level) would increase by a factor of $(1.001)^{10000}$, which is about 22,000! The delayed neutrons, however tiny the fraction, are able to provide the necessary cushion to allow a reactor to undergo power change in a timely manner.

Overall, in the field of nuclear reactor design the most essential quantity is the detailed spatial and energy distribution of neutron fluence rate, ϕ (in neutrons cm^{-2} s^{-1}), which can also be a function of time when a reactor is undergoing a transient in power. In principle, ϕ can be obtained by solving a set of neutron balance equations (i.e., the so-called "neutron diffusion" or "neutron transport" equations). However, because the neutron cross sections of the reactor components (most notably the water density) may change as temperature changes, for reactor transient analysis one must also engage in the thermal hydraulic calculations to88 obtain the local water density with small time steps. In modern days, these so-called coupled neutronics/thermal hydraulics calculations are carried out numerically by computer codes that include detailed neutron and gamma-ray cross section data library. Interested readers are encouraged to study reactor physics, which includes the methods for solving neutron diffusion equations and for calculating how nuclear fuels are depleted (via the fission reactions) in a reactor core.

One other unique aspect for designing a nuclear power reactor system is related to the material damage caused by ionizing radiations (mainly fast neutrons). Fast neutrons can undergo elastic collisions or (n, α) reactions with atomic nuclei; and the energetic recoil nuclei, the so-called "primary knock-on atom (PKA)", in turn, can cause collision cascades that produce point defects and dislocations in the material, resulting in change of material properties. At high neutron fluences, this can lead to embrittlement and swelling in metals (e.g., fuel rod cladding and reactor pressure vessel) and other materials (e.g., UO_2 fuel pellets). Room temperature tensile tests show that fast neutron irradiation causes significant increase in yield and tensile strength, along with a decreased ductility in these materials. The change of these properties, in turn, makes deformation more difficult. In fact, the lifetimes of many critical components of a nuclear reactor (i.e., fuel rod cladding, control rods, and reactor pressure vessel) are limited by the neutron damage. As such, material science research currently plays a pivotal role in the extension of the life of the existing fleet of nuclear reactors; in the deployment of new, modern light water reactors, advanced reactors with non-water coolants, and small modular reactors; and in storage, recycling, and disposal of used nuclear fuel. Understanding and overcoming material degradation in an extreme environment (i.e., high temperature, high pressure, and high neutron and gamma fluences) is essential for safe and efficient operation. In other words, the development of new materials may make new nuclear power reactors safer and more economical.

Lastly, there are still two more design concerns for fission reactor–based power production systems: the decay heat removal and the used fuel storage. Both are safety related, and their importance had been profoundly implicated in the three major nuclear power plant accidents: the Three-Mile Island accident that occurred in 1979, the Chernobyl accident that occurred in 1986, and the Fukushima accident that occurred in 2011. The decay heat of a nuclear reactor refers to the heat energy that is continuously released, even when the reactor is completely shut down with no fission reactions occurring. This extra energy mainly comes from the beta and gamma decays of the fission products. The decay heat power level for a typical PWR or BWR is about 6% of its full power immediately after a shutdown. It then decays exponentially to below 1% within a day. While 1% may sound small, for a typical 3-GWt reactor this amounts to 30 MWt! Five years after its removal from the reactor, the used fuel still releases ~1 kW/bundle of decay heat. Without adequate cooling, even the five-year-old used fuel can still melt. In other words, a nuclear power plant must be properly designed and built with robust cooling systems to guarantee adequate decay heat removal under all accident scenarios (e.g., an earthquake), when neither the reactor nor the offsite AC power is available. In fact, the lack of ability to remove the decay heat was the cause of severe core meltdowns in all three nuclear power accidents mentioned above.

11.2 Radioisotope Power Systems

Radioisotope power systems (or RPS) have played a critical role for more than five decades in the exploration of space, enabling missions of scientific discovery to destinations across the solar system. These systems provide electricity and heat that enable spacecraft and other apparatuses to undertake scientific missions to places beyond the capabilities of solar power, chemical batteries, and fuel cells. While some spacecraft, like Cassini, do run their systems directly off their RPS, others, like the Mars Science Laboratory rover, can use the RPS to charge batteries and run their systems and instruments off stored battery power. In either case, the RPS is attached directly to a spacecraft, much like a power cord being plugged in.

The most widely used RPS for producing electricity is called the radioisotope thermoelectric generator (RTG). It is an electrical generator that uses an array of thermocouples to convert the heat released by the decay of a suitable radioactive material into electricity by the Seebeck effect. This generator has no moving parts, and therefore requires no maintenance. Many RTGs of varying designs and power capacities have been build and used in the last five decades. The early ones deployed (or launched) by the United States from 1961 to 1975 follow the odd-numbered SNAP series. The acronym SNAP stands for System for Nuclear Auxiliary Power.

A variety of radioisotopes have been evaluated for space and terrestrial applications. The initial isotope selected as the fuel for the first RTG, SNAP-1, was Ce-144, which has a half-life of 290 days. Ce-144 was selected because it was one of the most abundant fission products available from reprocessing used reactor fuel. While its half-life is relatively short, it was thought to be compatible with the six-month military reconnaissance satellite mission envisioned at the time (around 1960). However, the high radiation field associated with the beta/gamma emission of Ce-144 made handling very difficult. As such, SNAP-1 was never used in space. In the late 1950s, Po-210 was used to fuel the small 5 W(e) SNAP-3 RTG. Po-210 is an alpha emitter. Large quantities of Po-210 can be made by irradiating Bi-209 targets with high neutron fluences in a nuclear reactor. The (n, γ) reaction with Bi-209 creates Bi-210, which quickly undergoes beta decay to become Po-210. The high power density ($\sim 1,320$ W/cm^3) and low gamma emissions made Po-210 easier to handle than Ce-144. However, the short 138-day half-life made Po-210 only suitable for limited-duration space power applications. In order to provide a long-lived radioisotope fuel, a large quantity of Sr-90 (another abundant fission product with a 28.8-year half-life) was extracted and made into an insoluble fuel form (strontium-titanate), which was used in several SNAP-7 RTGs. While Sr-90 and its daughter Y-90 are both beta emitters that require little shielding, the high-energy beta particles (mainly emitted from Y-90) produce significant bremsstrahlung radiation, which requires heavy shielding and makes it not suitable for space missions. As such, SNAP-7 RTGs were mainly deployed and used for terrestrial applications (e.g., navigation buoy, navigation light, floating weather station, et cetera).

By 1960, Pu-238 had been identified as the best radioisotope fuel for deep space missions because it has all the desirable properties: long half-life (87.7 years), alpha emissions with very little accompanied gamma rays, reasonably high power density, and useful fuel forms (as the metal or the oxide form). A Pu-238 fueled SNAP-3A RTG was launched on the Transit 4A Navy navigation satellite in June 1961—the first use of nuclear power in space. Pu-238 could be made by irradiating Np-237 targets with high neutron fluences in a nuclear reactor. The (n, γ) reaction with Np-237 creates Np-238, which quickly undergoes beta decay to become Pu-238. A number of RTGs were launched on NASA and Navy missions with Pu-238 dioxide microsphere and plutonia-molybdenum-cermet (PMC) fuel forms in the late 1960s and early-1970s. Since the mid-1970s, pressed Pu-238 oxide fuel forms have been exclusively used in all RPS launched into space. For the two Voyager missions to the outer planets (1977), a multihundred-watt (MHW) RTG was developed. It used Si-Ge thermocouples (replacing the Pb-Te thermocouples used in the earlier SNAP RTGs) and produced about 157 W(e) at the beginning of the mission. Each Voyager mission used three of these MHW RTGs. In the more recent space missions (e.g., Galileo to Jupiter in 1989, Ulysses to the Sun in 1990, and Cassini to Saturn in 1997), even larger power modules were needed. To meet these requirements, the

U.S. Department of Energy developed the general purpose heat source (GPHS) RTG. The GPHS-RTG is similar to the MHW-RTGs in that it also uses Pu-238 as the heat source and Si-Ge thermocouples to convert heat to electricity. Figure 11.4 shows just such a GPHS-RTG, currently used by the U.S. space program. This unit uses 18 of these GPHS modules, and initially produces about 4300 W of thermal energy. It weighs 56 kg, and has a length of 1.13 m and a diameter of 0.43 m.

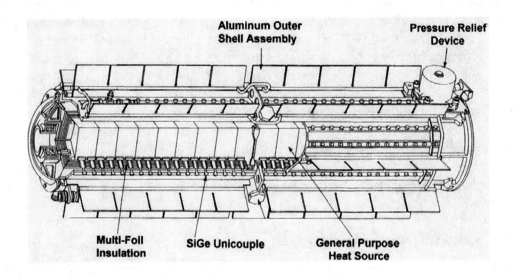

Figure 11.4. A general purpose heat source radioisotope thermoelectric generator (GPHS-RTG) currently used in the U.S. space program.
Source. Furlong and Wahlquist (1999).

The amount of Pu-238 that could be produced has always been a limiting factor in its use. At one time, Cm-244 was investigated as a potential alternative to Pu-238 because a large amount of Cm-244 was expected to become available, and because Cm-244 has similar properties to Pu-238. The idea, however, was abandoned, as a small fraction of Cm-244 undergoes spontaneous fission, which would significantly increase shielding requirements. For many years, Pu-238 was made available as a byproduct of the production of materials for nuclear weapons. The discontinuation of this production in the 1990s terminated the supply of Pu-238. During the 2000s, the U.S. government began purchasing small quantities of Pu-238 from Russia, but those acquisitions have also ended. As of this writing, the civilian stockpile of Pu-238 that can be used to power the RTGs for U.S. deep space probes has dwindled to only 35 kg, which is only enough to power two or three NASA missions.

To meet the future needs, the U.S. Department of Energy's Oak Ridge National Laboratory (ORNL) has recently restarted production of Pu-238. In this effort, the ORNL has developed a new production line that involves taking Np-237 feedstock, converting it to neptunium oxide, then mixing it with aluminum and pressing it into high-density pellets. These pellets are then irradiated with high neutron fluences in a nuclear reactor to convert Np-237 into Pu-238. After irradiation, the newly made Pu-238 is dissolved and separated from the leftover neptunium, oxidized, and pressed into pellets. The remaining neptunium is recycled to create more plutonium. As of this writing, the ORNL has just produced the first 50 g of plutonium oxide. According to ORNL, the laboratory is now working on ramping up the production to 1.5 kg per year.

11.3 Radiation-Based Medical Imaging Modalities

Radiation-based medical imaging modalities can be divided into two categories: transmission X-ray imaging, and nuclear medicine imaging. The first category itself includes two different modalities: two-dimensional (2-D) planar X-ray imaging and three-dimensional (3-D) X-ray computed tomography (CT). Both modalities use an external X-ray source to interrogate and obtain an anatomical image of the body. The second category also includes two different modalities: single photon emission computed tomography (SPECT) and positron emission tomography (PET). Both modalities introduce certain radiopharmaceuticals into the body and use instrumentation (radiation-sensitive detectors) to image the spatial distribution of the radiopharmaceuticals in the body. The nuclear medicine modalities are complementary to the transmission X-ray modalities in that they provide information regarding physiological and functional changes of organs. The sections below give brief introductions to these four imaging modalities.

11.3.1 Transmission X-Ray Imaging

All X-ray based imaging devices must include two major components: the X-ray source and the X-ray imaging system. In this section, we first introduce the X-ray source, and the introductions on 2-D X-ray planar imaging and 3-D X-ray CT then follow.

X-ray source

Figure 11.5 is a schematic diagram of a typical X-ray source used for diagnostic imaging. As shown, bremsstrahlung X-ray photons are produced via the bombardment of energetic electrons onto a tungsten target (the anode). The electrons are emitted from a heated tungsten filament (the cathode) and accelerated via the voltage difference applied between the cathode and the anode. Depending on the application, the voltage of a diagnostic X-ray source varies between 15 and 150 kV. This voltage (referred to as kVp) is used to specify the energy of the X-ray photons. For instance, the X-ray produced by a machine operated with 120 kV is referred to as 120-kVp X-ray.

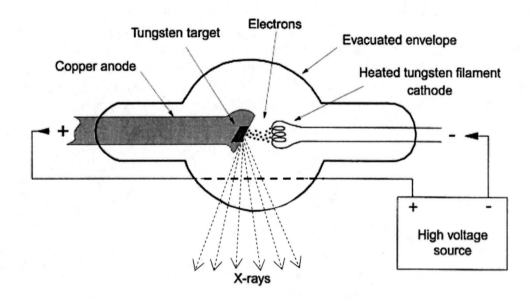

Figure 11.5. A schematic diagram of an X-ray source used for diagnostic imaging.

The photon energy spectrum of a kilo-voltage X-ray machine (used for medical or security diagnosis) has been discussed in Section 9.3 and is depicted by Figure 9.8(a). It includes a couple of line-based monoenergetic characteristic X-rays superimposed on top of the broad-based bremsstrahlung continuum. The intensity of the spectrum tapers down for high-energy photons and totally diminishes at the energy of the incident electron energy. The average energy of the photons is between 1/3 and 1/2 of the incident electron energy. That is, for a 120-kVp X-ray its average energy is between 40 and 60 keV.

Transmission 2-D planar X-ray imaging

Two-dimensional planar X-ray imaging technology is similar to that of a photographic camera in that each snapshot creates a 2-D image. It is specifically useful for examining broken or cracked bones inside a human body. It can also be used with an iodine-based X-ray contrast agent to obtain an image of blood vessels (the angiograms) or with a barium-based X-ray contrast agent to obtain images of the gastrointestinal tract of a patient. In addition, 2-D X-ray imaging technology is the basis for an interventional X-ray fluoroscopy system where continuous X-ray images (i.e., movie-like) are made to assist doctors during a surgery.

Figure 11.6 shows the geometric configuration of a patient undergoing a 2-D planar X-ray imaging procedure. As depicted, the 2-D broad beam of X-ray is brought to cover and penetrate the whole chest of the patient. The X-ray film (or digital imager) is placed on the opposite side of the patient to record the transmitted X-ray photons. X-ray film technology has been around for more than a century. The X-ray film itself is similar to that of a photographic film in that it is made of a sheet of transparent plastic film base coated on one side (or both sides) with a gelatin emulsion containing microscopically small light-sensitive silver halide crystals. In actual operation, the film is sandwiched with two X-ray intensifying screens and placed inside a light-tight cassette. The X-ray intensifying screen is made of a layer of high-Z phosphor (e.g., $Gd_2O_2S:Tb$, and $CaWO_4$). The purpose is to absorb most of the X-ray photons via photoelectric effect (Section 10.1) and to convert each photoelectron into many visible photons, which in turn create an image on the film. Without the intensifying screens, the film would only record a very small faction of the X-ray photons and thus result in a noisy image. Figure 11.7 is a normal chest X-ray image of a woman, showing the air-filled spaces of the lungs, the rib bones, and the more solid gray shape of the heart. Figure 11.8 is an X-ray angiogram of the right coronary artery of a man's heart. The image of the artery is clearly shown because the lumen is filled with an iodine-based contrast agent that preferentially absorbs the incident X-rays.

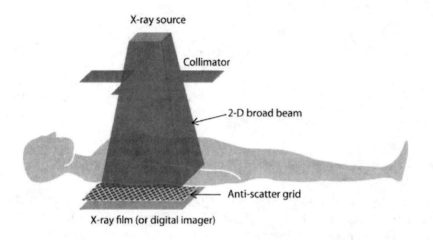

Figure 11.6. The geometric configuration of a patient undergoing a 2-D planar X-ray imaging procedure.

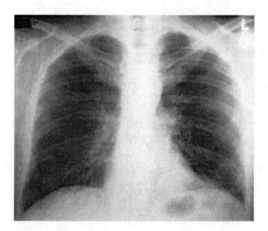

Figure 11.7. A 2-D planar chest X-ray image of a woman, showing the air-filled spaces of the lungs and the more solid gray shape of the heart.
Source. U.S. Food and Drug Administration (n.d.).

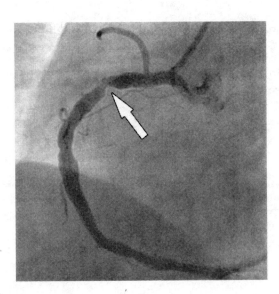

Figure 11.8. An X-ray angiogram of the right coronary artery of a man's heart. The arrow indicates a narrow passage (or stenosis).
Source. Baškot (2011).

Since the late 1990s, the flat panel X-ray imager (based on digital technology) has been slowly replacing film technology as the standard for 2-D planar X-ray imaging, including the mammography. A flat panel imager includes a layer of phosphor crystal similar to that used with the film, placed on top of an amorphous silicon (a-Si) detector array and a signal readout board. The a-Si detector array is manufactured using a process similar to that used to make LCD televisions and computer monitors. That is, millions of small pixels (e.g., 0.2 mm x 0.2 mm) each containing a thin-film transistor form a grid patterned in a-Si on a glass substrate. But, unlike an LCD, each a-Si pixel also contains a photodiode that generates an electrical signal in proportion to the light produced by the phosphor in front of the pixel. The signals from the photodiodes are amplified, digitized, and then displayed on a computer monitor as a 2-D image.

The contrast of a 2-D planar X-ray image is created based on the different amount of attenuation of the incident X-ray photons as they pass through an object (e.g., human body). Figure 11.9 is a simplified diagram illustrating how the contrast of the image is formed. Part (a) shows that an object (made of soft tissue) of uniform thickness l is irradiated with a parallel beam of X-ray photons with a uniform fluence ϕ_0. Because the middle section of the object contains a piece of bone (the darkened area, which has a greater linear attenuation coefficient than that of the soft tissue), the transmitted photon fluence in the middle section should be lower than that of the rest of the object (i.e., $\phi_2 < \phi_1$). Part (b) of Figure 11.9 shows that the difference between ϕ_1 and ϕ_2 would correspondingly produce different signal intensities I_1 and I_2 on the imager. From Equation 10.26, this can be expressed as

$$\phi_2 = \phi_0 e^{-[\mu_s(x_1+x_3)+\mu_b x_2]} < \phi_1 = \phi_0 e^{-\mu l}, \tag{11.1}$$

where μ_s and μ_b are the linear attenuation coefficients of the soft tissue and bone, respectively, and $\mu_b > \mu_s$. Because the incident X-ray photons contain a broad energy spectrum, and because the linear attenuation coefficients are dependent on the photon energy, a more precise expression of Equation 11.1 should include photon energy as a variable. That is,

$$\phi_2(E) = \phi_0(E)e^{-[\mu_s(E)(x_1+x_3)+\mu_b(E)x_2]} < \phi_1(E) = \phi_0(E)e^{-\mu_s(E)l}. \tag{11.2}$$

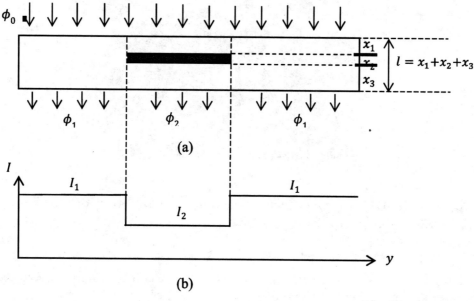

Figure 11.9. Contrast of an image created via the different amount of attenuation of X-ray photons passing through the object: (a) shows how the photons are attenuated as they pass through the object, and (b) shows the intensity of the image signals as a function of position (y).

Since the imager's response (i.e., X-ray detection efficiency) is also dependent on the X-ray photon energy, the image signal intensities corresponding to ϕ_1 and ϕ_2 should be the integrated responses over the entire energy spectrum. That is, $I_1 = \int R(E)\phi_1(E)dE$ and $I_2 = \int R(E)\phi_2(E)dE$, where $R(E)$ is the imager's response as a function of photon energy. The image contrast between the soft-tissue region and the bone-containing region is just the difference between I_1 and I_2. To have the best image contrast of the bone, one would want the incident photon energy to be slightly above the K-edge of calcium (~4 keV) so that the difference between μ_b and μ_s would be the largest. In the case of an angiogram, one would want the photon energy to be slightly greater than the K-edge of iodine (~33 keV). The value of μ_b for these photon energies, however, could be too large, so that the resulting values of ϕ_1, ϕ_2, I_1 and I_2 are too low. This, in turn, makes the image noisy. Accordingly, the optimal energy of the incident photons for obtaining the best image quality is determined based on the trade-off between contrast and noise of an image system. This energy (or energy range), depending on the application, is between 15 and 150 keV, which is significantly greater than the K-edge values of calcium and iodine.

Transmission 3-D computed tomography

The invention of X-ray computed tomography (CT) is generally credited to Allan MacLeod Cormack (1924–1998) and Godfrey Newbold Hounsfield (1919–2004), who were awarded with Nobel Prize in Physiology or Medicine in 1979. The mechanism of image formation in X-ray CT is entirely different from that of 2-D planar imaging devices. In X-ray CT, a 2-D cross-sectional image of a patient can be computationally constructed with the transmitted X-ray data collected from many directions. Figure 11.10 shows the geometric configuration of a patient undergoing an X-ray CT scan. As depicted, the X-ray source and detectors are on the opposite site of a ring structure, the central axis of which coincides with that of the patient. During a scanning procedure, the source/detector ring makes numerous rotations helically along the axis until it covers the entire section of interest (e.g., the abdomen) of the patient. The data of the transmitted X-ray collected in each rotation are sent to a computer to construct the 2-D cross-sectional image of the patient. Since each rotation only covers a thin slice (2–3 mm) of the patient's body, to cover the entire section of interest (e.g., the abdomen) may take more than one hundred slices. The 3-D image is formed by stacking many closely spaced, 2-D cross-sectional images.

Figure 11.11 is a parallel-beam geometry used to illustrate how the 2-D cross-sectional image in X-ray CT is obtained computationally. The elliptic object at the center represents the cross section of the patient. The outside circle represents the source/detector ring. The transmitted X-ray intensities are recorded for various values of θ (from 0° to 360°) as the source/detector ring makes a full rotation. The profile of the transmitted X-ray intensity for a specific value of θ can be expressed as

$$I(r,\theta) = I_0\, e^{-\int \mu(x,y)\,ds} = I_0\, e^{-\int \mu(x,y)\,ds}, \tag{11.3}$$

where $\mu(x,y)$ is the linear attenuation coefficient at the position (x,y) inside the patient's body, and it also represents the cross-sectional image of the patient. The goal of CT image reconstruction is to use a set of measured transmitted X-ray data, $I(r,\theta)$, to back calculate the image function, $\mu(x,y)$.

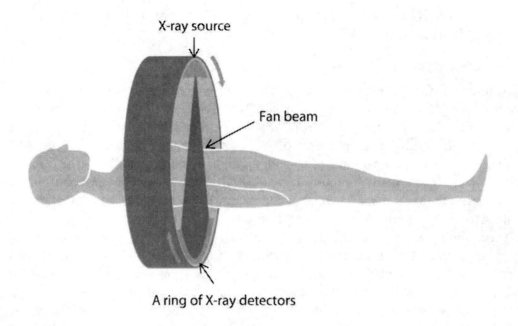

Figure 11.10. The geometric configuration of a patient undergoing a 3-D X-ray CT scan.

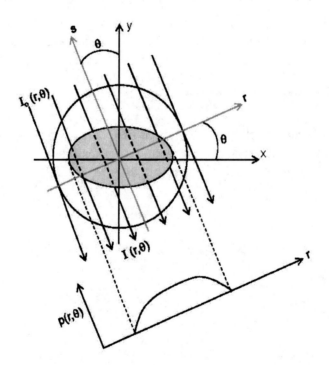

Figure 11.11. A parallel-beam geometry used to illustrate how the 2-D cross-sectional image in X-ray CT is obtained computationally.

From Figure 11.11, the relationships between x, y; r, s; and θ are found to be

$$x = r\cos\theta - s\sin\theta \text{ and } y = r\sin\theta + s\cos\theta. \tag{11.4}$$

To computationally obtain $\mu(x,y)$, one first recasts equation 11.3 as:

$$p(r,\theta_j) = -\ln\left[\frac{I(r,\theta_j)}{I_0}\right] = \int \mu(x,y)ds = \int \mu(r\cos\theta_j - s\sin\theta_j, r\sin\theta_j + s\cos\theta_j)\,ds,$$

$$\tag{11.5}$$

where $p(r,\theta_j)$ is referred to as the projection corresponding to the specific angle θ_j. The goal of CT image reconstruction is then to use a set of measured projections $p(r,\theta_j)$ to back calculate $\mu(x,y)$. This can be done via the so-called "filtered back-projection method." In the simple back-projection method (without filtering), equation 11.5 is discretized and approximated as

$$p(r,\theta_j) = \mu(x,y)_j s(r,\theta_j) \text{ or } \mu(x,y)_j = \frac{p(r,\theta_j)}{s(r,\theta_j)}, \tag{11.6}$$

where $s(r,\theta_j)$ is the distance for the incident X-ray to traverse the patient along direction θ_j. In other words, each projection $p(r,\theta_j)$ would provide its corresponding estimate of the image function $\mu(x,y)_j$. Since the estimate from each projection must have equal weight, the final estimate of $\mu(x,y)$ is then the average of the estimates from all projections. That is,

$$\mu(x,y) = \frac{1}{n}\sum_{j=1}^{n}\mu(x,y)_j = \frac{1}{n}\sum_{j=1}^{n}\frac{p(r,\theta_j)}{s(r,\theta_j)}, \tag{11.7}$$

where n is the total number of projections. The simple back-projection method described above, however, produces a so-called "halo effect" (shown in Figure 11.12), making the reconstructed image unacceptable.

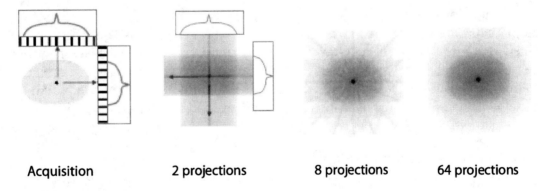

Acquisition   2 projections   8 projections   64 projections

Figure 11.12. The halo effect in a CT image reconstructed from the simple back-projection method.

The halo effect was understood to be caused by under sampling of the high-frequency part of the signals. To correct this effect, one may first apply the Fourier transform to the projection functions $p(r, \theta_j)$ to convert them onto the frequency domain. Next, one applies a weighting function (i.e., a filter) to the projection functions (in the frequency domain) to compensate for the under sampling of the high-frequency part of the signals. One then applies the inverse of the Fourier transform to the filtered projection functions to convert them back to the spatial domain. The filtered projection functions can then be used with equation 11.7 to obtain the image function, $\mu(x, y)$. This procedure effectively removes the halo effect, and it takes very little computational time. Figure 11.13 shows a cross-sectional image of a patient's abdomen constructed from the filtered back-projection method. The most notable advantage of CT images over 2-D planar images is their ability to distinguish the various soft-tissue organs even though the differences in the μ values of these organs are relatively small. Readers who are interested in learning more about the filtered back-projection method are referred to other textbooks specifically written for diagnostic medical imaging.

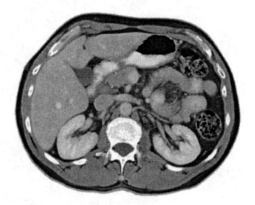

Figure 11.13. The cross-sectional image of a patient's abdomen constructed from the filtered back-projection method.
Source. U.S. Food and Drug Administration (n.d.).

The superior quality of a CT image, however, comes with the price of much greater radiation exposure. In fact, the exposure of a CT scan procedure is equivalent to that of a hundred or more planar chest X-ray procedures. Since radiation exposure is believed to increase an individual's risk of getting cancer, as well as many hereditary diseases, CT scans should not be taken unnecessarily. Currently, some 80 million CT scans are performed each year in the United States, and many of them are believed to be unnecessary.

11.3.2 Nuclear Medicine Imaging

The history of nuclear medicine imaging spans the past sixty years. Currently, more than twenty million nuclear medicine procedures using radiopharmaceuticals and imaging instruments are carried annually in the United States alone. In a nuclear medicine scan, a radiopharmaceutical is administered to the patient, and an imaging instrument that detects radiation (mainly gamma rays) is used to show physiological and functional changes in the body. Overall usage of nuclear medicine procedures is expanding rapidly, especially as the advanced technologies of single photon emission computed tomography (SPECT) and positron emission tomography (PET) are being introduced. Since both SPECT and PET use radiopharmaceuticals, in this section we first introduce the radiopharmaceuticals, and the introductions on SPECT and PET then follow separately.

Radiopharmaceuticals

A radiopharmaceutical is either a radionuclide alone, such as Tc-99m, or a radionuclide that is attached to a carrier molecule (a drug, protein, or peptide), which, when introduced into the body by injection, swallowing, or inhalation, accumulates in the organ or tissue of interest (National Research Council 2007). An ideal radionuclide should have a half-life that is long enough to accommodate the imaging procedures but not so long as to impose too much radiation on the patient. It must also emit gamma-ray (or X-ray) photons whose energies are high enough to come out the body to be externally detected with gamma-ray detectors. The typical photon energy range is between 70 and 200 keV. Photons with energies above 200 keV preferentially undergo Compton scatterings, making it difficult to collimate them as they exit the body. This, in turn, worsens spatial resolution of the image. Commonly used radionuclides for imaging purposes are shown in Table 11.1.

Table 11.1. Commonly used radionuclides in nuclear medicine imaging and their properties.

Radionuclide	Half-life	Gamma-ray energy (keV)	Imaging technique used
^{99m}Tc	6.02 hours	140	SPECT
^{67}Ga	3.26 days	93, 185, 300, 394	SPECT
^{201}Tl	3.04 days	167, 69–84 (X-rays)	SPECT
^{133}Xe	5.25 days	81	SPECT
^{111}In	2.8 days	171, 245	SPECT
^{131}I	8.03 days	364	SPECT
^{123}I	13.2 hours	159	SPECT
^{11}C	20.33 minutes	511	PET
^{13}N	9.97 minutes	511	PET
^{15}O	2.04 minutes	511	PET
^{18}F	109.75 minutes	511	PET

Note. SPECT = single photon emission computed tomography; PET = positron emission tomography.

Among the radionuclides used for SPECT, ^{99m}Tc is the only pure gamma emitter, and it is also the most widely used one. Other nuclides decay either via EC or β^- to the excited states of the daughter nuclides, which then undergo gamma and IC decays. A pure gamma emitter (i.e., ^{99m}Tc) is preferred because it results in a lower radiation dose to the patient. ^{99m}Tc also has two other advantages: 1) it can be produced from an on-site generator, whereas other nuclides must be produced from an off-site cyclotron or nuclear reactor, and 2) it can be chemically attached to a variety of ligands that have high selectivity for the organ of interest, with minimal distribution in other tissues. Figure 11.14 shows an on-site ^{99m}Tc generator. The generator contains a certain amount of ^{99}Mo adsorbed onto an alumina (Al_2O_3) column. ^{99}Mo undergoes β⁻ decay with a half-life of 66 hours and becomes ^{99m}Tc (refer to Figure 5.5). The ^{99m}Tc is typically recovered by passing a saline solution through the alumina column. The saline removes the ^{99m}Tc but leaves the ^{99}Mo in place. A ^{99m}Tc generator can be eluted several times a day for about a week before it needs to be replaced with a fresh generator. There are numerous ^{99m}Tc kits for producing radiopharmaceuticals to examine the brain, kidney, heart, bone, liver, and lungs. Currently, the world supply of ^{99}Mo is mainly provided by irradiating ^{235}U-bearing targets with thermal neutrons in nuclear reactors. Approximately 6% of the fission fragments of the neutron-induced fission of the ^{235}U nucleus are ^{99}Mo atoms. The weekly global demand for ^{99}Mo can be supplied by the fission of about 2 g of ^{235}U. The amount of ^{99}Mo that can be extracted has a mass of about 0.1 g, which is about that contained in a cook's pinch of salt!

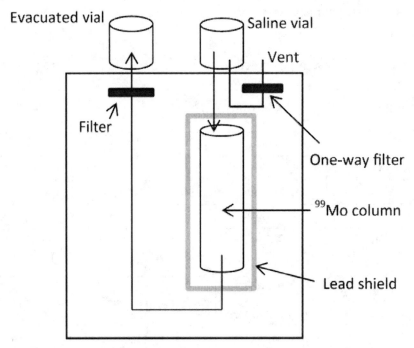

Figure 11.14. Schematic diagram showing the internal structure of a typical ^{99m}Tc generator.

Source. National Research Council (2009).

As shown in Table 11.1, PET radiopharmaceuticals are different from SPECT radiopharmaceuticals in that the former have radionuclides that are positron emitters, of which the majority have much shorter half-lives. As such, the radionuclides used for PET must be produced with on-site cyclotrons. The advantage of PET radiopharmaceuticals, however, is that the ligands used are common analogs of biological molecules, and therefore, tend to depict a true representation of biological processes after in vivo administration. For example, ^{18}F-fluorodeoxyglucose is an analog of glucose used for cellular metabolism, and $H_2{}^{15}O$ for cerebral perfusion. All the radionuclides used in PET can be produced from relatively small cyclotrons, using protons with an energy of ~10 MeV, or deuterons with an energy of ~5 MeV. Typical reactions include: $^{12}C(p,pn)^{11}C$, $^{14}N(p,\alpha)^{11}C$, $^{13}C(p,n)^{13}N$, $^{15}N(p,n)^{15}O$, $^{14}N(d,n)^{15}O$, and $^{18}O(p,n)^{18}F$. Among them, ^{18}F is by far the most widely used one for PET imaging, since it has a relatively long half-life (~110 min), allowing its supply to reach remote places.

Single photon emission computed tomography

The SPECT-based 3-D image of radionuclide distribution in a patient's body is obtained by using the data collected with a 2-D gamma camera. Figure 11.15 shows the schematic diagram of a gamma camera. The system is somewhat similar to that of the transmission 2-D planar X-ray imaging in that it also has an anti-scatter grid and a scintillating crystal that converts gamma rays (or X rays) to visible light, which is in turn converted to electrical signals.

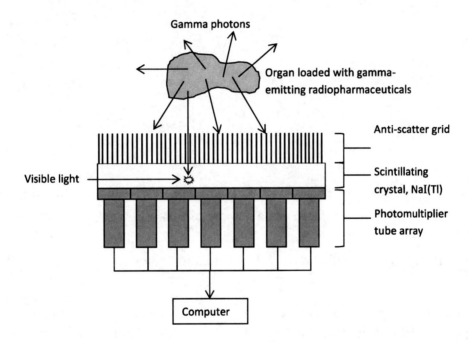

Figure 11.15. The schematic diagram of a 2-D gamma camera.

One major difference between the two is that in the transmission X-ray system, the incident X-rays are collimated into the same directions, whereas in SPECT the gamma photons are emitted in different directions. This difference, together with the higher energy of gamma photons used in SPECT (e.g., 140 keV from ^{99m}Tc), require that gamma camera employ a rather thick scintillating crystal in order to maximize the counting efficiency, and thus, minimize the radiation dose to the patient. The (x,y) position of a gamma photon (once detected) is determined by the weighted average according to the light intensities received by the individual photomultiplier tubes, with the largest weight assigned to the one receiving the highest light intensity. A 2-D image is formed in the x-y plane after a large number of gamma photons have been detected and their (x,y) positions determined. The use of gamma camera to form such a 2-D image is called "planar scintigraphy." It is often used to detect cancers in the bone and lungs. Figure 11.16 shows the 2-D image of a whole-body bone scan using ^{99m}Tc-methylenediphosphonate (MDP) and a gamma camera.

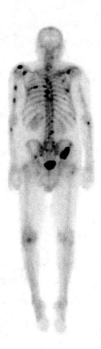

Figure 11.16. The 2-D image of a whole-body bone scan using ^{99m}Tc-methylenediphosphonate (MDP) and a gamma camera, showing multiple bone metastases from prostate cancer.

Source. https://en.wikipedia.org/wiki/Bone_scintigraphy.

A 2-D cross-sectional (slice) image of SPECT can be formed based on several gamma camera images taken from several different angles. The image construction method used is similar to that used for X-ray CT., but the image function for SPECT is totally different from that of X-ray CT. For SPECT, the projection function is defined as

$$p(r,\theta) = \int f(x,y)\, e^{-\int \mu(r,s')ds'}\, ds,\qquad (11.8)$$

where $f(x,y)$ is the cross-sectional distribution of the radiopharmaceuticals in a patient's body, and it is also the image function. In this case, the goal of SPECT image reconstruction is to use a set of measured projections $p(r,\theta_j)$ to back calculate $f(x,y)$. Both the filtered-projection method and the iterative method have been successfully used to obtain the 2-D slice images for SPECT. It should be noted, however, that for a variety of reasons the spatial resolutions of a SPECT scan are much worse than that of X-ray CT. Typical values are approximately 1–2 cm at large depths within the body and 5–8 mm close to the surface. Readers who are interested in learning more about the image reconstruction method used for SPECT are referred to other textbooks specifically written for diagnostic medical imaging. Figure 11.17 shows a SPECT image acquired from a ^{99m}Tc cerebral blood flow scan of an individual with Alzheimer's disease. The arrows indicate areas of diminished blood flow due to the disease.

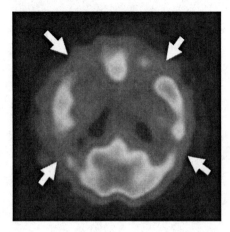

Figure 11.17. A SPECT image acquired from a ^{99m}Tc cerebral blood flow scan of an individual with Alzheimer's disease. The arrows indicate areas of diminished blood flow due to the disease. **Source.** National Research Council (2009).

Positron emission tomography

The design of a PET scanner is more similar to that of a CT scanner than to a SPECT system. The detection of a positron emission and its location is based on two opposing detectors simultaneously detecting the two back-to-back 511-keV photons, which are created due to the annihilation of the positron and the electron. Figure 11.18 shows the schematic diagram of a PET scanner. As indicated, the positron emitted from the radiopharmaceutical is locally annihilated with an electron and produces two back-to-back 511-keV photons. The image reconstruction methods used in PET are essentially the same as that used in SPECT (i.e., the filtered-projection method and the iterative method). Its spatial resolutions are also comparable to that of the SPECT.

Because of the increased sensitivity and specificity of PET scans in detecting various tumors, and fusion imaging using the combined modality of PET and X-ray CT, this has become the state-of-the-art technique for cancer diagnosis and treatment preparation. Data acquisition in PET/CT is performed in two steps: first CT, and then PET. The two scan images are then fused together. The fused image significantly improves the readability of a PET image because the high-resolution X-ray CT image provides clear anatomical features surrounding the tumor. Figure 11.19 illustrates such an effect. That is, the PET image shows a non-small cell lung carcinoma but with extremely poor reference to its location with respect to the surrounding tissues/organs. By properly fusing the PET image with the X-ray CT image, the tumor and its location then become clearly demonstrated.

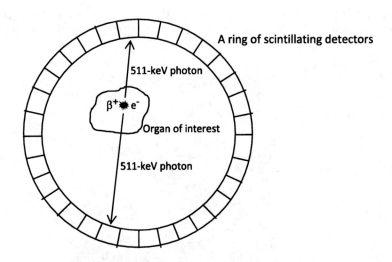

Figure 11.18. The schematic diagram of a PET scanner.

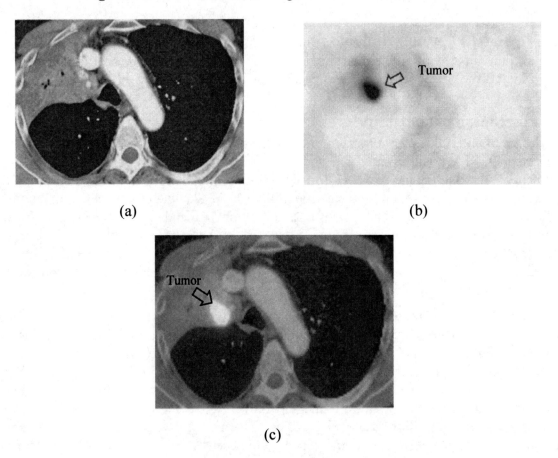

Figure 11.19. A study showing the effect of the fusion of PET and CT images: (a) CT, (b) PET, and (c) PET/CT fused images showing non-small cell lung carcinoma in the right upper lobe. **Source.** Antoch et al. (2003).

11.4 Radiation Therapy for Cancer Treatment

Radiation therapy has been for several decades one of the three most widely used modalities for cancer treatment, with the other two being surgery and chemotherapy. It likely will remain this way for many years to come. Radiation therapy uses X-rays, gamma rays, and charged particles (e.g., electrons and protons) to kill cancer cells. The radiation may be delivered by an external beam produced by a particle accelerator, or it may come from radioactive material placed in the body near cancer cells (internal radiation therapy, also known as "brachytherapy"). About fifty percent of all cancer patients receive some form of radiation therapy sometime during the course of their treatment.

While the use of radiation to treat cancer and other diseases can be traced back to the beginning of the last century, the fundamental understanding as to why radiation therapy is effective in treating cancer has not been clear until recently. We now know that ionizing radiation can cause double strand DNA breaks, which in turn will produce chromosome aberrations. Cells with chromosome aberrations will likely die during mitosis because they are not able to properly divide. Because cancer cells are less able to repair DNA damage and they also tend to undergo mitosis more frequently than normal cells, radiation tends to be more effective in killing cancer cells. Since radiation also kills normal cells, the goal of radiation therapy has been to maximize the radiation dose delivered to the tumor volume while minimizing the dose to the surrounding normal tissues.

Over the last century, the external radiation source used for cancer treatment has evolved from the early days' kilovoltage X-ray beams to today's megavoltage X-ray beams, produced from an electron linear accelerator (linac). The radioisotopes used for brachytherapy have also evolved from the early days' ^{226}Ra to include many others (e.g., ^{192}Ir, ^{125}I, and ^{103}Pd). However, since brachytherapy generally involves invasive procedures, it is relegated to second place behind external beam therapy in the treatment of cancer. A typical radiation oncology department today treats about eighty percent of its patients with the various external beam techniques, and about ten to twenty percent of its patients with brachytherapy (Podgorsak 2005) The sections below separately describe external beam radiation therapy and brachytherapy.

11.4.1 External Beam Radiation Therapy

External beam radiation therapy (EBRT) today is mostly based on a megavoltage X-ray beam produced from an electron linac. Figure 11.20 is the schematic diagram of a modern medical linac. As shown, the main beam-forming components include the following: electron gun, radio-frequency power generation system, accelerating waveguide, electron beam transport system, and X-ray beam collimation and monitoring system. The length of the accelerating waveguide depends on the final electron kinetic energy, and ranges from ~30 cm at 4 MeV to 150 cm at 25 MeV. The megavoltage X-rays are produced by slamming the electrons onto a tungsten target, the same method used to produce kilovoltage X-rays (Section 11.3.1.1 and Figure 11.5). At megavoltage electron energies, the bremsstrahlung X-ray photons produced in the tungsten target are mainly forwardly peaked so that the clinical photon beam is produced in the direction of the electron beam striking the target. The X-ray beam collimation of a modern medical linac is achieved with two or three collimator devices so that the beam shape closely follows that of the tumor.

In a modern linac treatment routine, the patient is placed on the treatment couch with the tumor volume positioned at the beam isocenter. To deliver a concentrated radiation dose to the tumor volume, the gantry is rotated about its axis (i.e., the patient) in one or more arcs. During the rotation the collimators continuously adjust the shape of the beam to match the shape of the tumor. Figure 11.21 shows a patient being positioned at a modern medical linac manufactured by Varian Medical Systems. The treatment head, the X-ray beam collimator, and the gantry are specifically pointed out. The patient is usually positioned in such a way that the geometric center of the tumor overlaps with the beam's isocenter. The entire treatment for each patient includes three basic steps:

1. The patient first undergoes a diagnostic imaging procedure (e.g., X-ray CT/PET) to delineate the tumor location and clinical target volume.
2. The image data obtained in the first step are then passed over to a treatment planning software to produce an optimized treatment scheme. The optimization process is largely based on the criteria that the tumor volume receives the prescribed dose and that the nearby critical organs and tissues are well spared.
3. The optimized treatment scheme is then implemented accordingly at the linac, and it is entirely controlled by the computer.

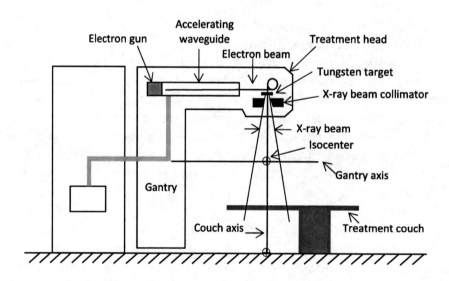

Figure 11.20. The schematic diagram of a modern medical linac.

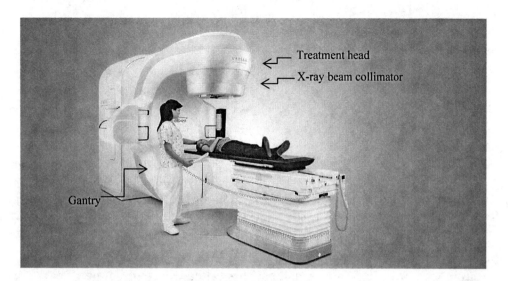

Figure 11.21. A patient being positioned on the treatment couch at a modern medical linac manufactured by Varian Medical Systems.

Most of the EBRT follows a conventional protocol that the radiation dose is delivered in many small fractions on a daily basis over the course of several weeks. For example, a commonly used scheme is to divide the prescribed radiation dose of 60 Gy (to the tumor) into 30 fractions, with 2 Gys per fraction per day. On the basis of five treatment days per week, the total treatment for the patient will last for six weeks. The above treatment protocol is generally believed to produce better clinical outcomes than a scheme where radiation dose is delivered in one or a few very large fractions (i.e., the hypofractionation scheme). The clinical outcomes are evaluated based on the tumor control probability and the probability of normal tissue complication. The explanation in favor of the conventional protocol is as follows: division of radiation delivery into many small fractions spares normal tissues through repair of sublethal DNA damage and repopulation of cells. Because some tumor cells are hypoxic (i.e., short of oxygen) and because the hypoxic cells are known to be resistant to radiation damage, dose fractionation may allow the hypoxic tumor cells be oxygenated and thus become more sensitive to radiation damage.

Since early 2000s, a new form of EBRT called stereotactic body radiation therapy (SBRT) has been successfully used in treating small size, early stage lung cancer, gastrointestinal tumors, and liver tumors. With SBRT, the radiation dose is delivered in one or a few (<5) large doses over the course of a few days. This hypofractionation scheme has become possible because modern medical linacs are equipped with collimators of millimeter-size precision, as well as on-board kilovoltage/megavoltage imagers that allow high doses be precisely delivered to the tumor, with very sharp dose gradient outside the tumor and into the surrounding normal tissue. While SBRT is not going to entirely replace the conventional EBRT, it is rapidly becoming a widely used form in treating a variety of early stage cancers.

11.4.2 Internal Radiation Therapy (or Brachytherapy)

In brachytherapy, radioactive isotopes are sealed in tiny capsules or "seeds." These seeds are placed very close to or inside the tumor using a variety of devices, such as needles or catheters. As isotopes decay, they give off radiation which then delivers a radiation dose to the nearby tissue. Because the radiation is emitted from the inside out, radiation dose distribution follows the $1/r^2$ law. As such, tumor tissue is more heavily irradiated as opposed to the surrounding normal tissues.

Several brachytherapy techniques are currently used in cancer treatment, depending on if the placement of the source seeds is temporary or permanent. For temporary brachytherapy, a high-activity source seed is placed near or within the tumor volume via a delivery device (a needle or a catheter). The source seed stays in the patient's body for only a short period of time (~10 minutes) to deliver the prescribed radiation dose, and both the source seed and the delivery device are removed after treatment. Because it uses a high-activity source, and because the treatment duration is short, the temporary brachytherapy is also referred to as a type of high-dose-rate (HDR) treatment. The most widely used radioisotope for HDR treatment is ^{192}Ir, which has a half-life of 73.8 days and emits photons with an average energy of 0.38 MeV. The typical activity of ^{192}Ir used for HDR treatment is 370 GBq (10 Ci). The ^{192}Ir-based HDR brachytherapy devices have been used to treat several types of cancer, including prostate cancer, breast cancer, cervical cancer, and esophageal cancer. Unlike the EBRT, most of the HDR treatments are done with a few large dose fractions. This is because the procedures involved in a HDR treatment are somewhat invasive.

For permanent brachytherapy, the source seeds are of low activities and are surgically implanted into the patient's body and left there, even after all the radioactivity has decayed away. Since the source capsule is made of biologically benign materials (e.g., titanium), leaving the decayed source seeds in the body does not cause any discomfort or harm to the patient. Because the source seeds are of low activities and because the treatment duration is long (a few months), the permanent brachytherapy is also referred to as a type of low-dose-rate (LDR) treatment. The widely used radioisotopes for permanent brachytherapy include ^{125}I and ^{103}Pd. ^{125}I has a half-life of 59.4 days and emits photons with an average energy of 28 keV. ^{103}Pd has a half-life of 17 days and emits photons with an average energy of 21 keV. Both isotopes are mainly used to treat prostate cancer. In a typical prostate cancer treatment procedure, more than one hundred source seeds are uniformly implanted into the prostate. The positioning of each source seed is guided by an ultrasound device. The low-energy photons emitted from ^{125}I and ^{103}Pd are unique in that they are locally absorbed in the vicinity of the tumor (to maximize the tumor dose) and that the amount of photons escaping the patient is negligible. The negligible photon escape is important as it allows the patient be released into the community without being a "radiation hazard" to others.

11.5 Radiation Protection and Safety

While ionizing radiation has been beneficial to human beings for power production, medical diagnosis, cancer treatment, and scientific research, it has been known since the early days that radiation can also harm people. There have been many radiation-induced injuries and deaths of both workers and the general public, all over the world. The most famous incidences are the Chernobyl disaster that occurred on April 26, 1986, at the Chernobyl nuclear power plant in Ukraine, and the Fukushima disaster that occurred on March 12, 2011, at several nuclear power plants in Fukushima, Japan. While there were few deaths directly attributed to the accidents (31 in Chernobyl and 0 in Fukushima), both accidents released huge quantities of radioactive materials into the atmosphere. The radioactive fallout eventually covered extensive geographical areas and caused harm to large populations. In addition to these accidental events, there is an increasing concern about so-called "radiological terrorism." Possible scenarios for radiological terrorism include the detonation of a nuclear weapon in or close to a major city, an attack on a nuclear power plant, and the detonation of a "dirty bomb," also called a "radiological dispersed device" (RDD). Consequently, the industries that involve the use of radiation are highly regulated. There have been rules and guidelines developed over the years to minimize radiation-induced harm to people. These rules and guidelines have been written into laws that are enforced by government agencies, such as the Nuclear Regulatory Commission and the Environmental Protection Agency. Every institution or organization that owns and uses radiation sources must have a radiation safety officer (or health physicist) to make sure that the rules and guidelines are being followed by their workers.

There are two types of harmful effects of radiation: the deterministic effect and the stochastic effect. The deterministic effect is usually associated with large radiation exposures. It occurs when a large number of the cells of an organ (or a tissue) are dead, resulting in the loss of organ or tissue function. There usually is a radiation dose threshold (which is organ/tissue specific) below which the effect does not occur. Once the dose exceeds the threshold, the severity of the effect increases with the dose. In fact, the deterministic effect is the major side effect for radiation therapy patients (Section 11.4). Examples of deterministic effect include cataracts, erythema, infertility, and blood forming deficiency. The worst deterministic effect, of course, is death, which occurs when the critical organs of the body have lost their functions.

The stochastic effect is usually associated with relatively small radiation exposures. The probability of having the effect is proportional to the radiation dose absorbed. Examples of stochastic effect include radiation-induced cancer and genetic effect. The most significant epidemiological study demonstrating the stochastic effect is that of the Japanese atomic bomb survivors. However, since the bomb survivors all received relatively large radiation exposures, it is unclear if a dose threshold exists for the stochastic effect. Other epidemiological studies on the populations that live in high levels of natural background radiation do not show the effect, indicating the existence of a dose threshold. The current practice in the radiation protection industry is based on the so-called "linear-no-threshold (LNT) hypothesis." It assumes that the stochastic effect of radiation is proportional to the dose an individual receives, regardless of how small the dose is (National Council on Radiation Protection and Measurements 2001).

11.6 Professional Society Websites

Readers who are interested in learning more about the profession of nuclear engineering are referred to the American Nuclear Society (ANS) website: http://www.ans.org. Those who are interested in learning more about the profession of medical physics are referred to the American Association of Physicists in Medicine (AAPM) website: https://www.aapm.org. Those who are interested in learning more about the profession of radiological health physics, radiation protection, and safety are referred to the website of the Health Physics Society (HPS) website: https://www.hps.org.

Bibliography

Antoch, Gerald, Jörg Stattaus, Andre T. Nemat, Simone Marnitz, Thomas Beyer, Hilmar Kuehl, Andreas Bockisch, Jörg F. Debatin, and Lutz S. Freudenberg. 2003. "Non-Small Cell Lung Cancer: Dual-Modality PET/CT in Preoperative Staging." *Radiology* 229 (2): 526–33.

Baškot, Branislav, ed. 2011. *Coronary Angiography – Advances in Noninvasive Imaging Approach for Evaluation of Coronary Artery Disease.* Rijeka, Croatia: InTech.

Furlong, Richard R., and Earl J. Wahlquist. 1999. "U.S. Space Missions Using Radioisotope Power Systems." *Nuclear News,* American Nuclear Society (April): 26-34.

National Council on Radiation Protection and Measurements. 2001. "Evaluation of the Linear-Nonthreshold Dose-Response Model for Ionizing Radiation." NCRP Report No. 136.

National Research Council, Committee on State of the Science of Nuclear Medicine. 2007. "Advancing Nuclear Medicine Through Innovation." http://www.nap.edu/read/11985/chapter/1.

National Research Council, Committee on Medical Isotope Production without Highly Enriched Uranium. 2009. "Medical Isotope Production Without Highly Enriched Uranium." http://www.nap.edu/read/12569/chapter/1.

Podgorsak, Ervin. B., ed. 2005. *Radiation Oncology Physics: A Handbook for Teachers and Students.* Vienna: International Atomic Energy Agency.

U.S. Food and Drug Administration (n.d.). "What is Computed Tomography?" http://www.fda.gov/Radiation-EmittingProducts/RadiationEmittingProductsandProcedures/MedicalImaging/MedicalX-Rays/ucm115318.htm.

Credits

APPENDIX A: PHYSICAL CONSTANTS, PARTICLE REST MASSES, AND CONVERSION FACTORS

Physical Constants

Charge of the electron $e = 1.6 \times 10^{-19}$ C

Planck constant $h = 6.626 \times 10^{-34}$ J s $= 4.136 \times 10^{-15}$ eV s

$\hbar = 1.0546 \times 10^{-34}$ J s $= 6.582 \times 10^{-16}$ eV s

Boltzmann constant $k = 1.38 \times 10^{-23}$ J K^{-1} $= 8.617 \times 10^{-5}$ eV K^{-1}

Speed of light in free space $c = 3.00 \times 10^{8}$ m s^{-1}

Permittivity of free space $\varepsilon_0 = 8.85 \times 10^{-12}$ F m^{-1}

Permeability of free space $\mu_0 = 4\pi \times 10^{-7}$ H m^{-1}

Avogadro constant $N_A = 6.02 \times 10^{26}$ kg-mol^{-1}

Rydberg constant $R = 1.10 \times 10^{7}$ m^{-1}

Bohr magneton $\mu_B = 9.27 \times 10^{-24}$ J T^{-1}

Nuclear magneton $\mu_N = 5.0508 \times 10^{-27}$ J T^{-1} $= 3.1525 \times 10^{-14}$ MeV T^{-1}

Fine structure constant $\alpha = 1/137$

$$hc = 1239.85 \text{ MeV fm}$$
$$\hbar c = 197.329 \text{ MeV fm}$$
$$e^2 / 4\pi\varepsilon_0 = 1.44 \text{ MeV fm}$$

Particle Rest Masses

Mass of the electron $m_e = 9.11 \times 10^{-31}$ kg $= 5.4858 \times 10^{-4}$ u $= 511$ keV/c^2

Mass of the proton $m_p = 1.673 \times 10^{-27}$ kg $= 1.007276$ u $= 938.28$ MeV/c^2

Mass of the neutron $m_n = 1.675 \times 10^{-27}$ kg $= 1.008665$ u $= 939.57$ MeV/c^2

Conversion Factors

Unified atomic mass unit $1\text{u} = 1.66 \times 10^{-27}$ kg $= 931.502$ MeV/c^2

Energy conversion 1 eV $= 1.6 \times 10^{-19}$ J

Cross section conversion: 1 barn $= 10^{-24}$ cm^2

Year in seconds: 1 yr $= 3.16 \times 10^{7}$ s

Atmospheric pressure 1 atmosphere $= 1.01 \times 10^{5}$ N m^{-2}

Acceleration due to gravity on Earth's surface $g = 9.81$ m s^{-2}

1 gram molecule at standard temperature and pressure occupies 22.4 liters

APPENDIX B: NUCLEAR DATA

The nuclear data for various isotopes have been directly extracted from the Nuclear Wallet Cards published by the National Nuclear Data Center: www.nndc.bnl.gov.

Explanation of the Table

Column 1, Nuclide (Z, El, A)

Nuclides are listed in order of increasing atomic number (Z), and are subordered by increasing mass number (A). All isotopic species, as well as all isomers with half-life ≥ 0.1 s , and some with half-life ≥ 0.1 ms that decay by SF, α, or p emissions, are included. A nuclide is given only if its mass estimate is known. Isomeric states are denoted by the symbol "m" after the mass number and are given in the order of increasing excitation energy. Where the ground state is not well established, all given states carry the symbol "m". The ^{235}U thermal fission products with fractional cumulative yields $\geq 10^{-6}$ are italicized in the table.

Column 3, Mass Excess, Δ

Mass excesses, M-A, are given in MeV with $\Delta(^{12}C) = 0$, by definition. For isomers, the values are obtained by adding the excitation energy to the Δ values. Wherever the excitation energy is not known, the mass excess for the next lower isomer is given. The values are given to the accuracy determined by the uncertainty in Δ (maximum of three figures after the decimal). The uncertainty is ≤ 9 in the last significant figure. An appended "s" denotes that the value is obtained from systematics.

Column 4, $T_{1/2}$, Γ or Abundance

The half-life and the abundance (in bold face) are shown, followed by their units (% symbol in the case of abundance), which are followed by the uncertainty, in italics, in the last significant figures. For example, 8.1 s *10* means 8.1 ± 1.0 s. For some very short-lived nuclei, level widths rather than half-lives are given. There also, the width is followed by units (e.g., eV, keV, or MeV), which are followed by the uncertainty in italics, if known. This field is left blank when the half-life is not known.

Column 5, $T_{1/2}$, Γ or Abundance

Decay modes are given in decreasing strength from left to right, followed by the percentage branching, if known ("w" indicates a weak branch). The percentage branching is omitted where there is no competing mode of decay or no other mode has been observed. A "?" symbol indicates an expected but not observed mode of decay. The various modes of decay are given below:

$\beta-$ β^- decay

ε	ε (electron capture), or $\varepsilon + \beta^+$, or β^+ decay
IT	isomeric transition through γ or IC
n, p, α, ...	neutron, proton, alpha, ... decay
SF	spontaneous fission
$2\beta-$, 3α, ...	double β^- decay, decay through emission of 3 α, ...
$\beta - n$, $\beta - p$, ...	delayed n, p, ... emission following β^- decay
εp, $\varepsilon \alpha$, ...	delayed p, α, ... emission following ε or β^+ decay

Credits

Appendix B: Adapted from National Nuclear Data Center.

Nuclide				Δ	T½, Γ, or	
Z	El	A	Jπ	(MeV)	Abundance	Decay Mode
0	n	1	1/2+	8.071	10.183 m *17*	β–
1	H	1	1/2+	7.289	**99.9885% 70**	
		2	1+	13.136	**0.0115% 70**	
		3	1/2+	14.950	12.32 y *2*	β–
		4	2–	24.6		n
		5	(1/2+)	32.89	5.7 MeV *21*	2n
		6	(2–)	41.9	1.6 MeV *4*	n
		7	(1/2+)	47.9	29×10⁻²³ y *7*	
2	He	3	1/2+	14.931	**0.000134% 3**	
		4	0+	2.425	**99.999866% 3**	
		5	3/2–	11.23	0.60 MeV *2*	α, n
		6	0+	17.592	801 ms *10*	β–
		7	(3/2)–	26.067	150 keV *20*	n
		8	0+	31.609	119.1 ms *12*	β–, β–n 16%
		9	1/2+	39.78		n
		10	0+	48.81	300 keV *200*	n
3	Li	3		29s	unbound	p?
		4	2–	25.3	6.03 MeV	p
		5	3/2–	11.68	≈1.5 MeV	p, α
		6	1+	14.087	**7.59% 4**	
		7	3/2–	14.907	**92.41% 4**	
		8	2+	20.945	839.9 ms *9*	β–, β–α
		9	3/2–	24.954	178.3 ms *4*	β–, β–n 50.8%
		10	(1–,2–)	33.05		n
		11	3/2–	40.728	8.75 ms *14*	β–, β–n 83%, β–2n 4.1%, β–nα 0.027%
		12		48.92	<10 ns	n?
		13		58.3		
4	Be	5	(1/2+)	37s		p
		6	0+	18.375	92 keV *6*	p, α
		7	3/2–	15.768	53.24 d *4*	ε
		8	0+	4.941	5.57 eV *25*	α
		9	3/2–	11.348	**100.%**	
		10	0+	12.607	1.387×10⁶ y *12*	β–
		11	1/2+	20.177	13.81 s *8*	β–, β–α 3.1%
		12	0+	25.076	21.49 ms *3*	β–, β–n ≤1%
		13	(1/2–)	33.21	2.7×10⁻²¹ s *18*	n
		14	0+	40.0	4.35 ms *17*	β–, β–n 81%, β–2n 5%
		15		49.8s	<200 ns	n?
		16	0+	57.7s	<200 ns	2n?
5	B	6		47s	unbound	2p?
		7	(3/2–)	27.87	1.4 MeV *2*	α, p
		8	2+	22.921	770 ms *3*	ε, εα
		9	3/2–	12.416	0.54 keV *21*	p, 2α
		10	3+	12.050	**19.9% 7**	
		11	3/2–	8.667	**80.1% 7**	
		12	1+	13.368	20.20 ms *2*	β–, β–3α 1.58%
		13	3/2–	16.562	17.33 ms *17*	β–
		14	2–	23.66	12.5 ms *5*	β–

Nuclide Z El A			Jπ	Δ (MeV)	T½, Γ, or Abundance	Decay Mode
5	B	15		28.96	9.93 ms *7*	β–, β–n 93.6%, β–2n 0.4%
		16	0–	37.12	<190 ps	n
		17	(3/2–)	43.8	5.08 ms *5*	β– , β–n 63%, β–2n 11%, β–3n 3.5 β–4n 0.4%
		18	(4–)	51.9s	<26 ns	n?
		19	(3/2–)	58.8s	2.92 ms *13*	β– , β–n 72%, β–2n 16%
		20		67.1s		
		21		75.7s		
6	C	8	0+	35.08	230 keV *50*	p , α
		9	(3/2–)	28.909	126.5 ms *9*	ε , εp 61.6%, εα 38.4%
		10	0+	15.698	19.308 s *4*	ε
		11	3/2–	10.650	20.334 m *24*	ε
		12	0+	0.000	**98.93% *8***	
		13	1/2–	3.125	**1.07% *8***	
		14	0+	3.020	5700 y *30*	β–
		15	1/2+	9.873	2.449 s *5*	β–
		16	0+	13.694	0.747 s *8*	β–, β–n 99%
		17	3/2+	21.03	193 ms *13*	β–, β–n 32%
		18	0+	24.92	92 ms *2*	β–, β–n 31.5%
		19	1/2+	32.41	49 ms *4*	β–, β–n 61%
		20	0+	37.6	14 ms *+6–5*	β–, β–n 72%
		21	(1/2+)	45.6s	<30 ns	n?
		22	0+	52.1s	6.1 ms *+14–12*	β–, β–n 61%, β–2n < 37%
		23		62.7s		
7	N	10		38.8		p
		11	1/2+	24.30	0.83 MeV *3*	p
		12	1+	17.338	11.000 ms *16*	ε
		13	1/2–	5.345	9.965 m *4*	ε
		14	1+	2.863	**99.636% *20***	
		15	1/2–	0.101	**0.364% *20***	
		16	2–	5.683	7.13 s *2*	β–, β–α 1.2×10^{-3}%
		17	1/2–	7.87	4.173 s *4*	β–, β–n 95.1%
		18	1–	13.11	620 ms *8*	β–, β–α 12.2%, β–n 7%
		19		15.86	336 ms *3*	β–, β–n 41.8%
		20	2–	21.76	136 ms *3*	β–, β–n 42.9%
		21	(1/2–)	25.25	83 ms *8*	β–, β–n 90.5%
		22	(0–,1–)	32.0	20 ms *2*	β–, β–n 33%, β–2n 12%
		23		38.4s	14.5 ms *14*	β–, β–n, β–2n
		24		47.5s	<52 ns	n?
		25		56.5s		
8	O	12	0+	32.05	0.40 MeV *25*	p
		13	(3/2–)	23.114	8.58 ms *5*	ε , εp
		14	0+	8.007	70.620 s *15*	ε
		15	1/2–	2.855	122.24 s *16*	ε

Nuclide Z	El	A	Jπ	Δ (MeV)	T½, Γ, or Abundance	Decay Mode
8	O	16	0+	−4.737	99.757% *16*	
		17	5/2+	−0.809	0.038% *1*	
		18	0+	−0.783	0.205% *14*	
		19	5/2+	3.333	26.88 s *5*	β–
		20	0+	3.796	13.51 s *5*	β–
		21	(5/2+)	8.06	3.42 s *10*	β–
		22	0+	9.28	2.25 s *9*	β–, β–n < 22%
		23	1/2+	14.62	97 ms *8*	β–, β–n 7%
		24	0+	18.5	65 ms *5*	β–, β–n 58%
		25		27.3		
		26	0+	35.1s	<40 ns	n?
		27		44.1s	<260 ns	n?
		28	0+	52.9s	<100 ns	n?
9	F	14	(2−)	31.96		p
		15	(1/2+)	16.81	1.0 MeV *2*	p
		16	0−	10.680	40 keV *20*	p
		17	5/2+	1.951	64.49 s *16*	ε
		18	1+	0.873	109.77 m *5*	ε
		19	1/2+	−1.487	100%	
		20	2+	−0.017	11.07 s *6*	β–
		21	5/2+	−0.047	4.158 s *20*	β–
		22	(4+)	2.79	4.23 s *4*	β–, β–n < 11%
		23	5/2+	3.3	2.23 s *14*	β–
		24	(1,2,3)+	7.56	390 ms *70*	β–, β–n < 5.9%
		25	5/2+	11.36	80 ms *9*	β–, β–n 23.1%
		26	(1+)	18.67	9.7 ms *7*	β–, β–n 11%
		27	(5/2+)	24.6	5.0 ms *2*	β–, β–n 77%
		28		33.1s	<40 ns	
		29	(5/2+)	40.0s	2.5 ms *3*	β–, β–n
		30		48.4s		n
		31		55.9s	>250 ns	β–n, β–
10	Ne	16	0+	24.00	9×10⁻²¹ s	2p
		17	1/2−	16.500	109.2 ms *6*	ε, εp, εα
		18	0+	5.317	1.6670 s *17*	ε
		19	1/2+	1.752	17.22 s *2*	ε
		20	0+	−7.042	90.48% *3*	
		21	3/2+	−5.731	0.27% *1*	
		22	0+	−8.024	9.25% *3*	
		23	5/2+	−5.154	37.24 s *12*	β–
		24	0+	−5.951	3.38 m *2*	β–
		25	1/2+	−2.06	602 ms *8*	β–
		26	0+	0.48	197 ms *1*	β–, β–n 0.13%
		27	(3/2+)	7.03	31.5 ms *13*	β–, β–n 2%
		28	0+	11.29	18.9 ms *4*	β–, β–n 12%, β– 3.6%
		29	(3/2+)	18.40	14.8 ms *3*	β–, β–n 28%, β–2n 4%
		30	0+	23.0	7.3 ms *3*	β–, β–n 13%, β– 8.9%
		31		31	3.4 ms *8*	β–, β–n
		32	0+	37.0s	3.5 ms *9*	β–, β–n
		33		46.0s	<180 ns	n

Nuclide Z El	A	Jπ	Δ (MeV)	T½, Γ, or Abundance	Decay Mode
10 Ne	34	0+	52.8s	>60 ns	β–n , β–
11 Na	18	1–	25.0	1.3×10^{-21} s 4	p
	19	(5/2+)	12.93	<40 ns	p
	20	2+	6.850	447.9 ms 23	ε , εα 20.05%
	21	3/2+	–2.184	22.49 s 4	ε
	22	3+	–5.181	2.6027 y 10	ε
	23	3/2+	–9.530	**100%**	
	24	4+	–8.417	14.997 h 12	β–
	24m	1+	–7.945	20.18 ms 10	IT 99.95%, β– ≈ 0.05%
	25	5/2+	–9.357	59.1 s 6	β–
	26	3+	–6.860	1.07128 s 25	β–
	27	5/2+	–5.517	301 ms 6	β–, β–n 0.13%
	28	1+	–0.99	30.5 ms 4	β–, β–n 0.58%
	29	3/2+	2.67	44.9 ms 12	β–, β–n 21.5%
	30	2+	8.37	48 ms 2	β–, β–n 30%, β–2n 1.15%, β–α 5.5×10^{-5}%
	31	3/2(+)	12.5	17.0 ms 4	β–, β–n 37%, β–2n 0.87%, β–3n < 0.05%
	32	(3–,4–)	18.8	13.2 ms 4	β–, β–n 24%, β–2n 8%
	33	(3/2+)	24.0s	8.0 ms 4	β–, β–n 47%, β–2n 13%
	34		31.3s	5.5 ms 10	β–, β–2n ≈ 50%, β–n ≈ 15%
	35		37.8s	1.5 ms 5	β–, β–n
	36		45.9s	<180 ns	n
	37		53.1s	>60 ns	β–n , β–
12 Mg	19		31.83	4.0 ps 15	2p
	20	0+	17.56	90.8 ms 24	ε , εp ≈ 27%
	21	5/2+	10.91	122 ms 3	ε , εp 32.6%, εα < 0.5%
	22	0+	–0.399	3.8755 s 12	ε
	23	3/2+	–5.473	11.317 s 11	ε
	24	0+	–13.933	**78.99% 4**	
	25	5/2+	–13.192	**10.00% 1**	
	26	0+	–16.214	**11.01% 3**	
	27	1/2+	–14.586	9.458 m 12	β–
	28	0+	–15.018	20.915 h 9	β–
	29	3/2+	–10.60	1.30 s 12	β–
	30	0+	–8.89	335 ms 17	β–
	31	1/2(+)	–3.19	232 ms 15	β–, β–n 1.7%
	32	0+	–0.91	86 ms 5	β–, β–n 5.5%
	33	3/2–	4.95	90.5 ms 16	β–, β–n 14%
	34	0+	8.56	20 ms 10	β–, β–n
	35	(7/2–)	15.6	70 ms 40	β–, β–n 52%
	36	0+	20.4	3.9 ms 13	β–, β–n
	37	(7/2–)	28.3s	>260 ns	β–, β–n
	38	0+	34.1s	>260 ns	β–, β–n
	39		42.3s	<180 ns	n

Nuclide Z El A	Jπ	Δ (MeV)	T½, Γ, or Abundance	Decay Mode
12 Mg 40	0+	48.6s	>170 ns	β−, β−n
13 Al 21	(5/2+)	27.1s	<35 ns	p
22	4+	18.2s	91.1 ms *5*	ε, εp 54.5%, ε2p 1.1%, εα 0.04%
23	5/2+	6.748	446 ms *6*	ε, εp 1.22%
24	4+	−0.048	2.053 s *4*	ε, εp 1.6×10⁻³%, εα 0.04%
24m	1+	0.378	130 ms *3*	IT 82.5%, ε 17.5%, εα 0.03%
25	5/2+	−8.916	7.183 s *12*	ε
26	5+	−12.210	7.17×10⁵ y *24*	ε
26m	0+	−11.982	6.3464 s *7*	ε
27	5/2+	−17.196	**100%**	
28	3+	−16.850	2.2414 m *12*	β−
29	5/2+	−18.215	6.56 m *6*	β−
30	3+	−15.87	3.62 s *6*	β−
31	(3/2,5/2)+	−14.95	644 ms *25*	β−
32	1+	−11.06	33.0 ms *2*	β−, β−n 0.7%
33	(5/2)+	−8.44	41.7 ms *2*	β−, β−n 8.5%
34		−3.05	42 ms *6*	β−, β−n 27%
35		−0.22	37.2 ms *8*	β−, β−n 38%
36		5.95	90 ms *40*	β−, β−n< 31%
37		9.8	10.7 ms *13*	β−
38		16.2	7.6 ms *6*	β−, β−n
39		21.0s	7.6 ms *16*	β−, β−n
40		28.0s	>260 ns	β−, β−n
41		33.9s	>260 ns	β−
42		41.5s	>170 ns	β−, β−n
43		48.4s	>170 ns	β−, β−n
14 Si 22	0+	33.0s	29 ms *2*	ε, εp 32%
23	(5/2)+	23.1s	42.3 ms *4*	ε, εp 71%, ε2p 3.6%
24	0+	10.75	140.5 ms *15*	ε, εp 45%
25	5/2+	3.83	220 ms *3*	ε, εp 35%
26	0+	−7.140	2.229 s *3*	ε
27	5/2+	−12.384	4.15 s *4*	ε
28	0+	−21.493	**92.223% *19***	
29	1/2+	−21.895	**4.685% *8***	
30	0+	−24.432	**3.092% *11***	
31	3/2+	−22.949	157.3 m *3*	β−
32	0+	−24.077	153 y *19*	β−
33	3/2+	−20.514	6.11 s *21*	β−
34	0+	−19.96	2.77 s *20*	β−
35		−14.36	0.78 s *12*	β−, β−n< 5%
36	0+	−12.42	0.45 s *6*	β−, β−n< 10%
37	(7/2−)	−6.59	90 ms *60*	β−, β−n 17%
38	0+	−4.17	>1 μs	β−, β−n
39		2.32	47.5 ms *20*	β−, β−n
40	0+	5.4	33.0 ms *10*	β−, β−n
41		12.1	20.0 ms *25*	β−, β−n ?
42	0+	16.6s	12.5 ms *35*	β−, β−n
43		23.1s	>60 ns	β−, β−n
44	0+	28.5s	>360 ns	β−, β−n

Nuclide Z El A	Jπ	Δ (MeV)	T½, Γ, or Abundance	Decay Mode
14 Si 45		37.2s		
15 P 24	(1+)	32.8s		ε? , p ?
25	(1/2+)	19.7s	<30 ns	p
26	(3+)	11.0s	43.7 ms *6*	ε , εp
27	1/2+	−0.71	260 ms *80*	ε , εp 0.07%
28	3+	−7.149	270.3 ms *5*	ε , εp 1.3×10^{-3}% , εα 8.6×10^{-4}%
29	1/2+	−16.952	4.142 s *15*	ε
30	1+	−20.200	2.498 m *4*	ε
31	1/2+	−24.441	**100%**	
32	1+	−24.304	14.262 d *14*	β−
33	1/2+	−26.337	25.35 d *11*	β−
34	1+	−24.548	12.43 s *8*	β−
35	1/2+	−24.857	47.3 s *7*	β−
36	4−	−20.25	5.6 s *3*	β−
37		−19.00	2.31 s *13*	β−
38	(0−:4−)	−14.64	0.64 s *14*	β− , β−n 12%
39	(1/2+)	−12.80	0.28 s *4*	β− , β−n 26%
40	(2−,3−)	−8.1	125 ms *25*	β− , β−n 15.8%
41	(1/2+)	−4.98	100 ms *5*	β− , β−n 30%
42		1.0	48.5 ms *15*	β− , β−n 50%
43	(1/2+)	4.7	36.5 ms *15*	β− , β−n
44		10.4s	18.5 ms *25*	β− , β−n
45		15.3s	>200 ns	β−
46		22.8s	>200 ns	β−
47		29.2s		
16 S 26	0+	27.1s	<79 ns	2p ?
27	(5/2+)	17.0s	15.5 ms *15*	ε , εp 2.3%, ε2p 1.1%
28	0+	4.1	125 ms *10*	ε , εp 20.7%
29	5/2+	−3.16	187 ms *4*	ε , εp 47%
30	0+	−14.062	1.178 s *5*	ε
31	1/2+	−19.043	2.572 s *13*	ε
32	0+	−26.015	**94.99%** *26*	
33	3/2+	−26.586	**0.75%** *2*	
34	0+	−29.931	**4.25%** *24*	
35	3/2+	−28.846	87.37 d *4*	β−
36	0+	−30.664	**0.01%** *1*	
37	7/2−	−26.896	5.05 m *2*	β−
38	0+	−26.861	170.3 m *7*	β−
39	(7/2)−	−23.16	11.5 s *5*	β−
40	0+	−22.9	8.8 s *22*	β−
41	(7/2−)	−19.09	1.99 s *5*	β− , β−n
42	0+	−17.7	1.03 s *3*	β−
43		−12.07	0.28 s *3*	β− , β−n 40%
44	0+	−9.1	100 ms *1*	β− , β−n 18%
45		−4.0	68 ms *2*	β− , β−n 54%
46	0+	0.0s	50 ms *8*	β−
47		7.4s		
48	0+	12.8s	≥200 ns	β−
49		21.2s	<200 ns	n
17 Cl 28	(1+)	27.5s		p ?

| Nuclide | | | | Δ | T½, Γ, or | |
Z El		A	Jπ	(MeV)	Abundance	Decay Mode
17 Cl		29	(3/2+)	13.8s	<20 ns	p
		30	(3+)	4.4s	<30 ns	p
		31		−7.07	150 ms *25*	ε , εp 0.7%
		32	1+	−13.335	298 ms *1*	ε , εα 0.05%, εp 0.03%
		33	3/2+	−21.003	2.511 s *4*	ε
		34	0+	−24.440	1.5264 s *14*	ε
		34m	3+	−24.294	32.00 m *4*	ε 55.4%, IT 44.6%
		35	3/2+	−29.013	**75.76% 10**	
		36	2+	−29.521	3.01×10⁵ y *2*	β− 98.1%, ε 1.9%
		37	3/2+	−31.761	**24.24% 10**	
		38	2−	−29.798	37.24 m *5*	β−
		38m	5−	−29.127	715 ms *3*	IT
		39	3/2+	−29.800	56.2 m *6*	β−
		40	2−	−27.56	1.35 m *2*	β−
		41	(1/2+)	−27.31	38.4 s *8*	β−
		42		−24.9	6.8 s *3*	β−
		43	(1/2+)	−24.4	3.13 s *9*	β−
		44	(2−)	−20.6	0.56 s *11*	β− , β−n < 8%
		45	(1/2+)	−18.36	413 ms *25*	β− , β−n 24%
		46		−13.8	232 ms *2*	β− , β−n 60%
		47		−10.1s	101 ms *6*	β− , β−n > 0%
		48		−4.1s	≥200 ns	β−
		49		1.1s	≥170 ns	β−
		50		8.4s	>620 ns	β− , β−n
		51	(3/2+)	14.5s	>200 ns	β−
18 Ar		30	0+	21.5s	<20 ns	p ?
		31	5/2(+)	11.3s	14.4 ms *6*	ε , εp 62%, ε2p 8.5%
		32	0+	−2.200	100.5 ms *3*	ε , εp 35.6%
		33	1/2+	−9.384	173.0 ms *20*	ε , εp 38.7%
		34	0+	−18.377	844.5 ms *34*	ε
		35	3/2+	−23.047	1.7756 s *10*	ε
		36	0+	−30.231	**0.3336% 21**	
		37	3/2+	−30.947	35.04 d *4*	ε
		38	0+	−34.714	**0.0629% 7**	
		39	7/2−	−33.242	269 y *3*	β−
		40	0+	−35.040	**99.6035% 25**	
		41	7/2−	−33.067	109.61 m *4*	β−
		42	0+	−34.422	32.9 y *11*	β−
		43	(5/2−)	−32.009	5.37 m *6*	β−
		44	0+	−32.673	11.87 m *5*	β−
		45	5/2−,7/2−	−29.770	21.48 s *15*	β−
		46	0+	−29.73	8.4 s *6*	β−
		47	(3/2)−	−25.21	1.23 s *3*	β− , β−n < 0.2%
		48	0+	−22.6s	475 ms *40*	β−
		49		−16.8s	170 ms *50*	β− , β−n 65%
		50	0+	−12.8s	85 ms *30*	β− , β−n 35%
		51		−5.9s	>200 ns	β−
		52	0+	−1.0s	>620 ns	β− ?
		53		7.1s	>620 ns	β− ?, β−n ?, β−2n ?
19 K		32		21.1s		p ?
		33		7.0s	<25 ns	p

Z	El	A	Jπ	Δ (MeV)	T½, Γ, or Abundance	Decay Mode
19	**K**	34	(1+)	−1.2s	<25 ns	p
		35	3/2+	−11.172	178 ms 8	ε, εp 0.37%
		36	2+	−17.417	342 ms 2	ε, εp 0.05%, εα 3.4×10⁻³%
		37	3/2+	−24.800	1.226 s 7	ε
		38	3+	−28.800	7.636 m 18	ε
		38m	0+	−28.670	924.3 ms 3	ε 99.97%, IT 0.03%
		39	3/2+	−33.807	**93.2581% 44**	
		40	4−	−33.535	1.248×10⁹ y 3 0.0117% 1	β− 89.28%, ε 10.72%
		41	3/2+	−35.560	**6.7302% 44**	
		42	2−	−35.022	12.321 h 25	β−
		43	3/2+	−36.575	22.3 h 1	β−
		44	2−	−35.781	22.13 m 19	β−
		45	3/2+	−36.615	17.81 m 61	β−
		46	(2−)	−35.413	105 s 10	β−
		47	1/2+	−35.708	17.50 s 24	β−
		48	(2−)	−32.285	6.8 s 2	β−, β−n 1.14%
		49	(1/2+,3/2+)	−29.611	1.26 s 5	β−, β−n 86%
		50	(0−,1−,2−)	−25.74	472 ms 4	β−, β−n 29%
		51	(1/2+,3/2+)	−21.6s	365 ms 5	β−, β−n 47%
		52	(2−)	−16.0s	118 ms 6	β−, β−n ≈ 73%
		53	(3/2+)	−11.1s	30 ms 5	β−, β−n ≈ 75%, β−2n< 1%
		54		−4.3s	10 ms 5	β−, β−n> 0%
		55		2s	>360 ns	β−, β−n
		56		8.7s	>620 ns	β−, β−n?, β−2n?
20	**Ca**	34	0+	13.9s	<35 ns	p
		35		4.8s	25.7 ms 2	ε, εp 95.9%, ε2p 4.1%
		36	0+	−6.45	102 ms 2	ε, εp 54.3%
		37	3/2+	−13.135	181.1 ms 10	ε, εp 82.1%
		38	0+	−22.058	440 ms 12	ε
		39	3/2+	−27.282	859.6 ms 14	ε
		40	0+	−34.846	>3.0×10²¹ y 96.94% 16	2ε
		41	7/2−	−35.137	1.02×10⁵ y 7	ε
		42	0+	−38.547	**0.647% 23**	
		43	7/2−	−38.408	**0.135% 10**	
		44	0+	−41.468	**2.09% 11**	
		45	7/2−	−40.812	162.61 d 9	β−
		46	0+	−43.139	>0.28×10¹⁶ y 0.004% 3	2β−
		47	7/2−	−42.345	4.536 d 3	β−
		48	0+	−44.223	>5.8×10²² y 0.187% 21	2β− 75%
		49	3/2−	−41.298	8.718 m 6	β−
		50	0+	−39.588	13.9 s 6	β−
		51	(3/2−)	−35.87	10.0 s 8	β−, β−n
		52	0+	−32.5	4.6 s 3	β−, β−n≤2%
		53	(3/2−,5/2−)	−27.5s	90 ms 15	β−, β−n>30%
		54	0+	−23.0s	86 ms 7	β−

Nuclide				Δ	T½, Γ, or	
Z	El	A	Jπ	(MeV)	Abundance	Decay Mode
20	Ca	55	(5/2–)	–17.0s	22 ms *2*	β–, β–n
		56	0+	–12.4s	11 ms *2*	β–, β–n?
		57		–5s	>620 ns	β–, β–n, β–2n
		58	0+	–0.3s	>620 ns	β–, β–n
21	Sc	36		15.5s		p?
		37		3.6s		p?
		38		–4.4s		p
		39	(7/2–)	–14.17	<300 ns	p
		40	4–	–20.523	182.3 ms *7*	ε, εp 0.44%, εα 0.02%
		41	7/2–	–28.642	596.3 ms *17*	ε
		42	0+	–32.121	681.3 ms *7*	ε
		42m	(7)+	–31.505	61.7 s *4*	ε
		43	7/2–	–36.188	3.891 h *12*	ε
		44	2+	–37.816	3.97 h *4*	ε
		44m	6+	–37.545	58.61 h *10*	IT 98.8%, ε 1.2%
		45	7/2–	–41.070	**100%**	
		45m	3/2+	–41.058	318 ms *7*	IT
		46	4+	–41.759	83.79 d *4*	β–
		46m	1–	–41.617	18.75 s *4*	IT
		47	7/2–	–44.336	3.3492 d *6*	β–
		48	6+	–44.502	43.67 h *9*	β–
		49	7/2–	–46.560	57.18 m *13*	β–
		50	5+	–44.55	102.5 s *5*	β–
		50m	2+,3+	–44.29	0.35 s *4*	IT>97.5%, β–<2.5%
		51	(7/2)–	–43.23	12.4 s *1*	β–
		52	3(+)	–40.4	8.2 s *2*	β–
		53	(7/2–)	–37.5s	2.4 s *6*	β–, β–n?
		54	(3)+	–33.7s	526 ms *15*	β–
		55	(7/2)–	–29.6	96 ms *2*	β–, β–n 17%
		56	(1+)	–24.5s	26 ms *6*	β–, β–n?
		56m	(5,6)+	–24.5s	75 ms *6*	β–, β–n>14%
		57	(7/2–)	–20.1s	22 ms *2*	β–, β–n
		58		–14.4s	12 ms *5*	β–, β–n
		59		–9.6s	>360 ns	β–, β–n
		60		–3.4s	>360 ns	β–, β–n
		61		1.6s	>360 ns	β–, β–n
22	Ti	38	0+	10.6s		
		39	(3/2+)	2.2s	31 ms +*6–4*	ε, εp
		40	0+	–8.9	52.4 ms *3*	ε, εp 97.5%
		41	3/2+	–15.1	80.4 ms *9*	ε, εp
		42	0+	–25.104	199 ms *6*	ε
		43	7/2–	–29.321	509 ms *5*	ε
		44	0+	–37.548	60.0 y *11*	ε
		45	7/2–	–39.008	184.8 m *5*	ε
		46	0+	–44.127	**8.25%** *3*	
		47	5/2–	–44.936	**7.44%** *2*	
		48	0+	–48.491	**73.72%** *3*	
		49	7/2–	–48.562	**5.41%** *2*	
		50	0+	–51.430	**5.18%** *2*	
		51	3/2–	–49.731	5.76 m *1*	β–
		52	0+	–49.468	1.7 m *1*	β–

Nuclide Z El A	Jπ	Δ (MeV)	T½, Γ, or Abundance	Decay Mode
22 Ti 53	(3/2)–	–46.8	32.7 s 9	β–
54	0+	–45.6	1.5 s 4	β–
55	(1/2)–	–41.7	1.3 s 1	β–
56	0+	–38.9	0.200 s 5	β–, β–n
57	(5/2–)	–33.5	98 ms 5	β–, β–n
58	0+	–30.7s	57 ms 10	β–, β–n
59	(5/2–)	–25.0s	27.5 ms 25	β–
60	0+	–21.5s	22.4 ms 25	β–
61	(1/2–)	–15.5s	15 ms 4	β–, β–n
62	0+	–11.8s	>620 ns	β–, β–n
63		–5.2s	>360 ns	β–, β–n
23 V 40		11.6s		p?
41		0.0s		p?
42		–7.6s	<55 ns	p
43		–18.0s	79.3 ms 24	ε
44	(2+)	–24.1	111 ms 7	ε, εα
44m	(6+)	–24.1	150 ms 3	ε
45	7/2–	–31.88	547 ms 6	ε
46	0+	–37.074	422.50 ms 11	ε
46m	3+	–36.272	1.02 ms 7	IT
47	3/2–	–42.005	32.6 m 3	ε
48	4+	–44.476	15.9735 d 25	ε
49	7/2–	–47.960	330 d 15	ε
50	6+	–49.224	>2.1×10¹⁷ y 0.250% 2	ε>92.9%, β–<7.1%
51	7/2–	–52.203	99.750% 2	
52	3+	–51.443	3.743 m 5	β–
53	7/2–	–51.849	1.543 m 14	β–
54	3+	–49.89	49.8 s 5	β–
55	(7/2–)	–49.2	6.54 s 15	β–
56	1+	–46.1	0.216 s 4	β–, β–n
57	(7/2–)	–44.2	0.32 s 3	β–, β–n
58	(1+)	–40.2	191 ms 10	β–, β–n
59	(5/2–)	–37.1	97 ms 2	β–, β–n<3%
60		–32.6	68 ms 5	β–
60m		–32.6	40 ms 15	β–, β–n
60m		–32.6	122 ms 18	β–, β–n
61	(3/2–)	–29.5s	52.6 ms 42	β–, β–n≥6%
62		–24.6s	33.5 ms 20	β–, β–n
63	7/2–	–21.1s	19.2 ms 24	β–, β–n≈35%
64		–15.6s	19 ms 8	β–
65		–11.3s	>360 ns	β–, β–n
66		–5.3s	>360 ns	β–, β–n
24 Cr 42	0+	6.5s	13.3 ms 10	ε, εp 94.4%
43	(3/2+)	–1.9s	20.6 ms 9	ε, εp 81%, ε2p 7.1%, ε3p 0.08%
44	0+	–13.1s	42.8 ms 6	ε, εp 14%
45	(7/2–)	–19.4s	60.9 ms 4	ε, εp 34.4%
46	0+	–29.47	0.26 s 6	ε
47	3/2–	–34.56	500 ms 15	ε
48	0+	–42.821	21.56 h 3	ε
49	5/2–	–45.332	42.3 m 1	ε

Nuclide Z El	A	Jπ	Δ (MeV)	T½, Γ, or Abundance	Decay Mode
24 Cr	50	0+	−50.261	>1.3×10^{18} y **4.345%** *13*	2ε
	51	7/2−	−51.451	27.7025 d *24*	ε
	52	0+	−55.418	**83.789%** *18*	
	53	3/2−	−55.285	**9.501%** *17*	
	54	0+	−56.933	**2.365%** *7*	
	55	3/2−	−55.108	3.497 m *3*	β−
	56	0+	−55.281	5.94 m *10*	β−
	57	(3/2)−	−52.524	21.1 s *10*	β−
	58	0+	−51.8	7.0 s *3*	β−
	59	(1/2−)	−47.9	1.05 s *9*	β−
	60	0+	−46.5	0.49 s *1*	β−
	61	(5/2−)	−42.2	243 ms *11*	β−, β−n
	62	0+	−40.4	206 ms *12*	β−, β−n
	63	1/2−	−35.6s	129 ms *2*	β−, β−n
	64	0+	−33.3s	42 ms *2*	β−
	65	(1/2−)	−27.8s	28 ms *3*	β−
	66	0+	−24.3s	23 ms *4*	β−
	67		−18.5s		β−?
	68	0+	−14.9s	>360 ns	β−, β−n
25 Mn	44	(2−)	6.7s	<105 ns	ε, p
	45		−5.1s		
	46	(4+)	−12.0s	36.2 ms *4*	ε, εp 57%
	47	(5/2−)	−22.3s	88.0 ms *13*	ε, εp<1.7%
	48	4+	−29.3	158.1 ms *22*	ε, εp 0.28%, εα<6.0×10^{-4}%
	49	5/2−	−37.61	382 ms *7*	ε
	50	0+	−42.627	283.19 ms *10*	ε
	50m	5+	−42.402	1.75 m *3*	ε
	51	5/2−	−48.243	46.2 m *1*	ε
	52	6+	−50.706	5.591 d *3*	ε
	52m	2+	−50.328	21.1 m *2*	ε 98.25%, IT 1.75%
	53	7/2−	−54.689	3.74×10^6 y *4*	ε
	54	3+	−55.556	312.12 d *6*	ε, β−<2.9×10^{-4}%
	55	5/2−	−57.711	**100%**	
	56	3+	−56.910	2.5789 h *1*	β−
	57	5/2−	−57.486	85.4 s *18*	β−
	58	1+	−55.827	3.0 s *1*	β−
	58m	4+	−55.755	65.4 s *5*	β−≈90%, IT≈10%
	59	(5/2)−	−55.525	4.59 s *5*	β−
	60	1+	−52.967	0.28 s *2*	β−
	60m	4+	−52.695	1.77 s *2*	β− 88.5%, IT 11.5%
	61	(5/2)−	−51.742	0.67 s *4*	β−
	62m	(3+)	−48.180	671 ms *5*	β−, β−n
	62m	(1+)	−48.180	92 ms *13*	β−, β−n
	63	5/2−	−46.886	0.275 s *4*	β−, β−n
	64	(1+)	−42.989	90 ms *4*	β−, β−n 33%
	64m	(4+)	−42.814	0.50 ms *5*	IT
	65	(5/2−)	−40.967	84 ms *8*	β−
	66		−36.75	65 ms *2*	β−
	67	(5/2+)	−32.8s	51 ms *4*	β−, β−n>10%
	68	(>3)	−28.0s	28 ms *3*	β−, β−n

Nuclide Z El A			Jπ	Δ (MeV)	T½, Γ, or Abundance	Decay Mode
25 Mn	69		5/2−	−24.4s	18 ms *4*	β−
	70			−19.2s	>360 ns	β− , β−n
	71				>637 ns	β− , β−n, β−2n
26 Fe	45		(3/2+)	13.8s	1.89 ms +*49−21*	2p 70%, ε≤30%, εp 19%, ε2p 7.8%, ε3p 3.3%
	46		0+	0.8s	13.0 ms *20*	ε , εp 78.7%
	47		(7/2−)	−6.6s	21.9 ms *2*	ε , εp 88.4%, ε2p
	48		0+	−18.16s	45.3 ms *6*	ε , εp 15.9%
	49		(7/2−)	−24.8s	64.7 ms *3*	ε , εp 56.7%
	50		0+	−34.49	155 ms *11*	ε , εp ?
	51		5/2−	−40.22	305 ms *5*	ε
	52		0+	−48.332	8.275 h *8*	ε
	52m		12+	−41.374	45.9 s *6*	ε , IT<4.0×10⁻³%
	53		7/2−	−50.946	8.51 m *2*	ε
	53m		19/2−	−47.906	2.54 m *2*	IT
	54		0+	−56.253	**5.845%** *35*	
	55		3/2−	−57.480	2.744 y *9*	ε
	56		0+	−60.606	**91.754%** *36*	
	57		1/2−	−60.181	**2.119%** *10*	
	58		0+	−62.154	**0.282%** *4*	
	59		3/2−	−60.664	44.495 d *9*	β−
	60		0+	−61.412	2.62×10⁶ y *4*	β−
	61		3/2−,5/2−	−58.920	5.98 m *6*	β−
	62		0+	−58.877	68 s *2*	β−
	63		(5/2−)	−55.635	6.1 s *6*	β−
	64		0+	−54.969	2.0 s *2*	β−
	65		(1/2−)	−51.221	0.81 s *5*	β−
	65m		(9/2+)	−50.819	1.12 s *15*	β−
	66		0+	−50.067	440 ms *60*	β−
	67		(1/2−)	−45.7	0.40 s *4*	β−
	68		0+	−43.1	180 ms *19*	β−
	69		1/2−	−38.4s	110 ms *6*	β−
	70		0+	−36.3s	71 ms *10*	β−
	71			−31.0s	28 ms *5*	β− , β−n
	72		0+	−28.3s	≥150 ns	β− , β−n 27.6%
	73				>633 ns	β− , β−n, β−2n
	74		0+		>638 ns	β− , β−n, β−2n
27 Co	47			10.3s		
	48			1.9s		
	49			−9.6s		
	50		(6+)	−17.2s	38.8 ms *2*	ε , εp 70.5%, ε2p
	51		(7/2−)	−27.3s	>200 ns	ε
	52		(6+)	−33.92s	115 ms *23*	ε
	53		(7/2−)	−42.658	240 ms *9*	ε
	53m		(19/2−)	−39.461	247 ms *12*	ε≈98.5%, p≈1.5%
	54		0+	−48.009	193.28 ms *7*	ε
	54m		7+	−47.812	1.48 m *2*	ε
	55		7/2−	−54.029	17.53 h *3*	ε
	56		4+	−56.039	77.236 d *26*	ε
	57		7/2−	−59.344	271.74 d *6*	ε
	58		2+	−59.846	70.86 d *6*	ε

Nuclide				Δ	T½, Γ, or	
Z	El	A	Jπ	(MeV)	Abundance	Decay Mode
27	**Co**	58m	5+	−59.821	9.10 h *9*	IT
		59	7/2−	−62.229	**100%**	
		60	5+	−61.649	1925.28 d *14*	β−
		60m	2+	−61.590	10.467 m *6*	IT 99.76%, β− 0.24%
		61	7/2−	−62.897	1.650 h *5*	β−
		62	2+	−61.43	1.50 m *4*	β−
		62m	5+	−61.41	13.91 m *5*	β−>99%, IT< 1%
		63	7/2−	−61.84	27.4 s *5*	β−
		64	1+	−59.79	0.30 s *3*	β−
		65	(7/2)−	−59.185	1.16 s *3*	β−
		66	(3+)	−56.41	0.20 s *2*	β−
		67	(7/2−)	−55.321	0.425 s *20*	β−
		68	(7−)	−51.9	0.199 s *21*	β−
		68m	(3+)	−51.9	1.6 s *3*	β−
		69	7/2−	−50.0	229 ms *24*	β−
		70	(6−)	−45.6	108 ms *7*	β−
		70m	(3+)	−45.6	0.50 s *18*	β−
		71	(7/2−)	−43.9	80 ms *3*	β−, β−n ≤ 6%
		72	(6−,7−)	−39.7s	59.9 ms *17*	β−, β−n ≥ 6%
		73		−37.2s	41 ms *4*	β−
		74	0+	−32.7s	25 ms *5*	β−, β−n ≈ 18%
		75	(7/2−)	−29.4s	>150 ns	β−
		76			>634 ns	β−, β−2n, β−n
28	**Ni**	48	0+	18.0s	2.1 ms +*14−6*	2p ≈ 70%, ε
		49		8.7s	7.5 ms *10*	ε, εp 83%
		50	0+	−3.6s	18.5 ms *12*	ε, εp 86.7%, ε2p
		51	(7/2−)	−11.5s	23.8 ms *2*	ε, εp 87.2%
		52	0+	−22.9s	40.8 ms *2*	ε, εp 31.4%
		53	(7/2−)	−29.7s	55.2 ms *7*	ε, εp 23.4%
		54	0+	−39.22	104 ms *7*	ε
		55	7/2−	−45.335	204.7 ms *37*	ε
		56	0+	−53.906	6.075 d *10*	ε
		57	3/2−	−56.083	35.60 h *6*	ε
		58	0+	−60.228	**68.077%** *9*	
		59	3/2−	−61.156	7.6×10⁴ y *5*	ε
		60	0+	−64.472	**26.223%** *8*	
		61	3/2−	−64.221	**1.1399%** *13*	
		62	0+	−66.745	**3.6346%** *40*	
		63	1/2−	−65.512	101.2 y *15*	β−
		64	0+	−67.098	**0.9255%** *19*	
		65	5/2−	−65.125	2.5175 h *5*	β−
		66	0+	−66.006	54.6 h *3*	β−
		67	(1/2)−	−63.742	21 s *1*	β−
		68	0+	−63.463	29 s *2*	β−
		68m	5−	−60.614	0.86 ms *5*	IT
		69	9/2+	−59.978	11.2 s *9*	β−
		69m	1/2−	−59.657	3.5 s *9*	β−
		70	0+	−59.213	6.0 s *3*	β−
		71	(9/2+)	−55.405	2.56 s *3*	β−
		71m	(1/2−)	−54.906	2.3 s *3*	β−
		72	0+	−54.225	1.57 s *5*	β−
		73	(9/2+)	−50.107	0.84 s *3*	β−

Nuclide Z El A	Jπ	Δ (MeV)	T½, Γ, or Abundance	Decay Mode
28 Ni 74	0+	−48.7s	0.68 s *18*	β−, β−n
75	(7/2+)	−44.1s	344 ms *25*	β−, β−n 10%
76	0+	−41.6s	0.238 s +*15−18*	β−, β−n
77		−36.7s	128 ms +*36−32*	β−, β−n 30%
78	0+	−34.1s	0.11 s +*10−6*	β−, β−n
79			>635 ns	β−, β−n, β−2n
29 Cu 52	(3+)	−1.9s		p
53	(3/2−)	−13.5s	<300 ns	ε, p
54	(3+)	−21.4s	<75 ns	p
55	(3/2−)	−31.6s	27 ms *8*	ε, εp 15%
56	(4+)	−38.2s	93 ms *3*	ε, εp 0.4%
57	3/2−	−47.308	196.3 ms *7*	ε
58	1+	−51.667	3.204 s *7*	ε
59	3/2−	−56.357	81.5 s *5*	ε
60	2+	−58.344	23.7 m *4*	ε
61	3/2−	−61.983	3.333 h *5*	ε
62	1+	−62.786	9.673 m *8*	ε
63	3/2−	−65.579	**69.15% *15***	
64	1+	−65.424	12.701 h *2*	ε 61.5%, β− 38.5%
65	3/2−	−67.263	**30.85% *15***	
66	1+	−66.257	5.120 m *14*	β−
67	3/2−	−67.318	61.83 h *12*	β−
68	1+	−65.567	30.9 s *6*	β−
68m	(6−)	−64.845	3.75 m *5*	IT 84%, β− 16%
69	3/2−	−65.736	2.85 m *15*	β−
70	(6−)	−62.976	44.5 s *2*	β−
70m	(3−)	−62.875	33 s *2*	β− 52%, IT 48%
70m	1+	−62.733	6.6 s *2*	β− 93.2%, IT 6.8%
71	3/2(−)	−62.711	19.4 s *16*	β−
72	(2)	−59.782	6.63 s *3*	β−
73	(3/2−)	−58.987	4.2 s *3*	β−
74	(1+,3+)	−56.006	1.594 s *10*	β−
75	(5/2−)	−54.471	1.222 s *8*	β−, β−n 3.5%
76	(3,4)	−50.975	637 ms *7*	β−, β−n 7.2%
76m		−50.975	1.27 s *30*	β−
77	(5/2−)	−48.3	468.1 ms *20*	β−, β−n 30.3%
78	(4−,5−,6−)	−44.5	335 ms *11*	β−, β−n>65%
79		−41.9s	188 ms *25*	β−, β−n 55%
80		−36.4s	0.17 s +*11−5*	β−
81			>632 ns	β−, β−2n, β−n
82			>636 ns	β−, β−n, β−2n
30 Zn 54	0+	−6.0s	1.59 ms +*60−35*	2p 92%
55	(5/2−)	−14.4s	19.8 ms *13*	ε, εp 91%
56	0+	−25.2s	30.0 ms *17*	ε, εp 86%
57	(7/2−)	−32.5s	38 ms *4*	ε, εp≥65%
58	0+	−42.30	86 ms *8*	ε, εp<3%
59	3/2−	−47.214	182.0 ms *18*	ε, εp 0.1%
60	0+	−54.173	2.38 m *5*	ε
61	3/2−	−56.34	89.1 s *2*	ε
61m	1/2−	−56.25	<430 ms	IT
61m	3/2−	−55.92	0.14 s *7*	IT
61m	5/2−	−55.59	<0.13 s	IT

Nuclide Z El A	Jπ	Δ (MeV)	T½, Γ, or Abundance	Decay Mode
30 Zn 62	0+	−61.167	9.186 h *13*	ε
63	3/2−	−62.213	38.47 m *5*	ε
64	0+	−66.003	≥7.0×10²⁰ y **49.17% 75**	2ε
65	5/2−	−65.911	243.93 d *9*	ε
66	0+	−68.899	**27.73% 98**	
67	5/2−	−67.880	**4.04% 16**	
68	0+	−70.006	**18.45% 63**	
69	1/2−	−68.417	56.4 m *9*	β−
69m	9/2+	−67.978	13.76 h *2*	IT 99.97%, β− 0.03%
70	0+	−69.564	≥2.3×10¹⁷ y **0.61% 10**	2β−
71	1/2−	−67.328	2.45 m *10*	β−
71m	9/2+	−67.170	3.96 h *5*	β−, IT≤0.05%
72	0+	−68.145	46.5 h *1*	β−
73	(1/2)−	−65.593	23.5 s *10*	β−
73m		−65.593	5.8 s *8*	β−, IT
73m	(5/2+)	−65.397	13.0 ms *2*	IT
74	0+	−65.756	95.6 s *12*	β−
75	(7/2+)	−62.558	10.2 s *2*	β−
76	0+	−62.303	5.7 s *3*	β−
77	(7/2+)	−58.789	2.08 s *5*	β−
77m	(1/2−)	−58.017	1.05 s *10*	IT>50%, β−<50%
78	0+	−57.483	1.47 s *15*	β−
79	(9/2+)	−53.432	0.995 s *19*	β−, β−n 1.3%
80	0+	−51.648	0.54 s *2*	β−, β−n 1%
81	(5/2+)	−46.199	304 ms *13*	β−, β−n 7.5%
82	0+	−42.6s	>150 ns	β−
83		−36.7s	>300 ns	β−, β−n
84	0+		>633 ns	β−, β−2n, β−n
85			>637 ns	β−?, β−n?, β−2n?
31 Ga 56		−4.2s		p?
57		−15.6s		p?
58		−23.8s		p?
59		−34.0s		p?
60	(2+)	−39.8s	70 ms *13*	ε 98.4%, εp 1.6%, εα<0.02%
61	3/2−	−47.09	167 ms *3*	ε, εp<0.25%
62	0+	−51.986	116.121 ms *21*	ε, εp
63	3/2−	−56.547	32.4 s *5*	ε
64	0+	−58.833	2.627 m *12*	ε
65	3/2−	−62.657	15.2 m *2*	ε
66	0+	−63.724	9.49 h *3*	ε
67	3/2−	−66.878	3.2617 d *5*	ε
68	1+	−67.085	67.71 m *9*	ε
69	3/2−	−69.327	**60.108% 9**	
70	1+	−68.910	21.14 m *3*	β− 99.59%, ε 0.41%
71	3/2−	−70.139	**39.892% 9**	
72	3−	−68.588	14.10 h *2*	β−
73	3/2−	−69.699	4.86 h *3*	β−
74	(3−)	−68.049	8.12 m *12*	β−
74m	(0)	−67.989	9.5 s *10*	IT 75%, β−<50%

Nuclide Z El A	Jπ	Δ (MeV)	T½, Γ, or Abundance	Decay Mode
31 Ga 75	3/2–	–68.464	126 s 2	β–
76	2+	–66.296	32.6 s 6	β–
77	3/2–	–65.992	13.2 s 2	β–
78	2+	–63.705	5.09 s 5	β–
79	3/2–	–62.547	2.847 s 3	β–, β–n 0.09%
80	3	–59.223	1.676 s 14	β–, β–n 0.86%
81	5/2–	–57.627	1.217 s 5	β–, β–n 11.9%
82	(1,2,3)	–52.930	0.599 s 2	β–, β–n 19.8%
83		–49.257	308.1 ms 10	β–, β–n 62.8%
84	(0–)	–44.3s	0.085 s 10	β–, β–n 74%
84m	(3–,4–)	–44.3s	<0.085 s	β–, β–n ?
85	(1/2–,3/2–)	–40.2s	<100 ms	β–, β–n >35%
86		–34.5s	>150 ns	β–, β–n
87			>634 ns	β–, β–n, β–2n
32 Ge 58	0+	–7.7s		2p ?
59		–16.5s		2p ?
60	0+	–27.6s	>110 ns	εp, ε
61	(3/2–)	–33.7s	44 ms 6	ε, εp >58%
62	0+	–42.2s	129 ms 35	ε, εp
63	3/2–	–46.92	150 ms 9	ε
64	0+	–54.315	63.7 s 25	ε
65	3/2–	–56.480	30.9 s 5	ε, εp 0.01%
66	0+	–61.606	2.26 h 5	ε
67	1/2–	–62.657	18.9 m 3	ε
68	0+	–66.978	270.95 d 16	ε
69	5/2–	–67.100	39.05 h 10	ε
70	0+	–70.561	**20.57% 27**	
71	1/2–	–69.906	11.43 d 3	ε
71m	9/2+	–69.708	20.41 ms 18	IT
72	0+	–72.585	**27.45% 32**	
73	9/2+	–71.297	**7.75% 12**	
73m	1/2–	–71.230	0.499 s 11	IT
74	0+	–73.422	**36.50% 20**	
75	1/2–	–71.856	82.78 m 4	β–
75m	7/2+	–71.716	47.7 s 5	IT 99.97%, β– 0.03%
76	0+	–73.212	**7.73% 12**	
77	7/2+	–71.213	11.30 h 1	β–
77m	1/2–	–71.053	52.9 s 6	β– 81%, IT 19%
78	0+	–71.862	88.0 m 10	β–
79	(1/2)–	–69.53	18.98 s 3	β–
79m	(7/2+)	–69.34	39.0 s 10	β– 96%, IT 4%
80	0+	–69.535	29.5 s 4	β–
81	(9/2+)	–66.291	7.6 s 6	β–
81m	(1/2+)	–65.612	7.6 s 6	β–
82	0+	–65.415	4.56 s 26	β–
83	(5/2)+	–60.976	1.85 s 6	β–
84	0+	–58.148	0.954 s 14	β–, β–n 10.2%
85	(1/2+,5/2+)	–53.123	0.56 s 5	β–, β–n 14%
86	0+	–49.8s	>150 ns	β–, β–n
87	(5/2+)	–44.2s	≈0.14 s	β–, β–n
88	0+	–40.2s	≥300 ns	β–
89		–33.8s	≥300 ns	β– ?

Nuclide Z El	A	Jπ	Δ (MeV)	T½, Γ, or Abundance	Decay Mode
32 Ge	90	0+		>635 ns	β–, β–n, β–2n
33 As	60		–6.1s		p?
	61		–17.8s		p?
	62		–24.8s		p?
	63	3/2–	–33.5s	<43 ns	p
	64		–39.4s	18 ms +43–7	ε
	65		–46.94	128 ms 16	ε
	66	(0+)	–52.03	95.77 ms 23	ε
	67	(5/2–)	–56.585	42.5 s 12	ε
	68	3+	–58.894	151.6 s 8	ε
	69	5/2–	–63.09	15.2 m 2	ε
	70	4+	–64.34	52.6 m 3	ε
	71	5/2–	–67.893	65.30 h 7	ε
	72	2–	–68.229	26.0 h 1	ε
	73	3/2–	–70.952	80.30 d 6	ε
	74	2–	–70.859	17.77 d 2	ε 66%, β– 34%
	75	3/2–	–73.033	**100%**	
	75m	9/2+	–72.729	17.62 ms 23	IT
	76	2–	–72.290	1.0942 d 7	β–
	77	3/2–	–73.916	38.83 h 5	β–
	78	2–	–72.817	90.7 m 2	β–
	79	3/2–	–73.636	9.01 m 15	β–
	80	1+	–72.17	15.2 s 2	β–
	81	3/2–	–72.533	33.3 s 8	β–
	82	(2–)	–70.103	19.1 s 5	β–
	82m	(5–)	–69.956	13.6 s 4	β–
	83	(5/2–,3/2–)	–69.669	13.4 s 3	β–
	84	(3–)	–65.853	4.2 s 5	β–, β–n 0.18%
	85	(3/2–)	–63.189	2.021 s 10	β–, β–n 59.4%
	86		–58.962	0.945 s 8	β–, β–n 26%
	87	(3/2–)	–55.617	0.56 s 8	β–, β–n 15.4%
	88		–50.9s	>300 ns	β–
	89		–46.9s	>300 ns	β–?, β–n?
	90		–41.3s	>300 ns	β–, β–n
	91		–36.9s	>150 ns	β–
	92		–31.0s		β–
34 Se	64	0+	–26.9s	>180 ns	ε
	65	(3/2–)	–32.9s	33 ms 4	ε, εp
	66	0+	–41.7s		
	67		–46.58	136 ms 12	ε, εp 0.5%
	68	0+	–54.189	35.5 s 7	ε
	69	(1/2–,3/2–)	–56.30	27.4 s 2	ε, εp 0.05%
	70	0+	–61.929	41.1 m 3	ε
	71	(5/2–)	–63.146	4.74 m 5	ε
	72	0+	–67.868	8.40 d 8	ε
	73	9/2+	–68.227	7.15 h 8	ε
	73m	3/2–	–68.201	39.8 m 13	IT 72.6%, ε 27.4%
	74	0+	–72.212	**0.89%** 4	
	75	5/2+	–72.169	119.79 d 4	ε
	76	0+	–75.251	**9.37%** 29	
	77	1/2–	–74.599	**7.63%** 16	
	77m	7/2+	–74.437	17.4 s 8	IT

Nuclide Z El A	Jπ	Δ (MeV)	T½, Γ, or Abundance	Decay Mode
34 Se 78	0+	−77.025	23.77% *28*	
79	7/2+	−75.917	2.95×10⁵ y *38*	β−
79m	1/2−	−75.821	3.92 m *1*	IT 99.94%, β− 0.06%
80	0+	−77.759	49.61% *41*	
81	1/2−	−76.389	18.45 m *12*	β−
81m	7/2+	−76.286	57.28 m *2*	IT 99.95%, β− 0.05%
82	0+	−77.594	8.73% *22*	
83	9/2+	−75.340	22.3 m *3*	β−
83m	1/2−	−75.112	70.1 s *4*	β−
84	0+	−75.947	3.26 m *10*	β−
85	(5/2+)	−72.413	32.9 s *3*	β−
86	0+	−70.503	14.3 s *3*	β−
87	(5/2+)	−66.426	5.50 s *12*	β−, β−n 0.2%
88	0+	−63.884	1.53 s *6*	β−, β−n 0.67%
89	(5/2+)	−58.992	0.41 s *4*	β−, β−n 7.8%
90	0+	−55.9s	>300 ns	β−, β−n
91		−50.3s	0.27 s *5*	β−, β−n 21%
92	0+	−46.7s		β−
93	(1/2+)	−40.7s		β−
94	0+	−36.8s	>150 ns	β−
95			>300 ns	β−?, β−n?, β−2n?
35 Br 67		−32.8s		p?
68		−38.7s	<1.2 μs	p?
69		−46.5s	<24 ns	p?
70	0+	−51.42	79.1 ms *8*	ε
70m	9+	−49.13	2.2 s *2*	ε
71	(5/2)−	−56.502	21.4 s *6*	ε
72	1+	−59.067	78.6 s *24*	ε
72m	(3−)	−58.966	10.6 s *3*	IT, ε
73	1/2−	−63.647	3.4 m *2*	ε
74	(0−)	−65.285	25.4 m *3*	ε
74m	4(+)	−65.271	46 m *2*	ε
75	3/2−	−69.107	96.7 m *13*	ε
76	1−	−70.288	16.2 h *2*	ε
76m	(4)+	−70.185	1.31 s *2*	IT>99.4%, ε<0.6%
77	3/2−	−73.234	57.036 h *6*	ε
77m	9/2+	−73.128	4.28 m *10*	IT
78	1+	−73.452	6.45 m *4*	ε≥99.99%, β−≤0.01%
79	3/2−	−76.068	50.69% *7*	
79m	9/2+	−75.860	5.1 s *4*	IT
80	1+	−75.889	17.68 m *2*	β− 91.7%, ε 8.3%
80m	5−	−75.803	4.4205 h *8*	IT
81	3/2−	−77.975	49.31% *7*	
82	5−	−77.497	35.282 h *7*	β−
82m	2−	−77.451	6.13 m *5*	IT 97.6%, β− 2.4%
83	3/2−	−79.006	2.40 h *2*	β−
84	2−	−77.79	31.76 m *8*	β−
84m	(6)−	−77.47	6.0 m *2*	β−
85	3/2−	−78.575	2.90 m *6*	β−
86	(1−)	−75.632	55.1 s *4*	β−
87	3/2−	−73.891	55.65 s *13*	β−, β−n 2.6%

Nuclide Z El A	Jπ	Δ (MeV)	T½, Γ, or Abundance	Decay Mode
35 Br 88	(2−)	−70.715	16.29 s *6*	β−, β−n 6.58%
89	(3/2−,5/2−)	−68.274	4.40 s *3*	β−, β−n 13.8%
90		−64.000	1.91 s *1*	β−, β−n 25.2%
91		−61.107	0.541 s *5*	β−, β−n 20%
92	(2−)	−56.232	0.343 s *15*	β−, β−n 33.1%
93	(5/2−)	−52.9s	102 ms *10*	β−, β−n 68%
94		−47.6s	70 ms *20*	β−, β−n 68%
95		−43.9s	≥150 ns	β−, β−n 34%
96		−38.3s	≥150 ns	β−, β−n 27.6%
97		−34.5s	>300 ns	β−
98			>634 ns	β−, β−n, β−2n
36 Kr 69		−32.4s	32 ms *10*	ε
70	0+	−41.6s	52 ms *17*	ε, εp≤1.3%
71	(5/2−)	−46.3	100 ms *3*	ε, εp 2.1%
72	0+	−53.940	17.1 s *2*	ε, εp<1.0×10⁻⁶%
73	3/2−	−56.551	27.3 s *10*	ε, εp 0.25%
74	0+	−62.331	11.50 m *11*	ε
75	5/2+	−64.323	4.29 m *17*	ε
76	0+	−69.014	14.8 h *1*	ε
77	5/2+	−70.169	74.4 m *6*	ε
78	0+	−74.179	≥1.5×10²¹ y **0.355%** *3*	2ε
79	1/2−	−74.442	35.04 h *10*	ε
79m	7/2+	−74.312	50 s *3*	IT
80	0+	−77.892	**2.286%** *10*	
81	7/2+	−77.694	2.29×10⁵ y *11*	ε
81m	1/2−	−77.503	13.10 s *3*	IT, ε 2.5×10⁻³%
82	0+	−80.590	**11.593%** *31*	
83	9/2+	−79.990	**11.500%** *19*	
83m	1/2−	−79.948	1.85 h *3*	IT
84	0+	−82.439	**56.987%** *15*	
85	9/2+	−81.480	10.752 y *25*	β−
85m	1/2−	−81.175	4.480 h *8*	β− 78.6%, IT 21.4%
86	0+	−83.266	**17.279%** *41*	
87	5/2+	−80.709	76.3 m *5*	β−
88	0+	−79.691	2.84 h *3*	β−
89	3/2(+)	−76.535	3.15 m *4*	β−
90	0+	−74.959	32.32 s *9*	β−
91	5/2(+)	−70.973	8.57 s *4*	β−
92	0+	−68.769	1.840 s *8*	β−, β−n 0.03%
93	1/2+	−64.135	1.286 s *10*	β−, β−n 1.95%
94	0+	−61.35	212 ms *5*	β−, β−n 1.11%
95	1/2(+)	−56.16	0.114 s *3*	β−, β−n 2.87%
96	0+	−53.08	80 ms *6*	β−, β−n 3.7%
97	(3/2+)	−47.4	63 ms *4*	β−, β−n 6.7%
98	0+	−44.5s	46 ms *8*	β−, β−n 7%
99		−38.8s	13 ms +*34−6*	β−, β−n 11%
100	0+	−35.2s	7 ms +*11−3*	β−, β−n
101			>635 ns	β−, β−n, β−2n
37 Rb 71		−32.3s		p?
72	(3+)	−38.1s	<1.2 μs	p?
73		−46.1s	<30 ns	ε?, p>0%

Nuclide Z El A	Jπ	Δ (MeV)	T½, Γ, or Abundance	Decay Mode
37 Rb 74	(0+)	−51.916	64.9 ms *5*	ε
75	(3/2−)	−57.218	19.0 s *12*	ε
76	1(−)	−60.478	36.5 s *6*	ε , εα 3.8×10⁻⁷%
77	3/2−	−64.830	3.77 m *4*	ε
78	0(+)	−66.936	17.66 m *3*	ε
78m	4(−)	−66.825	5.74 m *3*	ε 91%, IT 9%
79	5/2+	−70.802	22.9 m *5*	ε
80	1+	−72.175	33.4 s *7*	ε
81	3/2−	−75.456	4.572 h *4*	ε
81m	9/2+	−75.370	30.5 m *3*	IT 97.6%, ε 2.4%
82	1+	−76.187	1.2575 m *2*	ε
82m	5−	−76.118	6.472 h *6*	ε , IT<0.33%
83	5/2−	−79.070	86.2 d *1*	ε
84	2−	−79.756	32.82 d *7*	ε 96.1%, β− 3.9%
84m	6−	−79.292	20.26 m *4*	IT
85	5/2−	−82.167	**72.17%** *2*	
86	2−	−82.747	18.642 d *18*	β− 99.99%, ε 5.2×10⁻³%
86m	6−	−82.191	1.017 m *3*	IT, β−<0.3%
87	3/2−	−84.597	4.81×10¹⁰ y *9* 27.83% *2*	β−
88	2−	−82.608	17.773 m *11*	β−
89	3/2−	−81.712	15.15 m *12*	β−
90	0−	−79.364	158 s *5*	β−
90m	3−	−79.257	258 s *4*	β− 97.4%, IT 2.6%
91	3/2(−)	−77.746	58.4 s *4*	β−
92	0−	−74.772	4.492 s *20*	β− , β−n 0.01%
93	5/2−	−72.620	5.84 s *2*	β− , β−n 1.39%
94	3(−)	−68.561	2.702 s *5*	β− , β−n 10.5%
95	5/2−	−65.89	377.7 ms *8*	β− , β−n 8.7%
96	2(−)	−61.354	203 ms *3*	β− , β−n 13.3%
97	3/2+	−58.518	169.1 ms *6*	β− , β−n 25.5%
98	(0,1)	−54.03	102 ms *4*	β− , β−n 13.8%, β−2n 0.05%
98m	(3,4)	−53.76	96 ms *3*	β−
99	(5/2+)	−51.2	54 ms *4*	β− , β−n 15.8%
100	(3+,4−)	−46.5s	51 ms *8*	β− , β−n 6%, β−2n 0.16%
101	(3/2+)	−43.0s	32 ms *5*	β− , β−n 28%
102		−37.9s	37 ms *3*	β− , β−n 18%
103			>633 ns	β− , β−n
38 Sr 73		−32.0s	>25 ms	ε , εp>0%
74	0+	−40.8s	>1.2 μs	ε
75	(3/2−)	−46.6	88 ms *3*	ε , εp 5.2%
76	0+	−54.25	7.89 s *7*	ε , εp 3.4×10⁻⁵%
77	5/2+	−57.803	9.0 s *2*	ε , εp<0.25%
78	0+	−63.173	160 s *8*	ε
79	3/2(−)	−65.476	2.25 m *10*	ε
80	0+	−70.311	106.3 m *15*	ε
81	1/2−	−71.528	22.3 m *4*	ε
82	0+	−76.009	25.34 d *2*	ε
83	7/2+	−76.797	32.41 h *3*	ε

Nuclide Z El A	Jπ	Δ (MeV)	T½, Γ, or Abundance	Decay Mode
38 Sr 83m	1/2–	–76.538	4.95 s *12*	IT
84	0+	–80.649	**0.56%** *1*	
85	9/2+	–81.103	64.850 d *7*	ε
85m	1/2–	–80.864	67.63 m *4*	IT 86.6%, ε 13.4%
86	0+	–84.523	**9.86%** *1*	
87	9/2+	–84.880	**7.00%** *1*	
87m	1/2–	–84.492	2.815 h *12*	IT 99.7%, ε 0.3%
88	0+	–87.921	**82.58%** *1*	
89	5/2+	–86.208	50.53 d *7*	β–
90	0+	–85.949	28.90 y *3*	β–
91	5/2+	–83.652	9.63 h *5*	β–
92	0+	–82.867	2.66 h *4*	β–
93	5/2+	–80.086	7.43 m *3*	β–
94	0+	–78.843	75.3 s *2*	β–
95	1/2+	–75.123	23.90 s *14*	β–
96	0+	–72.932	1.07 s *1*	β–
97	1/2+	–68.591	429 ms *5*	β– , β–n ≤ 0.05%
98	0+	–66.436	0.653 s *2*	β– , β–n 0.25%
99	3/2+	–62.529	0.269 s *1*	β– , β–n 0.1%
100	0+	–59.833	202 ms *3*	β– , β–n 0.78%
101	(5/2–)	–55.56	118 ms *3*	β– , β–n 2.37%
102	0+	–52.4s	69 ms *6*	β– , β–n 5.5%
103		–47.5s	68 ms +*48–20*	β–
104	0+	–43.9s	43 ms +*9–7*	β–
105		–38.6s	40 ms +*36–13*	β–
106	0+		>392 ns	β– , β–n, β–2n
107			>395 ns	β– , β–n, β–2n
39 Y 76		–38.6s	>200 ns	ε , p
77	(5/2+)	–46.78s	57 ms +*22–12*	ε , εp, p
78	(0+)	–52.5s	53 ms *8*	ε , εp
78m	(5+)	–52.5s	5.8 s *6*	ε , εp
79	(5/2+)	–58.4	14.8 s *6*	ε , εp
80	(4–)	–61.148	30.1 s *5*	ε , εp
80m	(1–)	–60.919	4.8 s *3*	IT 81%, ε 19%
81	(5/2+)	–65.713	70.4 s *10*	ε
82	1+	–68.064	8.30 s *20*	ε
83	9/2+	–72.21	7.08 m *6*	ε
83m	3/2–	–72.14	2.85 m *2*	ε 60%, IT 40%
84	(6+)	–73.894	39.5 m *8*	ε
84m	1+	–73.827	4.6 s *2*	ε
85	(1/2)–	–77.84	2.68 h *5*	ε
85m	9/2+	–77.82	4.86 h *20*	ε , IT< 2.0×10⁻³%
86	4–	–79.28	14.74 h *2*	ε
86m	(8+)	–79.06	48 m *1*	IT 99.31%, ε 0.69%
87	1/2–	–83.018	79.8 h *3*	ε
87m	9/2+	–82.637	13.37 h *3*	IT 98.43%, ε 1.57%
88	4–	–84.298	106.626 d *21*	ε
89	1/2–	–87.709	**100%**	
89m	9/2+	–86.800	15.663 s *5*	IT
90	2–	–86.495	64.053 h *20*	β–
90m	7+	–85.813	3.19 h *6*	IT, β– 1.8×10⁻³%
91	1/2–	–86.352	58.51 d *6*	β–

Nuclide Z	El	A	Jπ	Δ (MeV)	T½, Γ, or Abundance	Decay Mode
39	Y	91m	9/2+	−85.796	49.71 m *4*	IT, β−< 1.5%
		92	2−	−84.817	3.54 h *1*	β−
		93	1/2−	−84.23	10.18 h *8*	β−
		93m	(9/2)+	−83.47	0.82 s *4*	IT
		94	2−	−82.352	18.7 m *1*	β−
		95	1/2−	−81.213	10.3 m *1*	β−
		96	0−	−78.344	5.34 s *5*	β−
		96m	8+	−77.204	9.6 s *2*	β−
		97	(1/2−)	−76.130	3.75 s *3*	β−, β−n 0.06%
		97m	(9/2)+	−75.463	1.17 s *3*	β−>99.3%, IT<0.7% β−n<0.08%
		97m	(27/2−)	−72.607	142 ms *8*	IT 98.4%, β− 1.6%
		98	(0)−	−72.303	0.548 s *2*	β−, β−n 0.33%
		98m	(4,5)	−71.893	2.0 s *2*	β−>80%, IT<20%, β−n 3.4%
		99	(5/2+)	−70.658	1.484 s *7*	β−, β−n 1.7%
		100	1−,2−	−67.34	735 ms *7*	β−, β−n 0.92%
		100m	(3,4,5)	−67.19	0.94 s *3*	β−
		101	(5/2+)	−65.070	0.45 s *2*	β−, β−n 1.94%
		102m	HighJ	−61.2s	0.36 s *4*	β−, β−n 4.9%
		102m	LowJ	−61.2s	0.298 s *9*	β−, β−n 4.9%
		103	(5/2+)	−58.50	0.23 s *2*	β−, β−n 8%
		104		−54.1s	197 ms *4*	β−, β−n
		105		−50.8s	85 ms +*5−4*	β−, β−n<82%
		106		−46.1s	62 ms +*25−14*	β−
		107	(5/2+)	−42.4s	41 ms +*15−9*	β−
		108		−37.3s	25 ms +*66−10*	β−, β−n
		109			>393 ns	β−, β−n, β−2n
40	Zr	78	0+	−41.3s	>170 ns	ε
		79		−47.1s	56 ms *30*	ε, εp
		80	0+	−56	4.6 s *6*	ε, εp
		81	(3/2−)	−58.4	5.5 s *4*	ε, εp 0.12%
		82	0+	−63.9s	32 s *5*	ε
		83	(1/2−)	−65.911	41.6 s *24*	ε, εp
		84	0+	−71.421	25.8 m *5*	ε
		85	(7/2+)	−73.175	7.86 m *4*	ε
		85m	(1/2−)	−72.883	10.9 s *3*	IT≤92%, ε>8%
		86	0+	−77.969	16.5 h *1*	ε
		87	(9/2)+	−79.347	1.68 h *1*	ε
		87m	(1/2)−	−79.011	14.0 s *2*	IT
		88	0+	−83.629	83.4 d *3*	ε
		89	9/2+	−84.876	78.41 h *12*	ε
		89m	1/2−	−84.288	4.161 m *17*	IT 93.77%, ε 6.23%
		90	0+	−88.774	**51.45% *40***	
		90m	5−	−86.455	809.2 ms *20*	IT
		91	5/2+	−87.897	**11.22% *5***	
		92	0+	−88.460	**17.15% *8***	
		93	5/2+	−87.123	1.61×10^{6} y *5*	β−
		94	0+	−87.272	**17.38% *28***	
		95	5/2+	−85.663	64.032 d *6*	β−
		96	0+	−85.447	2.35×10^{19} y *21* **2.80% *9***	2β−

Nuclide				Δ	T½, Γ, or	
Z	El	A	Jπ	(MeV)	Abundance	Decay Mode
40	**Zr**	*97*	1/2+	−82.951	16.749 h *8*	β–
		98	0+	−81.295	30.7 s *4*	β–
		99	(1/2+)	−77.63	2.1 s *1*	β–
		100	0+	−76.384	7.1 s *4*	β–
		101	(3/2+)	−73.173	2.3 s *1*	β–
		102	0+	−71.595	2.9 s *2*	β–
		103	(5/2−)	−67.824	1.32 s *11*	β–, β–n ≤ 1%
		104	0+	−65.733	0.87 s *6*	β–, β–n ≤ 1%
		105		−61.47	0.66 s *7*	β–, β–n ≤ 2%
		106	0+	−59.0s	191 ms *19*	β–, β–n ≤ 7%
		107		−54.3s	138 ms *4*	β–, β–n ≤ 23%
		108	0+	−51.4s	73 ms *4*	β–, β–n
		109		−46.2s	63 ms +*38–17*	β–, β–n
		110	0+	−42.9s	37 ms +*17–9*	β–
		111			>392 ns	β–, β–n, β–2n
		112	0+		>394 ns	β–, β–n, β–2n
41	**Nb**	*81*		−47.2s	<200 ns	ε
		82	(0+)	−52.2s	50 ms *5*	ε, εp
		83	(5/2+)	−58.4	3.8 s *2*	ε
		84	(1+,2+,3+)	−61.0s	9.8 s *9*	ε, εp
		85	(9/2+)	−66.279	20.5 s *12*	ε
		85m		−66.279	12 s *5*	ε, IT
		85m	(1/2−,3/2−)	−66.279	3.3 s *9*	ε, IT
		86	(6+)	−69.134	88 s *1*	ε
		87	(1/2−)	−73.874	3.75 m *9*	ε
		87m	(9/2+)	−73.870	2.6 m *1*	ε
		88	(8+)	−76.18	14.55 m *6*	ε
		88m	(4−)	−76.18	7.78 m *5*	ε
		89	(9/2+)	−80.65	2.03 h *7*	ε
		89m	(1/2)−	−80.61	66 m *2*	ε
		90	8+	−82.663	14.60 h *5*	ε
		90m	4−	−82.538	18.81 s *6*	IT
		91	9/2+	−86.639	6.8×10^2 y *13*	ε
		91m	1/2−	−86.534	60.86 d *22*	IT 96.6%, ε 3.4%
		92	(7)+	−86.454	3.47×10^7 y *24*	ε, β– < 0.05%
		92m	(2)+	−86.318	10.15 d *2*	ε
		93	9/2+	−87.214	**100%**	
		93m	1/2−	−87.183	16.12 y *12*	IT
		94	6+	−86.370	2.03×10^4 y *16*	β–
		94m	3+	−86.329	6.263 m *4*	IT 99.5%, β– 0.5%
		95	9/2+	−86.786	34.991 d *6*	β–
		95m	1/2−	−86.550	3.61 d *3*	IT 94.4%, β– 5.6%
		96	6+	−85.608	23.35 h *5*	β–
		97	9/2+	−85.610	72.1 m *7*	β–
		97m	1/2−	−84.867	58.7 s *18*	IT
		98	1+	−83.533	2.86 s *6*	β–
		98m	(5+)	−83.449	51.3 m *4*	β– 99.9%, IT < 0.2%
		99	9/2+	−82.33	15.0 s *2*	β–
		99m	1/2−	−81.96	2.5 m *2*	β– > 96.2%, IT < 3.8%
		100	1+	−79.806	1.5 s *2*	β–
		100m	(5+)	−79.492	2.99 s *11*	β–
		101	(5/2+)	−78.886	7.1 s *3*	β–

Nuclide			Jπ	Δ (MeV)	T½, Γ, or Abundance	Decay Mode
Z	El	A				
41	Nb	102	(4+)	−76.313	4.3 s 4	β−
		102m	1+	−76.313	1.3 s 2	β−
		103	(5/2+)	−75.023	1.5 s 2	β−
		104	(1+)	−71.828	4.9 s 3	β−, β−n 0.06%
		104m		−71.613	0.94 s 4	β−, β−n 0.05%
		105	(5/2+)	−69.910	2.95 s 6	β−, β−n 1.7%
		106		−66.197	0.93 s 4	β−, β−n 4.5%
		107		−63.718	300 ms 9	β−, β−n 8%
		108	(2+)	−59.6	220 ms 18	β−, β−n 8%
		109	(5/2)	−56.8s	106 ms 9	β−, β−n < 15%
		110		−52.3s	86 ms 6	β−, β−n 40%
		111	(5/2+)	−49.0s	51 ms +6−5	β−
		112	(2+)	−44.4s	33 ms +9−6	β−
		113		−40.6s	>300 ns	β−
		114			>392 ns	β−, β−n, β−2n
		115			>394 ns	β−, β−n, β−2n
42	Mo	83		−46.7s	6 ms +30−3	ε
		84	0+	−54.5s	2.3 s 3	ε, εp
		85	(1/2−)	−57.51	3.2 s 2	ε, εp ≈ 0.14%
		86	0+	−64.110	19.1 s 3	ε
		87	7/2+	−66.882	14.02 s 26	ε, εp 15%
		88	0+	−72.686	8.0 m 2	ε
		89	(9/2+)	−75.014	2.11 m 10	ε
		89m	(1/2−)	−74.627	190 ms 15	IT
		90	0+	−80.174	5.56 h 9	ε
		91	9/2+	−82.21	15.49 m 1	ε
		91m	1/2−	−81.56	64.6 s 6	ε 50%, IT 50%
		92	0+	−86.809	**14.53% 30**	
		93	5/2+	−86.807	4.0×10^3 y 8	ε
		93m	21/2+	−84.382	6.85 h 7	IT 99.88%, ε 0.12%
		94	0+	−88.414	**9.15% 9**	
		95	5/2+	−87.711	**15.84% 11**	
		96	0+	−88.794	**16.67% 15**	
		97	5/2+	−87.544	**9.60% 14**	
		98	0+	−88.116	**24.39% 37**	
		99	1/2+	−85.970	65.976 h 24	β−
		100	0+	−86.187	7.3×10^{18} y 4 **9.82% 31**	2β−
		101	1/2+	−83.514	14.61 m 3	β−
		102	0+	−83.572	11.3 m 2	β−
		103	(3/2+)	−80.970	67.5 s 15	β−
		104	0+	−80.359	60 s 2	β−
		105	(5/2−)	−77.346	35.6 s 16	β−
		106	0+	−76.144	8.73 s 12	β−
		107	(5/2+)	−72.561	3.5 s 5	β−
		108	0+	−70.765	1.09 s 2	β−, β−n < 0.5%
		109	(7/2−)	−66.68	660 ms 45	β−, β−n 1.3%
		110	0+	−64.55	0.27 s 1	β−, β−n 2%
		111		−60.1s	220 ms +41−36	β−, β−n ≤ 12%
		112	0+	−57.6s	120 ms +13−11	β−
		113		−52.9s	78 ms +6−5	β−
		114	0+	−50.0s	60 ms +13−9	β−

Nuclide Z El A	Jπ	Δ (MeV)	T½, Γ, or Abundance	Decay Mode
42 Mo 115		−44.7s	51 ms +79−19	β− , β−n
116	0+		>391 ns	β− , β−n
117			>393 ns	β− ?, β−n ?, β−2n ?
43 Tc 85		−46.0s	≈0.5 s	p?
86	(0+)	−51.3s	54 ms 7	ε , εp
87	(9/2+)	−57.690	2.2 s 2	ε
88m	(3+)	−61.679	5.8 s 2	ε
88m	(6+)	−61.679	6.4 s 8	ε
89	(9/2+)	−67.394	12.8 s 9	ε
89m	(1/2−)	−67.331	12.9 s 8	ε , IT< 0.01%
90m	1+	−70.723	8.7 s 2	ε
90m	(6+)	−70.223	49.2 s 4	ε
91	(9/2)+	−75.987	3.14 m 2	ε
91m	(1/2)−	−75.848	3.3 m 1	ε , IT< 1%
92	(8)+	−78.924	4.25 m 15	ε
93	9/2+	−83.606	2.75 h 5	ε
93m	1/2−	−83.214	43.5 m 10	IT 77.4%, ε 22.6%
94	7+	−84.158	293 m 1	ε
94m	(2)+	−84.082	52.0 m 10	ε , IT< 0.1%
95	9/2+	−86.021	20.0 h 1	ε
95m	1/2−	−85.982	61 d 2	ε 96.12%, IT 3.88%
96	7+	−85.821	4.28 d 7	ε
96m	4+	−85.787	51.5 m 10	IT 98%, ε 2%
97	9/2+	−87.224	4.21×10^6 y 16	ε
97m	1/2−	−87.127	91.0 d 6	IT 96.06%, ε 3.94%
98	(6)+	−86.431	4.2×10^6 y 3	β−
99	9/2+	−87.327	2.111×10^5 y 12	β−
99m	1/2−	−87.184	6.0067 h 5	IT , β− 3.7×10^{-3}%
100	1+	−86.020	15.46 s 19	β− , ε 2.6×10^{-3}%
101	9/2+	−86.34	14.02 m 1	β−
102	1+	−84.569	5.28 s 15	β−
102m	(4,5)	−84.569	4.35 m 7	β− 98%, IT 2%
103	5/2+	−84.600	54.2 s 8	β−
104	(3+)	−82.51	18.3 m 3	β−
105	(3/2−)	−82.29	7.6 m 1	β−
106	(2+)	−79.77	35.6 s 6	β−
107	(3/2−)	−78.746	21.2 s 2	β−
108	(2)+	−75.919	5.17 s 7	β−
109	(5/2+)	−74.279	0.86 s 4	β− , β−n 0.08%
110	(2+)	−71.030	0.92 s 3	β− , β−n 0.04%
111	(5/2+)	−69.02	350 ms 21	β− , β−n 0.85%
112		−65.253	0.29 s 2	β− , β−n 4%
113	>5/2	−62.88	160 ms +50−40	β− , β−n 2.1%
114m	>3	−58.9s	100 ms 20	β− , β−n ?
114m	(1+)	−58.9s	90 ms 20	β− , β−n ?
115		−56.1s	83 ms +20−13	β− , β−n
116		−51.5s	56 ms +15−10	β−
117	(5/2+)	−48.4s	85 ms +95−30	β−
118		−43.8s		β−
119			>392 ns	β− , β−n ?, β−2n ?
120			>394 ns	β− , β−n ?, β−2n ?
44 Ru 87		−45.9s	>1.5 μs	ε ?

Nuclide Z El A	Jπ	Δ (MeV)	T½, Γ, or Abundance	Decay Mode
44 Ru 88	0+	−54.4s	1.2 s +3−2	ε
89	(9/2+)	−58.1s	1.5 s 2	ε , εp< 0.15%
90	0+	−64.883	11.7 s 9	ε
91	(9/2+)	−68.238	7.9 s 4	ε
91m	(1/2−)	−68.238	7.6 s 8	IT , ε> 0%, εp> 0%
92	0+	−74.301	3.65 m 5	ε
93	(9/2)+	−77.213	59.7 s 6	ε
93m	(1/2)−	−76.479	10.8 s 3	ε 78%, IT 22%, εp 0.03%
94	0+	−82.579	51.8 m 6	ε
95	5/2+	−83.457	1.643 h 13	ε
96	0+	−86.080	5.54% 14	
97	5/2+	−86.120	2.83 d 23	ε
98	0+	−88.224	1.87% 3	
99	5/2+	−87.620	12.76% 14	
100	0+	−89.222	12.60% 7	
101	5/2+	−87.952	17.06% 2	
102	0+	−89.101	31.55% 14	
103	3/2+	−87.262	39.247 d 13	β−
104	0+	−88.092	18.62% 27	
105	3/2+	−85.931	4.44 h 2	β−
106	0+	−86.320	371.8 d 18	β−
107	(5/2)+	−83.859	3.75 m 5	β−
108	0+	−83.657	4.55 m 5	β−
109	(5/2+)	−80.734	34.5 s 10	β−
110	0+	−80.069	11.6 s 6	β−
111	5/2+	−76.781	2.12 s 7	β−
112	0+	−75.627	1.75 s 7	β−
113	(1/2+)	−71.87	0.80 s 5	β−
113m	(7/2−)	−71.87	510 ms 30	β−
114	0+	−70.21	0.52 s 5	β−
115	(3/2+)	−66.19	318 ms 19	β−
115m		−66.19	740 ms 80	β−, β−n
115m		−66.19	270 ms 38	β−, β−n
115m		−66.19	76 ms 6	β−, β−n
116	0+	−64.2s	204 ms +32−29	β−
117		−59.6s	142 ms +18−17	β−
118	0+	−57.3s	123 ms +48−35	β−, β−n
119		−52.6s	>300 ns	β−
120	0+	−50.0s	>150 ns	β−
121			>390 ns	β−, β−n
122	0+		>392 ns	β−, β−n
123			>394 ns	β−, β−n, β−2n
124	0+		>396 ns	β−, β−n
45 Rh 89		−46.0s	>1.5 μs	ε?, p?
90		−52.0s	12 ms +9−4	ε?
90m		−52.0s	1.0 s +3−2	ε?
91	(9/2+)	−58.8s	1.47 s 22	ε
91m	(1/2−)	−58.8s	1.46 s 11	ε
92?	(6+)	−62.999	4.66 s 25	ε
92m	(2+)	−62.999	0.53 s 37	ε
93	(9/2+)	−69.017	12.2 s 7	ε

Nuclide				Δ	T½, Γ, or	
Z	El	A	Jπ	(MeV)	Abundance	Decay Mode
45	Rh	94	(4+)	−72.907	66 s *6*	ε , εp 1.8%
		94m	(8+)	−72.607	25.8 s *2*	ε
		95	9/2+	−78.342	5.02 m *10*	ε
		95m	(1/2)−	−77.799	1.96 m *4*	IT 88%, ε 12%
		96	≥ 6+	−79.69	9.90 m *10*	ε
		96m	3+	−79.64	1.51 m *2*	IT 60%, ε 40%
		97	9/2+	−82.60	30.7 m *6*	ε
		97m	1/2−	−82.34	46.2 m *16*	ε 94.4%, IT 5.6%
		98	(2)+	−83.18	8.72 m *12*	ε
		98m	(5+)	−83.18	3.6 m *2*	IT 89%, ε 11%
		99	1/2−	−85.576	16.1 d *2*	ε
		99m	9/2+	−85.511	4.7 h *1*	ε > 99.84%, IT < 0.16%
		100	1−	−85.59	20.8 h *1*	ε
		100m	(5+)	−85.48	4.6 m *2*	IT ≈ 98.3%, ε ≈ 1.7%
		101	1/2−	−87.411	3.3 y *3*	ε
		101m	9/2+	−87.254	4.34 d *1*	ε 92.8%, IT 7.2%
		102	(1−,2−)	−86.778	207.3 d *17*	ε 78%, β− 22%
		102m	6(+)	−86.637	3.742 y *10*	ε 99.77%, IT 0.23%
		103	1/2−	−88.025	100%	
		103m	7/2+	−87.985	56.114 m *9*	IT
		104	1+	−86.953	42.3 s *4*	β− 99.55%, ε 0.45%
		104m	5+	−86.824	4.34 m *3*	IT 99.87%, β− 0.13%
		105	7/2+	−87.848	35.36 h *6*	β−
		105m	1/2−	−87.718	42.9 s *3*	IT
		106	1+	−86.360	30.07 s *35*	β−
		106m	(6)+	−86.223	131 m *2*	β−
		107	7/2+	−86.86	21.7 m *4*	β−
		108	1+	−85.03	16.8 s *5*	β−
		108m	(5+)	−85.03	6.0 m *3*	β−, IT
		109	7/2+	−85.010	80 s *2*	β−
		110m	(≥4)	−82.84	28.5 s *15*	β−
		110m	1+	−82.84	3.2 s *2*	β−
		111	(7/2+)	−82.304	11 s *1*	β−
		112m	1+	−79.73	3.45 s *37*	β−
		112m	(4,5,6)	−79.73	6.73 s *15*	β−
		113	(7/2+)	−78.767	2.80 s *12*	β−
		114	1+	−75.71	1.85 s *5*	β−
		114m	(7−)	−75.51	1.86 s *6*	β−
		115	(7/2+)	−74.229	0.99 s *5*	β−
		116	1+	−70.74	0.68 s *6*	β−
		116m	(6−)	−70.59	0.57 s *5*	β−
		117	(7/2+)	−68.897	0.44 s *4*	β−
		118		−64.89	266 ms +*22−21*	β−, β−n 3.1%
		119	(7/2+)	−62.8s	171 ms *18*	β−, β−n 6.4%
		120		−58.8s	136 ms +*14−13*	β−, β−n < 5.4%
		121		−56.4s	151 ms +*67−58*	β−, β−n
		122		−52.4s	>300 ns	β−, β−n
		123			>403 ns	β−, β−n
		124			>391 ns	β−, β−n, β−2n
		125			>393 ns	β−, β−n
		126			>395 ns	β−, β−2n, β−n

Z	El	A	Jπ	Δ (MeV)	T½, Γ, or Abundance	Decay Mode
46	Pd	91		−46.3s	>1 µs	ε ?
		92	0+	−55.1s	0.7 s +4−2	ε
		93	(9/2+)	−59.1s	1.00 s 9	ε , εp
		94	0+	−66.102	9.6 s 2	ε
		95	(9/2+)	−69.966	5 s 3	ε
		95m	(21/2+)	−68.091	13.3 s 3	ε 89%, IT 11%, εp 0.93%
		96	0+	−76.183	122 s 2	ε
		97	(5/2+)	−77.805	3.10 m 9	ε
		98	0+	−81.320	17.7 m 3	ε
		99	(5/2)+	−82.184	21.4 m 2	ε
		100	0+	−85.23	3.63 d 9	ε
		101	5/2+	−85.431	8.47 h 6	ε
		102	0+	−87.928	**1.02% 1**	
		103	5/2+	−87.482	16.991 d 19	ε
		104	0+	−89.393	**11.14% 8**	
		105	5/2+	−88.416	**22.33% 8**	
		106	0+	−89.905	**27.33% 3**	
		107	5/2+	−88.370	6.5×10^6 y 3	β−
		107m	11/2−	−88.155	21.3 s 5	IT
		108	0+	−89.521	**26.46% 9**	
		109	5/2+	−87.603	13.7012 h 24	β−
		109m	11/2−	−87.414	4.696 m 3	IT
		110	0+	−88.348	**11.72% 9**	
		111	5/2+	−86.003	23.4 m 2	β−
		111m	11/2−	−85.831	5.5 h 1	IT 73%, β− 27%
		112	0+	−86.323	21.03 h 5	β−
		113	(5/2+)	−83.590	93 s 5	β−
		113m	(9/2−)	−83.509	0.3 s 1	IT
		114	0+	−83.490	2.42 m 6	β−
		115	(5/2+)	−80.43	25 s 2	β−
		115m	(11/2−)	−80.34	50 s 3	β− 92%, IT 8%
		116	0+	−79.831	11.8 s 4	β−
		117	(5/2+)	−76.424	4.3 s 3	β−
		118	0+	−75.391	1.9 s 1	β−
		119		−71.407	0.92 s 1	β−
		120	0+	−70.309	0.5 s 1	β−
		121	(3/2+)	−66.3s	285 ms 24	β−, β−n ≤ 0.8%
		122	0+	−64.7s	175 ms 16	β− ≥ 97.5%, β−n ≤ 2.5%
		123		−60.6s	174 ms +38−34	β−
		124	0+	−58.8s	38 ms +38−19	β−
		125			>230 ns	β−, β−n
		126	0+		>230 ns	β−, β−n
		128	0+		>394 ns	β−, β−n
47	Ag	93		−46.3s		p, ε, εp
		94	(0+)	−52.4s	26 ms +26−9	ε, εp
		94m	(7+)	−52.4s	0.60 s 2	ε, εp 20%
		94m	(21+)	−45.7s	0.40 s 4	ε 95.4%, εp 27%, p 4.1%, 2p 0.5%
		95	(9/2+)	−59.6s	1.75 s 12	ε, εp
		95m	(1/2−)	−59.3s	<500 ms	IT

Nuclide Z El A	Jπ	Δ (MeV)	T½, Γ, or Abundance	Decay Mode
47 Ag 96m	(8)+	−64.62	4.40 s 6	ε, εp 8.5%
96m	(2+)	−64.62	6.9 s 6	ε, εp 18%
97	(9/2+)	−70.8	25.5 s 3	ε
98	(6+)	−73.05	47.5 s 3	ε, εp 1.1×10^{-3}%
99	(9/2)+	−76.712	124 s 3	ε
99m	(1/2−)	−76.206	10.5 s 5	IT
100	(5)+	−78.137	2.01 m 9	ε
100m	(2)+	−78.121	2.24 m 13	ε, IT
101	9/2+	−81.334	11.1 m 3	ε
101m	(1/2)−	−81.060	3.10 s 10	IT
102	5(+)	−82.246	12.9 m 3	ε
102m	2+	−82.237	7.7 m 5	ε 51%, IT 49%
103	7/2+	−84.800	65.7 m 7	ε
103m	1/2−	−84.665	5.7 s 3	IT
104	5+	−85.114	69.2 m 10	ε
104m	2+	−85.107	33.5 m 20	ε 99.93%, IT< 0.07%
105	1/2−	−87.070	41.29 d 7	ε
105m	7/2+	−87.045	7.23 m 16	IT 99.66%, ε 0.34%
106	1+	−86.940	23.96 m 4	ε 99.5%, β−< 1%
106m	6+	−86.850	8.28 d 2	ε
107	1/2−	−88.405	**51.839% 8**	
107m	7/2+	−88.312	44.3 s 2	IT
108	1+	−87.605	2.382 m 11	β− 97.15%, ε 2.85%
108m	6+	−87.495	438 y 9	ε 91.3%, IT 8.7%
109	1/2−	−88.719	**48.161% 8**	
109m	7/2+	−88.631	39.6 s 2	IT
110	1+	−87.457	24.6 s 2	β− 99.7%, ε 0.3%
110m	6+	−87.339	249.76 d 4	β− 98.64%, IT 1.36%
111	1/2−	−88.217	7.45 d 1	β−
111m	7/2+	−88.157	64.8 s 8	IT 99.3%, β− 0.7%
112	2(−)	−86.583	3.130 h 9	β−
113	1/2−	−87.03	5.37 h 5	β−
113m	7/2+	−86.99	68.7 s 16	IT 64%, β− 36%
114	1+	−84.930	4.6 s 1	β−
115	1/2−	−84.98	20.0 m 5	β−
115m	7/2+	−84.94	18.0 s 7	β− 79%, IT 21%
116	(0−)	−82.542	237 s 5	β−
116m	(3+)	−82.494	20 s 1	β− 93%, IT 7%
116m	(6−)	−82.412	9.3 s 3	β− 92%, IT 8%
117	(1/2−)	−82.18	72.8 s +20−7	β−
117m	(7/2+)	−82.15	5.34 s 5	β− 94%, IT 6%
118	1(−)	−79.553	3.76 s 15	β−
118m	4(+)	−79.425	2.0 s 2	β− 59%, IT 41%
119m	(1/2−)	−78.64	6.0 s 5	β−
119m	(7/2+)	−78.64	2.1 s 1	β−
120	3(+)	−75.651	1.23 s 4	β−, β−n< 3.0×10^{-3}%
120m	6(−)	−75.448	0.40 s 3	β− ≈63%, IT ≈37%
121	(7/2+)	−74.40	0.78 s 2	β−, β−n 0.08%
122	(3+)	−71.11	0.529 s 13	β− 99.8%, β−n 0.2%
122m	(1−)	−71.11	0.55 s 5	β−, IT, β−n
122m	(9−)	−71.03	0.20 s 5	β−, β−n
123	(7/2+)	−69.55	0.300 s 5	β−, β−n 0.55%

Nuclide				Δ	T½, Γ, or	
Z	El	A	Jπ	(MeV)	Abundance	Decay Mode
47	Ag	*124*	≥2	−66.2	0.172 s *5*	β−, β−n 1.3%
		125	(9/2+)	−64.4s	166 ms *7*	β−, β−n
		126		−60.9s	107 ms *12*	β−, β−n
		127		−58.8s	109 ms *25*	β−
		128		−54.9s	58 ms *5*	β−, β−n
		129	(9/2+)	−52.6s	46 ms +*5−9*	β−, β−n
		129m	(1/2−)	−52.6s	≈160 ms	β−, β−n
		130		−46.3s	≈50 ms	β−, β−n
48	Cd	95		−46.6s		εp?, ε?
		96	0+	−55.6s	1.03 s +*24−21*	ε
		97	(9/2+)	−60.5s	1.10 s *7*	ε, εp 12%
		97m	(25/2+)	−60.5s	3.70 s *8*	ε, εp 25%
		98	0+	−67.62	9.2 s *3*	ε, εp < 0.03%
		99	(5/2+)	−69.931	16 s *3*	ε, εα < 1.0×10⁻⁴%, εp 0.17%
		100	0+	−74.194	49.1 s *5*	ε
		101	(5/2+)	−75.836	1.36 m *5*	ε
		102	0+	−79.659	5.5 m *5*	ε
		103	(5/2)+	−80.652	7.3 m *1*	ε
		104	0+	−83.968	57.7 m *10*	ε
		105	5/2+	−84.333	55.5 m *4*	ε
		106	0+	−87.130	>3.6×10²⁰ y **1.25% 6**	2ε
		107	5/2+	−86.990	6.50 h *2*	ε
		108	0+	−89.252	>1.9×10¹⁸ y **0.89% 3**	2ε
		109	5/2+	−88.504	461.4 d *12*	ε
		110	0+	−90.350	**12.49% 18**	
		111	1/2+	−89.254	**12.80% 12**	
		111m	11/2−	−88.858	48.50 m *9*	IT
		112	0+	−90.577	**24.13% 21**	
		113	1/2+	−89.046	8.00×10¹⁵ y *26* **12.22% 12**	β−
		113m	11/2−	−88.783	14.1 y *5*	β− 99.86%, IT 0.14%
		114	0+	−90.018	>2.1×10¹⁸ y **28.73% 42**	2β−
		115	1/2+	−88.087	53.46 h *5*	β−
		115m	(11/2)−	−87.906	44.56 d *24*	β−
		116	0+	−88.716	3.3×10¹⁹ y *4* **7.49% 18**	2β−
		117	1/2+	−86.422	2.49 h *4*	β−
		117m	(11/2)−	−86.286	3.36 h *5*	β−
		118	0+	−86.71	50.3 m *2*	β−
		119	3/2+	−83.98	2.69 m *2*	β−
		119m	(11/2−)	−83.83	2.20 m *2*	β−
		120	0+	−83.957	50.80 s *21*	β−
		121	(3/2+)	−81.06	13.5 s *3*	β−
		121m	(11/2−)	−80.84	8.3 s *8*	β−
		122	0+	−80.616	5.24 s *3*	β−
		123	(3/2+)	−77.32	2.10 s *2*	β−
		123m	(11/2−)	−77.00	1.82 s *3*	β− ≤100%, IT
		124	0+	−76.697	1.25 s *2*	β−

Z	El	A	Jπ	Δ (MeV)	T½, Γ, or Abundance	Decay Mode
48	Cd	*125*	(3/2+)	−73.35	0.68 s *4*	β−
		125m	(11/2−)	−73.35	0.48 s *3*	β−
		126	0+	−72.256	0.515 s *17*	β−
		127	(3/2+)	−68.43	0.37 s *7*	β−
		128	0+	−67.25	0.28 s *4*	β−
		129	(3/2+)	−63.3s	0.27 s *4*	
		130	0+	−61.5	162 ms *7*	β− , β−n 3.5%
		131	(7/2−)	−55.4s	68 ms *3*	β− , β−n 3.5%
		132	0+	−50.9s	97 ms *10*	β− , β−n 60%
		133	(7/2−)		57 ms *10*	β− , β−n , β−2n
49	In	97		−47.2s		ε ?, p ?
		98		−53.9s	32 ms +*32–11*	ε
		98m		−53.9s	1.2 s +*12–4*	ε
		99		−61.4s	3.0 s *8*	ε
		100	(6+,7+)	−64.3	5.9 s *2*	ε , εp 1.6%
		101	(9/2+)	−68.6s	15.1 s *3*	ε , εp
		102	(6+)	−70.694	23.3 s *1*	ε , εp 9.3×10^{-3}%
		103	(9/2)+	−74.629	65 s *7*	ε
		103m	(1/2−)	−73.997	34 s *2*	ε 67%, IT 33%
		104	(6+)	−76.182	1.80 m *3*	ε
		104m	(3+)	−76.089	15.7 s *5*	IT 80%, ε 20%
		105	9/2+	−79.64	5.07 m *7*	ε
		105m	(1/2−)	−78.97	48 s *6*	IT
		106	7+	−80.60	6.2 m *1*	ε
		106m	(2)+	−80.57	5.2 m *1*	ε
		107	9/2+	−83.56	32.4 m *3*	ε
		107m	1/2−	−82.89	50.4 s *6*	IT
		108	7+	−84.116	58.0 m *12*	ε
		108m	2+	−84.086	39.6 m *7*	ε
		109	9/2+	−86.488	4.167 h *18*	ε
		109m	1/2−	−85.838	1.34 m *7*	IT
		109m	(19/2+)	−84.386	0.209 s *6*	IT
		110	7+	−86.47	4.9 h *1*	ε
		110m	2+	−86.41	69.1 m *5*	ε
		111	9/2+	−88.393	2.8047 d *4*	ε
		111m	1/2−	−87.856	7.7 m *2*	IT
		112	1+	−87.992	14.97 m *10*	ε 56%, β− 44%
		112m	4+	−87.835	20.56 m *6*	IT
		113	9/2+	−89.368	**4.29% *5***	
		113m	1/2−	−88.976	99.476 m *23*	IT
		114	1+	−88.570	71.9 s *1*	β− 99.5%, ε 0.5%
		114m	5+	−88.380	49.51 d *1*	IT 96.75%, ε 3.25%
		115	9/2+	−89.536	4.41×10^{14} y *25* 95.71% *5*	β−
		115m	1/2−	−89.200	4.486 h *4*	IT 95%, β− 5%
		116	1+	−88.249	14.10 s *3*	β− 99.98%, ε 0.02%
		116m	5+	−88.122	54.29 m *17*	β−
		116m	8−	−87.959	2.18 s *4*	IT
		117	9/2+	−88.943	43.2 m *3*	β−
		117m	1/2−	−88.628	116.2 m *3*	β− 52.9%, IT 47.1%
		118	1+	−87.228	5.0 s *5*	β−
		118m	5+	−87.168	4.45 m *5*	β−

Nuclide Z	El	A	Jπ	Δ (MeV)	T½, Γ, or Abundance	Decay Mode
49	In	118m	8–	–87.028	8.5 s *3*	IT 98.6%, β– 1.4%
		119	9/2+	–87.699	2.4 m *1*	β–
		119m	1/2–	–87.388	18.0 m *3*	β– 95.6%, IT 4.4%
		120	1+	–85.73	3.08 s *8*	β–
		120m	(8–)	–85.73	47.3 s *5*	β–
		120m	(5)+	–85.66	46.2 s *8*	β–
		121	9/2+	–85.84	23.1 s *6*	β–
		121m	1/2–	–85.52	3.88 m *10*	β– 98.8%, IT 1.2%
		122	1+	–83.57	1.5 s *3*	β–
		122m	5+	–83.53	10.3 s *6*	β–
		122m	(8–)	–83.28	10.8 s *4*	β–
		123	(9/2)+	–83.43	6.17 s *5*	β–
		123m	(1/2)–	–83.10	47.4 s *4*	β–
		124	(1)+	–80.87	3.12 s *9*	β–
		124m	(8–)	–80.82	3.7 s *2*	β–
		125	9/2+	–80.48	2.36 s *4*	β–
		125m	1/2(–)	–80.12	12.2 s *2*	β–
		126	3(+)	–77.81	1.53 s *1*	β–
		126m	(8–)	–77.71	1.64 s *5*	β–
		127	(9/2+)	–76.89	1.09 s *1*	β–, β–n ≤ 0.03%
		127m	(1/2–)	–76.43	3.67 s *4*	β–, β–n 0.69%
		127m	(21/2–)	–75.03	1.04 s *10*	β–
		128	(3)+	–74.36	0.84 s *6*	β–, β–n < 0.05%
		128m	(8–)	–74.02	0.72 s *10*	β–, β–n < 0.05%
		129	(9/2+)	–72.81	0.61 s *1*	β–, β–n 0.25%
		129m	(1/2–)	–72.44	1.23 s *3*	β–> 99.7%, β–n 2.5%, IT< 0.3%
		129m	(23/2–)	–71.18	0.67 s *10*	β–
		130	1(–)	–69.89	0.29 s *2*	β–, β–n 0.93%
		130m	(10–)	–69.84	0.54 s *1*	β–, β–n 1.65%
		130m	(5+)	–69.49	0.54 s *1*	β–, β–n 1.65%
		131	(9/2+)	–68.05	0.28 s *3*	β–, β–n ≤ 2%
		131m	(1/2–)	–67.75	0.35 s *5*	β– ≥ 99.98%, β–n ≤ 2%, IT ≤ 0.02%
		131m	(21/2+)	–64.29	0.32 s *6*	β–> 99%, IT< 1%, β–n ≈ 0.03%
		132	(7–)	–62.41	0.207 s *6*	β–, β–n 6.3%
		133	(9/2+)	–57.8s	165 ms *3*	β–, β–n 85%
		133m	(1/2–)	–57.4s	180 ms *15*	β–, IT, β–n
		134	(4– to 7–)	–52.0s	140 ms *4*	β–, β–n 65%
		135		–47.2s	92 ms *10*	β–, β–n
50	Sn	99		–47.7s		ε?, εp?
		100	0+	–56.9	0.86 s +37–20	ε, εp< 17%
		101	(5/2+)	–59.9s	1.7 s *3*	ε, εp 26%
		102	0+	–64.9	3.8 s *2*	ε
		103	(5/2+)	–66.97	7.0 s *2*	ε, εp 1.2%
		104	0+	–71.624	20.8 s *5*	ε
		105	(5/2+)	–73.337	32.7 s *5*	ε, εp 0.01%
		106	0+	–77.353	115 s *5*	ε
		107	(5/2+)	–78.512	2.90 m *5*	ε
		108	0+	–82.071	10.30 m *8*	ε
		109	5/2+	–82.632	18.0 m *2*	ε

Nuclide Z El A	Jπ	Δ (MeV)	T½, Γ, or Abundance	Decay Mode
50 Sn 110	0+	−85.84	4.11 h *10*	ε
111	7/2+	−85.941	35.3 m *6*	ε
112	0+	−88.657	<1.3×10²¹ y	2ε
			0.97% *1*	
113	1/2+	−88.330	115.09 d *3*	ε
113m	7/2+	−88.253	21.4 m *4*	IT 91.1%, ε 8.9%
114	0+	−90.559	**0.66%** *1*	
115	1/2+	−90.033	**0.34%** *1*	
116	0+	−91.525	**14.54%** *9*	
117	1/2+	−90.397	**7.68%** *7*	
117m	11/2−	−90.082	13.76 d *4*	IT
118	0+	−91.652	**24.22%** *9*	
119	1/2+	−90.065	**8.59%** *4*	
119m	11/2−	−89.976	293.1 d *7*	IT
120	0+	−91.098	**32.58%** *9*	
121	3/2+	−89.197	27.03 h *4*	β−
121m	11/2−	−89.191	43.9 y *5*	IT 77.6%, β− 22.4%
122	0+	−89.942	**4.63%** *3*	
123	11/2−	−87.817	129.2 d *4*	β−
123m	3/2+	−87.792	40.06 m *1*	β−
124	0+	−88.237	>1.2×10²¹ y	2β−
			5.79% *5*	
125	11/2−	−85.898	9.64 d *3*	β−
125m	3/2+	−85.870	9.52 m *5*	β−
126	0+	−86.02	2.30×10⁵ y *14*	β−
127	(11/2−)	−83.47	2.10 h *4*	β−
127m	(3/2+)	−83.46	4.13 m *3*	β−
128	0+	−83.34	59.07 m *14*	β−
128m	(7−)	−81.24	6.5 s *5*	IT
129	(3/2+)	−80.59	2.23 m *4*	β−
129m	(11/2−)	−80.56	6.9 m *1*	β−, IT< 2.0×10⁻³%
130	0+	−80.137	3.72 m *7*	β−
130m	(7−)	−78.190	1.7 m *1*	β−
131	(3/2+)	−77.271	56.0 s *5*	β−
131m	(11/2−)	−77.271	58.4 s *5*	β−, IT
132	0+	−76.548	39.7 s *8*	β−
133	7/2−	−70.85	1.46 s *3*	β−, β−n 0.03%
134	0+	−66.3	1.050 s *11*	β−, β−n 17%
135	(7/2−)	−60.6s	530 ms *20*	β−, β−n 21%
136	0+	−56.3s	0.25 s *3*	β−, β−n 30%
137		−50.3s	190 ms *60*	β−, β−n 58%
138	0+		>408 ns	β−, β−n
51 Sb 103		−56.2s	>1.5 μs	ε?
104		−59.2s	0.44 s +*15−11*	ε, εp< 7%, p< 1%
105	(5/2+)	−63.85	1.22 s *11*	ε 99%, p 1%
106	(2+)	−66.473	0.6 s *2*	ε
107	(5/2+)	−70.653	4.0 s *2*	ε
108	(4+)	−72.445	7.4 s *3*	ε
109	(5/2+)	−76.251	17.0 s *7*	ε
110	(3+,4+)	−77.449	23.0 s *4*	ε
111	(5/2+)	−80.836	75 s *1*	ε
112	3+	−81.60	51.4 s *10*	ε

Nuclide Z El A	Jπ	Δ (MeV)	T½, Γ, or Abundance	Decay Mode
51 Sb 113	5/2+	−84.42	6.67 m 7	ε
114	3+	−84.50	3.49 m 3	ε
115	5/2+	−87.00	32.1 m 3	ε
116	3+	−86.822	15.8 m 8	ε
116m	8−	−86.439	60.3 m 6	ε
117	5/2+	−88.642	2.80 h 1	ε
118	1+	−87.996	3.6 m 1	ε
118m	8−	−87.746	5.00 h 2	ε
119	5/2+	−89.474	38.19 h 22	ε
119m	(27/2+)	−86.632	0.85 s 9	IT
120	1+	−88.417	15.89 m 4	ε
120m	8−	−88.417	5.76 d 2	ε
121	5/2+	−89.599	**57.21% 5**	
122	2−	−88.334	2.7238 d 2	β− 97.59%, ε 2.41%
122m	(8)−	−88.170	4.191 m 3	IT
123	7/2+	−89.226	**42.79% 5**	
124	3−	−87.622	60.20 d 3	β−
124m	5+	−87.611	93 s 5	IT 75%, β− 25%
124m	(8)−	−87.585	20.2 m 2	IT
125	7/2+	−88.257	2.75856 y 25	β−
126	(8−)	−86.40	12.35 d 6	β−
126m	(5+)	−86.38	19.15 m 8	β− 86%, IT 14%
126m	(3−)	−86.36	≈11 s	IT
127	7/2+	−86.700	3.85 d 5	β−
128	8−	−84.61	9:01 h 4	β−
128m	5+	−84.61	10.4 m 2	β− 96.4%, IT 3.6%
129	7/2+	−84.63	4.40 h 1	β−
129m	(19/2−)	−82.78	17.7 m 1	β− 85%, IT 15%
130	(8−)	−82.29	39.5 m 8	β−
130m	(4,5)+	−82.29	6.3 m 2	β−
131	(7/2+)	−81.98	23.03 m 4	β−
132	(4)+	−79.67	2.79 m 7	β−
132m	(8−)	−79.67	4.10 m 5	β−
133	(7/2+)	−78.94	2.34 m 5	β−
134	(0−)	−74.17	0.78 s 6	β−
134m	(7−)	−73.89	10.07 s 5	β−, β−n 0.09%
135	(7/2+)	−69.79	1.679 s 15	β−, β−n 22%
136	1−	−64.5s	0.923 s 14	β−, β−n 16.3%
137	(7/2+)	−60.4s	492 ms 25	β−, β−n 49%
138		−54.8s	350 ms 15	β−, β−n 72%
139		−50.3s	93 ms +14−3	β−, β−n 90%
140			>407 ns	β−, β−n, β−2n
52 Te 105	(5/2+)	−52.6s	0.62 μs 7	α
106	0+	−58.2	70 μs 17	α
107		−60.54	3.1 ms 1	α 70%, ε 30%
108	0+	−65.783	2.1 s 1	ε 51%, α 49%, εp 2.4%
109	(5/2+)	−67.715	4.6 s 3	ε 96.1%, εp 9.4%, α 3.9%, εα< 5.0×10⁻³%
110	0+	−72.229	18.6 s 8	ε, α≈3.0×10⁻³%
111	(5/2)+	−73.587	19.3 s 4	ε, εp

Nuclide Z El A	Jπ	Δ (MeV)	T½, Γ, or Abundance	Decay Mode
52 Te 112	0+	−77.567	2.0 m *2*	ε
113	(7/2+)	−78.35	1.7 m *2*	ε
114	0+	−81.89	15.2 m *7*	ε
115	7/2+	−82.06	5.8 m *2*	ε
115m	(1/2)+	−82.04	6.7 m *4*	ε ≤ 100%, IT
116	0+	−85.27	2.49 h *4*	ε
117	1/2+	−85.10	62 m *2*	ε
117m	(11/2−)	−84.80	103 ms *3*	IT
118	0+	−87.68	6.00 d *2*	ε
119	1/2+	−87.181	16.05 h *5*	ε
119m	11/2−	−86.920	4.70 d *4*	ε, IT < 8.0×10^{-3}%
120	0+	−89.369	**0.09% *1***	
121	1/2+	−88.54	19.17 d *4*	ε
121m	11/2−	−88.25	164.2 d *8*	IT 88.6%, ε 11.4%
122	0+	−90.315	**2.55% *12***	
123	1/2+	−89.173	$>9.2 \times 10^{16}$ y **0.89% *3***	ε
123m	11/2−	−88.925	119.2 d *1*	IT
124	0+	−90.526	**4.74% *14***	
125	1/2+	−89.024	**7.07% *15***	
125m	11/2−	−88.879	57.40 d *15*	IT
126	0+	−90.066	**18.84% *25***	
127	3/2+	−88.283	9.35 h *7*	β−
127m	11/2−	−88.195	106.1 d *7*	IT 97.6%, β− 2.4%
128	0+	−88.993	2.41×10^{24} y *39* **31.74% *8***	2β−
129	3/2+	−87.004	69.6 m *3*	β−
129m	11/2−	−86.898	33.6 d *1*	IT 63%, β− 37%
130	0+	−87.352	$\geq 3.0 \times 10^{24}$ y **34.08% *62***	2β−
131	3/2+	−85.211	25.0 m *1*	β−
131m	11/2−	−85.029	33.25 h *25*	β− 74.1%, IT 25.9%
131m	(23/2+)	−83.271	93 ms *12*	IT
132	0+	−85.180	3.204 d *13*	β−
133	(3/2+)	−82.94	12.5 m *3*	β−
133m	(11/2−)	−82.61	55.4 m *4*	β− 83.5%, IT 16.5%
134	0+	−82.56	41.8 m *8*	β−
135	(7/2−)	−77.90	19.0 s *2*	β−
136	0+	−74.48	17.63 s *8*	β−, β−n 1.31%
137	(7/2−)	−69.3	2.49 s *5*	β−, β−n 2.99%
138	0+	−65.8	1.4 s *4*	β−, β−n 6.3%
139	(7/2−)	−60.4s	>150 ns	β−, β−n
140	0+	−56.6s	>300 ns	β−, β−n
141		−51.0s	>150 ns	β−?, β−n?
142	0+	−46.9s		
143			>408 ns	β−, β−n, β−2n
53 I 107		−49.6s		
108	(1)	−52.6s	36 ms *6*	α 91%, ε 9%, p < 1%
109	1/2+	−57.675	93.5 μs *3*	p 99.99%, α 0.01%
110		−60.46	0.65 s *2*	ε 83%, α 17%, εp 11%, εα 1.1%
111	(5/2+)	−64.953	2.5 s *2*	ε 99.9%, α ≈ 0.1%

Nuclide Z El A	Jπ	Δ (MeV)	T½, Γ, or Abundance	Decay Mode
53 I 112		−67.06	3.42 s *11*	ε , α ≈ 1.2×10⁻³%
113	5/2+	−71.119	6.6 s *2*	ε , α 3.3×10⁻⁷%
114	1+	−72.8s	2.1 s *2*	ε , εp
114m	(7)	−72.5s	6.2 s *5*	ε 91%, IT 9%
115	(5/2+)	−76.34	1.3 m *2*	ε
116	1+	−77.49	2.91 s *15*	ε
117	(5/2)+	−80.43	2.22 m *4*	ε
118	2−	−80.97	13.7 m *5*	ε
118m	(7−)	−80.87	8.5 m *5*	ε < 100%, IT
119	5/2+	−83.76	19.1 m *4*	ε
120	2−	−83.75	81.6 m *2*	ε
120m	(7−)	−83.43	53 m *4*	ε
121	5/2+	−86.253	2.12 h *1*	ε
122	1+	−86.081	3.63 m *6*	ε
123	5/2+	−87.945	13.2235 h *19*	ε
124	2−	−87.367	4.1760 d *3*	ε
125	5/2+	−88.838	59.407 d *10*	ε
126	2−	−87.912	12.93 d *5*	ε 52.7%, β− 47.3%
127	5/2+	−88.984	**100%**	
128	1+	−87.739	24.99 m *2*	β− 93.1%, ε 6.9%
129	7/2+	−88.507	1.57×10⁷ y *4*	β−
130	5+	−86.936	12.36 h *1*	β−
130m	2+	−86.896	8.84 m *6*	IT 84%, β− 16%
131	7/2+	−87.442	8.0252 d *6*	β−
132	4+	−85.698	2.295 h *13*	β−
132m	(8−)	−85.578	1.387 h *15*	IT 86%, β− 14%
133	7/2+	−85.886	20.83 h *8*	β−
133m	(19/2−)	−84.252	9 s *2*	IT
134	(4)+	−84.072	52.5 m *2*	β−
134m	(8)−	−83.756	3.52 m *4*	IT 97.7%, β− 2.3%
135	7/2+	−83.791	6.58 h *3*	β−
136	(1−)	−79.57	83.4 s *10*	β−
136m	(6−)	−78.93	46.9 s *10*	β−
137	(7/2+)	−76.51	24.5 s *2*	β− , β−n 7.14%
138	(2−)	−71.9s	6.23 s *3*	β− , β−n 5.56%
139	(7/2+)	−68.5	2.280 s *11*	β− , β−n 10%
140	(4−)	−63.6	0.86 s *4*	β− , β−n 9.3%
141		−60.3	0.43 s *2*	β− , β−n 21.2%
142		−55.0s	222 ms *12*	β− , β−n ?
143		−51.1s	130 ms *45*	β−?
144		−45.8s	>300 ns	β−?
145			>407 ns	β− , β−n
54 Xe 108	0+	−42.7s		
109	(7/2+)	−45.9s	13 ms *2*	α
110	0+	−51.9	93 ms *3*	α 64%, ε, εp
111	(7/2+)	−54.39	0.81 s *20*	ε 90%, α 10%
112	0+	−60.028	2.7 s *8*	ε 99.16%, α 0.84%
113	(5/2+)	−62.203	2.74 s *8*	ε , εp 7%, α ≈ 0.01%, εα ≈ 7.0×10⁻³%
114	0+	−67.08	10.0 s *4*	ε
115	(5/2+)	−68.66	18 s *4*	ε , εp 0.34%, α 3.0×10⁻⁴%

Nuclide				**Δ**	**T½, Γ, or**	
Z	**El**	**A**	**Jπ**	**(MeV)**	**Abundance**	**Decay Mode**
54	Xe	116	0+	−73.05	59 s *2*	ε
		117	5/2(+)	−74.18	61 s *2*	ε, εp 2.9×10⁻³%
		118	0+	−78.08	3.8 m *9*	ε
		119	(5/2+)	−78.79	5.8 m *3*	ε
		120	0+	−82.17	40 m *1*	ε
		121	5/2(+)	−82.47	40.1 m *20*	ε
		122	0+	−85.35	20.1 h *1*	ε
		123	(1/2)+	−85.249	2.08 h *2*	ε
		124	0+	−87.661	≥1.6×10¹⁴ y **0.0952% *3***	2ε
		125	1/2(+)	−87.193	16.9 h *2*	ε
		125m	9/2(−)	−86.940	57 s *1*	IT
		126	0+	−89.146	**0.0890% *2***	
		127	1/2+	−88.322	36.346 d *3*	ε
		127m	9/2−	−88.025	69.2 s *9*	IT
		128	0+	−89.860	**1.9102% *8***	
		129	1/2+	−88.696	**26.4006% *82***	
		129m	11/2−	−88.460	8.88 d *2*	IT
		130	0+	−89.880	**4.0710% *13***	
		131	3/2+	−88.413	**21.232% *30***	
		131m	11/2−	−88.249	11.84 d *4*	IT
		132	0+	−89.279	**26.9086% *33***	
		132m	(10+)	−86.527	8.39 ms *11*	IT
		133	3/2+	−87.643	5.2475 d *5*	β−
		133m	11/2−	−87.410	2.198 d *13*	IT
		134	0+	−88.124	>5.8×10²² y **10.4357% *21***	2β−
		134m	7−	−86.159	290 ms *17*	IT
		135	3/2+	−86.417	9.14 h *2*	β−
		135m	11/2−	−85.890	15.29 m *5*	IT>99.4%, β−<0.6%
		136	0+	−86.429	>2.4×10²¹ y **8.8573% *44***	2β−
		137	7/2−	−82.383	3.818 m *13*	β−
		138	0+	−79.975	14.08 m *8*	β−
		139	3/2−	−75.644	39.68 s *14*	β−
		140	0+	−72.986	13.60 s *10*	β−
		141	5/2(−)	−68.197	1.73 s *1*	β−, β−n 0.04%
		142	0+	−65.229	1.23 s *2*	β−, β−n 0.21%
		143	5/2−	−60.202	0.511 s *6*	β−, β−n 1%
		144	0+	−56.872	0.388 s *7*	β−, β−n 3%
		145		−51.49	188 ms *4*	β−, β−n 5%
		146	0+	−47.95	146 ms *6*	β−, β−n 6.9%
		147	(3/2−)	−42.5s	0.10 s +*10−5*	β−, β−n<8%
		148	0+		>408 ns	β−, β−n
55	Cs	112	(0+,3+)	−46.29	0.5 ms *1*	p
		113	(3/2+)	−51.765	16.7 μs *7*	p, α
		114	(1+)	−54.68	0.57 s *2*	ε 99.98%, εp 8.7%, εα 0.19%, α 0.02%
		115		−59.7s	1.4 s *8*	ε, εp≈0.07%
		116	(1+)	−62.1s	0.70 s *4*	ε, εp 2.8%, εα 0.05%
		116m	4+,5,6	−62.0s	3.85 s *13*	ε, εp 0.51%, εα 8.0×10⁻³%

Nuclide Z	El	A	Jπ	Δ (MeV)	T½, Γ, or Abundance	Decay Mode
55	Cs	117m	(9/2+)	−66.49	8.4 s *6*	ε
		117m	(3/2+)	−66.49	6.5 s *4*	ε
		118	2	−68.41	14 s *2*	ε , εp<0.04%, εα<2.4×10⁻³%
		118m	6,7,8	−68.41	17 s *3*	ε , εp<0.04%, εα<2.4×10⁻³%
		119	9/2+	−72.31	43.0 s *2*	ε
		119m	3/2(+)	−72.31	30.4 s *1*	ε
		120	2(+)	−73.888	61.3 s *11*	ε , εα 2.0×10⁻⁵% , εp 7.0×10⁻⁶%
		120m	(7−)	−73.888	57 s *6*	ε
		121	3/2(+)	−77.10	155 s *4*	ε
		121m	9/2(+)	−77.03	122 s *3*	ε 83%, IT 17%
		122	1+	−78.14	21.18 s *19*	ε
		122m	(5)−	−78.01	0.36 s *2*	IT
		122m	8(−)	−78.00	3.70 m *11*	ε
		123	1/2+	−81.04	5.88 m *3*	ε
		123m	(11/2)−	−80.89	1.64 s *12*	IT
		124	1+	−81.731	30.9 s *4*	ε
		124m	(7)+	−81.268	6.3 s *2*	IT
		125	1/2(+)	−84.087	46.7 m *1*	ε
		125m	(11/2−)	−83.821	0.90 ms *3*	IT
		126	1+	−84.34	1.64 m *2*	ε
		127	1/2+	−86.240	6.25 h *10*	ε
		128	1+	−85.931	3.66 m *2*	ε
		129	1/2+	−87.499	32.06 h *6*	ε
		130	1+	−86.899	29.21 m *4*	ε 98.4%, β− 1.6%
		130m	5−	−86.736	3.46 m *6*	IT 99.84%, ε 0.16%
		131	5/2+	−88.058	9.689 d *16*	ε
		132	2+	−87.155	6.480 d *6*	ε 98.13%, β− 1.87%
		133	7/2+	−88.070	100%	
		134	4+	−86.891	2.0652 y *4*	β−, ε 3.0×10⁻⁴%
		134m	8−	−86.752	2.912 h *2*	IT
		135	7/2+	−87.581	2.3×10⁶ y *3*	β−
		135m	19/2−	−85.948	53 m *2*	IT
		136	5+	−86.339	13.04 d *3*	β−
		136m	8−	−85.821	17.5 s *2*	β− , IT>0%
		137	7/2+	−86.545	30.08 y *9*	β−
		138	3−	−82.887	33.41 m *18*	β−
		138m	6−	−82.807	2.91 m *8*	IT 81%, β− 19%
		139	7/2+	−80.701	9.27 m *5*	β−
		140	1−	−77.050	63.7 s *3*	β−
		141	7/2+	−74.48	24.84 s *16*	β−, β−n 0.04%
		142	0−	−70.53	1.684 s *14*	β−, β−n 0.09%
		143	3/2+	−67.67	1.791 s *7*	β−, β−n 1.64%
		144	1(−)	−63.27	0.994 s *6*	β−, β−n 3.03%
		144m	(≥4)	−63.27	<1 s	β−
		145	3/2+	−60.06	0.587 s *5*	β−, β−n 14.7%
		146	1−	−55.57	0.321 s *2*	β−, β−n 14.2%
		147	(3/2+)	−52.02	0.230 s *1*	β−, β−n 28.5%
		148		−47.3	146 ms *6*	β−, β−n 25.1%
		149		−43.8s	>50 ms	β−, β−n

Nuclide			Jπ	Δ (MeV)	T½, Γ, or Abundance	Decay Mode
Z	El	A				
55	Cs	150		−39.0s	>50 ms	β−, β−n
		151		−35.1s	>50 ms	β−, β−n
56	Ba	112	0+	−36.1s		
		113		−39.8s		
		114	0+	−46.0	0.43 s +30−15	ε 99.1%, εp 20%, α 0.9%, ^{12}C < 0.0034%
		115	(5/2+)	−49.0s	0.45 s 5	ε, εp > 15%
		116	0+	−54.6s	1.3 s 2	ε, εp 3%
		117	(3/2)	−57.5	1.75 s 7	ε, εα > 0%, εp > 0%
		118	0+	−62.4s	5.5 s 2	ε, εp
		119	(5/2+)	−64.6	5.4 s 3	ε, εp < 25%
		120	0+	−68.9	24 s 2	ε
		121	5/2(+)	−70.7	29.7 s 15	ε
		122	0+	−74.61	1.95 m 15	ε
		123	5/2(+)	−75.65	2.7 m 4	ε
		124	0+	−79.09	11.0 m 5	ε
		125	1/2(+)	−79.67	3.3 m 3	ε
		126	0+	−82.67	100 m 2	ε
		127	1/2+	−82.82	12.7 m 4	ε
		127m	7/2−	−82.73	1.9 s 2	IT
		128	0+	−85.379	2.43 d 5	ε
		129	1/2+	−85.06	2.23 h 11	ε
		129m	7/2+	−85.06	2.16 h 2	ε ≤ 100%, IT
		130	0+	−87.261	**0.106% 1**	
		130m	8−	−84.786	9.4 ms 4	IT
		131	1/2+	−86.684	11.50 d 6	ε
		131m	9/2−	−86.496	14.6 m 2	IT
		132	0+	−88.434	>3.0×10^{21} y **0.101% 1**	2ε
		133	1/2+	−87.553	10.551 y 11	ε
		133m	11/2−	−87.265	38.93 h 10	IT 99.99%, ε 0.01%
		134	0+	−88.950	**2.417% 18**	
		135	3/2+	−87.850	**6.592% 12**	
		135m	11/2−	−87.582	28.7 h 2	IT
		136	0+	−88.887	**7.854% 24**	
		136m	7−	−86.856	0.3084 s 19	IT
		137	3/2+	−87.721	**11.232% 24**	
		137m	11/2−	−87.059	2.552 m 1	IT
		138	0+	−88.261	**71.698% 42**	
		139	7/2−	−84.914	83.06 m 28	β−
		140	0+	−83.270	12.7527 d 23	β−
		141	3/2−	−79.733	18.27 m 7	β−
		142	0+	−77.845	10.6 m 2	β−
		143	5/2−	−73.937	14.5 s 3	β−
		144	0+	−71.767	11.5 s 2	β−, β−n 3.6%
		145	5/2−	−67.516	4.31 s 16	β−
		146	0+	−64.94	2.22 s 7	β−
		147	(3/2−)	−60.26	0.894 s 10	β−, β−n 0.06%
		148	0+	−57.59	0.612 s 17	β−, β−n 0.4%
		149		−53.2s	0.344 s 7	β−, β−n 0.43%
		150	0+	−50.3s	0.3 s	β−, β−n

Z	Nuclide El	A	Jπ	Δ (MeV)	T½, Γ, or Abundance	Decay Mode
56	Ba	151		−45.6s	>300 ns	β−, β−n
		152	0+	−42.4s	>406 ns	β−, β−n
		153		−37.2s		β−?
57	La	117	(3/2+,3/2−)	−46.5s	23.5 ms 26	p 93.9%, ε 6.1%
		117m	(9/2+)	−46.3s	10 ms 5	p 97.4%, ε 2.6%
		118		−49.6s		ε ?
		119		−55.0s		ε ?
		120m		−57.7s	2.8 s 2	ε, εp > 0%
		121		−62.4s	5.3 s 2	ε
		122		−64.5s	8.6 s 5	ε, εp
		123		−68.7s	17 s 3	ε
		124m	(8−)	−70.26	29.21 s 17	ε
		124m		−70.26	21 s 4	ε
		125	(3/2+)	−73.76	64.8 s 12	ε
		125m		−73.65	0.39 s 4	
		126m	(5+)	−74.97	54 s 2	ε > 0%
		126m	(0−,1,2−)	−74.97	<50 s	ε, IT
		127	(11/2−)	−77.89	5.1 m 1	ε
		127m	(3/2+)	−77.88	3.7 m 4	ε, IT
		128	(5+)	−78.63	5.18 m 14	ε
		128m	(1+,2−)	−78.63	<1.4 m	ε
		129	3/2+	−81.33	11.6 m 2	ε
		129m	11/2−	−81.15	0.56 s 5	IT
		130	3(+)	−81.63	8.7 m 1	ε
		131	3/2+	−83.77	59 m 2	ε
		132	2−	−83.72	4.8 h 2	ε
		132m	6−	−83.53	24.3 m 5	IT 76%, ε 24%
		133	5/2+	−85.49	3.912 h 8	ε
		134	1+	−85.22	6.45 m 16	ε
		135	5/2+	−86.65	19.5 h 2	ε
		136	1+	−86.04	9.87 m 3	ε
		136m	(8+)	−85.81	114 ms 3	IT
		137	7/2+	−87.11	6×10⁴ y 2	ε
		138	5+	−86.521	1.02×10¹¹ y 1 0.08881% 71	ε 65.6%, β− 34.4%
		139	7/2+	−87.228	99.9119% 71	
		140	3−	−84.317	1.67855 d 12	β−
		141	(7/2+)	−82.934	3.92 h 3	β−
		142	2−	−80.022	91.1 m 5	β−
		143	(7/2)+	−78.171	14.2 m 1	β−
		144	(3−)	−74.83	40.8 s 4	β−
		145	(5/2+)	−72.83	24.8 s 20	β−
		146	2−	−69.05	6.27 s 10	β−
		146m	(6−)	−69.05	10.0 s 1	β−
		147	(3/2+)	−66.68	4.06 s 4	β−, β−n 0.04%
		148	(2−)	−62.71	1.26 s 8	β−, β−n 0.15%
		149	(3/2−)	−60.2	1.05 s 3	β−, β−n 1.43%
		150	(3+)	−56.6s	0.86 s 5	β−, β−n 2.7%
		151		−53.9s	>300 ns	β−, β−n
		152		−49.7s	>150 ns	β−
		153		−46.6s	>100 ns	β−?
		154		−42.0s		β−?

Nuclide Z El A	Jπ	Δ (MeV)	T½, Γ, or Abundance	Decay Mode
57 La 155		−38.5s		β−?
58 Ce 119		−43.9s		ε ?
120	0+	−49.5s		ε ?
121	(5/2)	−52.5s	1.1 s *1*	ε , εp≈1%
122	0+	−57.7s		ε , εp
123	(5/2)	−60.1s	3.8 s *2*	ε , εp>0%
124	0+	−64.6s	6 s *2*	ε
125	(7/2−)	−66.7s	9.7 s *3*	ε , εp
126	0+	−70.82	51.0 s *3*	ε
127	(1/2+)	−71.97	34 s *2*	ε
127m	(5/2+)	−71.97	28.6 s *7*	ε
128	0+	−75.53	3.93 m *2*	ε
129	5/2+	−76.29	3.5 m *5*	ε > 0%
130	0+	−79.42	22.9 m *5*	ε
131	7/2+	−79.71	10.3 m *3*	ε
131m	(1/2+)	−79.64	5.4 m *4*	ε , IT
132	0+	−82.47	3.51 h *11*	ε
132m	(8−)	−80.13	9.4 ms *3*	IT
133	1/2+	−82.42	97 m *4*	ε
133m	9/2−	−82.39	5.1 h *3*	ε , IT
134	0+	−84.83	3.16 d *4*	ε
135	1/2(+)	−84.62	17.7 h *3*	ε
135m	(11/2−)	−84.18	20 s *1*	IT
136	0+	−86.47	>0.7×10^{14} y **0.185% *2***	2ε
137	3/2+	−85.88	9.0 h *3*	ε
137m	11/2−	−85.63	34.4 h *3*	IT 99.21%, ε 0.79%
138	0+	−87.56	≥0.9×10^{14} y **0.251% *2***	2ε
138m	7−	−85.43	8.65 ms *20*	IT
139	3/2+	−86.949	137.641 d *20*	ε
139m	11/2−	−86.195	54.8 s *10*	IT
140	0+	−88.078	**88.450% *51***	
141	7/2−	−85.435	32.508 d *13*	β−
142	0+	−84.532	>5×10^{16} y **11.114% *51***	2β−
143	3/2−	−81.605	33.039 h *6*	β−
144	0+	−80.431	284.91 d *5*	β−
145	(5/2−)	−77.09	3.01 m *6*	β−
146	0+	−75.64	13.52 m *13*	β−
147	(5/2−)	−72.013	56.4 s *10*	β−
148	0+	−70.40	56 s *1*	β−
149	(3/2−)	−66.67	5.3 s *2*	β−
150	0+	−64.85	4.0 s *6*	β−
151	(5/2+)	−61.22	1.76 s *6*	β−
151m		−61.22	1.02 s *6*	β−
152	0+	−59.3s	1.4 s *2*	β−
153		−55.2s	>100 ns	β−?
154	0+	−52.7s	>100 ns	β−
155		−48.3s	>300 ns	β−?
156	0+	−45.3s		β−?
157		−40.4s		β−?

Nuclide Z El A	Jπ	Δ (MeV)	T½, Γ, or Abundance	Decay Mode
59 Pr 121	(3/2)	−41.4s	10 ms +6−3	p
122		−44.7s	≈0.5 s	ε ?
123		−50.1s	≈0.8 s	ε ?
124		−53.0s	1.2 s 2	ε , εp>0%
125		−57.7s	3.3 s 7	ε , εp
126	>3	−60.1s	3.14 s 22	ε , εp
127		−64.3s	4.2 s 3	ε
128	4,5,6	−66.33	2.84 s 9	ε
129	(11/2−)	−69.77	30 s 4	ε>0%
130?	(7,8)	−71.18	40 s 4	ε
130?	(4+,5+)	−71.18	40 s 4	ε
130?	(2+)	−71.18	40 s 4	ε
131	(3/2+)	−74.30	1.51 m 2	ε
131m	(11/2−)	−74.15	5.73 s 20	IT 96.4%, ε 3.6%
132	(2)+	−75.21	1.6 m 3	ε
133	(3/2+)	−77.94	6.5 m 3	ε
133m	(11/2−)	−77.74	1.1 s 2	IT
134m	(6−)	−78.51	≈11 m	ε
134m	2−	−78.51	17 m 2	ε
135	3/2(+)	−80.93	24 m 1	ε
136	2+	−81.33	13.1 m 1	ε
137	5/2+	−83.18	1.28 h 3	ε
138	1+	−83.13	1.45 m 5	ε
138m	7−	−82.76	2.12 h 4	ε
139	5/2+	−84.820	4.41 h 4	ε
140	1+	−84.690	3.39 m 1	ε
141	5/2+	−86.015	100%	
142	2−	−83.787	19.12 h 4	β− 99.98%, ε 0.02%
142m	5−	−83.783	14.6 m 5	IT
143	7/2+	−83.067	13.57 d 2	β−
144	0−	−80.749	17.28 m 5	β−
144m	3−	−80.690	7.2 m 3	IT 99.93%, β− 0.07%
145	7/2+	−79.626	5.984 h 10	β−
146	(2)−	−76.68	24.15 m 18	β−
147	(5/2+)	−75.44	13.4 m 3	β−
148	1−	−72.54	2.29 m 2	β−
148m	(4)	−72.44	2.01 m 7	β−
149	(5/2+)	−71.039	2.26 m 7	β−
150	(1)−	−68.299	6.19 s 16	β−
151	(3/2−)	−66.78	18.90 s 7	β−
152	(4+)	−63.76	3.57 s 18	β−
153		−61.58	4.28 s 11	β−
154	(3+)	−58.2	2.3 s 1	β−
155		−55.8s	>300 ns	β− ?
156		−51.9s	>300 ns	β− ?
157		−49.0s		β− ?
158		−44.7s		β− ?
159		−41.5s		β− ?
60 Nd 124	0+	−44.3s		ε ?
125	(5/2)	−47.4s	0.65 s 15	ε , εp>0%
126	0+	−52.6s	>200 ns	ε , εp
127		−55.3s	1.8 s 4	ε , εp

Nuclide Z El A	Jπ	Δ (MeV)	T½, Γ, or Abundance	Decay Mode
60 Nd 128	0+	−60.1s	5 s	ε , εp
129	(5/2+)	−62.2s	4.9 s *2*	ε>0%, εp>0%
130	0+	−66.60	21 s *3*	ε
131	(5/2+)	−67.77	25.4 s *9*	ε , εp>0%
132	0+	−71.43	94 s *8*	ε
133	(7/2+)	−72.33	70 s *10*	ε
133m	(1/2+)	−72.20	≈70 s	ε , IT
134	0+	−75.65	8.5 m *15*	ε
135	9/2(−)	−76.21	12.4 m *6*	ε
135m	(1/2+)	−76.15	5.5 m *5*	ε>99.97%, IT<0.03%
136	0+	−79.20	50.65 m *33*	ε
137	1/2+	−79.58	38.5 m *15*	ε
137m	11/2−	−79.06	1.60 s *15*	IT
138	0+	−82.02	5.04 h *9*	ε
139	3/2+	−82.01	29.7 m *5*	ε
139m	11/2−	−81.78	5.50 h *20*	ε 88.2%, IT 11.8%
140	0+	−84.25	3.37 d *2*	ε
140m	7−	−82.03	0.60 ms *5*	IT
141	3/2+	−84.192	2.49 h *3*	ε
141m	11/2−	−83.436	62.0 s *8*	IT , ε<0.05%
142	0+	−85.949	**27.152% *40***	
143	7/2−	−84.001	**12.174% *26***	
144	0+	−83.747	2.29×10^{15} y *16* **23.798% *19***	α
145	7/2−	−81.431	**8.293% *12***	
146	0+	−80.925	**17.189% *32***	
147	5/2−	−78.146	10.98 d *1*	β−
148	0+	−77.406	**5.756% *21***	
149	5/2−	−74.374	1.728 h *1*	β−
150	0+	−73.683	0.79×10^{19} y *7* **5.638% *28***	
151	3/2+	−70.946	12.44 m *7*	β−
152	0+	−70.15	11.4 m *2*	β−
153	(3/2)−	−67.34	31.6 s *10*	β−
154	0+	−65.7	25.9 s *2*	β−
155		−62.5s	8.9 s *2*	β−
156	0+	−60.5	5.06 s *13*	β−
157		−56.8s	>100 ns	β−?
158	0+	−54.4s	>50 ns	β−
159		−50.2s		β−?
160	0+	−47.4s		β−?
161		−43.0s		β−?
61 Pm 126		−38.8s		ε?
127		−44.4s		p?, ε?
128		−47.6s	1.0 s *3*	ε , α, εp
129	(5/2−)	−52.5s	2.4 s *9*	ε
130	(4,5,6)	−55.2s	2.6 s *2*	ε , εp
131	(11/2−)	−59.6s	6.3 s *8*	ε
132	(3+)	−61.6s	6.2 s *6*	ε , εp≈5.0×10^{-5}%
133	(3/2+)	−65.41	13.5 s *21*	ε
133m	(11/2−)	−65.28	<8.8 s	IT , ε

Nuclide Z El A	Jπ	Δ (MeV)	T½, Γ, or Abundance	Decay Mode
61 Pm 134	(2+)	−66.74	≈5 s	ε
134m	(5+)	−66.74	22 s *1*	ε
135m	(3/2+,5/2+)	−69.98	49 s *3*	ε
135m	(11/2−)	−69.91	45 s *4*	ε
136m	(5−)	−71.20	107 s *6*	ε
136m	(2+)	−71.20	47 s *2*	ε
137	11/2−	−74.07	2.4 m *1*	ε
138		−74.94	10 s *2*	ε
138m		−74.92	3.24 m *5*	ε
139	(5/2)+	−77.50	4.15 m *5*	ε
139m	(11/2)−	−77.31	180 ms *20*	IT 99.94%, ε 0.06%
140	1+	−78.21	9.2 s *2*	ε
140m	8−	−78.21	5.95 m *5*	ε
141	5/2+	−80.52	20.90 m *5*	ε
142	1+	−81.16	40.5 s *5*	ε
142m	(8)−	−80.27	2.0 ms *2*	IT
143	5/2+	−82.960	265 d *7*	ε
144	5−	−81.415	363 d *14*	ε
145	5/2+	−81.267	17.7 y *4*	ε, α 2.8×10⁻⁷%
146	3−	−79.453	5.53 y *5*	ε 66%, β− 34%
147	7/2+	−79.041	2.6234 y *2*	β−
148	1−	−76.865	5.368 d *2*	β−
148m	5−,6−	−76.727	41.29 d *11*	β− 95.8%, IT 4.2%
149	7/2+	−76.063	53.08 h *5*	β−
150	(1−)	−73.60	2.68 h *2*	β−
151	5/2+	−73.388	28.40 h *4*	β−
152	1+	−71.25	4.12 m *8*	β−
152m	(8)	−71.11	13.8 m *2*	β−, IT≥0%
152m	4−	−71.11	7.52 m *8*	β−
153	5/2−	−70.68	5.25 m *2*	β−
154	(3,4)	−68.49	2.68 m *7*	β−
154m	(0−,1−)	−68.49	1.73 m *10*	β−
155	5/2−	−66.97	41.5 s *2*	β−
156m	4−	−64.21	26.70 s *10*	β−
157	(5/2−)	−62.4	10.56 s *10*	β−
158		−59.1	4.8 s *5*	β−
159		−56.8	1.5 s *2*	β−
160		−53.1s		β−?
161		−50.4s		β−?
162		−46.3s		β−?
163		−43.1s		β−?
62 Sm 128	0+	−38.0s		ε?, p?
129	(1/2+,3/2+)	−41.3s	0.55 s *10*	ε, εp>0%
130	0+	−46.9s		ε
131		−49.6s	1.2 s *2*	ε, εp>0%
132	0+	−54.7s	4.0 s *3*	ε, εp
133	(5/2+)	−56.8s	2.89 s *16*	ε, εp>0%
133m	(1/2−)	−56.8s	3.5 s *4*	ε, IT, εp
134	0+	−61.2s	9.5 s *8*	ε
135	(3/2+,5/2+)	−62.9	10.3 s *5*	ε, εp 0.02%
136	0+	−66.81	47 s *2*	ε
137	(9/2−)	−68.03	45 s *1*	ε

Nuclide				Δ	T½, Γ, or	
Z	**El**	**A**	**Jπ**	**(MeV)**	**Abundance**	**Decay Mode**
62	**Sm**	138	0+	−71.50	3.1 m *2*	ε
		139	1/2+	−72.38	2.57 m *10*	ε
		139m	11/2−	−71.92	10.7 s *6*	IT 93.7%, ε 6.3%
		140	0+	−75.46	14.82 m *12*	ε
		141	1/2+	−75.934	10.2 m *2*	ε
		141m	11/2−	−75.758	22.6 m *2*	ε 99.69%, IT 0.31%
		142	0+	−78.987	72.49 m *5*	ε
		143	3/2+	−79.516	8.75 m *6*	ε
		143m	11/2−	−78.762	66 s *2*	IT 99.76%, ε 0.24%
		143m	23/2(−)	−76.722	30 ms *3*	IT
		144	0+	−81.965	**3.07% *7***	
		145	7/2−	−80.651	340 d *3*	ε
		146	0+	−80.995	10.3×10^7 y *5*	α
		147	7/2−	−79.265	1.060×10^{11} y *11*	α
					14.99% *18*	
		148	0+	−79.335	7×10^{15} y *3*	α
					11.24% *10*	
		149	7/2−	−77.135	**13.82% *7***	
		150	0+	−77.050	**7.38% *1***	
		151	5/2−	−74.575	90 y *8*	β−
		152	0+	−74.762	**26.75% *16***	
		153	3/2+	−72.559	46.284 h *4*	β−
		153m	11/2−	−72.461	10.6 ms *3*	IT
		154	0+	−72.454	**22.75% *29***	
		155	3/2−	−70.190	22.3 m *2*	β−
		156	0+	−69.362	9.4 h *2*	β−
		157	(3/2−)	−66.72	8.03 m *7*	β−
		158	0+	−65.21	5.30 m *3*	β−
		159	5/2−	−62.24	11.37 s *15*	β−
		160	0+	−60.4s	9.6 s *3*	β−
		161		−56.8	4.8 s *4*	β−
		162	0+	−54.8s	2.4 s *5*	β−
		163		−50.9s		β−?
		164	0+	−48.2s		β−?
		165		−43.8s		β−?
63	**Eu**	130	(1+)	−33.0s	0.90 ms +*49−29*	p
		131	3/2+	−38.7s	17.8 ms *19*	p 89%, ε 11%
		132		−41.9s		p, ε
		133		−47.1s		ε?
		134		−49.7s	0.5 s *2*	ε, εp>0%
		135		−54.1s	1.5 s *2*	ε, εp
		136m	(7+)	−56.1s	3.3 s *3*	ε, εp 0.09%
		136m	(3+)	−56.1s	3.8 s *3*	ε, εp 0.09%
		137	(11/2−)	−60.0s	11 s *2*	ε
		138	(6−)	−61.75	12.1 s *6*	ε
		139	(11/2)−	−65.40	17.9 s *6*	ε
		140	1+	−66.99	1.51 s *2*	ε
		140m	(5−)	−66.99	125 ms *2*	IT, ε<1%
		141	5/2+	−69.93	40.7 s *7*	ε
		141m	11/2−	−69.83	2.7 s *3*	IT 87%, ε 13%
		142	1+	−71.31	2.34 s *12*	ε
		142m	8−	−71.31	1.223 m *8*	ε

Nuclide Z El A	Jπ	Δ (MeV)	T½, Γ, or Abundance	Decay Mode
63 Eu 143	5/2+	−74.24	2.59 m *2*	ε
144	1+	−75.62	10.2 s *1*	ε
145	5/2+	−77.991	5.93 d *4*	ε
146	4−	−77.117	4.61 d *3*	ε
147	5/2+	−77.544	24.1 d *6*	ε , α 2.2×10⁻³%
148	5−	−76.30	54.5 d *5*	ε , α 9.4×10⁻⁷%
149	5/2+	−76.440	93.1 d *4*	ε
150	5−	−74.791	36.9 y *9*	ε
150m	0−	−74.749	12.8 h *1*	β− 89%, ε 11%, IT≤5.0×10⁻⁸%
151	5/2+	−74.651	≥1.7×10¹⁸ y 47.81% *3*	α
152	3−	−72.887	13.528 y *14*	ε 72.1%, β− 27.9%
152m	0−	−72.841	9.3116 h *13*	β− 72%, ε 28%
152m	8−	−72.739	96 m *1*	IT
153	5/2+	−73.366	**52.19% *6***	
154	3−	−71.736	8.601 y *10*	β− 99.98%, ε 0.02%
154m	8−	−71.591	46.3 m *4*	IT
155	5/2+	−71.816	4.753 y *14*	β−
156	0+	−70.085	15.19 d *8*	β−
157	5/2+	−69.459	15.18 h *3*	β−
158	(1−)	−67.20	45.9 m *2*	β−
159	5/2+	−66.045	18.1 m *1*	β−
160	1	−63.24	38 s *4*	β−
161		−61.80	26 s *3*	β−
162		−58.69	10.6 s *10*	β−
163		−56.80	7.7 s *4*	β−
164		−53.4s	4.2 s *2*	β−
165		−50.8s	2.3 s *2*	β−
166		−46.8s		β− ?
167		−43.8s		β− ?
64 Gd 133		−35.6s		
134	0+	−41.1s		ε ?
135	(5/2+)	−44.0s	1.1 s *2*	ε , εp 18%
136	0+	−48.9s	≥200 ns	
137	(7/2)	−51.2s	2.2 s *2*	ε , εp
138	0+	−55.7s	4.7 s *9*	ε
139	(9/2−)	−57.6s	5.8 s *9*	εp>0%, ε>0%
139m		−57.6s	4.8 s *9*	εp>0%, ε>0%
140	0+	−61.78	15.8 s *4*	ε
141	1/2+	−63.22	14 s *4*	ε , εp 0.03%
141m	11/2−	−62.85	24.5 s *5*	ε 89%, IT 11%
142	0+	−66.96	70.2 s *6*	ε
143	(1/2)+	−68.2	39 s *2*	ε
143m	(11/2−)	−68.1	110.0 s *14*	ε
144	0+	−71.76	4.47 m *6*	ε
145	1/2+	−72.93	23.0 m *4*	ε
145m	11/2−	−72.18	85 s *3*	IT 94.3%, ε 5.7%
146	0+	−76.087	48.27 d *10*	ε
147	7/2−	−75.356	38.06 h *12*	ε
148	0+	−76.269	70.9 y *10*	α
149	7/2−	−75.126	9.28 d *10*	ε , α 4.3×10⁻⁴%

Z	Nuclide El	A	Jπ	Δ (MeV)	T½, Γ, or Abundance	Decay Mode
64	**Gd**	150	0+	−75.763	1.79×10^6 y 8	α
		151	7/2−	−74.187	123.9 d 10	ε, α≈8.0×10^{-7}%
		152	0+	−74.706	1.08×10^{14} y 8	α
					0.20% 1	
		153	3/2−	−72.882	240.4 d 10	ε
		154	0+	−73.705	**2.18%** 3	
		155	3/2−	−72.069	**14.80%** 12	
		155m	11/2−	−71.948	31.97 ms 27	IT
		156	0+	−72.534	**20.47%** 9	
		157	3/2−	−70.823	**15.65%** 2	
		158	0+	−70.689	**24.84%** 7	
		159	3/2−	−68.560	18.479 h 4	β−
		160	0+	−67.940	>3.1×10^{19} y	2β−
					21.86% 19	
		161	5/2−	−65.505	3.66 m 5	β−
		162	0+	−64.279	8.4 m 2	β−
		163	(5/2−,7/2+)	−61.47	68 s 3	β−
		164	0+	−59.9s	45 s 3	β−
		165		−56.6s	10.3 s 16	β−
		166	0+	−54.5s	4.8 s 10	β−
		167		−50.8s		β−?
		168	0+	−48.3s		β−?
		169		−44.2s		β−?
65	**Tb**	135	(7/2−)	−32.6s	0.94 ms +33−22	p
		136		−35.9s		ε?
		137		−40.7s		p?, ε?
		138m		−43.5s	≥200 ns	ε, p
		139		−48.0s	1.6 s 2	ε, εp?
		140	(7+)	−50.5	2.0 s 5	ε, εp 0.26%
		141	(5/2−)	−54.5	3.5 s 2	ε
		141m		−54.5	7.9 s 6	ε
		142	1+	−56.6	597 ms 17	ε, εp 2.2×10^{-3}%
		142m	5−	−56.3	303 ms 17	IT
		143	(11/2−)	−60.42	12 s 1	ε
		143m		−60.42	<21 s	ε
		144	1+	−62.37	≈1 s	ε
		144m	(6−)	−61.97	4.25 s 15	IT 66%, ε 34%
		145		−65.88		ε?
		145m	(11/2−)	−65.88	30.9 s 6	ε
		146	1+	−67.76	8 s 4	ε
		146m	5−	−67.76	23 s 2	ε
		146m	(10+)	−66.98	1.18 ms 2	IT
		147	(1/2+)	−70.742	1.64 h 3	ε
		147m	(11/2−)	−70.691	1.83 m 6	ε
		148	2−	−70.54	60 m 1	ε
		148m	(9)+	−70.45	2.20 m 5	ε
		149	1/2+	−71.489	4.118 h 25	ε 83.3%, α 16.7%
		149m	11/2−	−71.453	4.16 m 4	ε 99.98%, α 0.02%
		150	(2−)	−71.105	3.48 h 16	ε, α<0.05%
		150m	9+	−70.631	5.8 m 2	ε
		151	1/2(+)	−71.622	17.609 h 14	ε 99.99%, α 9.5×10^{-3}%

	Nuclide			Δ	T½, Γ, or	
Z	El	A	Jπ	(MeV)	Abundance	Decay Mode
65	Tb	151m	(11/2−)	−71.522	25 s 3	IT 93.4%, ε 6.6%
		152	2−	−70.72	17.5 h 1	ε, α<7.0×10⁻⁷%
		152m	8+	−70.21	4.2 m 1	IT 78.8%, ε 21.2%
		153	5/2+	−71.313	2.34 d 1	ε
		154	0	−70.15	21.5 h 4	ε, β−<0.1%
		154m	7−	−70.15	22.7 h 5	ε 98.2%, IT 1.8%
		154m	3−	−70.15	9.4 h 4	ε 78.2%, IT 21.8%, β−<0.1%
		155	3/2+	−71.25	5.32 d 6	ε
		156	3−	−70.090	5.35 d 10	ε
		156m	(7−)	−70.040	24.4 h 10	IT
		156m	(0+)	−70.002	5.3 h 2	IT<100%, ε>0%
		157	3/2+	−70.762	71 y 7	ε
		158	3−	−69.469	180 y 11	ε 83.4%, β− 16.6%
		158m	0−	−69.359	10.70 s 17	IT, β−<0.6%, ε<0.01%
		158m	7−	−69.081	0.40 ms 4	IT
		159	3/2+	−69.531	100%	
		160	3−	−67.835	72.3 d 2	β−
		161	3/2+	−67.460	6.89 d 2	β−
		162	1−	−65.67	7.60 m 15	β−
		163	3/2+	−64.594	19.5 m 3	β−
		164	(5+)	−62.1	3.0 m 1	β−
		165	(3/2+)	−60.7s	2.11 m 10	β−
		166	(2−)	−57.88	25.1 s 21	β−
		167	(3/2+)	−55.9s	19.4 s 27	β−
		168	(4−)	−52.6s	8.2 s 13	β−
		169		−50.2s		β−?
		170		−46.5s		β−?
		171		−43.8s		β−?
66	Dy	138	0+	−34.8s		ε?
		139	(7/2+)	−37.6s	0.6 s 2	ε, εp
		140	0+	−42.7s		ε
		141	(9/2−)	−45.2s	0.9 s 2	ε, εp
		142	0+	−49.9s	2.3 s 3	ε, εp 0.06%
		143	(1/2+)	−52.17	5.6 s 10	ε, εp
		143m	(11/2−)	−51.86	3.0 s 3	ε, εp
		144	0+	−56.570	9.1 s 4	ε, εp
		145	(1/2+)	−58.242	6 s 2	ε, εp≈50%
		145m	(11/2−)	−58.124	14.1 s 7	ε, εp≈50%
		146	0+	−62.554	29 s 3	ε
		146m	(10+)	−59.618	150 ms 20	IT
		147	(1/2+)	−64.194	67 s 7	ε, εp 0.05%
		147m	(11/2−)	−63.444	55.2 s 5	ε 68.9%, IT 31.1%
		148	0+	−67.859	3.3 m 2	ε
		149	(7/2−)	−67.702	4.20 m 14	ε
		149m	(27/2−)	−65.041	0.490 s 15	IT 99.3%, ε 0.7%
		150	0+	−69.310	7.17 m 5	ε 64%, α 36%
		151	7/2(−)	−68.752	17.9 m 3	ε 94.4%, α 5.6%
		152	0+	−70.118	2.38 h 2	ε 99.9%, α 0.1%
		153	7/2(−)	−69.142	6.4 h 1	ε 99.99%, α 9.4×10⁻³%

Nuclide Z El A	Jπ	Δ (MeV)	T½, Γ, or Abundance	Decay Mode
66 Dy 154	0+	−70.392	3.0×10⁶ y *15*	α
155	3/2−	−69.15	9.9 h *2*	ε
156	0+	−70.522	**0.056% *3***	
157	3/2−	−69.420	8.14 h *4*	ε
157m	11/2−	−69.221	21.6 ms *16*	IT
158	0+	−70.404	**0.095% *3***	
159	3/2−	−69.166	144.4 d *2*	ε
160	0+	−69.671	**2.329% *18***	
161	5/2+	−68.054	**18.889% *42***	
162	0+	−68.179	**25.475% *36***	
163	5/2−	−66.379	**24.896% *42***	
164	0+	−65.966	**28.260% *54***	
165	7/2+	−63.610	2.334 h *1*	β−
165m	1/2−	−63.502	1.257 m *6*	IT 97.76%, β− 2.24%
166	0+	−62.583	81.6 h *1*	β−
167	(1/2−)	−59.93	6.20 m *8*	β−
168	0+	−58.6	8.7 m *3*	β−
169	(5/2)−	−55.6	39 s *8*	β−
170	0+	−53.7s		β−
171		−50.1s		β−?
172	0+	−47.8s		β−?
173		−43.7s		β−?
67 Ho 140	(6−,0−,8+)	−29.2s	6 ms *3*	p
141	7/2−	−34.3s	4.1 ms *3*	p
142	(7−,8+)	−37.2s	0.4 s *1*	ε , εp>0%
143	(11/2−)	−42.0s		ε?, εp?
144	(5−)	−44.609	0.7 s *1*	ε , εp
145	(11/2−)	−49.120	2.4 s *1*	ε
146	(10+)	−51.238	3.6 s *3*	ε
147	(11/2−)	−55.757	5.8 s *4*	ε
148	(1+)	−57.99	2.2 s *11*	ε
148m	(6)−	−57.99	9.59 s *15*	ε , εp 0.08%
148m	(10+)	−57.30	2.35 ms *4*	IT
149	(11/2−)	−61.66	21.1 s *2*	ε
149m	(1/2+)	−61.62	56 s *3*	ε
150	2−	−61.95	72 s *4*	ε
150m	(9)+	−61.45	24.1 s *5*	ε ,
151	(11/2−)	−63.622	35.2 s *1*	ε 78%, α 22%
151m	(1/2+)	−63.581	47.2 s *13*	α 80%, ε 20%
152	2−	−63.61	161.8 s *3*	ε 88%, α 12%
152m	9+	−63.45	50.0 s *4*	ε 89.2%, α 10.8%
153	11/2−	−65.012	2.01 m *3*	ε 99.95%, α 0.05%
153m	1/2+	−64.943	9.3 m *5*	ε 99.82%, α 0.18%
154	2−	−64.639	11.76 m *19*	ε 99.98%, α 0.02%
154m	8+	−64.639	3.10 m *14*	ε , α< 1.0×10⁻³%
155	5/2+	−66.04	48 m *1*	ε
155m	11/2−	−65.90	0.88 ms *8*	IT
156	4−	−65.47	56 m *1*	ε
156m	1−	−65.42	9.5 s *15*	IT
156m	9+	−65.42	7.8 m *3*	ε 75%, IT 25%
157	7/2−	−66.83	12.6 m *2*	ε
158	5+	−66.18	11.3 m *4*	ε

Nuclide Z El A	Jπ	Δ (MeV)	T½, Γ, or Abundance	Decay Mode
67 Ho 158m	2–	–66.12	28 m 2	IT > 81%, ε < 19%
158m	(9+)	–66.00	21.3 m 23	ε ≥ 93%, IT ≤ 7%
159	7/2–	–67.328	33.05 m 11	ε
159m	1/2+	–67.122	8.30 s 8	IT
160	5+	–66.38	25.6 m 3	ε
160m	2–	–66.32	5.02 h 5	IT 73%, ε 27%
160m	(9+)	–66.21	3 s	IT
161	7/2–	–67.195	2.48 h 5	ε
161m	1/2+	–66.984	6.76 s 7	IT
162	1+	–66.040	15.0 m 10	ε
162m	6–	–65.934	67.0 m 7	IT 62%, ε 38%
163	7/2–	–66.376	4570 y 25	ε
163m	1/2+	–66.078	1.09 s 3	IT
164	1+	–64.980	29 m 1	ε 60%, β– 40%
164m	6–	–64.840	37.5 m +15–5	IT
165	7/2–	–64.897	100%	
166	0–	–63.070	26.824 h 12	β–
166m	7–	–63.064	1.20×10^3 y 18	β–
167	7/2–	–62.279	3.003 h 18	β–
168	3+	–60.06	2.99 m 7	β–
168m	(6+)	–60.00	132 s 4	IT ≥ 99.5%, β– ≤ 0.5%
169	7/2–	–58.80	4.72 m 10	β–
170	(6+)	–56.24	2.76 m 5	β–
170m	(1+)	–56.12	43 s 2	β–
171	(7/2–)	–54.5	53 s 2	β–
172		–51.5s	25 s 3	β–
173		–49.2s		β– ?
174		–45.7s		β– ?
175		–43.1s		β– ?
68 Er 142	0+	–28.1s		
143		–31.2s		ε ?
144	0+	–36.7s	≥ 200 ns	ε
145	(1/2+)	–39.4s		ε ?
145m	(11/2–)	–39.2s	1.0 s 3	ε, εp
146	0+	–44.322	1.7 s 6	ε, εp
147	(1/2+)	–46.61	2.5 s 2	ε, εp > 0%
147m	(11/2–)	–46.61	1.6 s 2	ε, εp > 0%
148	0+	–51.48	4.6 s 2	ε
149	(1/2+)	–53.74	4 s 2	ε, εp 7%
149m	(11/2–)	–53.00	8.9 s 2	ε 96.5%, IT 3.5%, εp 0.18%
150	0+	–57.83	18.5 s 7	ε
151	(7/2–)	–58.26	23.5 s 20	ε
151m	(27/2–)	–55.68	0.58 s 2	IT 95.3%, ε 4.7%
152	0+	–60.500	10.3 s 1	α 90%, ε 10%
153	(7/2–)	–60.475	37.1 s 2	α 53%, ε 47%
154	0+	–62.606	3.73 m 9	ε 99.53%, α 0.47%
155	7/2–	–62.209	5.3 m 3	ε 99.98%, α 0.02%
156	0+	–64.21	19.5 m 10	ε, α 1.7×10^{-5}%
157	3/2–	–63.41	18.65 m 10	ε
157m	(9/2+)	–63.26	76 ms 6	IT
158	0+	–65.30	2.29 h 6	ε

Nuclide				Δ	T½, Γ, or	
Z	El	A	Jπ	(MeV)	Abundance	Decay Mode
68	Er	159	3/2−	−64.560	36 m *1*	ε
		160	0+	−66.06	28.58 h *9*	ε
		161	3/2−	−65.199	3.21 h *3*	ε
		162	0+	−66.332	**0.139%** *5*	
		163	5/2−	−65.166	75.0 m *4*	ε
		164	0+	−65.941	**1.601%** *3*	
		165	5/2−	−64.520	10.36 h *4*	ε
		166	0+	−64.924	**33.503%** *36*	
		167	7/2+	−63.289	**22.869%** *9*	
		167m	1/2−	−63.081	2.269 s *6*	IT
		168	0+	−62.989	**26.978%** *18*	
		169	1/2−	−60.921	9.392 d *18*	β−
		170	0+	−60.108	**14.910%** *36*	
		171	5/2−	−57.718	7.516 h *2*	β−
		172	0+	−56.482	49.3 h *3*	β−
		173	(7/2−)	−53.7s	1.4 m *1*	β−
		174	0+	−51.9s	3.2 m *2*	β−
		175	(9/2+)	−48.7s	1.2 m *3*	β−
		176	0+	−46.6s		β−?
		177		−42.9s		β−?
69	Tm	144	(10+)	−22.2s	1.9 μs +*12−5*	p>0%
		145	(11/2−)	−27.7s	3.17 μs *20*	p
		146	(5−)	−31.2s	80 ms *10*	p, ε
		146m	(8+)	−31.1s	200 ms *10*	p, ε
		147	11/2−	−35.974	0.58 s *3*	ε 85%, p 15%
		147m	3/2+	−35.906	0.36 ms *4*	p
		148m	(10+)	−38.76	0.7 s *2*	ε
		149	(11/2−)	−43.9s	0.9 s *2*	ε, εp 0.2%
		150	(6−)	−46.5s	2.20 s *6*	ε
		150m	(10+)	−45.8s	5.2 ms *3*	IT
		151	(11/2−)	−50.78	4.17 s *11*	ε
		151m	(1/2+)	−50.78	6.6 s *20*	ε
		152	(2)−	−51.77	8.0 s *10*	ε
		152m	(9)+	−51.77	5.2 s *6*	ε
		153	(11/2−)	−53.99	1.48 s *1*	α 91%, ε 9%
		153m	(1/2+)	−53.95	2.5 s *2*	α 92%, ε 8%
		154	(2−)	−54.43	8.1 s *3*	α 54%, ε 46%
		154m	9+	−54.43	3.30 s *7*	α 58%, ε 42%, IT
		155	11/2−	−56.626	21.6 s *2*	ε 99.11%, α 0.89%
		155m	1/2+	−56.585	45 s *3*	ε>98%, α<2%
		156	2−	−56.84	83.8 s *18*	ε 99.94%, α 0.06%
		157	1/2+	−58.71	3.63 m *9*	ε
		158	2−	−58.70	3.98 m *6*	ε
		158m	(5+)	−58.70	≈20 s	ε?
		159	5/2+	−60.57	9.13 m *16*	ε
		160	1−	−60.30	9.4 m *3*	ε
		160m	5	−60.23	74.5 s *15*	IT 85%, ε 15%
		161	7/2+	−61.90	30.2 m *8*	ε
		162	1−	−61.47	21.70 m *19*	ε
		162m	5+	−61.47	24.3 s *17*	IT 81%, ε 19%
		163	1/2+	−62.727	1.810 h *5*	ε
		164	1+	−61.90	2.0 m *1*	ε

Nuclide Z El A	Jπ	Δ (MeV)	T½, Γ, or Abundance	Decay Mode
69 Tm 164m	6–	–61.90	5.1 m *1*	IT ≈ 80%, ε ≈ 20%
165	1/2+	–62.928	30.06 h *3*	ε
166	2+	–61.89	7.70 h *3*	ε
166m	(6–)	–61.78	340 ms *25*	IT
167	1/2+	–62.542	9.25 d *2*	ε
168	3+	–61.312	93.1 d *2*	ε 99.99%, β– 0.01%
169	1/2+	–61.274	**100%**	
170	1–	–59.795	128.6 d *3*	β– 99.87%, ε 0.13%
171	1/2+	–59.210	1.92 y *1*	β–
172	2–	–57.373	63.6 h *2*	β–
173	(1/2+)	–56.253	8.24 h *8*	β–
174	(4)–	–53.86	5.4 m *1*	β–
174m	0+	–53.61	2.29 s *1*	IT 99%, β– < 1%
175	(1/2+)	–52.31	15.2 m *5*	β–
176	(4+)	–49.4	1.9 m *1*	β–
177m	(7/2–)	–47.5s	90 s *6*	β–
178		–44.1s	>300 ns	β–
179		–41.6s		β– ?
70 Yb 148	0+	–30.2s		ε ?
149	(1/2+,3/2+)	–33.2s	0.7 s *2*	ε , εp
150	0+	–38.6s	≥200 ns	ε ?
151	(1/2+)	–41.5	1.6 s *1*	ε , εp > 0%
151m	(11/2–)	–41.5	1.6 s *1*	ε , IT ≈ 0.4%, εp
152	0+	–46.3	3.03 s *6*	ε , εp
153	7/2–	–47.1s	4.2 s *2*	α 60%, ε 40%
154	0+	–49.93	0.409 s *2*	α 92.6%, ε 7.4%
155	(7/2–)	–50.50	1.793 s *19*	α 89%, ε 11%
156	0+	–53.265	26.1 s *7*	ε 90%, α 10%
157	7/2–	–53.43	38.6 s *10*	ε 99.5%, α 0.5%
158	0+	–56.008	1.49 m *13*	α ≈ 2.1×10⁻³%, ε
159	5/2(–)	–55.84	1.67 m *9*	ε
160	0+	–58.16	4.8 m *2*	ε
161	3/2–	–57.84	4.2 m *2*	ε
162	0+	–59.83	18.87 m *19*	ε
163	3/2–	–59.30	11.05 m *35*	ε
164	0+	–61.02	75.8 m *17*	ε
165	5/2–	–60.29	9.9 m *3*	ε
166	0+	–61.594	56.7 h *1*	ε
167	5/2–	–60.588	17.5 m *2*	ε
168	0+	–61.580	**0.123%** *3*	
169	7/2+	–60.376	32.018 d *5*	ε
169m	1/2–	–60.352	46 s *2*	IT
170	0+	–60.763	**2.982%** *39*	
171	1/2–	–59.306	**14.09%** *14*	
171m	7/2+	–59.211	5.25 ms *24*	IT
172	0+	–59.255	**21.68%** *13*	
173	5/2–	–57.551	**16.103%** *63*	
174	0+	–56.944	**32.026%** *80*	
175	(7/2–)	–54.695	4.185 d *1*	β–
175m	1/2–	–54.180	68.2 ms *3*	IT
176	0+	–53.488	**12.996%** *83*	
176m	8–	–52.438	11.4 s *3*	IT

Nuclide				Δ	T½, Γ, or	
Z	El	A	Jπ	(MeV)	Abundance	Decay Mode
70	Yb	177	(9/2+)	−50.983	1.911 h *3*	β−
		177m	(1/2−)	−50.652	6.41 s *2*	IT
		178	0+	−49.69	74 m *3*	β−
		179	(1/2−)	−46.4s	8.0 m *4*	β−
		180	0+	−44.4s	2.4 m *5*	β−
		181		−40.8s		β−?
71	Lu	150	(2+)	−24.6s	45 ms *3*	p 70.9%, ε 29.1%
		151	11/2−	−30.1s	80.6 ms *20*	p 63.4%, ε 36.6%
		152	(4−,5−,6−)	−33.4s	0.7 s *1*	ε , εp 15%
		153	11/2−	−38.4	0.9 s *2*	α≈70%, ε≈30%
		154	(2−)	−39.6s		
		154m	(9+)	−39.6s	1.12 s *8*	ε
		155	11/2−	−42.55	68 ms *1*	α 90%, ε 10%
		155m	1/2+	−42.53	138 ms *8*	α 76%, ε 24%
		155m	(25/2−)	−40.77	2.69 ms *3*	α
		156	(2)−	−43.75	494 ms *12*	α≈95%, ε≈5%
		156m	9+	−43.75	198 ms *2*	α
		157	(1/2+,3/2+)	−46.46	6.8 s *18*	α>0%
		157m	(11/2−)	−46.43	4.79 s *12*	ε 94%, α 6%
		158		−47.21	10.6 s *3*	ε 99.09%, α 0.91%
		159		−49.71	12.1 s *10*	ε , α 0.1%
		160		−50.27	36.1 s *3*	ε , α≤1.0×10⁻⁴%
		160m		−50.27	40 s *1*	ε≤100%, α
		161	1/2+	−52.56	77 s *2*	ε
		161m	(9/2−)	−52.40	7.3 ms *4*	IT
		162	1−	−52.84	1.37 m *2*	ε≤100%
		162m		−52.84	1.9 m	ε≤100%
		162m	(4−)	−52.84	1.5 m	ε≤100%
		163	1/2(+)	−54.79	3.97 m *13*	ε
		164	1(−)	−54.64	3.14 m *3*	ε
		165	1/2+	−56.44	10.74 m *10*	ε
		166	6−	−56.02	2.65 m *10*	ε
		166m	3(−)	−55.99	1.41 m *10*	ε 58%, IT 42%
		166m	0−	−55.98	2.12 m *10*	ε>80%, IT<20%
		167	7/2+	−57.50	51.5 m *10*	ε
		167m	1/2+	−57.50	≥1 m	ε , IT
		168	6(−)	−57.07	5.5 m *1*	ε
		168m	3+	−56.87	6.7 m *4*	ε>99.6%, IT<0.8%
		169	7/2+	−58.083	34.06 h *5*	ε
		169m	1/2−	−58.054	160 s *10*	IT
		170	0+	−57.30	2.012 d *20*	ε
		170m	(4)−	−57.21	0.67 s *10*	IT
		171	7/2+	−57.828	8.24 d *3*	ε
		171m	1/2−	−57.757	79 s *2*	IT
		172	4−	−56.736	6.70 d *3*	ε
		172m	1−	−56.694	3.7 m *5*	IT
		173	7/2+	−56.881	1.37 y *1*	ε
		174	(1)−	−55.570	3.31 y *5*	ε
		174m	(6)−	−55.399	142 d *2*	IT 99.38%, ε 0.62%
		175	7/2+	−55.166	**97.401% *13***	
		176	7−	−53.382	3.76×10¹⁰ y *7* **2.599% *13***	β−

Nuclide				Δ	T½, Γ, or	
Z	El	A	Jπ	(MeV)	Abundance	Decay Mode
71	Lu	176m	1–	–53.259	3.664 h *19*	β– 99.9%, ε 0.09%
		177	7/2+	–52.384	6.647 d *4*	β–
		177m	23/2–	–51.414	160.44 d *6*	β– 78.6%, IT 21.4%
		177m	(39/2–)	–49.644	6 m +*3*–*2*	β–, IT?
		178	1(+)	–50.338	28.4 m *2*	β–
		178m	(9–)	–50.214	23.1 m *3*	β–
		179	7/2+	–49.059	4.59 h *6*	β–
		179m	1/2+	–48.467	3.1 ms *9*	IT
		180	5+	–46.68	5.7 m *1*	β–
		181	(7/2+)	–44.7s	3.5 m *3*	β–
		182		–41.9s	2.0 m *2*	β–
		183	(7/2+)	–39.5s	58 s *4*	β–
		184	(3+)	–36.4s	19 s *2*	β–
72	Hf	153		–27.3s	>60 ns	ε?
		154	0+	–32.7s	2 s *1*	ε, α?
		155		–34.1s	0.84 s *3*	ε
		156	0+	–37.9	23 ms *1*	α
		156m	8+	–35.9	0.52 ms *1*	α
		157	7/2–	–38.8s	110 ms *6*	α 86%, ε 14%
		158	0+	–42.10	2.85 s *7*	ε 55.7%, α 44.3%
		159	7/2–	–42.85	5.6 s *4*	ε 65%, α 35%
		160	0+	–45.938	13.6 s *2*	ε 99.3%, α 0.7%
		161		–46.32	18.2 s *5*	ε >99.87%, α <0.13%
		162	0+	–49.166	39.4 s *9*	ε 99.99%, α 8.0×10⁻³%
		163		–49.29	40.0 s *6*	ε, α <1.0×10⁻⁴%
		164	0+	–51.83	111 s *8*	ε
		165	(5/2–)	–51.63	76 s *4*	ε
		166	0+	–53.86	6.77 m *30*	ε
		167	(5/2)–	–53.47	2.05 m *5*	ε
		168	0+	–55.36	25.95 m *20*	ε
		169	5/2–	–54.72	3.24 m *4*	ε
		170	0+	–56.25	16.01 h *13*	ε
		171	7/2+	–55.43	12.1 h *4*	ε
		171m	1/2–	–55.41	29.5 s *9*	IT ≤100%, ε
		172	0+	–56.40	1.87 y *3*	ε
		173	1/2–	–55.41	23.6 h *1*	ε
		174	0+	–55.845	2.0×10¹⁵ y *4* 0.16% *1*	α
		175	5/2(–)	–54.482	70 d *2*	ε
		176	0+	–54.576	**5.26% *7***	
		177	7/2–	–52.885	**18.60% *9***	
		177m	23/2+	–51.569	1.09 s *5*	IT
		177m	37/2–	–50.145	51.4 m *5*	IT
		178	0+	–52.439	**27.28% *7***	
		178m	8–	–51.292	4.0 s *2*	IT
		178m	16+	–49.993	31 y *1*	IT
		179	9/2+	–50.467	**13.62% *2***	
		179m	1/2–	–50.092	18.67 s *4*	IT
		179m	25/2–	–49.361	25.05 d *25*	IT
		180	0+	–49.783	**35.08% *16***	
		180m	8–	–48.641	5.47 h *4*	IT 99.7%, β– 0.3%

Nuclide Z El A	Jπ	Δ (MeV)	T½, Γ, or Abundance	Decay Mode
72 Hf 181	1/2−	−47.407	42.39 d *6*	β−
181m	(25/2−)	−45.665	1.5 ms *5*	IT
182	0+	−46.053	8.90×10⁶ y *9*	β−
182m	(8−)	−44.880	61.5 m *15*	β− 54%, IT 46%
183	(3/2−)	−43.29	1.018 h *2*	β−
184	0+	−41.50	4.12 h *5*	β−
184m	(8−)	−40.23	48 s *10*	IT
185		−38.4s	3.5 m *6*	β−
186	0+	−36.4s	2.6 m *12*	β−
187m		−32.8s	0.27 µs *8*	β−
188	0+	−30.9s		β−
189				
73 Ta 155m	11/2−	−24.0s	2.9 ms +*15−11*	p
156	(2−)	−25.8s	144 ms *24*	p, ε
156m	9+	−25.7s	0.36 s *4*	ε 95.8%, p 4.2%
157	1/2+	−29.6	10.1 ms *4*	α 96.6%, p 3.4%
157m	11/2−	−29.6	4.3 ms *1*	α
157m	(25/2−)	−28.0	1.7 ms *1*	α
158	(2−)	−31.0s	55 ms *15*	α≈91%, ε≈9%
158m	(9+)	−30.9s	36.7 ms *15*	α 95%, ε 5%
159	1/2+	−34.44	0.83 s *18*	ε 66%, α 34%
159m	11/2−	−34.38	0.56 s *6*	α 55%, ε 45%
160		−35.87	1.55 s *4*	ε 66%, α 34%
160m		−35.87	1.7 s *2*	
161	(1/2+)	−38.71		ε, α
161m	(11/2−)	−38.71	3.08 s *11*	ε, α
162		−39.78	3.57 s *12*	ε 99.93%, α 0.07%
163		−42.54	10.6 s *18*	ε≈99.8%, α≈0.2%
164	(3+)	−43.28	14.2 s *3*	ε
165		−45.85	31.0 s *15*	ε
166	(2)+	−46.10	34.4 s *5*	ε
167	(3/2+)	−48.35	80 s *4*	ε
168	(2−,3+)	−48.39	2.0 m *1*	ε
169	(5/2+)	−50.29	4.9 m *4*	ε
170	(3+)	−50.14	6.76 m *6*	ε
171	(5/2−)	−51.72	23.3 m *3*	ε
172	(3+)	−51.33	36.8 m *3*	ε
173	5/2−	−52.40	3.14 h *13*	ε
174	3+	−51.74	1.14 h *8*	ε
175	7/2+	−52.41	10.5 h *2*	ε
176	(1)−	−51.37	8.09 h *5*	ε
177	7/2+	−51.719	56.56 h *6*	ε
178m	(1+)	−50.50	9.31 m *3*	ε
178m	7−	−50.50	2.36 h *8*	ε
178m	15−	−49.03	58 ms *4*	IT
178m	(21−)	−47.60	290 ms *12*	IT
179	7/2+	−50.361	1.82 y *3*	ε
179m	(25/2+)	−49.044	9.0 ms *2*	IT
179m	(37/2+)	−47.722	54.1 ms *17*	IT
180	1+	−48.936	8.154 h *6*	ε 86%, β− 14%
180m	9−	−48.859	>1.2×10¹⁵ y	ε ?
			0.01201% *32*	

Nuclide Z	El	A	Jπ	Δ (MeV)	T½, Γ, or Abundance	Decay Mode
73	Ta	180m	9–	−48.859	>1.2×10^{15} y	β–?
					0.01201% *32*	
		181	7/2+	−48.441	99.98799% *32*	
		182	3–	−46.433	114.74 d *12*	β–
		182m	5+	−46.417	283 ms *3*	IT
		182m	10–	−45.913	15.84 m *10*	IT
		183	7/2+	−45.296	5.1 d *1*	β–
		184	(5–)	−42.84	8.7 h *1*	β–
		185	(7/2+)	−41.40	49.4 m *15*	β–
		185m	(21/2)	−40.14	>1 ms	
		186	(2–,3–)	−38.61	10.5 m *3*	β–
		186m		−38.61	1.54 m *5*	β–
		187	(7/2+)	−36.8s	2.3 m *6*	β–
		187m	(27/2–)	−35.0s	22 s *9*	β–?, IT?
		187m	(41/2+)	−33.8s	>5 m	β–?, IT?
		188		−33.7s	19.6 s *20*	β–
		189?		−31.8s	1.6 μs *2*	β–?
		190		−28.7s	5.3 s *7*	β–
		191		−26.5s	>300 ns	β–?
		192	(1,2)	−23.1s	2.2 s *7*	β–
74	W	157	(7/2–)	−19.3s	275 ms *40*	ε
		158	0+	−23.7s	1.25 ms *21*	α
		158m	(8+)	−21.8s	0.143 ms *19*	IT, α
		159		−25.2s	7.3 ms *27*	α≈99.9%, ε≈0.1%
		160	0+	−29.4	91 ms *5*	α 87%
		161		−30.4s	409 ms *18*	α 73%, ε 27%
		162	0+	−34.00	1.36 s *7*	ε 54.8%, α 45.2%
		163	7/2–	−34.91	2.67 s *10*	ε 86%, α 14%
		164	0+	−38.235	6.3 s *2*	ε 96.2%, α 3.8%
		165	(5/2–)	−38.86	5.1 s *5*	ε, α<0.2%
		166	0+	−41.88	19.2 s *6*	ε 99.96%, α 0.04%
		167	(+)	−42.09	19.9 s *5*	ε 99.96%, α 0.04%
		168	0+	−44.90	50.9 s *19*	ε, α 3.2×10^{-3}%
		169	(5/2–)	−44.92	74 s *6*	ε
		170	0+	−47.29	2.42 m *4*	ε
		171	(5/2–)	−47.09	2.38 m *4*	ε
		172	0+	−49.10	6.6 m *9*	ε
		173	5/2–	−48.73	7.6 m *2*	ε
		174	0+	−50.23	33.2 m *21*	ε
		175	(1/2–)	−49.63	35.2 m *6*	ε
		176	0+	−50.64	2.5 h *1*	ε
		177	1/2–	−49.70	132 m *2*	ε
		178	0+	−50.41	21.6 d *3*	ε
		179	7/2–	−49.29	37.05 m *16*	ε
		179m	1/2–	−49.07	6.40 m *7*	IT 99.71%, ε 0.29%
		180	0+	−49.636	≥6.6×10^{17} y	2ε
					0.12% *1*	
		181	9/2+	−48.253	121.2 d *2*	ε
		182	0+	−48.247	26.50% *16*	
		183	1/2–	−46.367	>1.3×10^{19} y	α
					14.31% *4*	
		183m	11/2+	−46.057	5.2 s *3*	IT

Nuclide Z El A	Jπ	Δ (MeV)	T½, Γ, or Abundance	Decay Mode
74 W 184	0+	−45.707	**30.64% 2**	
185	3/2−	−43.389	75.1 d 3	β−
185m	11/2+	−43.192	1.67 m 3	IT
186	0+	−42.510	>2.3×10¹⁹ y	2β−
			28.43% 19	
186m	(16+)	−38.967	>3 ms	IT
187	3/2−	−39.906	24.000 h 4	β−
188	0+	−38.669	69.78 d 5	β−
189	(3/2−)	−35.5	10.7 m 5	β−
190	0+	−34.3	30.0 m 15	β−
190m	(10−)	−31.9	≤3.1 ms	IT
191		−31.1s	>300 ns	β−?
192	0+	−29.6s		β−?
193		−26.2s	>300 ns	β−?
194	0+	−24.4s	>300 ns	β−?
75 Re 159	(1/2+)	−14.8s		
160	(2−)	−16.7s	0.82 ms +15−9	p 91%, α 9%
161	1/2+	−20.9	0.44 ms 1	p, α≤1.4%
161m	11/2−	−20.8	14.7 ms 3	α 93%, p 7%
162	(2−)	−22.4s	107 ms 13	α 94%, ε 6%
162m	(9+)	−22.2s	77 ms 9	α 91%, ε 9%
163	1/2+	−26.01	390 ms 72	ε 68%, α 32%
163m	11/2−	−25.89	214 ms 5	α 66%, ε 34%
164		−27.52	0.85 s +14−11	α≈58%, ε≈42%
164m		−27.45	0.86 s +15−11	IT, α≈3%
165	(1/2+)	−30.65	≈1 s	α, ε
165m	(11/2−)	−30.60	2.1 s 3	ε 87%, α 13%
166		−31.89	2.25 s 21	ε>76%, α<24%
167	(9/2−)	−34.84s	5.9 s 3	ε≈99%, α≈1%
167m		−34.84s	3.4 s 4	α
168	(7+)	−35.79	4.4 s 1	ε, α≈5.0×10⁻³%
169	(9/2−)	−38.41	8.1 s 5	ε, α<0.01%
169m	(5/2+,3/2+)	−38.41	15.1 s 15	ε, IT, α≈0.2%
170	(5+)	−38.92	9.2 s 2	ε
171	(9/2−)	−41.25	15.2 s 4	ε
172m	(2)	−41.52	55 s 5	ε
172m	(5)	−41.52	15 s 3	ε
173	(5/2−)	−43.55	1.98 m 26	ε
174	(≤ 4)	−43.67	2.40 m 4	ε
175	(5/2−)	−45.29	5.89 m 5	ε
176	(3+)	−45.06	5.3 m 3	ε
177	5/2−	−46.27	14 m 1	ε
178	(3+)	−45.65	13.2 m 2	ε
179	5/2+	−46.58	19.5 m 1	ε
179m	47/2,49/2+	−41.18	0.466 ms 15	IT
180	(1)−	−45.84	2.44 m 6	ε
181	5/2+	−46.52	19.9 h 7	ε
182	7+	−45.4	64.0 h 5	ε
182m	2+	−45.4	12.7 h 2	ε
183	5/2+	−45.811	70.0 d 14	ε
183m	(25/2)+	−43.903	1.04 ms 4	IT
184	3(−)	−44.224	35.4 d 7	ε

Nuclide				Δ	T½, Γ, or	
Z	**El**	**A**	**Jπ**	**(MeV)**	**Abundance**	**Decay Mode**
75	**Re**	184m	8(+)	−44.036	169 d *8*	IT 74.5%, ε 25.5%
		185	5/2+	−43.822	**37.40% *2***	
		186	1−	−41.930	3.7186 d *5*	β− 92.53%, ε 7.47%
		186m	(8+)	−41.781	2.0×10⁵ y	IT
		187	5/2+	−41.218	4.33×10¹⁰ y *7*	β−,
					62.60% *2*	α<1.0×10⁻⁴%
		188	1−	−39.018	17.003 h *3*	β−
		188m	(6)−	−38.846	18.59 m *4*	IT
		189	5/2+	−37.980	24.3 h *4*	β−
		190	(2)−	−35.6	3.1 m *3*	β−
		190m	(6−)	−35.4	3.2 h *2*	β− 54.4%, IT 45.6%
		191	(3/2+,1/2+)	−34.35	9.8 m *5*	β−
		192		−31.8s	16 s *1*	β−
		193?		−30.2s		
		194m		−27.4s	5 s *1*	β−
		194m		−27.4s	25 s *8*	β−
		194m		−27.4s	100 s *10*	β−
		195		−25.6s	6 s *1*	β−
		196		−22.5s	3 s +*1*−*2*	β−
		198				
76	**Os**	161	(7/2−)	−9.9s	0.64 ms *6*	α
		162	0+	−14.5s	2.1 ms *1*	α≈99%
		163	(7/2−)	−16.1s	5.5 ms *6*	α, ε
		164	0+	−20.5	21 ms *1*	α 98%, ε 2%
		165	(7/2−)	−21.6s	71 ms *3*	α>60%, ε<40%
		166	0+	−25.44	199 ms *3*	α 72%, ε 18%
		167	(7/2−)	−26.50	0.81 s *6*	α 57%, ε 43%
		168	0+	−29.992	2.1 s *1*	ε 57%, α 43%
		169	(5/2−)	−30.72	3.43 s *14*	ε 86.3%, α 13.7%
		170	0+	−33.92	7.37 s *18*	ε 90.5%, α 9.5%
		171	(5/2−)	−34.29	8.3 s *2*	ε 98.2%, α 1.8%
		172	0+	−37.24	19.2 s *9*	ε 99.8%, α 0.2%
		173	(5/2−)	−37.44	22.4 s *9*	ε, α 0.4%
		174	0+	−40.00	44 s *4*	ε 99.98%, α 0.02%
		175	(5/2−)	−40.11	1.4 m *1*	ε
		176	0+	−42.10	3.6 m *5*	ε
		177	1/2−	−41.95	3.0 m *2*	ε
		178	0+	−43.55	5.0 m *4*	ε, α
		179	1/2−	−43.02	6.5 m *3*	ε
		180	0+	−44.35	21.5 m *4*	ε
		181	1/2−	−43.55	105 m *3*	ε
		181m	7/2−	−43.50	2.7 m *1*	ε, IT≤3%
		182	0+	−44.61	21.84 h *20*	ε
		182m	(8)−	−42.78	0.78 ms *7*	IT
		183	9/2+	−43.66	13.0 h *5*	ε
		183m	1/2−	−43.49	9.9 h *3*	ε 85%, IT 15%
		184	0+	−44.256	>5.6×10¹³ y	α
					0.02% *1*	
		185	1/2−	−42.809	93.6 d *5*	ε
		186	0+	−43.002	2.0×10¹⁵ y *11*	α
					1.59% *3*	
		187	1/2−	−41.220	**1.96% *2***	

Nuclide Z El A	Jπ	Δ (MeV)	T½, Γ, or Abundance	Decay Mode
76 Os 188	0+	−41.139	**13.24%** *8*	
189	3/2−	−38.988	**16.15%** *5*	
189m	9/2−	−38.957	5.81 h *6*	IT
190	0+	−38.709	**26.26%** *2*	
190m	(10)−	−37.004	9.9 m *1*	IT
191	9/2−	−36.396	15.4 d *1*	β−
191m	3/2−	−36.322	13.10 h *5*	IT
192	0+	−35.883	**40.78%** *19*	
192m	(10−)	−33.868	5.9 s *1*	IT>87%, β−<13%
193	3/2−	−33.395	30.11 h *1*	β−
194	0+	−32.437	6.0 y *2*	β−
195		−29.7	≈9 m	β−
196	0+	−28.28	34.9 m *2*	β−
197		−25.3s	2.8 m *6*	β−
198	0+	−23.8s		β−
199		−20.5s	5 s +*4−2*	β−
200	0+	−18.9s	6 s +*4−3*	β−
201			>300 ns	β−?
202	0+		>300 ns	β−?
77 Ir 164m	(9+)	−7.3s	94 μs *27*	p>0%, α, ε
165	(1/2+)	−11.6s	<1 μs	p?, α?
165m	11/2−	−11.4s	0.30 ms *6*	p 87%, α 13%
166	(2−)	−13.2s	10.5 ms *22*	α 93%, p 7%
166m	(9+)	−13.0s	15.1 ms *9*	α 98.2%, p 1.8%
167	1/2+	−17.08	35.2 ms *20*	α 48%, p 32%, ε 20%
167m	11/2−	−16.90	25.7 ms *8*	α 80%, ε 20%, p 0.4%
168		−18.72	222 ms +*60−40*	α≤100%, ε, p
168m		−18.72	159 ms +*16−13*	α 77%, ε≤23%, p
169	(1/2+)	−22.08	0.353 s *4*	α 45%, ε, p
169m	(11/2−)	−21.93	0.281 s *4*	α 72%, ε, p
170	(3−)	−23.36s	0.87 s +*18−12*	ε 94.8%, α 5.2%
170m	(8+)	−23.36s	811 ms *18*	IT≤62%, ε≤62%, α 38%
171	(1/2+)	−26.43	3.2 s +*13−7*	α>0%, p, ε
171m	(11/2−)	−26.43	1.40 s *10*	α 58%, p≤42%, ε≤42%
172	(3+)	−27.38	4.4 s *3*	ε 98%, α≈2%
172m	(7+)	−27.24	2.0 s *1*	ε 77%, α 23%
173	(3/2+,5/2+)	−30.27	9.0 s *8*	ε>93%, α<7%
173m	(11/2−)	−30.04	2.4 s *9*	ε, α 7%
174	(3+)	−30.87	7.9 s *6*	ε 99.5%, α 0.5%
174m	(7+)	−30.67	4.9 s *3*	ε 97.5%, α 2.5%
175	(5/2−)	−33.39	9 s *2*	ε 99.15%, α 0.85%
176		−33.86	8.7 s *5*	ε 96.9%, α 3.1%
177	5/2−	−36.05	30 s *2*	ε 99.94%, α 0.06%
178		−36.25	12 s *2*	ε
179	(5/2)−	−38.08	79 s *1*	ε
180	(4,5)	−37.98	1.5 m *1*	ε
181	5/2−	−39.47	4.90 m *15*	ε
182	3+	−39.05	15 m *1*	ε
183	5/2−	−40.20	57 m *4*	ε
184	5−	−39.61	3.09 h *3*	ε

Nuclide Z El A	Jπ	Δ (MeV)	T½, Γ, or Abundance	Decay Mode
77 Ir 185	5/2–	–40.33	14.4 h *1*	ε
186	5+	–39.17	16.64 h *3*	ε
186m	2–	–39.17	1.90 h *5*	ε ≈ 75%, IT ≈ 25%
187	3/2+	–39.532	10.5 h *3*	ε
187m	9/2–	–39.346	30.3 ms *6*	IT
188	1–	–38.351	41.5 h *5*	ε
188m		–37.428	4.2 ms *2*	ε ?, IT
189	3/2+	–38.46	13.2 d *1*	ε
189m	11/2–	–38.08	13.3 ms *3*	IT
189m	(25/2)+	–36.12	3.7 ms *2*	IT
190	4–	–36.755	11.78 d *10*	ε
190m	(1–)	–36.729	1.120 h *3*	IT
190m	(11)–	–36.379	3.087 h *12*	ε 91.4%, IT 8.6%
191	3/2+	–36.710	**37.3%** *2*	
191m	11/2–	–36.539	4.899 s *23*	IT
191m		–34.663	5.5 s *7*	IT
192	4+	–34.837	73.829 d *11*	β– 95.24%, ε 4.76%
192m	1–	–34.780	1.45 m *5*	IT 99.98%, β– 0.02%
192m	(11–)	–34.669	241 y *9*	IT
193	3/2+	–34.538	**62.7%** *2*	
193m	11/2–	–34.458	10.53 d *4*	IT
194	1–	–32.533	19.28 h *13*	β–
194m	4+	–32.386	31.85 ms *24*	IT
194m	(10,11)	–32.343	171 d *11*	β–
195	3/2+	–31.694	2.5 h *2*	β–
195m	11/2–	–31.594	3.8 h *2*	β– 95%, IT 5%
196	(0–)	–29.44	52 s *1*	β–
196m	(10,11–)	–29.03	1.40 h *2*	β–, IT < 0.3%
197	3/2+	–28.26	5.8 m *5*	β–
197m	11/2–	–28.15	8.9 m *3*	β– 99.75%, IT 0.25%
198		–25.8s	8 s *1*	β–
199		–24.40	6 s +*5*–*4*	β–
200		–21.6s	>300 ns	β–
201		–19.9s	>300 ns	β–
202	(1–,2–)	–17.0s	11 s *3*	β–
203			>300 ns	β– ?
204				
78 Pt 166	0+	–4.8s	300 μs *100*	α
167		–6.5s	0.9 ms *3*	α
168	0+	–11.0	2.02 ms *10*	α
169	(7/2–)	–12.4s	7.0 ms *2*	α
170	0+	–16.30	13.8 ms *5*	α 98%, ε
171	(7/2–)	–17.47	45.5 ms *25*	α 90%, ε 10%
172	0+	–21.10	97.6 ms *13*	α 94%, ε 6%
173	(5/2–)	–21.94	382 ms *2*	α, ε ?
174	0+	–25.31	0.889 s *17*	α 76%, ε 24%
175	7/2–	–25.69	2.53 s *6*	α 64%, ε 36%
176	0+	–28.93	6.33 s *15*	ε 60%, α 40%
177	5/2–	–29.37	10.6 s *4*	ε 94.3%, α 5.7%
178	0+	–32.00	20.7 s *7*	ε 92.3%, α 7.7%
179	1/2–	–32.270	21.2 s *4*	ε 99.76%, α 0.24%
180	0+	–34.44	56 s *2*	ε, α ≈ 0.3%

Nuclide Z El A	Jπ	Δ (MeV)	T½, Γ, or Abundance	Decay Mode
78 Pt 181	1/2–	–34.37	52.0 s *22*	ε, α≈0.08%
182	0+	–36.17	2.67 m *12*	ε 99.96%, α 0.04%
183	1/2–	–35.77	6.5 m *10*	ε, α≈1.3×10⁻³%
183m	(7/2)–	–35.74	43 s *5*	ε, α<4.0×10⁻⁴%, IT
184	0+	–37.33	17.3 m *2*	ε, α≈1.0×10⁻³%
184m	8–	–35.49	1.01 ms *5*	IT
185	9/2+	–36.68	70.9 m *24*	ε<100%
185m	1/2–	–36.58	33.0 m *8*	ε 99%, IT<2%
186	0+	–37.86	2.08 h *5*	ε, α≈1.4×10⁻⁴%
187	3/2–	–36.71	2.35 h *3*	ε
188	0+	–37.828	10.2 d *3*	ε, α 2.6×10⁻⁵%
189	3/2–	–36.49	10.87 h *12*	ε
190	0+	–37.325	6.5×10¹¹ y *3* 0.012% *2*	α
191	3/2–	–35.701	2.83 d *2*	ε
192	0+	–36.292	**0.782%** *24*	
193	1/2–	–34.481	50 y *6*	ε
193m	13/2+	–34.331	4.33 d *3*	IT
194	0+	–34.762	**32.86%** *40*	
195	1/2–	–32.796	**33.78%** *24*	
195m	13/2+	–32.537	4.010 d *5*	IT
196	0+	–32.646	**25.21%** *34*	
197	1/2–	–30.421	19.8915 h *19*	β–
197m	13/2+	–30.021	95.41 m *18*	IT 96.7%, β– 3.3%
198	0+	–29.905	**7.36%** *13*	
199	5/2–	–27.390	30.80 m *21*	β–
199m	(13/2)+	–26.966	13.6 s *4*	IT
200	0+	–26.60	12.6 h *3*	β–
201	(5/2–)	–23.74	2.5 m *1*	β–
202	0+	–22.6s	44 h *15*	β–
202m	(7–)	–20.8s	0.28 ms +*42–19*	IT
203	(1/2–)	–19.7s	10 s *3*	β–
204	0+	–18.1s	10.3 s *14*	β–
205		–12.8s	>300 ns	β–
79 Au 169		–1.8s		p?, α?
170	(2–)	–3.6s	286 μs +*50–40*	p 89%, α 11%
170m	(9+)	–3.6s	617 μs +*50–40*	p 58%, α 42%
171	(1/2+)	–7.57	17 μs +*9–5*	p, α
171m	(11/2–)	–7.32	1.02 ms *10*	α 54%, p 46%
172		–9.37	22 ms +*6–4*	α, ε, p
172m		–9.37	7.7 ms *14*	α, p<0.02%, ε
173	(1/2+)	–12.82	25 ms *1*	α 94%, ε, p
173m	(11/2–)	–12.61	14.0 ms *9*	α 92%, p, ε
174		–14.24s	139 ms *3*	α>0%
175	(1/2+)	–17.44		ε?, α?
175m	(11/2–)	–17.44	156 ms *5*	α 94%, ε 6%
176		–18.40		
176m	(3–)	–18.40	1.05 s *1*	ε, α
176m	(9+)	–18.40	1.36 s *2*	
177	(1/2+,3/2+)	–21.55	1.53 s *7*	α 40%, ε
177m	11/2–	–21.39	1.00 s *20*	α 66%, ε
178		–22.33	2.6 s *5*	ε≤60%, α≥40%

Nuclide Z El A	Jπ	Δ (MeV)	T½, Γ, or Abundance	Decay Mode
79 Au 179	(1/2+,3/2+)	−24.98	7.1 s *3*	ε 78%, α 22%
180		−25.60	8.1 s *3*	ε ≤ 98.2%, α ≥ 1.8%
181	(3/2−)	−27.87	13.7 s *14*	ε 97.3%, α 2.7%
182	(2+)	−28.30	15.5 s *4*	ε 99.87%, α 0.13%
183	(5/2)−	−30.19	42.8 s *10*	ε 99.45%, α 0.55%
184	5+	−30.32	20.6 s *9*	ε , α ≤ 0.02%
184m	2+	−30.25	47.6 s *14*	ε 70%, IT 30%, α ≤ 0.02%
185	5/2−	−31.87	4.25 m *6*	ε 99.74%, α 0.26%
185m		−31.87	6.8 m *3*	ε < 100%, IT
186	3−	−31.71	10.7 m *5*	ε , α 8.0×10⁻⁴%
187	1/2(+)	−33.01	8.3 m *2*	ε , α 3.0×10⁻³%
187m	9/2(−)	−32.88	2.3 s *1*	IT
188	1(−)	−32.30	8.84 m *6*	ε
189	1/2+	−33.58	28.7 m *3*	ε , α < 3.0×10⁻⁵%
189m	11/2−	−33.33	4.59 m *11*	ε
190	1−	−32.88	42.8 m *10*	ε , α < 1.0×10⁻⁶%
190m	(11−)	−32.88	125 ms *20*	IT
191	3/2+	−33.81	3.18 h *8*	ε
191m	(11/2−)	−33.54	0.92 s *11*	IT
192	1−	−32.78	4.94 h *9*	ε
192m	(5)+	−32.64	29 ms	IT
192m	(11−)	−32.34	160 ms *20*	IT
193	3/2+	−33.405	17.65 h *15*	ε
193m	11/2−	−33.115	3.9 s *3*	IT 99.97%, ε ≈ 0.03%
194	1−	−32.26	38.02 h *10*	ε
194m	(5+)	−32.15	600 ms *8*	IT
194m	(11−)	−31.79	420 ms *10*	IT
195	3/2+	−32.569	186.098 d *47*	ε
195m	11/2−	−32.250	30.5 s *2*	IT
196	2−	−31.139	6.1669 d *6*	ε 93%, β− 7%
196m	5+	−31.054	8.1 s *2*	IT
196m	12−	−30.543	9.6 h *1*	IT
197	3/2+	−31.140	100%	
197m	11/2−	−30.731	7.73 s *6*	IT
198	2−	−29.581	2.6948 d *12*	β−
198m	(12−)	−28.769	2.272 d *16*	IT
199	3/2+	−29.094	3.139 d *7*	β−
199m	(11/2)−	−28.545	0.44 ms *3*	IT
200	(1−)	−27.27	48.4 m *3*	β−
200m	12−	−26.31	18.7 h *5*	β− 84%, IT 16%
201	3/2+	−26.401	26.0 m *8*	β−
202	(1−)	−24.4	28.4 s *12*	β−
203	3/2+	−23.143	60 s *6*	β−
204	(2−)	−20.8s	39.8 s *9*	β−
205	(3/2+)	−18.9s	32.5 s *14*	β−
205m	(11/2−)	−18.0s	6 s *2*	β− , IT
206		−14.3s	>300 ns	β−
207		−10.8s	>300 ns	β− , β−n
208		−6.1s	>300 ns	β− , β−n
209		−2.5s	>300 ns	β− , β−n
210		2.3s	>300 ns	β− , β−n

Nuclide Z El A	Jπ	Δ (MeV)	T½, Γ, or Abundance	Decay Mode
80 Hg 171		3.5s	59 μs +36−16	α
172	0+	−1.1	231 μs 9	α
173		−2.6s	0.6 ms +5−2	α
174	0+	−6.65	2.1 ms +18−7	α 99.6%
175	(7/2−)	−7.97	10.6 ms 4	α
176	0+	−11.78	20.3 ms 14	α 94%
177	(7/2−)	−12.78	118 ms 8	α
178	0+	−16.31	266.5 ms 24	α≈70%, ε≈30%
179	(7/2−)	−16.92	1.05 s 3	α 55%, ε 45%, εp≈0.15%
180	0+	−20.25	2.58 s 1	ε 52%, α 48%
181	1/2−	−20.66	3.6 s 1	ε 73%, α 27%, εp 0.01%, εα 9.0×10⁻⁶%
182	0+	−23.576	10.83 s 6	ε 84.8%, α 15.2%
183	1/2−	−23.806	9.4 s 7	ε 88.3%, α 11.7%, εp 2.6×10⁻⁴%
184	0+	−26.35	30.87 s 26	ε 98.89%, α 1.11%
185	1/2−	−26.17	49.1 s 10	ε 94%, α 6%
185m	13/2+	−26.08	21.6 s 15	IT 54%, ε 46%, α≈0.03%
186	0+	−28.54	1.38 m 6	ε 99.98%, α 0.02%
187	3/2(−)	−28.12	2.4 m 3	ε, α<3.7×10⁻⁴%
187m	13/2(+)	−28.12	1.9 m 3	ε, α<3.7×10⁻⁴%
188	0+	−30.20	3.25 m 15	ε, α 3.7×10⁻⁵%
189	3/2−	−29.63	7.6 m 1	ε, α<3.0×10⁻⁵%
189m	13/2+	−29.63	8.6 m 1	ε, α<3.0×10⁻⁵%
190	0+	−31.37	20.0 m 5	ε, α<3.4×10⁻⁷%
191	3/2(−)	−30.59	49 m 10	ε, α 5.0×10⁻⁶%
191m	13/2(+)	−30.59	50.8 m 15	ε
192	0+	−32.01	4.85 h 20	ε
193	3/2(−)	−31.06	3.80 h 15	ε
193m	13/2(+)	−30.92	11.8 h 2	ε 92.8%, IT 7.2%
194	0+	−32.19	444 y 77	ε
195	1/2−	−31.00	10.53 h 3	ε
195m	13/2+	−30.82	41.6 h 8	IT 54.2%, ε 45.8%
196	0+	−31.826	0.15% 1	
197	1/2−	−30.540	64.14 h 5	ε
197m	13/2+	−30.241	23.8 h 1	IT 91.4%, ε 8.6%
198	0+	−30.954	9.97% 20	
199	1/2−	−29.546	16.87% 22	
199m	13/2+	−29.014	42.67 m 9	IT
200	0+	−29.503	23.10% 19	
201	3/2−	−27.662	13.18% 9	
202	0+	−27.345	29.86% 26	
203	5/2−	−25.269	46.594 d 12	β−
204	0+	−24.690	6.87% 15	
205	1/2−	−22.287	5.14 m 9	β−
205m	13/2+	−20.731	1.09 ms 4	IT
206	0+	−20.95	8.32 m 7	β−
207	(9/2+)	−16.2	2.9 m 2	β−
208	0+	−13.27	41 m +5−4	β−

Nuclide Z El A	Jπ	Δ (MeV)	T½, Γ, or Abundance	Decay Mode
80 Hg 209		−8.5s	35 s +9−6	β−
210	0+	−5.4s	>300 ns	β−?
211		−0.5s	>300 ns	β−, β−n
212	0+	2.8s	>300 ns	β−, β−n
213		7.8s	>300 ns	β−, β−n
214	0+	11.2s	>300 ns	β−, β−n
215		16.3s	>300 ns	β−, β−n
216	0+	19.9s	>300 ns	β−, β−n
81 Tl 176	(3−,4−,5−)	0.58	5.2 ms +30−14	p
177	(1/2+)	−3.33	18 ms 5	α 73%, p 27%
178		−4.8s	254 ms +11−9	α≈53%, ε≈47%
179	(1/2+)	−8.30	0.23 s 4	α<100%, ε, p
179m	(11/2−)	−8.30	1.5 ms 3	α≤100%, p, ε, IT
180	(4−,5−)	−9.26	1.09 s 1	ε 94%, α 6%, εSF≈1.0×10⁻⁴%
181	(1/2+)	−12.799	3.2 s 3	ε, α≤10%
181m	(9/2−)	−11.963	1.40 ms 3	IT 99.6%, α 0.4%
182	(7+)	−13.35	3.1 s 10	ε 97.5%, α<5%
183	(1/2+)	−16.589	6.9 s 7	α, ε>0%
183m	(9/2−)	−15.959	53.3 ms 3	IT, ε, α 2%
184		−16.89	10.1 s 5	ε 97.9%, α 2.1%
185	(1/2+)	−19.75	19.5 s 5	ε
185m	(9/2−)	−19.30	1.93 s 8	α, IT
186m	(7+)	−19.87	27.5 s 10	ε, α≈6.0×10⁻³%
186m	(10−)	−19.50	2.9 s 2	IT
187	(1/2+)	−22.443	≈51 s	ε, α≈0.03%
187m	(9/2−)	−22.109	15.60 s 12	ε<99.9%, IT<99.9%, α 0.15%
188m	(2−)	−22.35	71 s 2	ε
188m	(7+)	−22.35	71 s 1	ε
188m	(9−)	−22.08	41 ms 4	IT, ε
189	(1/2+)	−24.60	2.3 m 2	ε
189m	(9/2−)	−24.34	1.4 m 1	ε<100%, IT<4%
190m	2(−)	−24.31	2.6 m 3	ε
190m	7(+)	−24.31	3.7 m 3	ε
190m	(8−)	−24.15	0.75 ms 4	IT
191	(1/2+)	−26.282		
191m	9/2(−)	−26.282	5.22 m 16	
192	(2−)	−25.87	9.6 m 4	ε
192m	(7+)	−25.72	10.8 m 2	ε
193	1/2(+)	−27.30	21.6 m 8	ε
193m	(9/2−)	−26.93	2.11 m 15	IT≤75%, ε≥25%
194	2−	−26.8	33.0 m 5	ε, α<1.0×10⁻⁷%
194m	(7+)	−26.8	32.8 m 2	ε
195	1/2+	−28.16	1.16 h 5	ε
195m	9/2−	−27.67	3.6 s 4	IT
196	2−	−27.50	1.84 h 3	ε
196m	(7+)	−27.10	1.41 h 2	ε 96.2%, IT 3.8%
197	1/2+	−28.34	2.84 h 4	ε
197m	9/2−	−27.73	0.54 s 1	IT
198	2−	−27.49	5.3 h 5	ε
198m	7+	−26.95	1.87 h 3	ε 55.9%, IT 44.1%

Nuclide				Δ	T½, Γ, or	
Z	El	A	Jπ	(MeV)	Abundance	Decay Mode
81	Tl	198m	(10–)	–26.75	32.1 ms *10*	IT
		199	1/2+	–28.06	7.42 h *8*	ε
		199m	9/2–	–27.31	28.4 ms *2*	IT
		200	2–	–27.047	26.1 h *1*	ε
		200m	7+	–26.293	34.0 ms *9*	IT
		201	1/2+	–27.18	3.0421 d *17*	ε
		201m	(9/2–)	–26.26	2.01 ms *7*	IT
		202	2–	–25.99	12.31 d *8*	ε
		203	1/2+	–25.762	**29.524%** *1*	
		204	2–	–24.346	3.783 y *12*	β– 97.08%, ε 2.92%
		205	1/2+	–23.821	**70.48%** *1*	
		206	0–	–22.254	4.202 m *11*	β–
		206m	(12–)	–19.611	3.74 m *3*	IT
		207	1/2+	–21.034	4.77 m *3*	β–
		207m	11/2–	–19.686	1.33 s *11*	IT
		208	5+	–16.752	3.053 m *4*	β–
		209	(1/2+)	–13.637	2.161 m *7*	β–
		210	(5+)	–9.25	1.30 m *3*	β–, β–n $7.0{\times}10^{-3}$%
		211		–5.9s	>300 ns	β–?
		212		–1.5s	>300 ns	β–?
		213		1.76	101 s *+486–46*	β–
		214		6.5s	>300 ns	β–, β–n
		215		10.1s	>300 ns	β–, β–n
		216		14.7s	>300 ns	β–, β–n
		217		18.4s	>300 ns	β–, β–n
82	Pb	178	0+	3.57	0.12 ms *+22–5*	α
		179	(9/2–)	2.05	3.5 ms *+14–8*	α
		180	0+	–1.93	4.2 ms *5*	α
		181	(9/2–)	–3.10	36 ms *2*	α
		181m	(13/2+)	–3.10	45 ms *20*	α < 100%
		182	0+	–6.82	55 ms *5*	α ≈ 98%, ε ≈ 2%
		183	(3/2–)	–7.57	535 ms *30*	α ≈ 90%
		183m	(13/2+)	–7.47	415 ms *20*	α
		184	0+	–11.05	490 ms *25*	α 80%, ε 20%
		185	3/2–	–11.54	6.3 s *4*	ε, α 34%
		185m	13/2+	–11.54	4.3 s *2*	α 50%, ε
		186	0+	–14.68	4.82 s *3*	ε 60%, α 40%
		187	(13/2+)	–14.990	18.3 s *3*	ε 88%, α 12%
		187m	(3/2–)	–14.957	15.2 s *3*	ε 90.5%, α 9.5%
		188	0+	–17.82	25.1 s *1*	ε 90.7%, α 9.3%
		189	(3/2–)	–17.88	39 s *8*	ε, α < 1%
		189m	(13/2+)	–17.84	50 s *3*	ε, α < 1%
		190	0+	–20.42	71 s *1*	ε 99.6%, α 0.4%
		191	(3/2–)	–20.25	1.33 m *8*	ε 99.99%, α 0.01%
		191m	(13/2+)	–20.25	2.18 m *8*	ε, α ≈ 0.02%
		192	0+	–22.56	3.5 m *1*	ε 99.99%, α $5.9{\times}10^{-3}$%
		193	(3/2–)	–22.19		ε
		193m	(13/2+)	–22.19	5.8 m *2*	ε
		194	0+	–24.21	10.7 m *6*	ε, α $7.3{\times}10^{-6}$%
		195	3/2–	–23.71	≈15 m	ε
		195m	13/2+	–23.51	15.0 m *12*	ε

Nuclide Z El A	Jπ	Δ (MeV)	T½, Γ, or Abundance	Decay Mode
82 Pb 196	0+	−25.36	37 m *3*	ε , α≤3.0×10⁻⁵%
197	3/2−	−24.748	8.1 m *17*	ε
197m	13/2+	−24.429	42.9 m *9*	ε 81%, IT 19%
198	0+	−26.05	2.4 h *1*	ε
199	3/2−	−25.231	90 m *10*	ε
199m	(13/2+)	−24.806	12.2 m *3*	IT ≈93%, ε ≈7%
200	0+	−26.25	21.5 h *4*	ε
201	5/2−	−25.26	9.33 h *3*	ε
201m	13/2+	−24.63	60.8 s *18*	IT
202	0+	−25.937	52.5×10³ y *28*	ε
202m	9−	−23.767	3.54 h *2*	IT 90.5%, ε 9.5%
203	5/2−	−24.787	51.92 h *3*	ε
203m	13/2+	−23.962	6.21 s *11*	IT
203m	29/2−	−21.838	480 ms *7*	IT
204	0+	−25.110	≥1.4×10¹⁷ y 1.4% *1*	α
204m	9−	−22.924	66.93 m *10*	IT
205	5/2−	−23.770	1.73×10⁷ y *7*	ε
205m	13/2+	−22.756	5.55 ms *2*	IT
206	0+	−23.786	**24.1%** *1*	
207	1/2−	−22.452	**22.1%** *1*	
207m	13/2+	−20.819	0.806 s *5*	IT
208	0+	−21.749	**52.4%** *1*	
209	9/2+	−17.615	3.253 h *14*	β−
210	0+	−14.729	22.20 y *22*	β−, α 1.9×10⁻⁶%
211	9/2+	−10.491	36.1 m *2*	β−
212	0+	−7.553	10.64 h *1*	β−
213	(9/2+)	−3.200	10.2 m *3*	β−
214	0+	−0.181	26.8 m *9*	β−
215		4.5s	147 s *12*	β−
216	0+	7.7s	>300 ns	β−
217		12.4s	>300 ns	β−
218	0+	15.6s	>300 ns	β−
219		20.5s	>300 ns	β−
220	0+	23.9s	>300 ns	β−
83 Bi 184m		1.19	13 ms *2*	α
184m		1.19	6.6 ms *15*	α
185	1/2+	−2.3s	58 μs *4*	p 90%, α 10%
186	(3+)	−3.17	15.0 ms *17*	α
186m	(10−)	−3.17	9.8 ms *13*	α
187	(9/2−)	−6.39	37 ms *2*	α
187m	(1/2+)	−6.27	0.370 ms *20*	α
188m	(10−)	−7.20	265 ms *15*	α , ε?
188m	(3+)	−7.20	60 ms *3*	α , ε?
189	(9/2−)	−10.06	674 ms *11*	α>50%, ε<50%
189m	(1/2+)	−9.88	5.0 ms *1*	α>50%, ε<50%
190m	(3+)	−10.59	6.3 s *1*	α 90%, ε 10%
190m	(10−)	−10.59	6.2 s *1*	α 70%, ε 30%
191	(9/2−)	−13.240	12.4 s *3*	α 51%, ε 49%
191m	(1/2+)	−12.999	125 ms *13*	α 68%, IT 32%, ε
192	(3+)	−13.55	34.6 s *9*	ε 88%, α 12%
192m	(10−)	−13.40	39.6 s *4*	ε 90%, α 10%

Nuclide Z El A	Jπ	Δ (MeV)	T½, Γ, or Abundance	Decay Mode
83 Bi 193	(9/2−)	−15.872	63.6 s *30*	ε 96.5%, α 3.5%
193m	(1/2+)	−15.564	3.2 s *5*	α 84%, ε 16%
194	(3+)	−15.97	95 s *3*	ε 99.54%, α 0.46%
194m	(6+,7+)	−15.97	125 s *2*	ε
194m	(10−)	−15.97	115 s *4*	ε 99.8%, α 0.2%
195	(9/2−)	−18.025	183 s *4*	ε 99.97%, α 0.03%
195m	(1/2+)	−17.624	87 s *1*	ε 67%, α 33%
196	(3+)	−18.01	308 s *12*	ε , α 1.2×10⁻³%
196m	(7+)	−17.84	0.6 s *5*	ε , IT
196m	(10−)	−17.74	240 s *3*	ε 74.2%, IT 25.8%, α 3.8×10⁻⁴%
197	(9/2−)	−19.686	9.33 m *50*	ε , α 1.0×10⁻⁴%
197m	(1/2+)	−19.186	5.04 m *16*	α 55%, ε 45%, IT< 0.3%
198	(2+,3+)	−19.37	10.3 m *3*	ε
198m	(7+)	−19.37	11.6 m *3*	ε
198m	10−	−19.12	7.7 s *5*	IT
199	9/2−	−20.80	27 m *1*	ε
199m	(1/2+)	−20.13	24.70 m *15*	ε 99%, IT≤2%, α≈0.01%
200	7+	−20.37	36.4 m *5*	ε
200m	(2+)	−20.37	31 m *2*	ε≤100%
200m	(10−)	−19.94	0.40 s *5*	IT
201	9/2−	−21.42	103 m *3*	ε
201m	1/2+	−20.57	57.5 m *21*	ε>91.1%, IT≤8.6%, α≈0.3%
202	5+	−20.74	1.71 h *4*	ε
203	9/2−	−21.52	11.76 h *5*	ε
203m	1/2+	−20.43	305 ms *5*	IT
204	6+	−20.645	11.22 h *10*	ε
204m	10−	−19.840	13.0 ms *1*	IT
204m	17+	−17.812	1.07 ms *3*	IT
205	9/2−	−21.064	15.31 d *4*	ε
206	6+	−20.028	6.243 d *3*	ε
206m	10−	−18.983	0.89 ms *1*	IT
207	9/2−	−20.055	31.55 y *4*	ε
208	5+	−18.870	3.68×10⁵ y *4*	ε
208m	10−	−17.299	2.58 ms *4*	IT
209	9/2−	−18.259	100%	
210	1−	−14.792	5.012 d *5*	β− , α 1.3×10⁻⁴%
210m	9−	−14.521	3.04×10⁶ y *6*	α
211	9/2−	−11.858	2.14 m *2*	α 99.72%, β− 0.28%
212	1(−)	−8.120	60.55 m *6*	β− 64.06%, α 35.94%
212m	(8−,9−)	−7.870	25.0 m *2*	α 67%, β− 33%, β−α 30%
212m	≥16	−6.210	7.0 m *3*	β−
213	9/2−	−5.230	45.59 m *6*	β− 97.8%, α 2.2%
214	1−	−1.20	19.9 m *4*	β− 99.98%, α 0.02%
215	(9/2−)	1.65	7.6 m *2*	β−
215m	>23/2−	3.00	36.9 s *6*	IT 76.2%, β− 23.8%
216	(6−,7−)	5.87	2.25 m *5*	β−≤100%
216m	(3)	5.87	6.6 m *21*	β−≤100%

Nuclide Z El A	Jπ	Δ (MeV)	T½, Γ, or Abundance	Decay Mode
83 Bi 217	(9/2−)	8.9s	98.5 s *8*	β−
218		13.2s	33 s *1*	β−
219		16.3s	>300 ns	β−
220		20.7s	>300 ns	β−
221		24.0s	>300 ns	β− , β−n
222		28.4s	>300 ns	β−
223		31.9s	>300 ns	β− , β−n
224		36.4s	>300 ns	β− , β−n
84 Po 186	0+	4.10		
187	(1/2−,5/2−)	2.83	1.40 ms *25*	α
188	0+	−0.54	0.275 ms *30*	ε , α
189	(7/2−)	−1.42	3.5 ms *5*	α
190	0+	−4.56	2.46 ms *5*	α
191	(3/2−)	−5.05	22 ms *1*	α 99%
191m	(13/2+)	−5.01	93 ms *3*	α 96%
192	0+	−8.07	32.2 ms *3*	α≈99.5%, ε≈0.5%
193m	(13/2+)	−8.36	245 ms *22*	α≤100%
193m	(3/2−)	−8.36	370 ms +*46−40*	α≤100%
194	0+	−11.01	0.392 s *4*	α , ε
195	(3/2−)	−11.07	4.64 s *9*	α 75%, ε 25%
195m	(13/2+)	−10.84	1.92 s *2*	α≈90%, ε≈10%, IT<0.01%
196	0+	−13.47	5.8 s *2*	α≈98%, ε≈2%
197	(3/2−)	−13.36	84 s *16*	ε 56%, α 44%
197m	(13/2+)	−13.15	32 s *2*	α 84%, ε 16%, IT 0.01%
198	0+	−15.47	1.77 m *3*	α 57%, ε 43%
199	(3/2−)	−15.21	5.47 m *15*	ε 92.5%, α 7.5%
199m	(13/2+)	−14.90	4.17 m *5*	ε 73.5%, α 24%, IT 2.5%
200	0+	−16.95	11.51 m *8*	ε 88.9%, α 11.1%
201	3/2−	−16.524	15.6 m *1*	ε 98.87%, α 1.13%
201m	13/2+	−16.100	8.96 m *12*	IT 56.2%, ε 41.4%, α 2.4%
202	0+	−17.92	44.6 m *4*	ε 98.08%, α 1.92%
203	5/2−	−17.310	36.7 m *5*	ε 99.89%, α 0.11%
203m	13/2+	−16.668	45 s *2*	IT , ε
204	0+	−18.34	3.519 h *12*	ε 99.33%, α 0.67%
205	5/2−	−17.51	1.74 h *8*	ε 99.96%, α 0.04%
205m	13/2+	−16.63	0.645 ms *20*	IT
205m	19/2−	−16.05	57.4 ms *9*	IT
206	0+	−18.185	8.8 d *1*	ε 94.55%, α 5.45%
207	5/2−	−17.146	5.80 h *2*	ε 99.98%, α 0.02%
207m	19/2−	−15.763	2.79 s *8*	IT
208	0+	−17.470	2.898 y *2*	α , ε 4.0×10⁻³%
209	1/2−	−16.366	102 y *5*	α 99.52%, ε 0.48%
210	0+	−15.953	138.376 d *2*	α
211	9/2+	−12.433	0.516 s *3*	α
211m	(25/2+)	−10.971	25.2 s *6*	α 99.98%, IT 0.02%
212	0+	−10.370	0.299 μs *2*	α
212m	(18+)	−7.448	45.1 s *6*	α 99.93%, IT 0.07%
213	9/2+	−6.654	3.72 μs *2*	α

Nuclide Z El A			Jπ	Δ (MeV)	T½, Γ, or Abundance	Decay Mode
84	Po	214	0+	−4.470	164.3 μs *20*	α
		215	9/2+	−0.540	1.781 ms *4*	α, β− 2.3×10⁻⁴%
		216	0+	1.778	0.145 s *2*	α
		217	(9/2+)	5.886	1.53 s *5*	α
		218	0+	8.357	3.098 m *12*	α 99.98%, β− 0.02%
		219		12.6s	>300 ns	β−
		220	0+	15.3s	>300 ns	β−
		221		19.78	112 s +*58−28*	β−?
		222	0+	22.48	550 s *430*	β−?
		223		26.8s	>300 ns	β−
		224	0+	29.7s	>300 ns	β−
		225		34.3s	>300 ns	β−
		226	0+	37.3s	>300 ns	β−
		227		42.0s	>300 ns	β−
85	At	191	(1/2+)	3.86	1.7 ms +*11−5*	α
		191m	(7/2−)	3.92	2.1 ms +*4−3*	α
		192m		2.92	11.5 ms *6*	α
		192m	(9−,10−)	2.92	88 ms *6*	α
		193	(1/2+)	−0.06	28 ms +*5−4*	α
		193m	(7/2−)	−0.06	21 ms *5*	α
		193m	(13/2+)	−0.03	27 ms +*4−3*	IT 76%, α 24%
		194m	(9−10−)	−0.70	310 ms *8*	α
		194m		−0.70	253 ms *10*	α
		195	1/2+	−3.476	328 ms *20*	α
		195m	7/2−	−3.476	147 ms *5*	α
		196	(3+)	−3.92	0.388 s *7*	α≈95.1%, ε≈4.9%
		197	(9/2−)	−6.34	0.388 s *6*	α 96.1%, ε 3.9%
		197m	(1/2+)	−6.29	2.0 s *2*	α≤100%, ε, IT≤4.0×10⁻³%
		198	(3+)	−6.65	3.8 s *4*	α 90%, ε 10%
		198m	(10−)	−6.55	1.04 s *15*	α 84%, ε 16%
		199	(9/2−)	−8.822	7.03 s *15*	α 90%, ε 10%
		200	(3+)	−8.99	43 s *1*	α 52%, ε 48%
		200m	(7+)	−8.88	47 s *1*	ε≤57%, α 43%
		200m	(10−)	−8.64	7.3 s +*26−15*	ε<89.5%, IT<89.5%, α≈10.5%
		201	(9/2−)	−10.789	85.2 s *16*	α 71%, ε 29%
		202	(2+,3+)	−10.59	184 s *1*	ε 63%, α 37%
		202m	(7+)	−10.59	182 s *2*	ε 91.3%, α 8.7%
		202m	(10−)	−10.20	0.46 s *5*	IT 99.9%, α 0.1%
		203	9/2−	−12.16	7.4 m *2*	ε 69%, α 31%
		204	7+	−11.88	9.12 m *11*	ε 96.09%, α 3.91%
		204m	10−	−11.29	108 ms *10*	IT
		205	9/2−	−12.97	26.9 m *8*	ε 90%, α 10%
		206	(5)+	−12.43	30.6 m *8*	ε 99.1%, α 0.9%
		207	9/2−	−13.23	1.81 h *3*	ε 91.4%, α 8.6%
		208	6+	−12.469	1.63 h *3*	ε 99.45%, α 0.55%
		209	9/2−	−12.882	5.41 h *5*	ε 95.9%, α 4.1%
		210	(5)+	−11.972	8.1 h *4*	ε 99.82%, α 0.18%
		211	9/2−	−11.648	7.214 h *7*	ε 58.2%, α 41.8%
		212	(1−)	−8.628	0.314 s *2*	α, ε<0.03%, β−<2.0×10⁻⁶%

Nuclide Z El A	Jπ	Δ (MeV)	T½, Γ, or Abundance	Decay Mode
85 At 212m	(9–)	–8.405	0.119 s 3	α>99%, IT<1%
213	9/2–	–6.580	125 ns 6	α
214	1–	–3.380	558 ns 10	α
215	9/2–	–1.255	0.10 ms 2	α
216	1–	2.254	0.30 ms 3	α, β–<6.0×10⁻³%, ε<3.0×10⁻⁷%
217	9/2–	4.395	32.3 ms 4	α 99.99%, β– 7.0×10⁻³%
218		8.10	1.5 s 3	α 99.9%, β– 0.1%
219		10.397	56 s 3	α≈97%, β–≈3%
220	3	14.35	3.71 m 4	β– 92%, α 8%
221		16.8s	2.3 m 2	β–
222		20.6s	54 s 10	β–
223		23.4s	50 s 7	β–
224		27.71	76 s +138–23	β–?
225		30.2s	>300 ns	β–
226		34.2s	>300 ns	β–
227		37.2s	>300 ns	β–
228		41.4s	>300 ns	β–
229		44.6s	>300 ns	β–, β–n
86 Rn 193	(3/2–)	9.05	1.15 ms 27	α
194	0+	5.72	0.78 ms 16	α
195	3/2–	5.06	6 ms +3–2	α
195m	13/2+	5.12	5 ms +3–2	α
196	0+	1.97	4.4 ms +13–9	α 99.9%, ε≈0.1%
197	(3/2–)	1.48	53 ms +7–5	α
197m	(13/2+)	1.48	25 ms +3–2	α
198	0+	–1.23	65 ms 3	α, ε
199	(3/2–)	–1.51	0.59 s 3	α 94%, ε 6%
199m	(13/2+)	–1.33	0.31 s 2	α 97%, ε 3%
200	0+	–4.01	1.03 s +20–11	α 86%, ε 14%
201	(3/2–)	–4.07	7.0 s 4	α, ε
201m	(13/2+)	–4.07	3.8 s 1	ε, α
202	0+	–6.28	9.7 s 1	α 78%, ε 22%
203	(3/2–)	–6.16	44 s 2	α 66%, ε 34%
203m	(13/2+)	–5.80	26.9 s 5	α 75%, ε 25%
204	0+	–7.98	74.5 s 14	α 72.4%, ε 27.6%
205	5/2–	–7.71	170 s 4	ε 75.4%, α 24.6%
206	0+	–9.12	5.67 m 17	α 62%, ε 38%
207	5/2–	–8.634	9.25 m 17	ε 79%, α 21%
208	0+	–9.66	24.35 m 14	α 62%, ε 38%
209	5/2–	–8.93	28.5 m 10	ε 83%, α 17%
210	0+	–9.601	2.4 h 1	α 96%, ε 4%
211	1/2–	–8.756	14.6 h 2	ε 72.6%, α 27.4%
212	0+	–8.660	23.9 m 12	α
213	(9/2+)	–5.699	19.5 ms 1	α
214	0+	–4.320	0.27 μs 2	α
215	9/2+	–1.169	2.30 μs 10	α
216	0+	0.254	45 μs 5	α
217	9/2+	3.657	0.54 ms 5	α
218	0+	5.216	35 ms 5	α
219	5/2+	8.831	3.96 s 1	α

Nuclide Z El A	Jπ	Δ (MeV)	T½, Γ, or Abundance	Decay Mode
86 Rn 220	0+	10.607	55.6 s *1*	α
221	7/2+	14.473	25 m *2*	β– 78%, α 22%
222	0+	16.373	3.8235 d *3*	α
223	7/2	20.40	24.3 m *4*	β–
224	0+	22.43	107 m *3*	β–
225	7/2–	26.56	4.66 m *4*	β–
226	0+	28.74	7.4 m *1*	β–
227		32.87	20.8 s *7*	β–
228	0+	35.25	65 s *2*	β–
229		39.36	12.0 s +*12–13*	β–
230	0+	42.1s	>300 ns	β–
231		46.5s	>300 ns	β–
87 Fr 199		6.76	12 ms +*10–4*	α>0%, ε
200	(3+)	6.12	49 ms *4*	α
201	(9/2–)	3.60	62 ms *5*	α
201m	(1/2+)	3.60	19 ms +*19–6*	α
202	(3+)	3.16	0.30 s *5*	α
202m	(10–)	3.16	0.29 s *5*	α
203	(9/2–)	0.877	0.55 s *1*	α≤100%
204	(3+)	0.61	1.8 s *3*	α 92%, ε 8%
204m	(7+)	0.65	1.6 s +*5–3*	α 90%, ε 10%
204m	(10–)	0.92	0.8 s *2*	α 74%, ε 26%
205	(9/2–)	−1.309	3.97 s *4*	α 98.5%, ε 1.5%
206	(2+,3+)	−1.24	≈16 s	α≈84%, ε≈16%
206m	(7+)	−1.24	≈16 s	α≈84%, ε≈16%
206m	(10–)	−0.71	0.7 s *1*	IT 95%, α 5%
207	9/2–	−2.84	14.8 s *1*	α 95%, ε 5%
208	7+	−2.67	59.1 s *3*	α 89%, ε 11%
209	9/2–	−3.77	50.5 s *7*	α 89%, ε 11%
210	6+	−3.33	3.18 m *6*	α 71%, ε 29%
211	9/2–	−4.14	3.10 m *2*	α 87%, ε 13%
212	5+	−3.515	20.0 m *6*	ε 57%, α 43%
213	9/2–	−3.553	34.82 s *14*	α 99.44%, ε 0.56%
214	(1–)	−0.959	5.0 ms *2*	α
214m	(8–)	−0.837	3.35 ms *5*	α
215	9/2–	0.317	86 ns *5*	α
216	(1–)	2.970	700 ns *20*	α
217	9/2–	4.313	19 μs *3*	α
218	1–	7.058	1.0 ms *6*	α
218m		7.144	22.0 ms *5*	α≤100%, IT
219	9/2–	8.617	20 ms *2*	α
220	1+	11.480	27.4 s *3*	α 99.65%, β– 0.35%
221	5/2–	13.278	286.1 s *10*	α, β–<0.1%
222	2–	16.35	14.2 m *3*	β–
223	3/2(−)	18.384	22.00 m *7*	β– 99.99%, α 6.0×10⁻³%
224	1–	21.65	3.33 m *10*	β–
225	3/2–	23.82	3.95 m *14*	β–
226	1–	27.4	49 s *1*	β–
227	1/2+	29.7	2.47 m *3*	β–
228	2–	33.3s	38 s *1*	β–≤100%
229	(1/2+)	35.82	50.2 s *20*	β–

Nuclide Z El A	Jπ	Δ (MeV)	T½, Γ, or Abundance	Decay Mode
87 Fr 230		39.50	19.1 s 5	β–
231	(1/2+)	42.3s	17.6 s 6	β–
232	(5)	46.1s	5.5 s 6	β–
233		49.2s	>300 ns	β–
88 Ra 201m	(13/2+)	11.8s	1.6 ms +77–7	α, ε
202	0+	9.09	16 ms +30–7	α
203	(3/2–)	8.66	31 ms +17–9	α
203m	(13/2+)	8.66	24 ms +6–4	α
204	0+	6.06	57 ms +11–5	α
205	(3/2–)	5.84	210 ms +60–40	α≤100%, ε
205m	(13/2+)	5.84	170 ms +60–40	α≤100%, ε
206	0+	3.56	0.24 s 2	α
207	(3/2–,5/2–)	3.54	1.35 s –13+22	α≈86%, ε≈14%
207m	(13/2+)	4.09	59 ms 4	IT≥85%, α≤15%
208	0+	1.71	1.3 s 2	α 95%, ε 5%
209	5/2–	1.85	4.6 s 2	α≈90%, ε≈10%
210	0+	0.46	3.7 s 2	α≈96%, ε≈4%
211	5/2(–)	0.832	13 s 2	α>93%, ε<7%
212	0+	–0.20	13.0 s 2	α≈85%, ε≈15%
213	1/2–	0.36	2.73 m 5	α 80%, ε 20%
213m	(17/2–)	2.13	2.20 ms 5	IT≈99.4%, α≈0.6%
214	0+	0.095	2.46 s 3	α 99.94%, ε 0.06%
215	(9/2+)	2.532	1.55 ms 7	α
216	0+	3.290	182 ns 10	α, ε< 1.0×10^{-8}%
217	(9/2+)	5.886	1.6 μs 2	α
218	0+	6.65	25.2 μs 3	α
219	(7/2)+	9.393	10 ms 3	α
220	0+	10.272	18 ms 2	α
221	5/2+	12.963	28 s 2	α, ^{14}C 1×10^{-12}%
222	0+	14.320	38.0 s 5	α, ^{14}C 3.0×10^{-8}%
223	3/2+	17.234	11.43 d 5	α, ^{14}C 8.9×10^{-8}%
224	0+	18.821	3.6319 d 23	α, ^{14}C 4.0×10^{-9}%
225	1/2+	21.995	14.9 d 2	β–
226	0+	23.668	1600 y 7	α, ^{14}C 3.2×10^{-9}%
227	3/2+	27.178	42.2 m 5	β–
228	0+	28.946	5.75 y 3	β–
229	5/2+	32.56	4.0 m 2	β–
230	0+	34.52	93 m 2	β–
231	(5/2+)	38.22	104.1 s 8	β–
232	0+	40.50	4.2 m 8	β–
233		44.6s	30 s 5	β–
234	0+	47.2s	30 s 10	β–
235		51.4s		
89 Ac 206	(3+)	13.53	22 ms +9 5	α
206m	(10–)	13.53	33 ms +22–9	α
207	(9/2–)	11.15	27 ms +11–6	α
208	(3+)	10.76	95 ms +24–16	α≈99%, ε≈1%
208m	(10–)	11.27	25 ms +9–5	α≈90%, ε≈10%
209	(9/2–)	8.84	0.10 s 5	α≈99%, ε≈1%
210		8.79	0.35 s 5	α 91%, ε≈9%
211		7.20	0.21 s 3	α
212		7.27	0.93 s 5	α≈57%, ε≈43%

Nuclide Z El A	Jπ	Δ (MeV)	T½, Γ, or Abundance	Decay Mode
89 Ac 213		6.16	738 ms *16*	α≤100%
214	(5+)	6.44	8.2 s *2*	α≥89%, ε≤11%
215	9/2–	6.03	0.17 s *1*	α 99.91%, ε 0.09%
216	(1–)	8.14	440 μs *16*	α
216m	(9–)	8.19	441 μs *7*	α
217	9/2–	8.70	69 ns *4*	α, ε≤2%
218	(1–)	10.84	1.08 μs *9*	α
219	9/2–	11.57	11.8 μs *15*	α
220	(3–)	13.742	26.4 ms *2*	α, ε 5.0×10⁻⁴%
221	(3/2–)	14.52	52 ms *2*	α
222	1–	16.620	5.0 s *5*	α 99%, ε 1%
222m		16.620	63 s *3*	α≥88%, IT≤10%, ε≥0.7%
223	(5/2–)	17.826	2.10 m *5*	α 99%, ε 1%
224	0–	20.231	2.78 h *17*	ε 90.9%, α 9.1%, β–< 1.6%
225	(3/2–)	21.638	10.0 d *1*	α, ¹⁴C 4×10⁻¹²%
226	(1)	24.309	29.37 h *12*	β– 83%, ε 17%, α 6.0×10⁻³%
227	3/2–	25.851	21.772 y *3*	β– 98.62%, α 1.38%
228	3+	28.900	6.15 h *2*	β–
229	(3/2+)	30.75	62.7 m *5*	β–
230	(1+)	33.8	122 s *3*	β–, β–F 1.2×10⁻⁶%
231	(1/2+)	35.9	7.5 m *1*	β–
232	(1+)	39.2	119 s *5*	β–
233	(1/2+)	41.5s	145 s *10*	β–
234		45.0s	44 s *7*	β–
235		47.6s	60 s *4*	β–
236		51.27		β–?
237		54.3s		
90 Th 208	0+	16.68	1.7 ms +*17–6*	α
209	(5/2–)	16.54	2.5 ms +*17–7*	α
210	0+	14.06	16 ms *4*	α 99%, ε≈1%
211		13.90	0.04 s +*3–1*	α
212	0+	12.10	31.7 ms *13*	α, ε≈0.3%
213		12.12	144 ms *21*	α≤100%
214	0+	10.71	87 ms *10*	α
215	(1/2–)	10.921	1.2 s *2*	α
216	0+	10.29	26.0 ms *2*	α, ε≈0.01%
216m	8+	12.33	134 μs *4*	α 2.8%, IT
217	(9/2+)	12.22	0.241 ms *5*	α
218	0+	12.37	117 ns *9*	α
219		14.47	1.05 μs *3*	α
220	0+	14.67	9.7 μs *6*	α, ε 2.0×10⁻⁷%
221	(7/2+)	16.937	1.68 ms *6*	α
222	0+	17.20	2.8 ms *3*	α
223	(5/2)+	19.384	0.60 s *2*	α
224	0+	20.00	0.81 s *10*	α
225	(3/2+)	22.309	8.75 m *4*	α≈90%, ε≈10%
226	0+	23.196	30.57 m *10*	α
227	1/2+	25.806	18.68 d *9*	α
228	0+	26.766	1.9116 y *16*	α, ²⁰O 1×10⁻¹¹%

Nuclide Z El A	Jπ	Δ (MeV)	T½, Γ, or Abundance	Decay Mode
90 Th 229	5/2+	29.587	7932 y *28*	α
229m	(3/2+)	29.587	2 m *1*	IT?
230	0+	30.863	7.54×10^4 y *3*	α, ^{24}Ne 6×10^{-11}%, SF $\leq 4 \times 10^{-12}$%
231	5/2+	33.816	25.52 h *1*	β–, α ≈ 4×10^{-11}%
232	0+	35.452	1.40×10^{10} y *1* 100%	α, SF 1.1×10^{-9}%
233	1/2+	38.737	21.83 m *4*	β–
234	0+	40.615	24.10 d *3*	β–
235	(1/2+)	44.26	7.2 m *1*	β–
236	0+	46.5s	37.3 m *15*	β–
237	(5/2+)	50.2s	4.7 m *6*	β–
238	0+	52.6s	9.4 m *20*	β–
239		56.6s		
91 Pa 212		21.61	5.1 ms *+61–19*	α
213		19.66	5.3 ms *+40–16*	α
214		19.49	17 ms *3*	α ≤ 100%
215		17.87	14 ms *2*	α
216		17.80	0.15 s *+6–4*	α ≈ 98%, ε ≈ 2%
217		17.07	3.6 ms *8*	α
217m		18.92	1.2 ms *2*	α 73%, IT 27%
218		18.68	113 μs *10*	α
219m	9/2–	18.54	53 ns *10*	α
220m		20.40	0.78 μs *16*	α, ε 3.0×10^{-7}%
221	9/2–	20.38	5.9 μs *17*	α
222		22.11s	2.9 ms *+6–4*	α
223		22.32	5.1 ms *6*	α
224		23.861	0.85 s *2*	α
225		24.34	1.7 s *2*	α
226		26.03	1.8 m *2*	α 74%, ε 26%
227	(5/2–)	26.831	38.3 m *3*	α 85%, ε 15%
228	3+	28.921	22.4 h *10*	ε 98.15%, α 1.85%
229	(5/2+)	29.898	1.50 d *5*	ε 99.52%, α 0.48%
230	(2–)	32.173	17.4 d *5*	ε 92.2%, β– 7.8%, α 3.2×10^{-3}%
231	3/2–	33.425	3.276×10^4 y *11*	α, SF $\leq 2 \times 10^{-11}$%
232	(2–)	35.941	1.32 d *2*	β–, ε
233	3/2–	37.491	26.975 d *13*	β–
234	4+	40.342	6.70 h *5*	β–
234m	(0–)	40.416	1.159 m *11*	β– 99.84%, IT 0.16%
235	(3/2–)	42.33	24.44 m *11*	β–
236	1(–)	45.3	9.1 m *1*	β–
237	(1/2+)	47.6	8.7 m *2*	β–
238	(3–)	50.77	2.27 m *9*	β–
239	(3/2)	53.3s	1.8 h *5*	β–
240		56.8s		β–?
241		59.7s		
92 U 217		22.71	16 ms *+21–6*	α ≤ 100%
218	0+	21.91	0.51 ms *+17–10*	α
218m	(8+)	24.02	0.56 ms *+26–14*	α
219		23.30	42 μs *+34–13*	α
220	0+	23.0s		α?, ε?

Z	Nuclide El	A	Jπ	Δ (MeV)	T½, Γ, or Abundance	Decay Mode
92	U	221	(9/2+)	24.6s	700 ns	
		222	0+	24.3s	1.0 μs +*12–4*	α
		223		25.84	18 μs +*10–5*	α, ε 0.2%
		224	0+	25.71	0.9 ms *3*	α
		225		27.38	95 ms *15*	α
		226	0+	27.33	0.35 s *15*	α
		227	(3/2+)	29.02	1.1 m *1*	α
		228	0+	29.22	9.1 m *2*	α>95%, ε<5%
		229	(3/2+)	31.209	58 m *3*	ε≈80%, α≈20%
		230	0+	31.613	20.8 d	α, SF<1×10⁻¹⁰%, ²²Ne 5×10⁻¹²%
		231	(5/2–)	33.807	4.2 d *1*	ε, α≈4.0×10⁻³%
		232	0+	34.604	68.9 y *4*	α, SF 3×10⁻¹²%
		233	5/2+	36.921	1.592×10⁵ y *2*	α, ²⁴Ne 9×10⁻¹⁰%, SF<6×10⁻¹¹%, ²⁸Mg<1.×10⁻¹³%
		234	0+	38.148	2.455×10⁵ y *6* **0.0054%** *5*	α, SF 1.6×10⁻⁹%, Mg 1×10⁻¹¹%, Ne 9×10⁻¹²%
		235	7/2–	40.921	7.04×10⁸ y *1* **0.7204%** *6*	α, SF 7.0×10⁻⁹%, ²⁸Mg 8.×10⁻¹⁰%, Ne≈8.×10⁻¹⁰%
		235m	1/2+	40.921	≈26 m	IT
		236	0+	42.447	2.342×10⁷ y *4*	α, SF 9.4×10⁻⁸%
		237	1/2+	45.393	6.75 d *1*	β–
		238	0+	47.310	4.468×10⁹ y *3* **99.2742%** *10*	α, SF 5.5×10⁻⁵%
		239	5/2+	50.575	23.45 m *2*	β–
		240	0+	52.716	14.1 h *1*	β–
		241		56.2s		β–?
		242	0+	58.6s	16.8 m *5*	β–
		243		62.4s		
93	Np	225	(9/2–)	31.59		α
		226		32.74s	35 ms *10*	α
		227		32.56	0.51 s *6*	α
		228		33.59	61.4 s *14*	ε 60%, α 40%
		229		33.78	4.0 m *2*	α 68%, ε 32%
		230		35.24	4.6 m *3*	ε≤97%, α≥3%
		231	(5/2)	35.62	48.8 m *2*	ε 98%, α 2%
		232	(4+)	37.4s	14.7 m *3*	ε, α 2.0×10⁻⁴%
		233	(5/2+)	37.95	36.2 m *1*	ε, α≤1.0×10⁻³%
		234	(0+)	39.957	4.4 d *1*	ε
		235	5/2+	41.045	396.1 d *12*	ε, α 2.6×10⁻³%
		236	(6–)	43.37	153×10³ y *5*	ε 86.3%, β– 13.5%, α 0.16%
		236m	1	43.37	22.5 h *4*	β– 50%, ε 50%
		237	5/2+	44.874	2.144×10⁶ y *7*	α, SF≤2×10⁻¹⁰%
		238	2+	47.457	2.117 d *2*	β–
		239	5/2+	49.313	2.356 d *3*	β–
		240	(5+)	52.32	61.9 m *2*	β–

Nuclide Z El A	Jπ	Δ (MeV)	T½, Γ, or Abundance	Decay Mode
93 Np 240m	(1+)	52.32	7.22 m 2	β– 99.88%, IT 0.12%
241	5/2+	54.26	13.9 m 2	β–
242	(1+)	57.4	2.2 m 2	β–
242m	(6+)	57.4	5.5 m 1	β–
243	(5/2–)	59.88s	1.85 m 15	β–
244	(7–)	63.2s	2.29 m 16	β–
245		65.9s		
94 Pu 228	0+	36.08	1.1 s +20–5	α
229	(3/2+)	37.39	67 s +41–19	ε 50%, α 50%, SF < 7%
230	0+	36.93	102 s 10	α ≤ 100%
231	(3/2+)	38.28	8.6 m 5	ε ≤ 99.8%, α > 0.2%
232	0+	38.36	33.8 m 7	ε 90%, α 10%
233		40.05	20.9 m 4	ε 99.88%, α 0.12%
234	0+	40.348	8.8 h 1	ε ≈ 94%, α ≈ 6%
235	(5/2+)	42.18	25.3 m 5	ε, α 2.8×10⁻³%
236	0+	42.896	2.858 y 8	α, SF 1.9×10⁻⁷%
237	7/2–	45.094	45.64 d 4	ε, α 4.2×10⁻³%
237m	1/2+	45.240	0.18 s 2	IT
238	0+	46.166	87.7 y 1	α, SF 1.9×10⁻⁷%
239	1/2+	48.591	24110 y 30	α, SF 3.×10⁻¹⁰%
240	0+	50.128	6561 y 7	α, SF 5.7×10⁻⁶%
241	5/2+	52.958	14.325 y 6	β–, α 2.5×10⁻³%, SF < 2×10⁻¹⁴%
242	0+	54.719	3.75×10⁵ y 2	α, SF 5.5×10⁻⁴%
243	7/2+	57.756	4.956 h 3	β–
244	0+	59.806	8.00×10⁷ y 9	α 99.88%, SF 0.12%
245	(9/2–)	63.18	10.5 h 1	β–
246	0+	65.40	10.84 d 2	β–
247		69.1s	2.27 d 23	β–
95 Am 230			≈17 s	ε
231		42.4s		α?, ε?
232		43.4s	79 s 2	ε ≈ 97%, α ≈ 3%
233		43.2s	3.2 m 8	α > 3%, ε
234		44.5s	2.32 m 8	ε, α
235	5/2–	44.62	10.3 m 6	ε 99.6%, α 0.4%
236	5–	46.0s	3.6 m 2	α, ε
236m	(1–)	46.0s	2.9 m 2	α, ε
237	5/2(–)	46.57s	73.6 m 8	ε 99.97%, α 0.03%
238	1+	48.42	98 m 2	ε, α 1.0×10⁻⁴%
239	(5/2)–	49.393	11.9 h 1	ε 99.99%, α 0.01%
240	(3–)	51.51	50.8 h 3	ε, α 1.9×10⁻⁴%
240m		54.51	0.94 ms 4	SF ≤ 100%
241	5/2–	52.937	432.6 y 6	α, SF 4×10⁻¹⁰%
242	1–	55.471	16.02 h 2	β– 82.7%, ε 17.3%
242m	5–	55.520	141 y 2	IT 99.55%, α 0.45%, SF < 4.7×10⁻⁹%
242m	(2+,3–)	57.671	14.0 ms 10	SF, IT, α < 5.0×10⁻³%
243	5/2–	57.177	7370 y 40	α, SF 3.7×10⁻⁹%
244	(6–)	59.882	10.1 h 1	β–
244m		59.882	0.90 ms 15	SF ≤ 100%
244m	1+	59.968	26 m 1	β– 99.96%, ε 0.04%

Nuclide Z El A	Jπ	Δ (MeV)	T½, Γ, or Abundance	Decay Mode
95 Am 245	(5/2)+	61.901	2.05 h *1*	β–
246	(7–)	65.00	39 m *3*	β–
246m	2(–)	65.00	25.0 m *2*	β– , IT< 0.02%
247	(5/2)	67.2s	23.0 m *13*	β–
248		70.6s	≈10 m	β–
249		73.1s		β– ?
96 Cm 233	(3/2+)	47.29	23 s +*13–6*	ε 80%, α 20%
234	0+	46.72	51 s *12*	α≈40%, SF≈40%, ε≈20%
235		47.9s		α?, ε ?
236	0+	47.86		ε, α
237		49.25		ε, α< 1%
238	0+	49.44	2.4 h *1*	ε≥90%, α≤10%
239	(7/2–)	51.15	≈2.9 h	ε, α< 0.1%
240	0+	51.719	27 d *1*	SF 3.9×10^{-6}% , α>99.5%, ε<0.5%
241	1/2+	53.704	32.8 d *2*	ε 99%, α 1%
242	0+	54.806	162.8 d *2*	α, SF 6.2×10^{-6}% , ^{34}Si 1.×10^{-14}%
243	5/2+	57.184	29.1 y *1*	α 99.71%, ε 0.29%, SF 5.3×10^{-9}%
244	0+	58.455	18.1 y *1*	α, SF 1.4×10^{-4}%
244m	6+	59.495	34 ms *2*	IT
245	7/2+	61.006	8423 y *74*	α, SF 6.1×10^{-7}%
246	0+	62.619	4706 y *40*	α 99.97%, SF 0.03%
247	9/2–	65.535	1.56×10^7 y *5*	α
248	0+	67.393	3.48×10^5 y *6*	α 91.61%, SF 8.39%
249	1/2+	70.751	64.15 m *3*	β–
250	0+	72.99	≈8.3×10^3 y	SF≈74%, α≈18%, β–≈8%
251	(1/2+)	76.65	16.8 m *2*	β–
252	0+	79.1s	<2 d	
97 Bk 234			1.4×10^2 s +*14–5*	α≥80%, ε≤20%
235		52.7s		ε?, α?
236		53.4s		
237		53.1s	≈1 m	ε?, α?
238		54.3s	144 s *5*	ε, εSF 0.048%
239m	(7/2+,3/2–)	54.3s		ε>99%, α< 1%, SF< 1%
240		55.7s	4.8 m *8*	ε, εSF 2.0×10^{-3}%
241	(7/2+)	56.1s	4.6 m *4*	α, ε
242		57.7s	7.0 m *13*	ε≤100%
243	(3/2–)	58.692	4.5 h *2*	ε≈99.85%, α≈0.15%
244	(4–)	60.72	4.35 h *15*	ε 99.99%, α 6.0×10^{-3}%
245	3/2–	61.816	4.95 d *3*	ε 99.88%, α 0.12%
246m	2(–)	63.97	1.80 d *2*	ε
247	(3/2–)	65.491	1380 y *250*	α≤100%
248		68.08s	>9 y	α
248m	1(–)	68.08s	23.7 h *2*	β– 70%, ε 30%
249	7/2+	69.850	330 d *4*	β–, α 1.4×10^{-3}% , SF 4.7×10^{-8}%

Nuclide Z El A	Jπ	Δ (MeV)	T½, Γ, or Abundance	Decay Mode
97 Bk 250	2–	72.952	3.212 h 5	β–
251	(3/2–)	75.23	55.6 m 11	β–
252		78.5s		
253		80.9s		β–?
254		84.4s		
98 Cf 237	(3/2+)	57.94	0.8 s 2	SF 70%, α 30%
238	0+	57.2s	21 ms 2	SF
239		58.1s	39 s +37–12	ε , α
240	0+	58.01	64 s 9	α 98.5%, SF 1.5%
241	(7/2–)	59.3s	3.78 m 70	ε≈75%, α≈25%
242	0+	59.38	3.7 m 5	α 80%, ε 20%, SF≤0.01%
243	(1/2+)	60.9s	10.7 m 5	ε≈86%, α≈14%
244	0+	61.473	19.4 m 6	α≤100%
245	1/2+	63.388	45.0 m 15	ε 64.7%, α 35.3%
246	0+	64.093	35.7 h 5	α, ε< 4.0×10⁻³%, SF 2.4×10⁻⁴%
246m		66.593	45 ns 10	SF≤100%
247	(7/2+)	66.10	3.11 h 3	ε 99.97%, α 0.04%
248	0+	67.241	333.5 d 28	α, SF 2.9×10⁻³%
249	9/2–	69.726	351 y 2	α, SF 5.0×10⁻⁷%
250	0+	71.173	13.08 y 9	α 99.92%, SF 0.08%
251	1/2+	74.137	898 y 44	α, SF
252	0+	76.035	2.645 y 8	α 96.91%, SF 3.09%
253	(7/2+)	79.302	17.81 d 8	β– 99.69%, α 0.31%
254	0+	81.34	60.5 d 2	SF 99.69%, α 0.31%
255	(7/2+)	84.8s	85 m 18	β–
256	0+	87.0s	12.3 m 12	SF, β–<1%, α≈1.0×10⁻⁶%
99 Es 240		64.2s		α?, ε?
241		63.8s	8 s +6–5	ε , α
242		64.9s	17.8 s 16	α 57%, ε 43%
243	(7/2+)	64.7s	23 s 3	α 61%, ε 39%, SF<1%
244		66.0s	37 s 4	ε 96%, α 4%
245	(3/2–)	66.4s	1.1 m 1	ε 60%, α 40%
246m		67.9s	7.5 m 5	ε 90.1%, α 9.9%
247	(7/2+)	68.58	4.55 m 26	ε≈93%, α≈7%
247m		68.58	625 d 84	α
248	(2–,0+)	70.30s	27 m 5	ε 99.7%, α≈0.25%
249	7/2+	71.18s	102.2 m 6	ε 99.43%, α 0.57%
250	(6+)	73.2s	8.6 h 1	ε>97%, α<3%
250m	1(–)	73.2s	2.22 h 5	ε≤100%
251	(3/2–)	74.513	33 h 1	ε 99.5%, α 0.5%
252	(5–)	77.29	471.7 d 19	α 78%, ε 22%
253	7/2+	79.015	20.47 d 3	SF 8.7×10⁻⁶%, α
254	(7+)	81.993	275.7 d 5	α, β– 1.7×10⁻⁴%, SF<3.0×10⁻⁶%
254m	2+	82.077	39.3 h 2	β– 98%, IT<3%, α 0.32%, ε 0.08%, SF<0.05%
255	(7/2+)	84.09	39.8 d 12	β– 92%, α 8%, SF 4.1×10⁻³%

Nuclide Z El A	Jπ	Δ (MeV)	T½, Γ, or Abundance	Decay Mode
99 Es 256	(1+,0−)	87.2s	25.4 m *24*	β−
256m	(8+)	87.2s	7.6 h	β−
257		89.4s	7.7 d *2*	β− , SF
258		92.7s		α?, ε ?
100 Fm 241			0.73 ms *6*	SF > 78%, α < 14%, ε < 12%
242	0+	68.4s	<4 μs	SF ≤ 100%
243	(7/2+)	69.3s	231 ms *9*	α 91%, SF 9%, ε < 10%
244	0+	69.0s	3.12 ms *8*	SF > 97%, ε < 2%, α < 1%
245		70.2s	4.2 s *13*	α ≤ 100%
246	0+	70.19	1.54 s *4*	α 93.2%, SF 6.8%, ε ≤ 1.3%
247	(7/2+)	71.6s	31 s *1*	α ≥ 84%, ε ≤ 16%
247m	(1/2+)	71.6s	5.1 s *2*	α 84%
248	0+	71.894	36 s *2*	α 93%, ε 7%, SF 0.1%
249	(7/2+)	73.521	2.6 m *7*	ε 67%, α 33%
250	0+	74.074	30 m *3*	α > 90%, ε < 10%, SF 6.9×10^{-3}%
250m		74.074	1.93 s *15*	IT
251	(9/2−)	75.95	5.30 h *8*	ε 98.2%, α 1.8%
252	0+	76.818	25.39 h *4*	SF 2.3×10^{-3}% , α
253	(1/2)+	79.349	3.00 d *12*	ε 88%, α 12%
254	0+	80.905	3.240 h *2*	α 99.94%, SF 0.06%
255	7/2+	83.801	20.07 h *7*	α , SF 2.4×10^{-5}%
256	0+	85.487	157.6 m *13*	SF 91.9%, α 8.1%
257	(9/2+)	88.590	100.5 d *2*	α 99.79%, SF 0.21%
258	0+	90.4s	370 μs *43*	SF ≤ 100%
259		93.7s	1.5 s *3*	SF
260	0+	95.8s	≈4 ms	SF
101 Md 245	(1/2−)	75.3s	0.90 ms *25*	α, SF
245m	(7/2)	75.6s	0.35 s *+23−16*	ε , α
246m		76.2s	0.9 s *2*	α
246m		76.2s	4.4 s *8*	ε > 77%, α < 23%
246m		76.2s	0.9 s *2*	SF?, ε ?
247	(7/2−)	75.9s	1.2 s *1*	α 99.9%, SF < 0.1%
247m	(1/2−)	75.9s	0.25 s *4*	α 79%, SF 21%
248		77.1s	13 s *+15−4*	α 58%, ε 42%
249	(7/2−)	77.3s	21.7 s *20*	α > 60%, ε ≤ 40%
249m	(1/2−)	77.3s	1.9 s *9*	α?
250		78.6s	25 s *+10−5*	ε 93%, α 7%
251	(7/2−)	78.97	4.3 m *6*	ε 90%, α 10%
252		80.5s	2.3 m *8*	ε ≤ 100%
253	(7/2−)	81.18s	6 m *+12−3*	ε ≤ 100%, α
254m		83.5s	28 m *8*	ε ≤ 100%
254m		83.5s	10 m *3*	ε ≤ 100%
255	(7/2−)	84.844	27 m *2*	ε 92%, α 8%, SF < 0.15%
256	(1−)	87.61	77 m *2*	ε 90.8%, α 9.2%, SF < 3%
257	(7/2−)	88.997	5.52 h *5*	ε 85%, α 15%, SF < 1%
258		91.689	51.5 d *3*	α , SF

Nuclide Z El A	Jπ	Δ (MeV)	T½, Γ, or Abundance	Decay Mode
101 Md 258m		91.689	57.0 m *9*	ε ≥ 70%, SF
259		93.6s	96 m *3*	SF, α < 1.3%
260		96.6s	31.8 d *5*	SF ≥ 42%, α ≤ 25%, ε ≤ 23%, β− ≤ 10%
261		98.6s		α?
262		101.6s		SF?, α?
102 No 248	0+	80.6s	<2 μs	SF?
249		81.8s		
250	0+	81.6s	4.2 μs *+12−9*	SF, α < 2%
251	(7/2+)	82.8s	0.80 s *1*	α 84%, SF < 0.3%, ε
251m	(1/2+)	82.9s	1.02 s *3*	α
252	0+	82.867	2.47 s *2*	α 70.7%, SF 29.3%, ε < 1.1%
252m	(8−)	82.867	110 ms *10*	IT
253	(9/2−)	84.360	1.62 m *15*	α ≈ 80%, ε
254	0+	84.72	51 s *10*	α 90%, ε 10%, SF 0.17%
254m	0+	84.72	0.28 s *4*	IT > 80%
255	1/2+	86.81	3.52 m *21*	ε 70%, α 30%
256	0+	87.825	2.91 s *5*	α 99.47%, SF 0.53%
257	(7/2+)	90.251	25 s *3*	α ≤ 100%, SF ≤ 1.5%
258	0+	91.5s	1.2 ms *2*	SF ≤ 100%
259		94.1s	58 m *5*	α 75%, ε 25%, SF < 10%
260	0+	95.6s	106 ms *8*	SF
261	(3/2+)	98.5s		α?
262	0+	100.1s	≈5 ms	SF
263		103.1s		α?, SF?
264	0+	105.2s		α?
103 Lr 251		87.9s		ε?, α?
252		88.7s	0.27 s *+18−8*	α, ε
253	(7/2−)	88.7s	0.57 s *+7−6*	α ≈ 98.7%, SF ≈ 1.3%
253m	(1/2−)	88.7s	1.49 s *+30−21*	α 92%, SF 8%
254		89.9s	18.4 s *18*	α 71.7%, ε 28.3%
255	1/2−	89.95	31.1 s *13*	α 85%, ε 15%
255m	7/2−	89.98	2.53 s *13*	IT 60%, α 40%
256		91.75	27 s *3*	α 85%, ε 15%, SF < 0.03%
257		92.61s	≈4 s	α ≤ 100%
258		94.8s	4.1 s *3*	α > 95%, SF < 5%
259		95.85s	6.2 s *3*	α 78%, SF 22%
260		98.3s	180 s *30*	α 80%, ε < 40%, SF < 10%
261		99.6s	39 m *12*	SF
262		102.0s	≈4 h	SF < 10%, ε, α
263		103.7s		α?
264		106.4s		SF?, α?
265		108.3s		SF?, α?
266		111.4s		α?, SF?
104 Rf 253m		93.8s	48 μs *+17−10*	SF ≤ 100%, α
253m		93.8s	≈1.8 s	α ≈ 50%, SF ≈ 50%

Nuclide Z El A	Jπ	Δ (MeV)	T½, Γ, or Abundance	Decay Mode
104 Rf 254	0+	93.2s	23 μs *3*	SF ≤ 100%
255	(9/2−)	94.2s	2.3 s +*8−5*	α 52%, SF 48%, ε ? 1%
256	0+	94.22	6.4 ms *2*	SF 99.68%, α 0.32%
257	(1/2+)	95.87	4.7 s *3*	α < 100%, SF ≤ 1.4%, ε > 0%
257m	(11/2−)	95.87	4.1 s *7*	α < 100%, SF ≤ 1.4%, ε > 0%
258	0+	96.34	14.7 ms +*12−10*	SF 69%, α 31%
259		98.36s	3.2 s *6*	α 92%, SF 8%
259m		98.36s	2.5 s +*4−3*	ε 15%
260	0+	99.2s	21 ms *1*	SF ≤ 100%, α?
261m		101.32	1.9 s *4*	SF 73%, α 27%
261m		101.32	78 s +*11−6*	α > 74%, ε < 15%, SF < 11%
262	0+	102.4s	2.3 s *4*	SF ≤ 100%, α < 3%
263		104.8s	10 m *2*	SF, α
264	0+	106.2s		α?
265m		108.8s		SF
266	0+	110.2s		SF?, α?
267		113.4s		
268	0+	115.4s		α?, SF?
105 Db 255		99.7s	1.6 s +*6−4*	α 80%, SF ≈ 20%
256		100.5s	1.9 s *4*	α ≈ 70%, ε ≈ 30%, SF ≈ 0.02%
257	(9/2+)	100.3s	1.82 s +*27−21*	α 94%, SF ≈ 6%
257m		100.3s	0.58 s +*13−9*	α, SF
258		101.8s	4.2 s +*4−3*	α 65%, ε 35%, SF < 1%
258m		101.8s	20 s *10*	ε
259		101.99	0.51 s *16*	α
260		103.36	1.52 s *13*	α ≥ 90.4%, SF ≤ 9.6%, ε < 2.5%
261		104.2s	1.8 s *4*	α ≥ 82%, SF ≤ 18%
262		106.3s	35 s *5*	α ≈ 67%, SF
263		107.1s	27 s +*10−7*	SF 55%, α 41%, ε 3%
264		109.4s		α?
265		110.5s		α?
266		112.7s		α?, SF?
267m		114.2s	73 m +*350−33*	SF
268m		117.0s	32 h +*11−7*	SF
269		119.1s		α?, SF?
270m		122.0s	23 h	SF, α
106 Sg 258	0+	105.3s	2.9 ms +*13−7*	SF ≤ 100%, α?
259	(1/2+)	106.5s	0.32 s +*8−6*	α 96%, SF 4%
259m		106.5s	0.28 s *5*	
260	0+	106.54	3.6 ms *9*	SF 50%, α 50%
260m		106.54	4.95 ms *33*	SF 71%, α 29%
261		108.01	0.23 s *6*	α, SF < 1%
262	0+	108.4s	6.9 ms +*38−18*	SF ≥ 78%, α ≤ 22%
263		110.19s	1.0 s *2*	α > 70%, SF < 30%
263m		110.19s	0.12 s	IT, α
264	0+	110.8s	37 ms +*27−11*	SF, α < 36%
265m		112.8s	16.2 s +*47−35*	α ≥ 65%, SF ≤ 35%

Nuclide Z El A	Jπ	Δ (MeV)	T½, Γ, or Abundance	Decay Mode
106 Sg 265m		113.0s	8.9 s +27−19	
266	0+	113.7s	21 s +20−12	SF > 50%, α > 18%
267		115.9s		
268	0+	116.9s		SF?, α?
269		120.0s		
270	0+	121.3s		α?, SF?
271m		124.4s	2.4 m +43−10	α ≈ 50%, SF ≈ 50%
272	0+	126.4s		α?, SF?
273		129.8s		SF?
107 Bh 260		113.3s	35 ms +19−9	α ≤ 100%
261		113.2s	11.8 ms +39−24	α
262m		114.5s	22 ms 4	α < 100%
262m		114.5s	83 ms 14	α < 100%
263		114.5s		α?
264		115.7s	0.44 s +60−16	α ≤ 100%
265		116.4s	0.9 s +7−3	α
266m		118.2s	1.7 s +82−8	α
267m		118.9s	17 s +14−6	α
268		120.9s		
269		121.7s		
270?		124.2s	6×10^1 s +29−3	α
271?		125.8s		α?
272m		128.6s	10 s +12−4	α
273		130.5s		α?, SF?
274		133.3s	0.9 m +42−4	α, SF
275		135.4s		SF?
108 Hs 263		120.0s	0.74 ms +48−21	α ≤ 100%, SF < 8.4%
264	0+	119.56	≈0.8 ms	SF ≈ 50%, α ≈ 50%
265		121.17	1.9 ms 2	α < 100%, SF ≤ 1%
265m		121.47	0.3 ms +2−1	α < 100%
266	0+	121.1s	2.3 ms +13−6	α, SF < 1.4%
267	(3/2+)	122.65s	52 ms +13−8	α ≥ 80%, SF < 20%
267m		122.65s	0.8 s +38−4	α
268	0+	122.8s	0.4 s +18−2	α
269		124.6s	3.6 s +8−14	α
269m		124.6s	9.7 s +97−33	α
270	0+	125.1s	22 s	α
271		127.8s		α?, SF?
272	0+	129.1s		SF?, α?
273		132.1s		α
274	0+	133.3s		SF?, α?
275m		136.3s	0.15 s +27−6	α
276	0+	138.0s		α?, SF?
277		141.1s		
109 Mt 265		126.6s		α?
266m		128.0s	1.7 ms +18−16	α ≤ 100%
267		127.8s		α?
268m		128.9s	21 ms +8−5	α
269		129.3s		
270m		130.8s	5.0 ms +24−3	α
271		131.5s		α?

Nuclide			Jπ	Δ (MeV)	T½, Γ, or Abundance	Decay Mode
Z	**El**	**A**				
109	**Mt**	272		133.7s		α?, SF?
		273		134.8s		α?, SF?
		274m		137.1s	0.44 s +81–17	α, SF
		275?		138.4s	9.7 ms +460–44	α
		276m		140.9s	0.72 s +87–25	α
		277		142.5s		
		278m		145.1s	8 s +37–4	α, SF
		279		146.8s		α?, SF?
110	**Ds**	267m		134.3s	2.8 μs +133–12	α
		268?	0+	133.6s	1	α
		269m		135.03	179 μs +245–66	α
		270	0+	134.7s	0.10 ms +14–4	α, SF<0.2%
		270m		135.9s	6.0 ms +82–22	α>70%, IT≤30%
		271		135.95s	1.63 ms +44–29	α
		271m		135.95s	69 ms +56–21	α>0%, IT?
		272	0+	136.0s		SF
		273		138.4s	0.17 ms +17–6	α
		274?	0+	138.9s		SF?, α?
		275?		141.2s		α?
		276?	0+	142.2s		SF?, α?
		277?		145.3s		α?
		278?	0+	145.8s		SF?, α?
		279m		148.6s	0.18 s +5–3	SF≈90%, α≈10%
		280	0+	149.6s		
		281		152.4s	20 s +20–7	SF 85%, α 15%
		281m		152.4s	9.6 s +50–25	SF
111	**Rg**	272m		142.8s	3.8 ms +14–8	α
		273		143.1s		α?
		274m		144.7s	6.4 ms +307–29	α
		275?		145.4s		α?
		276?		147.4s		α?, SF?
		277?		148.4s		SF?, α?
		278m		150.4s	4.2 ms +76–17	α, SF
		279m		151.3s	0.17 s +81–8	α
		280m		153.4s	3.6 s +43–13	α
		281m		154.6s	26 s +25–8	SF, α
		282m		156.7s	0.5 s +25–2	α, SF
		283?		158.1s		SF?, α?
112	**Cn**	276	0+	150.6s		
		277		152.4s		
		278?	0+	152.7s		α?, SF?
		279?		154.7s		SF?, α?
		280?	0+	155.4s		α?, SF?
		281m		158.1s		α
		282m		158.2s	0.50 ms +33–14	SF
		283m		160.7s	4.0 s +13–7	α≥90%, SF≤10%
		283m		160.7s	6.9 s +69–23	SF 50%, α 50%
		284m		161.5s	101 ms +41–22	SF
		285		164.1s	30 s +30–10	α
113		278m		159.0s	0.24 ms +114–11	α
		279		159.5s		

| Nuclide | | | | Δ | T½, Γ, or | |
Z	El	A	Jπ	(MeV)	Abundance	Decay Mode
113		280		161.2s		
		281		161.9s		
		282m		163.6s	0.07 s +13–3	α
		283m		164.0s	100 ms +490–45	α
		284m		166.0s	0.48 s +58–17	α
		285m		166.9s	5.5 s +50–18	α, SF
		286m		168.9s	20 s +94–9	α, SF
		287?		170.1s		α?, SF?
114		285m		171.2s		α
		286m	0+	171.0s	0.16 s +7–3	SF≈60%, α≈40%
		287		173.2s	0.51 s +18–10	α
		288	0+	174.0s	0.52 s +22–13	α
		289		176.5s	0.97 s +97–32	α
		289m		176.5s	2.7 s +14–7	α
115		287?		177.2s	32 ms +155–14	α
		288m		179.0s	87 ms +105–30	α
		289		179.8s	0.22 s +26–8	α, SF
		290		181.6s	16 ms +76–7	α, SF
		291?		182.8s		α?, SF?
116		289		184.8s		
		290	0+	184.4s	15 ms +26–6	α
		291		186.6s	6.3 ms +116–25	α
		292	0+	187.2s	18 ms +16–6	α
		293		189.6s	53 ms +62–19	α
117		291?		191.0s		SF?, α?
		292?		192.7s		SF?, α?
		293		193.4s	14 ms +11–4	α, SF
		294		195.1s	0.08 s +37–4	α
118		294		198.7s	0.9 ms +11–3	α, SF≤50%
		295		200.7s		

INDEX

CPSIA information can be obtained
at www.ICGtesting.com
Printed in the USA
FSOW02n2030090917
38534FS